12

BB

2

DISCUSSIONS ON
CHILD DEVELOPMENT

VOLUMES ONE TO FOUR

DISCUSSIONS ON
Child Development

A Consideration of the Biological, Psychological, and
Cultural Approaches to the Understanding
of Human Development and Behaviour

EDITORS

J. M. TANNER

BÄRBEL INHELDER

*The Proceedings of the Meetings of the
World Health Organization Study Group
on the Psychobiological Development of the Child
Geneva 1953-1956*

INTERNATIONAL UNIVERSITIES PRESS, INC.
NEW YORK

The series first published in the United States of America in 1960
by International Universities Press, Inc.
239 Park Avenue South, New York, N.Y. 10003

First one-volume edition 1971

ISBN 0-8236-1380-1

Volume I ⓒ *Tavistock Publications 1956*
Volume II ⓒ *Tavistock Publications 1956*
Volume III ⓒ *Tavistock Publications 1958*
Volume IV ⓒ *Tavistock Publications 1960*
One-volume edition ⓒ *Tavistock Publications 1971*

Library of Congress Catalog Card Number : 75-140319

Manufactured in Great Britain

DISCUSSIONS ON
CHILD DEVELOPMENT

VOLUME ONE

The Proceedings of the First Meeting of the
World Health Organization Study Group
on the Psychobiological Development of the Child
Geneva 1953

MEMBERS OF STUDY GROUP

DR. JOHN BOWLBY   *Psychoanalysis*
Director, Children's Department
Tavistock Clinic, London

DR. FRANK FREMONT-SMITH   *Research Promotion*
Chairman
Josiah Macy, Jr. Foundation, New York

DR. G. R. HARGREAVES   *Psychiatry*
Formerly Chief, Mental Health Section
World Health Organization
Professor of Psychiatry, Leeds University

MLLE. BÄRBEL INHELDER   *Psychology*
Professeur de Psychologie de l'Enfant
Institut des Sciences de l'Education de
l'Université de Genève

DR. KONRAD Z. LORENZ   *Ethology*
Forschungsstelle für
Verhaltensphysiologie des Max-Planck
Institutes für Meeresbiologie
Buldern über Dulmen, West Germany

DR. MARGARET MEAD   *Cultural Anthropology*
Associate Director Dept. of
Anthropology
American Museum of Natural History,
New York

DR. K. A. MELIN   *Electrophysiology*
Director, Clinic for Convulsive Disorders,
Stora Sköndal, Stockholm

DR. MARCEL MONNIER   *Electrophysiology*
Chargé de Cours de Neurophysiologie
appliquée Université de Genève

PROFESSOR JEAN PIAGET   *Psychology*
Professeur de Psychologie à la Sorbonne
et à l'Université de Genève

DR. A. RÉMOND   *Electrophysiology*
Chargé de Recherches, Centre National
de la Recherche Scientifique, Paris

DR. R. R. STRUTHERS *Research Promotion*

Formerly, Associate Director
Rockefeller Foundation, Paris

DR. J. M. TANNER *Human Biology*

Formerly Senior Lecturer,
Sherrington School of Physiology,
St. Thomas's Hospital
Lecturer, Institute of Child Health
University of London

DR. W. GREY WALTER *Electrophysiology*

Director of Research
Burden Neurological Institute, Bristol

RENÉ ZAZZO *Psychology*

Directeur du Laboratoire de Psychobiologie de l'Enfant
Institut des Hautes Etudes, Paris

GUESTS

DR. J. C. CAROTHERS *Psychiatry*

Psychiatrist, St. James' Hospital
Portsmouth, England

DR. E. E. KRAPF *Psychiatry*

Associate Professor of Psychiatry
University of Buenos Aires

DR. CHARLES ODIER *Psychoanalysis*

Château de Vernand, Lausanne

PREFACE

This volume, and others which will follow it, give an account of an activity of the World Health Organization—the Research Study Group on the Psychobiological Development of the Child.

The popular view of the World Health Organization associates it chiefly with practical activities concerned with the application of existing knowledge through public health services and as far as the great majority of the Organization's activities have been concerned this view is accurate. More than half the Organization's funds have from its creation in 1948 been devoted to such programmes as the control of communicable diseases.

But the Organization differs from the International Health bodies which preceded it in having placed upon it a specific obligation to 'foster activities in the field of mental health, especially those affecting the harmony of human relations'. In this field the mass programmes appropriate to such problems as the control of malaria are not applicable. In the mental health field there are no equivalents to D.D.T. and penicillin, and aetiological knowledge is scanty.

Although the Organization has devoted most of its energies, and its funds, to the preventive application of knowledge gained by research in national institutions, it is also obligated by its constitution to promote and conduct research and it was as a contribution to the promotion of research that the Research Study Group was formed. It was not an isolated activity but was part of one of the natural trends of development of the mental health programme which began in 1949.

The World Health Organization makes considerable use of Expert Committees (small groups of distinguished workers in a given field drawn from different countries) to advise it on the development of its technical policy. Such an Expert Committee on Mental Health was convened in 1949. This Committee recommended that it was desirable that the Mental Health Programme should concentrate especially on the psychiatry of childhood. It emphasized the fact that others apart from psychiatrists must be called on to contribute in this field and mentioned specifically the anthropologist, the sociologist, and the social and developmental psychologist. In its report the Committee urged that W.H.O. should also 'actively encourage research which sets out to fill gaps in fundamental knowledge' in the mental health field, and in this connection it specifically mentioned 'Research into the biological, psychological, and cultural determinants of personality structure'. It is evident, however, that since the funds available for the mental health programme have been small—less than two per cent of the Organization's budget—the Organization could not itself finance research on any appreciable scale. The Organization's contribution has, therefore, been directed toward the co-ordinating, surveying, and stimulating of research.

Two such W.H.O. surveys on different aspects of the Mental Health of

9

Childhood were widely read. The first of these was 'The Psychiatric Aspects of Juvenile Delinquency' by the late Dr. Lucien Bovet, and the second by Dr. John Bowlby on 'Maternal Care and Mental Health' surveyed existing research on the psychological effects of the continued separation of infants from their mothers, or mother substitutes.

Both these surveys posed questions which gave rise to the thought of a multiprofessional discussion group on child development problems. The thought was crystallized into a concrete plan by the stimulus of the Oxford Conference of the Mental Health Research Fund on 'Prospects in Psychiatric Research' held in 1952, and the model on which the plan was based was the informal conferences of the Josiah Macy Junior Foundation.

The aim of the Group was to bring together once a year for four or five years, during a period of a week, a small number of internationally eminent workers in the different disciplines which study different aspects of the psychobiological development of the child.

The aim of the meeting was not the reading of papers, the passing of resolutions, or the issuing of a report, but the provision of an opportunity for mutual understanding to develop between workers in different disciplines, and on the basis of that understanding the attempt to relate the findings of one discipline to those of another and the hope that new research, and particularly joint research, might be undertaken. The Organization was fortunate in obtaining, as chairman of the Group, Dr. Frank Fremont-Smith, of the Josiah Macy Junior Foundation. His personal qualities, and his great experience of conferences of this type, created in this international group (despite the problems of simultaneous interpretation) the atmosphere and enthusiasm which made the success of the group possible.

It was not originally intended that the proceedings of the meetings should be published; but the mimeographed transcript which was produced for the benefit of the members evoked such interest in those outside the group who read it that many requests for copies began to be received. Hence the decision to publish this series. To make the publication possible considerable editing has been necessary since the original transcript had to be reduced by about two-thirds. The Group is much indebted to one of its members, Dr. J. M. Tanner, for carrying out this task so skilfully.

Finally, as the Chief of the Mental Health Section of the World Health Organization at the time these meetings were convened, I should like to express my personal appreciation to Dr. Brock Chisholm and Dr. Marcolino Candau, the first two Directors General of the Organization, and to Dr. Norman Begg, Regional Director for Europe, for their support of a venture which, although not connected with the day-to-day practice of current public health work, may yet through some of its many repercussions have its significance for public health workers of future generations.

G. R. HARGREAVES

Leeds University

Lately Chief, Mental Health Section, World Health Organization

CONTENTS

CONTENTS

Introduction

FREMONT-SMITH (Chairman):

Je suis tout à fait content d'être ici avec vous, mais malheureuse-ment je ne peux pas parler le français, and so I will go on, not speaking in good English, but in the patois of the U.S.A. What I now have to say is intended to be introductory, and to tell you what we would like to have as the mood of the conference. I have been co-opted to this job because it was hoped that we could use at least some of the Macy Foundation conference methods in this meeting, and so first I should say a little about them. The Macy Foundation is a charitable body that makes grants for research. In the course of doing this the Foundation directors and officers became disturbed by the narrowness of the approach of the investigators who asked us for help. Their projects were drawn up from a unilateral point of view, and it seemed more and more that, to make advances in practically any problem in science, one needed the participation of several dis-ciplines. We found that the investigator was frequently ignorant of the contribution already made or potentially to be made by another discipline, and too often was uninterested. The general position that we held was that nature is all of one piece and that the departments of universities, the specialities which had grown up for good and necessary reasons, tended artificially to divide that nature and to set up barriers which prevented communication between the different disciplines. Our conference programme arose as an effort to rein-tegrate the scientist's approach to nature's secrets, to try to bring a genuine multi-disciplinary point of view to bear on problems. How-ever, we discovered that this was not as simple as it might seem. We tried at first to crowd the meeting with speakers representing different fields, as in the usual kind of meeting. It didn't get us very far. We tried to bring together the two or three men from different depart-ments in one university who were working on the same problem. They didn't like it. Often they didn't even like each other. We then gradually began to focus more and more on what are the obstructions

13

between disciplines and now we look upon our conferences as experiments in communication and as efforts to identify and remove, if possible, some of these obstructions.

One thing that seemed to come out of this thinking was that there is an over-emphasis, derived, I think, primarily from our universities, on the intellectual side of learning and the intellectual side of science —and I mean intellect as opposed to emotion, the logical as opposed to the creative—and we felt that we would like to do something to redress the balance. We felt that the lecture system of the universities had reached a point where it was practically limited to the making of statements *at* people rather than being concerned with communication *with* people. This applies also to the papers at the ordinary scientific meetings, which are usually a series of statements made *at* people, statements which give great satisfaction to the speaker but little to the listener. Since the scientific programme is crowded, only one or two questions may be raised at the end of each statement, and then one goes on with the next paper. We wondered if something might not be accomplished if we reversed the process and tried to make the questions and answers, the discussion, the heart of our conference, and the papers as small a factor as possible. Gradually we pushed the papers back and brought the discussion forward so that now we have somebody who makes introductory remarks for about twenty minutes, which serve as the basis of discussion for the rest of the day. We tried to bring the discussions that ordinarily take place in the corridor outside the scientific meetings into the meetings themselves.

With respect to making statements at people rather than communicating with them, it seems to me that we should pay more attention to the listener. We should ask ourselves what kind of a receiving set the other fellow has got. Some of the difficulties of communication are linguistic; but others are to do with the imprint of authority, which makes it impossible for us really to hear a viewpoint which challenges the authority with which we have identified ourselves— sometimes it is our own authority. In days gone by I think it was possible for a person to remain relatively static for long periods of time, but today I think we must expect change. But change is something which produces anxiety, and anxiety is apt to be transformed into hostility. And I think that is one of the reasons why, when someone is challenged with an idea which would produce a change in his approach to the problem, so often the response is a hostile one. These resistances, these obstructions to communication, these distorting lenses, may change with different environmental situations. When the environment is a chill and anxious environment, the lenses go on—it's like the guard the boxer puts up. But if there's a warm

14

and friendly atmosphere, then the glasses come off, the guard is lowered, and the way is open for communication. That's one of the reasons why people must have an opportunity to be associated with each other informally. It's one of the reasons why having the same group, with a few additions, meet again and again and again often helps so singularly well to provide a basis for communication.

We try to encourage the participants in our meetings to speak freely, not to hesitate to ask a foolish question, because how can they be sure it won't evoke wisdom in someone else? We are not here in this kind of group to solve a point, to defend a view, but rather to examine our own blind spots, or at least to give others a chance to point them out to us. In this way we hope that we can open the doors to the kind of communication that previously hasn't been possible. This kind of meeting should be primarily for the cross-fertilization of ideas, for the meeting of minds, for the stimulation of curiosity, and for examining and bringing out the resources of the group. The resources of each of us are certainly not known to the others, and some of them possibly not to ourselves, because we have all stored many memories and experiences which we cannot bring to the surface at will on a given problem, but which may be there in the background of our memories, and brought out by someone else's remark.

We will now introduce ourselves to each other. I will start with myself and then ask each of you to say in a few words how you got the kind of interest that brought you to this meeting. I had an Hungarian mother, which has helped to give me a warm feeling towards the Continent, and a father of New England origin, and I'd like you to feel that when I am quite wild and woolly it's the romantic, dynamic, Magyar spirit bursting out and when I'm sensible and calm and intelligent then it's the New England spirit, which, of course, came from Great Britain. I graduated from the Harvard Medical School in 1921 and had a training in pathology and then another year and a half in medicine, and then went to the Department of Neuropathology in the Harvard Medical School under Dr. Stanley Cobb and did research on cerebro-spinal fluid, and on body fluids in general: respectable, solid, basic research. Then, when I was measuring cerebro-spinal fluid in a manometer, I discovered that even such a simple measurement as that could not be made accurately unless I had some knowledge of the emotional state of the patient, because if the patient was tense he might either hold his breath and give himself a high venous pressure, and too high a pressure in the cerebro-spinal fluid, or, on the other hand, he might react by over-ventilation, lower his venous pressure and get too low a cerebro-spinal fluid pressure; in this way I was introduced into psychosomatic

15

problems. Then, since Dr. Cobb had many patients with epilepsy, I became very much interested in this problem and particularly in the factors which precipitated convulsions, and especially in emotional factors as one of the precipitating agents. And from there it turned out that the emotional factors which precipitated such attacks were very often factors of which the patient was unaware: old conflicts, for which the patient had an amnesia, so that I became more and more drawn from the psychosomatic into the psychiatric field, and although never properly trained in psychiatry nor properly analysed, I did have a personal analysis, which was very good for me, and some psychiatric training. Then I came into the Macy Foundation in 1936 and since then I have been in a curious situation. You all know the definition of the specialist who gradually gets to know more and more about less and less until he knows practically everything about nothing, and the generalist who gets to know less and less about more and more until he knows practically nothing about anything; but I am a mixture of those two, because I get exposed to an enormous range of conferences where the participants are groups of highly trained specialists.

MONNIER:

After medical studies in Geneva, Zürich, and Vienna, I worked in the Physiological Institute of Zürich, where I wrote my doctor's thesis under the direction of Professor W. R. Hess. I was already interested at that time in the correlations between psychological functions and the vegetative nervous system. From 1931 to 1934 I got a training in psychiatry as assistant at the Psychiatrische Universitätsklinik of Zürich, and from 1934 to 1937 a training in neurology at the Clinique des Maladies Nerveuses at the Salpêtrière in Paris. I went then as a Rockefeller Fellow to the Neurological Institute of Northwestern University in Chicago, where I studied the functions of the reticular system of the brainstem under the direction of Professor S. W. Ranson. During 1938, I worked as assistant in the Service de Neurologie de l'Hôpital Cantonal de Genève and in 1939 I became Chef des Travaux at the Institut de Physiologie de Genève.

In 1941 I went to Zürich as Chef des Travaux at the Physiological Institute, where I worked again with Professor W. R. Hess. I was interested in the integrative activity of the nervous system and had the opportunity of studying, with Professor H. Willi, head of the Kantonales Säuglingsheim, the development of motor functions in normal and anencephalic newborns. In 1948, I returned to Geneva to start the Laboratoire de Neurophysiologie appliquée, which had as its purpose the bridging of the gap between experimental and clinical neurophysiology. Here I had the opportunity to develop with Professor Piaget and Mlle Inhelder a co-operative study of the correlation between mental development as analysed by various psychological tests, and the development of the electrical activity of the brain, analysed by means of electroencephalography. This is one of the reasons why I am here.

STRUTHERS:

I don't know of anyone who is in this group who has less right to be here than I have as I am not trained as a scientist in any particular field. I had some experience in the army in the first war as a physician and also in general practice in the country and I eventually entered paediatrics, in the days when most of paediatric work was a question of whether you had sufficient lactic acid in the baby's feed. After twenty years in general paediatric practice in Montreal, during which I did some work on childhood tuberculosis as a social problem, and on the definition of activity of rheumatic fever in children, I found that my main interest was in undergraduate medical education. Because of that interest I am now dedicated to work in the Rockefeller Foundation as Director for Medical Programmes in Europe. The only justification for my attendance here is that I can qualify under Dr. Fremont-Smith's definition of one of those who knows less and less about more and more, and I think I have almost reached the apogee of knowing nothing.

TANNER:

I am a human biologist, with particular interests in physiology, child development, and genetics. I had originally a mathematical training at school, with the intention of becoming an army engineer. However, this project had never really appealed to me, and a few days before it came to fruition I deserted and began a pre-medical course. This I greatly enjoyed and soon I had a particular interest in genetics and evolutionary theory. Early in the war I was a medical student and the Rockefeller Foundation generously offered to take some of us from Britain over to America and to train us there because of the difficulties we were facing in the hospitals in London. I had at that time done a small amount of research work in pure physiology and my interests by this time had become, if not focused, at least fairly concrete, so that when I was asked about them at the interview associated with this trip, I said 'I want to work in the place where physiology, psychology, and sociology meet'. This is a stand from which I have never really departed. So, having had my anatomical

17

and physiological training in England I had my clinical training at the University of Pennsylvania, and later on as a house physician on the medical service of the Johns Hopkins Hospital.

Following that, I came back again to England and being now quite clear that I wanted to become, if necessary all by myself, a human biologist, I spent the next two years in psychiatry, dealing almost exclusively with the superficial psychotherapy of neuroses of a combat type. I was particularly concerned at that time with group therapy. At the end of this period, having learned just enough about psychology and psychiatry to understand the language, I went to Oxford University as lecturer in Physical Anthropology. I did that because it seemed to me that if one was concerned with studying human biology and behaviour one should build one's science from the ground up, studying first of all the simplest thing there is to study in the human, which is what he looks like.

At Oxford I spent a great deal of time getting to know the literature on the physical growth of the child, and trying to define and classify differences in physique among adults. I think the interest of these physical differences lies in the light they may throw on differences in physiological function and in behaviour. After I had spent three years at Oxford learning, by the well-known mechanism of teaching, the subject of physical anthropology, I went back to be a professional physiologist at St. Thomas's Hospital in London University, where I now teach physiology and do research work on the physiological differences between people, their genetical basis and their anatomical correlates.

There is one other thing I should tell you. I feel very likely that my best function here may be more to answer questions that the ethologists and the psychologists may bring up than to propose anything of my own, and therefore the more I tell you about the fields in which you may reasonably expect to get a sensible answer out of me the better. For the last four years I have been closely associated with a study on human growth run and financed by the Ministry of Health outside London and here we have a longitudinal growth-study, the first of its kind in England, modelled to a considerable extent on those which are doing such good work in the United States. We have there about 250 children and a group of us, collected mainly from various departments of London University, descend on these children two consecutive days every month. We therefore see every child within two weeks of its birthday or half-birthday; we see every child every six months, or every three months during puberty. At the present time we do a number of physical measurements of the children, we take photographs in a rather highly standardized and particular way which enables us to measure them, and we take a considerable

18

number of X-rays, the function of which is to differentiate bone and muscle and fat so as to see the growth of the different sorts of tissue in children. We have dental people who take X-rays of the jaws and are concerned with the development of the teeth; and a paediatrician who does the clinical examinations. We are dealing with bone-ages, teeth-development-ages and such-like things, subjects in which you may be interested. We do not have—and I regard it as a very grave gap in our investigation; it is a matter of money and space as usual—anybody who is studying the physiological and biochemical development of the children, so I have no personal experience of that. However, I am quite well acquainted with such literature as there is on it. Also we do not have at the present time any psychiatric or psychological studies in progress, and this is a field about which I wish to be informed, and know, practically speaking, nothing.

MEAD:

I started my training as an anthropologist at the age of about three, which gives me some sort of qualification for working on the problem of children. My mother was a sociologist who was working on the adjustment of Italian immigrants in the United States, and my grandmother was very much interested in child thought and imagination. She was a teacher of young children. So I was trained on my younger sisters to record children's behaviour, and by the time I was nine or ten I was a fairly competent recorder. We don't know yet whether starting that early does any good or not, but I went on a fairly straight line, having come out of this sort of academic expectation. I took my M.A. in psychology and worked initially on the effect of language spoken in the home of immigrants on their performance in intelligence tests at school, and that meant working through the literature on the relationship of intelligence testing to race. I then went into anthropology under Franz Boas. I suppose I belong ethnically to that very small and rapidly vanishing minority called 'Old Americans', as I have no ties that can be traced to Europe. I am tenth-generation American, so that Europe to me is a strange and new place that I have come face to face with, with very little chance of following any ties back.

In my anthropological work under Franz Boas I gained integration with European scientific thought, because Boas always gave us the first reference in German, the second in French, and sometimes one in English. My first anthropological work was on the extent to which the phenomena of adolescence could be regarded as biological and the extent to which they were culturally influenced. That was 1925. Since that time I have worked in eight different primitive societies,

19

taking to them the problems that were developing in the field of human behaviour over that period. During my second field trip in 1928 I took Professor Piaget's early work to the field and attempted to test it out. I am now going back this June, twenty-five years later, to re-study the same community, and I will be able to take this next twenty-five years of Professor Piaget's work with me. In the same way I have used from time to time one set of psychological formulations and at another stage some other or later development.

During the last twenty years I have been under the protective aegis of the Macy Foundation and all its cross-cultural and cross-disciplinary and cross-everything enterprises. I have been exposed to a very large number of conferences such as this, which have brought new problems, which one could use to take back to the field. As Dr. Tanner said of himself, I may be more useful in answering questions than in presenting material, because one of the characteristics of ethnological work is that we deal with whole cultures and so many varieties of material that it would be rather difficult to anticipate just which kind of material would be most useful. At the same time the anthropologist can take any hypothesis back into the field and subject it to new tests. My major function in these conferences was first to say whether the hypothesis was culturally limited or not. Is it physiological to nod your head to say 'yes', and did the negative head shake come from the child avoiding the mother's breast? Is it culturally stylized? Secondly, to present hypotheses which come out of the material. In most cases primitive material cannot supply proof. We deal with too small populations over too short a period of time. We are a hypothesis-criticizing, -correcting, and -producing agency rather than a proof-producing agency.

GREY WALTER:

Well, sir, I may add to your confession of cosmopolitanism that I have an American mother and an English father, and that I share a birthplace with Norbert Wiener, T. S. Eliot, and Harry Truman. I was born in Missouri. For that reason my life has been one long illustration of the need to 'show me'.

I am an experimental scientific worker. I started my training in the University of Cambridge as a fairly pure neurophysiologist in the school of Adrian and Matthews, and I spent five years there, studying the detailed neurophysiology of the peripheral nervous system. I then had the honour of being delegated by my professor, Sir Joseph Barcroft, to work with a Rockefeller Fellow—one of the first and few who came from Leningrad—on conditioned reflexes. I was given the task of acting as his assistant and becoming familiar

20

with the classical techniques of the Pavlovian School. I spent two years at that work, having a good background already of neurophysiology. I was enabled first of all to introduce a number of modernizations into the Pavlovian technique, to assure myself of the essential accuracy of the Pavlovian hypotheses, and to become much impressed with the manner in which the Pavlovian workers at that time were able to distinguish factors related to personality in their experimental creatures, both animal and man. Since that time, as you know, that particular aspect of Pavlovian work has been rejected and denied by the Soviet authorities, and very few people, I think, understand how important the typology of Pavlov was, in the early days, to the development and scope of the Pavlovian theories.

After we had realized that to extend the work in Cambridge would cost far more money than was available, I had the good fortune to be appointed as a Rockefeller Fellow at the Maudsley Hospital in London, where my approach to the human problem was directed and inspired by Professor Golla, who was then setting up a new laboratory for the multi-disciplinary study of the human organism; I had the role there of physiologist. There I was introduced to the study of the electrical activity of the brain, which as a physiologist I had previously considered to be inaccurate and unlikely to lead to any information, the brain being, of course, at that time a most objectionable subject of study. I had the opportunity to visit many European centres of brain physiology preparatory to setting up our own laboratory. I met Berger and Foerster and various other workers in the field of brain physiology. Our laboratory was set up mainly for the application of electroencephalography to psychiatric problems, but we were very soon more heavily involved with neurology, and I devoted a number of years to the study of organic lesions of the nervous system. It was rather a tough apprenticeship for a physiologist, having to relearn neuroanatomy and apply it to what was then an extremely inaccurate and troublesome method of study.

At the end of my period at the Maudsley, just before the War, I moved with Golla to Bristol, where I am now, and once again had to redirect my ideas towards the more generalized physiology of the human nervous system. Our plans were interrupted by the War. During the War we devoted our attention mainly to the problem of head injuries and epilepsy in Service personnel, but at the same time occurred the opportunity to deal with more normal physiology in matters quite relevant to the meeting here, that is the problem of children evacuated from the cities. Hundreds of ill-behaved and, in fact, horrible creatures descended upon us from the slums of big cities, presenting one of the most serious problems which my country has had to face: the disposal of these young creatures in schools, billets, and so forth. We found that the application of physiological techniques to the separation, selection, and classification of these children was astonishingly valuable. From that time dates my interest in the relevance of the physiology of the nervous system to the study of how children grow up, how the influences of environment and heredity, nurture and nature, combine to make the child as it is.

These interests have been paramount in my scientific thinking, combined obviously with the early influence of the Pavlovian School, and I have attempted particularly to quantify methods of study, to develop men and machines able to make objective and concrete appreciation of the problems which we encounter in this sort of work. This approach seems to me to have been neglected in the past, and ignorance here is liable to produce considerable misunderstanding if projected further.

ZAZZO:

As my name suggests, I am descended from Italian stock on my father's side. I was born in Paris in 1910 from a Burgundian mother and a Parisian father. My early teachers were Piéron and particularly Wallon. In 1933, having finished my studies at the Sorbonne, I decided to go abroad. Chance, or rather political events, led me overseas. I intended to go to Vienna to work with Freud, but the circumstances were not very favourable so I decided, while waiting for the situation to improve, to go to the U.S.A., where I worked for six months with Gesell in his Institute at Yale University. I came back to France in the Spring of 1934 and it was then that I started work directly under Wallon.

In 1940 I published my first book, which was devoted to American psychology. This was also at a difficult period, and the following incident is worth quoting. French censorship, under German control, required me to delete all the Jewish names from my book. Naturally this was rather awkward. I solved the problem by taking the names out of the preface and putting them back in the following chapters; and so I was able to ascertain that the censorship did not read beyond the first chapter. At this time, in 1940, I was working at the Psycho-pathological Laboratory at the Henri Rousselle Hospital.

Four years ago I took over from Professor Wallon as Director of the Laboratory of the Psychobiology of the Child. My present research bears more particularly on the psychology of epilepsy. Our team of workers is dealing with the classical problem of mental deficiency, certain types of which we are trying to redefine. It is an old problem but always seems new.

22

For the last few years my 'hobby-horse' has been the study of the foundations of personality, using various methods, especially with twins.

Finally, on the question of method I would like to mention that I have attempted to reconcile the clinical method taught by Professor Wallon and the statistical, quantitative, approach. There are difficulties, which are, moreover, exaggerated by doctrinal oppositions and opposition between groups which regard themselves as strictly clinical or strictly psychostatistical; but, as I say, I endeavour to reconcile these two points of view, both of which seem to me essential for the understanding of human nature.

MELIN:

I am a paediatrician. After my medical examination I studied paediatrics in Stockholm, and very soon I was directed by my chief, Professor Lichtenstein, towards the field of children's convulsive disorders. This was at a time when electroencephalography was not at all known as a clinical method in Sweden. It was not possible to learn about it at home, and that led to my visiting the United States, where I studied at Harvard Medical School, mainly in the clinic of Lennox, and also at Johns Hopkins Hospital and the Neurological Institute with Hoefer. I went back to Sweden again and continued in this field. However, I found it very difficult to judge pathological conditions, knowing almost nothing at all about the normal in children. It has therefore been a constant struggle during the years to find out what is normal in children, especially in the field of the electrical development of the brain. My interest has been mainly in that direction and I have tried to work in this field from the electroencephalographic point of view. I am, however, still a pure paediatrician, and I have still my main interest focused on work with children suffering from convulsive disorders.

RÉMOND:

I began my studies in Picardy, in the north of France, and continued at the Faculty of Medicine of the University of Paris. There I was particularly interested in the study of the nervous system of the adult and the child. One of my best-liked tutors, Professor Baudouin, was the first in France (in 1936) to become interested in electroencephalography. In 1939 I was already thinking of concentrating on neurophysiological research.

In 1941 I started working regularly in Professor Baudouin's laboratory, where I studied mainly the electrical activity of the brain of sick children, with the assistance of Professor Heuyer and Professor

23

Debré. I was lucky enough in 1945 to work for a year in the U.S.A., in Professor Detlew Bronk's laboratory at Philadelphia; there I was able to become familiar with the techniques of neurophysiology. Although these techniques had perhaps not entirely escaped notice in France during the war, little was known of the details. I was able to study particularly the polarographic recording of oxygen and apply it to the study of cortical metabolism.

Since 1946 I have been with the Centre Nationale de la Recherche Scientifique and have concentrated on the electrophysiology of the brain.

I went back to the U.S.A. in 1952 to work with Professor McCulloch in Chicago, and since my return I have again held the post of Head of the Laboratory of Electroencephalography and Applied Neurophysiology. As a daily routine in this laboratory we make electroencephalograms of about twenty persons presenting different lesions of the brain. Having made most interesting contacts at the Salpêtrière in a neurological milieu which is already long established, I want to profit by the atmosphere which exists there to base on it research in human neurophysiology.

Regarding the research which I have followed or carried out myself, I should like to mention that in our laboratory we are attempting much more than in the past to 'define' the normal individual. Since we are constantly working with sick persons we cannot always know where the pathological begins and the normal ends. What is the normal individual? What is the normal child? One might ask whether normality exists.

Among the groups of people we try to study I should like to refer to a very restricted one, of pilot apprentices. In order to show the difficulties we are faced with I would mention that individuals of twenty to twenty-four years in this group who appeared absolutely normal according to screening, definitions and tests, seem to us, used to observing adults, to be immature as regards the electrical activity of the brain. I mention this fact before we start on our work in order to ask each of you to underline as far as possible what you consider normal and to tell us what importance the definition of normal has in the fields you represent. How can we obtain this definition? Why should we obtain it?

KRAPF:

I think I might, with due apologies to Dr. Lorenz, describe myself as some sort of bird of migration. I was born and studied medicine in Germany and took my degree at Leipzig University, and tnen I started on my first Transatlantic migration, to the Argentine, from which I came back in order to concentrate on neurology and psychiatry at the University of Munich, at the University of Paris, and for some time also in Zürich. Eventually I wound up being a lecturer in psychiatry and neurology at the University of Cologne, where I remained until Hitler came into power and, as Hitler and I couldn't see eye to eye on many things, I decided that I'd rather withdraw to South America again, and so I settled in 1933 in Argentina. Since then I've commuted between South America and Europe. Eventually I became an Associate Professor of Psychiatry in Buenos Aires, and somewhat belatedly the University of Cologne also conferred the title of Professor on me.

As to professional experience, there I think I am a bird of migration too. I started on neurological lines, did a certain amount of what is called solid research on the neurological aspects of psychiatry, until I found out that I couldn't do without some other sort of training; so I underwent my personal psychoanalysis, and since then have been commuting between neurological and psychoanalytic psychiatry. I feel that birds of migration in a way have some sort of stability, they always fly by the same route, and if there are two schools of psychiatry—one in which one tries to explain everything in physiological terms, and the other one where everything is couched in psychological terms—I have always been most interested in the gap in between, which is in my opinion neither quite as wide as some people seem to think, nor quite as narrow as some others believe. I think it is a most fascinating task to see how things can happen in physiology through psychological stimuli, and how psychological events use physiological channels in order to manifest themselves, and in this context lately I have been interested in the 'gap' in epilepsy and the convulsive states generally, and in the so-called psychopathic personalities, two subjects which are particularly closely related to some of the most outstanding neurophysiological problems in children. Lately also I have been particularly interested in the implications of speech pathology from the point of view both of psychology and brain pathology.

BOWLBY:

I am a Londoner born and bred. My father's family came from Yorkshire, my mother's from Wales, and my father was a surgeon. I had rather a wayward youth, inasmuch as I toyed with being a sailor and went to the Royal Naval College; I then took up medicine, then switched to child psychology, and it was unfortunate that it was at my most wayward that my father died. This was at a point when, after reading natural sciences, medicine, and psychology at

25

Cambridge, I decided to give up medicine in order to take up education. I spent twelve months in one of the progressive and free schools, which was a very valuable experience, because I saw a number of disturbed children at first hand, I lived with them, indeed I had to look after them, and I met there the first 'affectionless character' of my career.

Fortunately, I was very wisely advised at this point to finish my medical training and train in psychoanalysis. So I went to London, to University College Hospital. Then I specialized in psychiatry at the Maudsley Hospital and continued my training in psychoanalysis; I finished that and took up child psychiatry and child guidance. Between 1936 and 1940 I was concerned with child guidance and it was really at that time that I became convinced in my own heart that certain events of early childhood were of critical importance in determining personality development—particularly the child's relationship to his mother, and the mother's unconscious attitude to the child, based on her own childhood experiences. I ought to say that my concentration on the mother-child relationship was largely due to the influence of Melanie Klein. Now, I was eager to make scientific these clinical observations on mother-child relationships, and I seized on the particular relationship between the experience of a child being separated from his mother and the psychopathic affectionless character, not because it was the most important, but because it seemed to me the most concrete and the simplest to study.

Then came the war. I spent five years in the army as an army psychiatrist, and much of my time was spent in officer-selection work. I received a post-graduate education in psychology in the army and a training in research method. I also learnt that the way to get people of diverse backgrounds and disciplines and outlooks to work together was to give them one single task.

After the war I was offered a full-time post at the Tavistock Clinic, where I have been for the last seven years, in charge of the Child Guidance Department; there I have had one foot in the clinical field and one foot in research, trying to 'scientificate' the clinical field. I think when I returned to child guidance after the war I did so with some doubt as to whether my clinical convictions of pre-war days were going to stand up to further scrutiny, and I was rather delighted to find that they all did, or at least they seemed to.

I returned very swiftly to my hobby-horse, mother-child separation. It seemed to me that it was one of the few islands of dry ground in a rather swampy scientific field, and that one had here a definable experience which demonstrably could sometimes produce a particular type of personality outcome. I have stuck very rigidly to it, with two or three purposes in mind. The first has been to substantiate a claim that all child psychiatrists make, that these early experiences between the parent and child are really as important as we think they are, in contrast to the view of many who ridicule it. The second purpose is to make clear that here is an aetiological factor calling for preventive action in the mental health field, something clear cut and concrete that people can get hold of. The third purpose is research; I felt that we had here a scientific phenomenon to the study of which many techniques could be brought which might lead to a unification of different points of view. My own techniques were those of psychoanalysis and child psychiatry but I hoped to bring to bear on this one single problem a variety of disciplines. It was my good fortune in 1950 to be invited by W.H.O. to read the literature on this subject and really get to grips with it. Since then I have been interested in getting hold of any scientific knowledge which seemed to lead to an understanding of why it is that that particular sort of experience, the child being separated from his mother for many months, could not only have an effect on the character but have a *permanent* effect. What is the cause of the permanence? Well, that led me, amongst other things, to be interested in Professor Lorenz's work; the phenomenon of imprinting at once struck me as possibly important to my work. Whether it really has anything to do with the effects of separation we shall see. The other thing that fascinated me in his work was the mother-child relationship of animals. The mother-child relationship is manifestly an example of instinct, in the ethological meaning of the word, and it is also at the centre of psychoanalysis.

Other things which have been interesting me more recently have been the phenomena of behaviour under stress and experimental neurosis because, here again, one is faced with peculiar forms of learning which have a remarkable quality of persistence. My interest in this Study Group is the hope that some other disciplines could help me in my quest. I must confess to a rather one-track, one-problem mind.

LORENZ:

I am born and bred Austrian, from near Vienna. My scientific career, rather like that of Dr. Mead, started at the age of five, when I got a nest of ducklings as an Easter present, and I may say that the ducklings and I became imprinted upon each other, and curiously enough the history of my teacher Heinroth, who has done most of his work on *Anatidae*, begins in exactly the same way, with a gosling, not a duckling, but also at five years. Well, that may be a coincidence. Then, at about twelve years, I became acquainted with Charles

27

Darwin, by means of a popular booklet (DARWIN, 1872), and from then on I became a passionate evolutionist, and besides started to become a comparative zoologist, which my father, who was an orthopaedic surgeon, tried to prevent by ordering me to study medicine. This afterwards saved my life, when I was in Russia. Nevertheless, I resented it strongly at the time, and when I was a graduate student, I attached myself to Professor Hochstetter, who was the best morphologist and comparative anatomist living, and decided to become a comparative anatomist, not changing my preference for evolution, though. I did not give up keeping live animals, but regarded it as a hobby, a plaything. Now, at Hochstetter's chair, I learnt how one ought to proceed in investigating and reconstructing the course of evolution. Then I learnt among other things one fundamental sentence, which my teacher Hochstetter used to repeat again and again, 'Primitive animals do not exist, only primitive *characters* do.'

Then I made my discovery; it wasn't mine, it was actually Charles Whitman's, but I didn't know it. I discovered instinctive movement. I discovered for myself that innate movements are just as conservative characters in the species or genus as are any claws or bones. The museum zoologist is apt to think that what is most resistant and keepable in the museum must be so in evolution, but it isn't true.

Then, when I was just full of the first discovery, I discovered Heinroth, and I saw that he knew the same thing, and I found out that comparative morphology of movement might be worth while studying. At the same time I was not, and Heinroth was not, interested in the physiology or in the psychological importance of instinctive movements. We were interested in comparative characters. We were interested in finding more and more *characters* that could be used in reconstructing evolution. And simply because there were not enough morphological characters available, we proceeded to spread our search to behaviour patterns and found that these very often are even more conservative and reliable landmarks of phylogeny than the colours of plumage or the form of bones. In view of the fact that instinctive movements were discovered in this particular way it always seems somewhat paradoxical to me that there still are people who try to deny their very existence.

And now on the strength of Heinroth's authority, I decided to make my profession out of what had been my hobby up to that time in the study of animals, and I quit my position as an assistant in the anatomical institute, and became docent in Vienna for comparative psychology. At the time that was impossible, because in Vienna the very Catholic régime prohibited animals having souls and therefore a psychology of animals was impossible; and so I got a lectureship

28

for comparative anatomy and—hush-hush—psychology. I have never delivered a lecture on comparative anatomy in my life. Then I became professor of psychology in Koenigsberg, together with the pragmatist philosopher Eduard Baumgarten, a disciple and ardent admirer of John Dewey. Together we had a great number of good fights with Neo-Kantian philosophers, and, in general, it was a very nice collaboration between philosophical anthropology and ethology.

For a very short time I became a soldier and then was recruited as an army surgeon because I had a full doctor's degree of medicine. From then on I worked as a psychiatrist and neurologist, having been promoted to the rank of an Unterarzt, which is a sergeant. I was for two years in Posen, under a very intelligent teacher, Dr. Weigl, who was interested in the study of neurosis. It was interesting to me that neurosis developed in people who had an instinctive inhibition towards killing. Such people were my patients because they couldn't kill any more, and what struck me as most gruesome was that there were so *few* of them—one would have expected many more. Then I was transferred to the front and immediately caught by the Russians, and then I went on being a neurologist and a psychologist in Russia, without any interruption. There I was treated very decently indeed for four years and wrote a volume of my textbook (Lorenz, in press) there, and was able to bring it home. Then I came to Vienna and again developed my little Institute of Comparative Ethology in Altenberg, with the help of the Austrian Academy of Sciences, which was financed by the English poet and writer, J. B. Priestley, who gave all the royalties of his plays and publications in Austria to the Austrian Academy of Sciences. My work went on very prettily on that but the family finances did not; we had to sell one piece of ground after the other; Altenberg became smaller and smaller. Then I got a call to the University of Bristol, where I was to do comparative ethological work on the beautiful collection of ducks and geese collected by my friend Peter Scott, and simultaneously I got an appointment by the Max-Planck-Gesellschaft to take over a newly-established Institute, and I decided to take the latter, although after very much hesitation.

Our present work tends to become interested, as you see, in knowing more and more about less and less; the problems begin to specialize more and more and therefore I think it is very good for me to take part in this meeting to widen my interests again. It is a great satisfaction to me that comparative ethology is something that child psychologists and psychiatrists begin to get interested in, because what we do is only to create a base; whether you can use it is something beyond my knowledge. Well, I hope you can.

29

BOWLBY:

May I ask one question? I would like to know when the term 'ethology' was coined, and by whom.

LORENZ:

The term ethology was created by Heinroth, who, with Whitman, was the pioneer of that science. It's an interesting fact, though, that neither knew of the other's existence, still less about his work; Heinroth called one of his first and most important papers 'Beiträge zur Biologie, insbesondere Psychologie und Ethologie der Anatiden' (1911). The subject of this paper is constituted by the *innate* activities and reactions of the birds in question. Tinbergen took over the term ethology, which I consider rather a pity, because it creates misunderstandings with psychologists and philosophers. Neither Heinroth nor Tinbergen cared in the least about human psychology and philosophy, sciences in which the words ethos and ethics have a very different meaning. So they did not mind the ambiguity of the word ethology. But I think it is too late to do anything about it now, we are called, we are branded, 'ethologists'. I never use the term ethology in German, though; I say *'Vergleichende Verhaltenslehre'*. The German ending *-lehre* has the advantage over the English -ology that you can join it on to practically anything. You could not say 'Comparative Behaviourology' in English—and that is what probably influenced Tinbergen. But the word ethology is really awful, I concede that to any psychologist.

INHELDER:

I am Swiss, and spent my childhood and adolescence in eastern Switzerland. Being the daughter of a zoologist I amused myself, as naïvely as many other children do, rearing various animals, including tortoises, without in the least suspecting the role Dr. Grey Walter would one day make them play in cybernetics. I went to the University in Geneva where I studied under Professors Claparède and Piaget.

At the Institute of the Sciences of Education in Geneva it is common practice to throw students into the water to teach them to swim. So from the very beginning M. Piaget asked me to participate in his work and assigned me a piece of experimental research; it was a matter of studying how a child forms the idea of physical conservation. M. Piaget proposed that I should do this by dissolving pieces of sugar in water to see whether the children believed in the destruction of matter or supposed that it was conserved, and to see what atomistic intuition they had (PIAGET and INHELDER, 1941).

30

At the beginning of the war I was asked to establish in German-speaking Switzerland a centre for the psychology of school children with the main object of discovering and diagnosing cases of mental retardation. The psychological research on development I had carried out previously with a purely scientific and theoretical aim was then most useful to me. The stages in the genesis of the concepts of conservation supplied me with a scale of development on which the phenomena of mental deficiency showed as delays and fixations (INHELDER, 1943). In my case-finding investigations, which led me from one school to another, I resolutely devoted to a scientific cause the few pieces of sugar allowed per month at that time!

In 1943 I was recalled to the Institute, to act firstly as 'Chef des travaux', then as 'Chargée de Cours', and from 1948 as Professor of Child Psychology. My main activity, however, is still directed towards research.

With a group of assistants I train the young students in the use of scientific and clinical methods by allowing them to participate in our work. In recent years we have concentrated on the genesis of spatial concepts (PIAGET and INHELDER, 1946; PIAGET, INHELDER and SZEMINSKA, 1948) and of physical and mathematical concepts (PIAGET and INHELDER, 1951). At the moment we are hoping to conclude a series of studies on experimental and inductive reasoning in children and adolescents (INHELDER, 1948, 1951).

In recent years we have been working in a highly specialized, restricted area: that of the genesis of intellectual functions in children. This specialization was a result of the need to push our research deeper, but until it rests on a neurological basis and as long as we remain ignorant of the emotional and social background of the child I consider it to be hanging in mid-air. As I wish to incorporate our results in a comprehensive study I welcome the possibility of collaborating with Dr. Monnier and Dr. Odier. I am particularly glad of the opportunity of participating in this meeting and hope not only to obtain information but also to make new plans for research.

PIAGET:

I was born at Neuchâtel, in Switzerland. I was less precocious than Dr. Mead and Dr. Lorenz because I was already fifteen when my first work was published. This work dealt with a special field of zoology—the study of terrestrial molluscs.

The way I came to study child psychology was far from orthodox. I had studied natural sciences, and my doctor's thesis dealt, of course, with molluscs. What interested me most were the problems of adaptation, of the relation between an organ and its environment and the

31

problem of variation as a function of environment and as a function of structure. But while I was preparing my doctorate in zoology I was taking a very lively interest in the problems of knowledge, of epistemology, of logic, and the history of sciences, etc. At the same time I was highly suspicious of philosophers who I thought had treated the problem of knowledge in a fashion that was far too speculative and not sufficiently experimental. I then considered devising a genetic theory of knowledge, studying knowledge as a function of its growth and development, so I felt I should read psychology. I thought I would spend four or five years studying the development of logic and the intellectual functions in the child and the growth of intelligence during the child's development; these studies have lasted more than thirty years and are not yet finished.

To begin with I concentrated mainly on the problem of logic in the child, then on the concepts that are basic to science: number, space, time, etc. My method of studying logic in the child was much too verbal at first, dealing particularly with the relation between thought and language. Gradually I discovered that for this study it was essential to go back to the actions themselves, to the reasoning which is carried out not through language but through manipulation of objects. Starting with my books on the first and second years of child development my technique has always been to study reasoning through objects set up so that the child could make certain experiments.

This study of the child's actions brought me to a conception of logic based on operations—an operation being considered as internalized action which becomes reversible, that is to say can be carried out in both directions, and links up with others. In the sphere of intelligence operations always constitute whole structures, rather like the Gestalt in the sphere of perception; the structures being, however, larger, more mobile and essentially reversible, and capable of co-ordination. For several years we have studied these structures in the infant, then in the child of seven to twelve years, and, finally, thanks to the recent work of Mlle Inhelder, in adolescence. These structures are of great interest. As one arrives at a certain degree of generalization in the study of operative structures one finds again the fundamental structures of mathematics; algebraic structures such as the group, or structures based on the idea of order, such as the lattice concept, and topological structures, etc. We are studying the achievement of these structures in the adolescent and their development during childhood, and they seem to give some hope of co-ordination between psychology and neurology. It is evident that such general structures are based on the activity of the brain. Although perhaps no neurological contact is possible at present, except for attempts—such as those of Pitts and McCulloch—to apply logical structures to neuron structures, I think nevertheless that now we can go further in developing the comparison between the various cybernetic models and the activity of intelligence, as we have tried to define it. Moreover the attempt to discover all possible connexions between these fields comes within the frame of reference of this meeting.

ODIER:

Dr. Mead told us that she began her career at the age of three. By comparison I feel like a newcomer, because my entry into the corporation dates only from my Oedipus complex, at the age of five or six.

I had the rare good fortune to have a father who was most interested in all the questions I asked and took the trouble to reply. I went through the phase called 'questionnisme' in French. As you can imagine I gradually realized that my good father did not know everything, that many problems remained unsolved, and I thought it was the duty of my generation to study them more closely. That is the origin of my vocation, for all my questions were connected with the thoughts, intentions, and opinions of grown-ups.

I will pass over a few years and come to an important event which occurred during my medical studies. Professor Flournoy gave a summer course in psychology and I had the privilege of making his personal acquaintance. I would mention that Professor Flournoy was the first person from a French-speaking country to become interested in a certain method, a certain psychological conception, taught at that time by a Dr. Freud in Vienna.

Later, after the first war, I spent two years in the department of neurology at the Salpêtrière, mainly under Professor Pierre Marie and Professor Souques, who was Charcot's first pupil. I worked in a section for wounded soldiers where cases of mental shock were unfortunately fairly frequent. I saw several cases of post-shock syndrome psychoanalysed for months or even years with truly remarkable results. The patients recovered despite the opinion of the psychoanalysts, who considered the aetiology of the syndromes to be purely psychogenic. Because of this period spent in Paris I always think of the possibility of faulty diagnosis and consider the delicate question of physiogenesis or psychogenesis.

Later I studied in Vienna. It was then that I deviated. I was going to be led astray into psychiatry. One day, looking through the programme of courses, I found that Freud was giving a course on the theory of instinct. Remembering my conversations with Flournoy and Claparède, I decided to follow this course. There were ten or eleven students—twelve on a good day.

B

33

After that I worked in the Psychoanalytic Institute in Berlin. I was psychoanalysed and received psychoanalytic training. My teachers were Freud's first pupils: Sachs, Abraham, Rado, and even Jung.

I spent another period in Paris where I had been asked to contribute to the creation and organization of the Institut de Psychanalyse and the Revue Française de Psychanalyse.

Gradually, however, I became aware of what I might call a lacuna in Freud's theory—the psychology and activity of the ego. At that time it was very bad form to mention the ego in a psychoanalytic discussion, but I discovered that this evaluation was only a resistance, or rather a defence mechanism; actually my colleagues certainly felt that something was wrong. It must be admitted that data on the ego in Freud's theory were precarious, insufficient and sometimes even contradictory. Therefore in Paris, in order to try to bridge this gap, I turned to the work of the genetic psychology school and plunged into the works of Piaget. I was immediately struck by the many connexions between neurotic thinking and all the mechanisms described by Freud, and infant thinking as described by Piaget and his followers. In my course at the Institute of Psychoanalysis I tried to establish links between stages of development of thinking and intelligence as described by Piaget and instinctive-affective stages described by Freud. I immediately ran into great difficulties, I found that it was exceedingly difficult to connect these different stages, as if the child adopted either the theories of Freud or those of Piaget, developing in one direction or the other.

However, there are two points on which I think a correspondence exists, and which play an exceedingly important part in the psycho-biological or biologico-psychological development of the child, particularly in this highly complex evolution which should culminate in the socialization of the individual. These two points are: firstly, everything connected with the mechanisms of the super-ego and, secondly, everything connected with the well-known Oedipus complex. The latter, in my opinion, is a most important and critical phase in the development of the individual; I would almost say a second critical phase, admitting the great importance of the first critical phase so well described by Dr. Bowlby. The Oedipus complex is not a sign of illness; if it develops normally it is, on the contrary, a factor making for balance and development.

CAROTHERS:

It is perhaps relevant to my career that I was born in South Africa and lived for several years of early childhood in South Africa, and had an African nanny. Then I went to England, was educated there,

34

and so to hospital and took a medical degree about 1926. After qualification, I went to Kenya Colony as a medical officer of the Government and for nine years worked as a general medical officer throughout all parts of the Colony. I did medicine and surgery and midwifery and saw the people in their homes and in the hospitals and the out-patient departments of the little hospitals throughout the Colony, and throughout those nine years I must have seen a number which runs into six figures of the population of Kenya.

Round about 1937 the Colony had developed to the point where it was considered necessary for a medical man to be permanently attached to the Mental Hospital. There had been for some time before that a mental hospital, but it had been regarded only as a place where any doctor who happened to be near at hand could look in from time to time and deal with emergencies. There were two schools of thought in this matter—one school thought that they should get an expert from England who could study the African and the African language after he arrived; the other school of thought felt that they should get somebody from the Colony who knew the people and the language and could take his degree in psychiatry at a later time. The first school won the day and an expert was brought from England, but this arrangement did not last very long, and nine months later I was called upon to fill the breach. I don't know to this day why I was chosen, but I accepted the post and after taking it on I became more and more intrigued and interested in the work; but I had no opportunity to return to England for many years, because the war intervened, and I had to do my psychiatric study of the people on the basis of textbooks, and of talking to occasional people who knew something about the subject and who were passing through the country, and I found myself in very great difficulties over diagnosis, and finally decided that I must be a very bad diagnostician.

However, the opportunity came in 1946 to return to England and take the Diploma of Psychological Medicine in London, and then it dawned upon me that my difficulties were partly due to the fact that the pictures of disease as described in European textbooks of psychiatry are not at all completely applicable to the pictures that one sees in Africa, and this has been the theme of my interest for the last several years—are these differences real and if so what accounts for them. In regard to this meeting on the psychobiology of the child I should say that it seems to me that in many ways the African, as an individual, stops short at the second stage that Professor Piaget has described and I would like to know why this is so.

35

Physical and Physiological Aspects
of Child Development

TANNER:

I am sorry to say that during the next fifteen minutes I am going to make a considerable number of statements without giving you the detailed evidence for many of them. It seems to be the only way I can effectively get across what I have to say, which will really constitute my feelings about the growth process, based entirely on morphological and physiological growth and not on the psychological aspects, about which I have no personal experience. These ideas may or may not clash with the ideas coming from the psychological side.

General

I think anybody who has studied the growth curves of infants and children must be struck by the fact that the whole affair is quite extraordinarily regular. Different external dimensions and different organs grow at different rates, because the head end of the foetus develops in general earlier than the tail end; thus the head after birth grows slowly, the legs, less advanced, grow quickly. But as far as is known each dimension follows a perfectly regular rate-of-growth curve with no breaks or spurts as long as the environment is optimal. The one possible exception to this statement is the mid-growth spurt, an acceleration which *may* occur and be confined to breadth and width dimensions between about five and a half and seven and a half years. The evidence for its existence is dubious, and the subject needs restudying on more exact longitudinal growth data. At *adolescence* a striking growth spurt occurs in all external dimensions except fat. Immediately prior to this adolescent spurt there is a wave of fat increase, followed during the spurt by fat loss.

All this is even true of the growth of single individuals, which after all is almost more than one could demand. There are bound to be variations in any process, yet they are not sufficiently large, short of

FIG. 1

GRAPH SHOWING CHIEF TYPES OF POSTNATAL GROWTH OF VARIOUS PARTS AND ORGANS OF THE BODY

(From Scammon, 1930, *The Measurement of Man*, Univ. Minnesota Press)

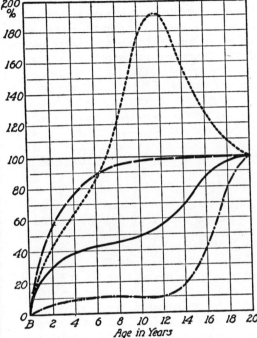

LYMPHOID TYPE
Thymus, Lymph-nodes, Intestinal lymphoid masses.

NEURAL TYPE
Brain and its parts, Dura, Spinal cord, Optic apparatus, many head dimensions.

GENERAL TYPE
Body as a whole, External dimensions (with exception of head and neck), Respiratory and digestive organs, Kidneys, Aorta and pulmonary trunks, Spleen, Musculature as a whole, Skeleton as a whole, Blood volume.

GENITAL TYPE
Testis, Ovary, Epididymis, Uterine tube, Prostate, Prostatic urethra, Seminal vesicles.

Curves drawn to same scale by plotting as percentage of adult (20-year-old) values at successive ages

malnutrition and suchlike, to disturb the regular genesis of the curves that one sees. Curves of a smaller period may be imposed on the general curves. For example, there are differences between the seasons; a child grows more in height in the spring and more in weight in the autumn. This is very well established and the magnitude of the effect is considerable, but again it does not disturb the general underlying regularity of the process. I cannot help feeling there is a certain inevitability about growth which forcibly reminds one of the sort of development that, for example, Dr. Lorenz is interested in. The mechanism unwinds; it is not as though it is being pushed particularly to do so, but it just unwinds unless you get in the way and stop it.

Fig. 1 is a very famous illustration from SCAMMON (1930) that many of you will know. It shows some growth curves from birth to age twenty. These four curves are of different tissues, to demonstrate that, though each different part of the human organism has a regular curve, these curves are not all the same. You will see that the growth of the brain and the spinal cord reach the adult level early. What Scammon calls the general type of curve characterizes the growth of most of the external dimensions such as shoulder breadth, width of the chest, height and, approximately, weight. These dimensions grow fairly fast after birth, then they slow down for a while and then have a great spurt at adolescence. There are two other forms of growth illustrated in the figure; there is the growth of the genitalia, which lie dormant until adolescence and then suddenly catch up with the rest of the organism; and there is the growth of the lymphatic tissue which is rather considerably different from the others. The lymphatic tissue grows to a supra-adult magnitude and then at about adolescence it decreases all over the body, even in organs which consist chiefly of other tissues.

The same events are shown in Fig. 2 in terms of velocity. These velocity curves, that is curves of rate of growth, seem to me often more informative than distance curves when discussing physical and physiological growth. One can see from this figure that after birth one grows more and more slowly. The brain practically stops growing in magnitude by four or five years old, for example. The growth of the external dimensions—body weight is plotted here, but it could equally well be stature, or some other measurement—decreases also in the same way, but then has the adolescent spurt. The weight of the testes shows a much greater adolescent spurt. Lastly, the thymus and the lymphatic tissues after their initial decrease actually have a negative velocity—as we have seen in the previous figure.

In Fig. 3 are the growth curves of the hip width of a group of girls studied more or less longitudinally. Above is the distance curve, plotting the average width of the hips each year; below is the velocity curve, showing the rate of growth in hip width. The time of fastest growth for a dimension like hip width is before birth, at about six to seven intra-uterine months; after this the velocity decreases steadily except that the decrease is interrupted twice. There *may* be an increase of velocity at about five and a half to seven and a half years, the 'mid-growth' spurt (TANNER, 1947). Then there is the adolescent spurt about whose existence there is no question whatever.

There is one other point worth mentioning before I leave these figures; the mechanism of form change. We do not look exactly the same as we did when babies, and this form change is due to some parts growing faster than others at various times. For example, supposing one believes in the mid-growth spurt; there does seem to be a

38

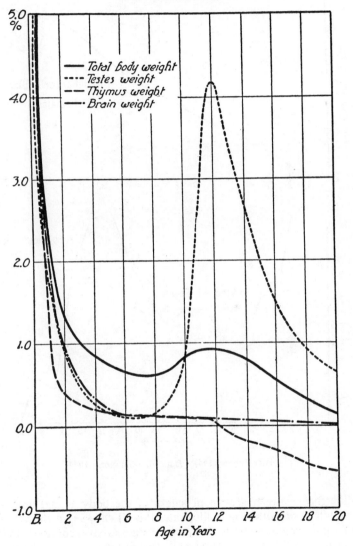

FIG. 2

GROWTH CURVES OF FIG. 1. PLOTTED AS
VELOCITY CURVES

(From Scammon, 1930, *The Measurement of Man*,
Univ. Minnesota Press)

— Total body weight
···· Testes weight
— — Thymus weight
—·— Brain weight

Age in Years

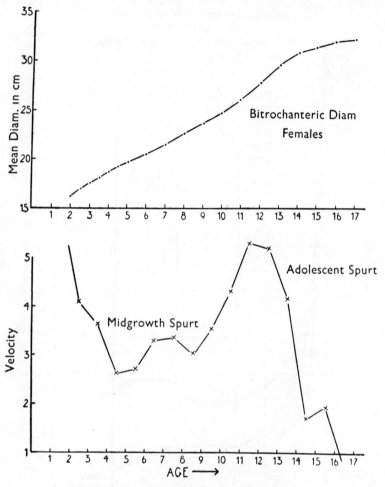

After Tanner (1947); Data from Simmons (1944)

difference between growth in length of the body at that time and growth in breadth. Fig. 4 illustrates this. It shows that the velocity of trunk length, arm length, and leg length (above) continues to fall during the mid-growth period while that of hip width, chest breadth, thigh circumference (below), increases.

40

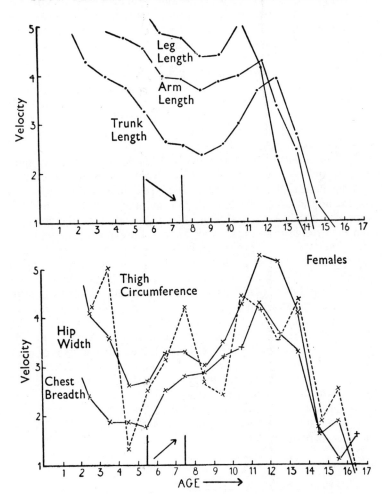

FIG. 4

CONTRASTED VELOCITY CURVES OF TRUNK-LENGTH, ARM-LENGTH AND LEG-LENGTH (above) AND HIP-WIDTH, CHEST-BREADTH AND THIGH-CIRCUMFERENCE (below) TO SHOW DIFFERENCE DURING MID-GROWTH PERIOD

After Tanner (1947); Data from Simmons (1944) and Boynton (1936)

41

A few words now about the development of the nervous system. We know very little about this. We lack even the simplest anatomical facts about the development of the human brain, such as, for example, growth curves of the nuclei of the thalamus or hypothalamus. The external growth of the brain approaches completion earlier than any other bodily dimension, and there is little or no new nerve cell formation after birth, or even for some time before. At least this is true of the cerebral cortex, which is the only part about whose growth we have any good information. Very little indeed is known of the growth of the subcortical structures; the times of appearance of the various nuclei and tracts are for the most part unknown. Presumably there is a regular sequence in their development comparable to that of the ossification centres. There is the same ignorance about the development of the sense organs.

By nine months after birth, the brain is 50 per cent of its adult weight, and by two years it is 75 per cent. At about three intrauterine months the cells become organized into the layers of the cortex, and at about six intra-uterine months the layering and the appearance that we are familiar with in the adult is present. After that the cytoplasm of the cells grows, and the cell processes enlarge, but no new cells, or very few new cells, seem to appear. One can only suppose, of course, that after this time new tracts are beginning to function, connexions are being made, and neuroglia and blood vessels are growing. CONEL (1952) has studied the cerebral cortex from birth to six months and makes one very interesting point: the primary motor area is the most advanced of any part of the cerebral cortex, he primary sensory areas are the next most advanced, and the primary auditory and visual areas follow them. In the case of each sensation the association areas are less advanced than the primary receptive areas. The cingulate gyrus, the hippocampus, and the insula, which are concerned particularly in circuits which include subcortical structures, and as a rough generalization can be said to be concerned mainly with the emotions, are developmentally behind the sensory areas at that time.

REMOND:

What do you mean by 'advanced'?

TANNER:

Conel takes the following grounds. Increase in the width of the horizontal layer of the cells; decrease in number of nerve cells per millimetre; increase in size of nerve cells; increase and differentiation in the chromophil substance and in the neurofibrils. In principle Conel's point is that any particular part of the cortex changes in several ways as time goes by; and when he says that one area is more advanced than the other, he means that the changes are further along in time.

KRAPF:

Is there no reference whatsoever to the myelinization of the fibres?

TANNER:

Yes, he takes nine points altogether as his criteria, and the ninth is myelinization, which he regards, if I understand him, as not one of the most important.

That brings us to the end, as far as I am aware, of the information on the growth of the nervous system. It does not appear to have an adolescent spurt like most parts I mentioned. The skull, as a matter of fact, does have quite a little adolescent spurt, but it is said that the brain does not—I do not see how anybody can tell, with the studies that have been done up to the present time.

Physiological Development

Now I want to go on to endocrinological and biochemical development. There is remarkably little to say, once again. Indeed of all our lacks in the study of the growing child, this is perhaps the greatest. There are no longitudinal studies of hormone excretion or hormone blood levels, except over the span of a single year. There are a few cross-sectional studies from which the course of events is known very roughly. So far as this limited information goes, there is no striking change in hormonal or other internal environment from six months up to puberty. Some parts of the pituitary, some parts of the adrenal cortex, and the gonads do not function until puberty; other hormones seem to be secreted in proportion to the size of the growing child. Striking changes in the internal environment occur at adolescence, however.

One of the more interesting things that I can tell you, I think, is about the adrenal cortex which currently is believed to secrete at least three, and possibly more, sorts of hormones. One of these sorts, the gluco-corticoids, or 11-oxysteroids, hormones which are concerned in the response to stress, are secreted from very shortly after birth at the same intensity as in the adult, per surface area: there is less in absolute amount than in the adult, but then the child is not so big (TALBOT, WOOD, WORCESTER, CHRISTO, CAMPBELL and ZYGMUNTOWICZ, 1951).

43

FREMONT-SMITH:

Is that based on urinary excretions?

TANNER:

It is based on urinary excretions only.

FREMONT-SMITH:

So we are really still ignorant as to the actual rate of the formation, other than by this indirect method?

TANNER:

That is perfectly true. Although the blood studies that have been done do appear to concur with the twenty-four-hour excretion studies, one must be careful how one argues from twenty-four-hour excretions back to such things as blood levels and rates of secretion.

The neutral 17-ketosteroids, which are in general end-products of androgenic hormones produced in the adrenal cortex and testis, appear to start being excreted about nine or ten, in the male as well as in the female. Some people have referred to this, rather inelegantly, I think, as the 'adrenarche'. This is an inaccurate term because, as I said, one part of the adrenal has been going hard at it ever since birth. About other hormones we have no information whatever, and I ought to stress the fact that even the information I have given you is very insecurely based and subject to change as methods and data improve.

Now I want to consider *interrelations during development*. The functional state of a nervous centre may often depend on the internal environment of the body. For example, the nervous pattern of copulation and orgasm is complete in man by early childhood, but is not normally stimulated to action until sex hormones begin to be secreted, and lower its threshold to stimuli.

Conversely the whole train of events constituting adolescence is initiated by the hypothalamus (or by higher centres in the brain). The time of the beginning of adolescence seems to depend on the brain reaching a certain stage of maturation. Possibly the hypothalamic centre responsible is the very last part of the brain to become mature and functional. The postponement of adolescence is seen only in the primates, and seems to be an evolutionary point of some importance (TANNER, 1953).

You know, of course, that sometimes pathologically early adolescence occurs in girls and boys, and when this happens the events of adolescence proceed all the way to spermatogenesis in the male and, if the circumstances are favourable, to pregnancy in the female. This raises another very interesting problem. The hormones of the anterior pituitary are present in the anterior pituitary from birth onwards, as far as we know; certainly they are present very early. They are not normally released until a certain time, probably controlled fundamentally by genetical factors, and proximately by the maturation of the hypothalamus. Tumours in the hypothalamus may cause release of anterior pituitary hormones, which bring about the secretion of testosterone or oestrogen, as the case may be, and the changes of puberty, including spermatogenesis and the production of ova. There are two exceedingly interesting papers about this; one is by Gesell and others (GESELL, THOMS, HARTMAN and THOMPSON, 1939) and another is hidden in a journal called the *Reports of the Royal Berkshire Hospital* (LE MARQUAND and RUSSELL, 1934). Le Marquand's case concerned a boy of two years old. He did not quite go to spermatogenesis, but he had adult-sized genitalia and had erections. He did not have any seminal emissions. Presumably there wasn't any semen to emit, but he had the sex-drive quantitatively appropriate to the adult. On the other hand, he behaved in a way which was more appropriate, both from an analytical point of view, and as far as common sense would have it, to the two-year-old child. He would attempt to rub his penis up against women's legs, meanwhile sucking his thumb. He had no idea about adult sex behaviour, but presumably he had his nervous reproductive centres stimulated by the hormone. Evidently the hormones had got out of step with his brain, and there must have been further maturation processes due to occur in the brain before he could produce adult sex behaviour.* In the Gesell case a similar divergence between mental and reproductive maturation occurred in a girl aged about four when she began to menstruate. Her brain, of course, was nearer to adult concepts. The whole business of adolescence is highly instructive, because we know much more about adolescence on the physical and physiological side than about any other period of childhood. Questions about the hormone secretion and growth at that period really can be answered now to some extent, whereas questions about the earlier periods cannot be at all.

Now lastly, I would like to draw your attention to a short list of some questions and of data required for answering them; then try finally to give you some picture of the growth process.

* This child was also said to have shown quite abnormally precocious interest in and skill at manipulating mechanical things such as farm tractors, motor cars, and motor cycles.

45

Some Questions

(i) Is advancement in physical development as judged by bone maturity and other means related to the age at which children reach the psychological milestones?

(ii) Hormonal and internal environments differ fairly consistently from one child to another; is early psychological development related to these differences?

(iii) Endomorphic children appear to have earlier adolescence than endopenic ones; do they also have an earlier psychological development?

(iv) Girls are ahead of boys in physical development up to puberty. Are they ahead also in psychological development? Do both effects disappear when (iii) is taken into account?

(v) What is the relation between finalization of E.E.G. pattern and time at which the adolescent growth spurt starts?

Some Data Required

To settle some of these and numerous other questions we therefore need:

(*a*) descriptions of the growth of the brain in the human. Such studies should give cell counts of the various parts and nuclei, allowing inferences as to when anatomical development of each ceases. They should also give details of myelinization and of any other histochemical criteria allowing inferences as to the state of functional development;

(*b*) longitudinal studies of endocrine and biochemical development in association with highly accurate measurement of physical growth in a group of children;

(*c*) both (*a*) and (*b*) in apes, with facilities for experimental alterations of both brain function and internal environment.

Summary

The growth process seems to me best visualized as a series of waves of activity. There is a fundamental ground plan to this which consists of a steadily decreasing velocity of growth from early intra-uterine life onwards, and on it is superimposed at least one wave of increased velocity at adolescence, and possibly another. The waves of growth do not hit each part at the same time. First the brain is growing faster and then the chest is growing faster and then the length of the legs is growing faster. We can see the flowing of that wave of activation, or whatever one likes to call it, very well in the sequence of the epiphysial unions. This is a very constant sequence, and it is not much affected by whether everything is occurring relatively early or

46

relatively late. Girls are ahead of boys in physical development at birth and they remain ahead all the way through. Their epiphyses join in the same sequence as in the boys but always earlier, and their adolescence is about two years earlier.

The only thing to which I can liken this whole process is a series of clocks which are wound up and gradually run down. Now, of course, you can interfere with the running down of them by sticking your fingers in the way, which is what happens if you malnourish the child. But let us forget about that for the moment and get to the fundamental things, presuming that everything is all right for the child. The clocks run down one after the other and as one runs down it seems to initiate the running down of the next one, and so on. Consider adolescence—something in the mid-brain reaches a particular point of development, and at that point impulses go for the first time to the pituitary, and the next clock, the pubescent endocrine one, begins at this time to run down and drags the child through that phase. When we think of phases of development in this way it seems to me quite irrelevant to talk about critical phases as though there are times when an organism is particularly susceptible or particularly in danger of some influence. I do not think there is at present any evidence in physical or physiological growth for sharply defined critical periods in man, but there is, I think, a probability that an outside influence can make itself felt only between two points of time in the growth pattern. Searching my mind for an example of this, I can only find a very bad one. It is a natural one, but you will see why it is bad. If you give follicle-stimulating hormone of the anterior pituitary to a child before a certain stage of intra-uterine development it has no effect, because the ovaries cannot secrete oestrogen. If you give it after the menopause (that is, after rather a long period of growth has gone by), it has no effect either. If you give it in between, then it produces oestrogen secretion and all the things that go with that, including, of course, behaviour changes. One can conceive of susceptible periods like this occurring in the growth of the child very easily. I don't think, in fact, that there is any evidence that such things are there, but that may well be merely because we haven't got the evidence. Dr. Lorenz's experiments on mother-following in the goose and others are certainly evidence that at particular times certain neurons (if I may change languages) are capable of having their usual connexions made in a different way, though, as far as I am aware, no cast-iron evidence on the physical and physiological side exists about this.

That is all I want to say to start with. May I repeat that I feel that probably my best use in this group is to answer such questions as you wish to put on basic data from the physical side.

LORENZ:

I should like to ask a question about critical periods, and to give an example how it is in birds. There is something like the critical period, something like the finger that is stuck into the clock which is running down. There are periods when certain organs are growing fast and must grow fast, and evidently cannot stop growing. If you take a young goose in the middle stage of growth and malnourish it, it just grows much more slowly; then if you feed it up again it simply grows fast again and develops into a normal bird. Now in water-fowl, the wings grow quite slowly, nearly not at all, until shortly before fledging, and then suddenly there is a tremendous spurt, they catch up with the rest of the bird. Now if, during that period, you subject the animal to malnutrition, then the wing goes on growing as if nothing had happened to the bird, the wing is hardly affected, but the bird gets thinner and thinner and usually gets tuberculosis and dies. I would like to ask if there is something similar in the case of children, for example, towards puberty.

TANNER:

I would rather doubt that. I think the evidence is at least very equivocal. I am most interested by what you have to say, and I would be even more so to discover by what mechanism, I suppose endocrine, the bird gets its nitrogen and so forth out of itself and into its wings. Of your first example there is evidence in man; the child will starve and be generally retarded and then come back to normal later on when he is well nourished once again.

FREMONT-SMITH:

In pregnancy I think there is an equivalent. I think that the foetus does get the nourishment even in malnutrition, and I think also that in breast feeding to a considerable extent the milk continues at the expense of other portions of the body.

STRUTHERS:

But the foetus gets smaller.

FREMONT-SMITH:

Yes, but there is a tendency for the foetus to be preserved at the expense of the mother.

LORENZ:

I have a better example. There is some such relation between the important and the unimportant feathers on birds. For instance, certain feathers must be kept for one year and some others are shed within a few weeks after fledging. If malnutrition causes a shortage of horn-producing substance the horn that is available goes into the primaries and the primaries are the last feathers to be affected by malnutrition. Some other feathers may be so dystrophied as to be hardly present at all. I have some sheldrakes at home that had to economize on horn substance, but in all of them the primaries are beautiful. Cold-blooded vertebrates can grow as slowly as they please. They do not mind malnutrition at all. A newt can catch up at any period of its life; when you start feeding it again it will grow. The bird cannot do this.

GREY WALTER:

I want to put the general zoological proposition that those characters which are phylogenetically the most recently acquired are the ones which ontogenetically are the most favoured in times of stress or emergency. As Dr. Tanner told us, the data on brain growth are extremely sparse and ill-favoured; but in the few measurements that have been made of the weight, sizes, and general proportions of different parts of the brain when people have been subjected to malnutrition, inanition, and stress, such as in the concentration camps in Germany, those parts of the brain which have retained most of their normal structure were those which developed last: that is the association, temporal, and frontal regions, while the primary motor and sensory regions tended to be relatively under-nourished and dystrophic (WULFF, personal communication).

FREMONT-SMITH:

I would like to raise a question which might underline a good deal of the discussion. I am thinking of the concept of innateness. It seems to me there is possibly an implicit idea that the environment can be passive and that the organism then just unfolds actively in it. Now I do not know whether anybody means that, but I would at least like to put into words the opposite point of view that there is a constant interaction and that all behaviour of which growth is a manifestation is a result of interaction between organism and environment with an intricate interplay in a reverberatory process, but there is no time when the environment is inoperative. Therefore, if we endeavoured to change the environment in a pertinent way, we would be able to modify any form of so-called innate or unfolding behaviour. When we do not see this it is only because the environment remains constant for the particular manifestation of growth or behaviour or unfolding.

LORENZ:

Well, I should consider that any genetically determined character is determined only in respect to a certain range of modifiability. If you take any instinctive action of a bird you can only decrease the intensity along a quite definite gradation down to zero; you can't do anything else. You would not get the slightest actual qualitative variation of his instinctive activity. If you take any more highly differentiated character, let us say, the structure of a bird's feather, its form cannot be changed as can the leaves of certain plants. I think the question of whether a character is modifiable, and to what extent it is modifiable, to what extent it is interactive with environment or whether it may be totally independent, endogenous, is a question which can only be answered by an experiment for each individual case. You cannot say out of hand that all is dependent on environment or that all is independent of environment.

FREMONT-SMITH:

The point I am trying to make is: is it on theoretical grounds tenable to assume that no conceivable change of blood chemistry, irradiation, operative procedure can change this particular character? It does seem to me hard to accept that theoretically. It seems to me that manifestations of behaviour are always interactions of the organism with the environment, because there is no such thing as organism without environment.

TANNER:

In theory, of course, no genetic mechanism can operate *in vacuo*; if the animal is completely starved, there is not much environment, and there is very soon no animal. Nevertheless, particular characters —I entirely agree with what Dr. Lorenz says—vary from being not at all dependent on the environment, except that if there is a lack of a particular amino-acid, etc., they just won't develop at all and you get a thoroughly pathological beast, to the other extreme of being genetically scarcely controlled at all. I feel that the placing in opposition of environmental and genetic features in a general sort of way is quite misconceived, because each problem is a quantitative and a particular one, and is neither qualitative nor general in any sense.

This, I think, brings us to a matter of importance for future research. The question arises as to how much the human skeleton, for example, can be modified during growth by various environmental factors. We don't know the answer to this, and as Dr. Lorenz has implied, and as I fully agree, it will not be the same for all parts of the skeleton. About the only thing that we do know is that you can retard puberty.

At the behavioural level this discussion leads on to things which seem to me intensely important, because, if I understand Dr. Bowlby rightly, what he says about the effects on children who were separated from their mothers at particular periods of growth is that environmental factors have irreversibly changed behaviour. In neurological language this implies that environmental factors have produced altered formations of neurological connexions in the brain and/or syntheses of different proteins in the neurons. To my mind one—though by no means the only—way in which Dr. Bowlby's thesis could be validated, would be by experiments to determine that these physical alterations have in fact occurred. There we have got to rely, I suppose, on the electroencephalographers, because there is nothing much else we can do with the brain except take electric currents off it. You can investigate this with animals, though.

KRAPF:

I wanted to bring up another point and to link it up with one that Dr. Fremont-Smith has made. I do not feel quite happy about some of the implications of Conel's ideas on the cerebral growth of the brain. I am referring to the remark that the first centres to develop are the primary motor, primary sensory, primary visual, and primary auditory, and that the cingulum and those structures generally referred to as emotional develop later. It seems to me that we ought to make a distinction between what we might call morphological growth and functional growth, especially with reference to myelinization, because of course it is quite true, cytologically speaking, those centres are the first to develop, but from the point of view of myelinization of pathways quite different centres have precedence. The vestibular structures, for example, are fully myelinized at the age of four intra-uterine months (MINKOWSKI, 1924, 1925). From the point of view of myelinization (see KRAPF, 1950) not only the vestibular but also the cingulum and the olfactory structures seem to develop before those others. It would seem that the functional growth as witnessed by myelinization has primary importance, and this is where I think the subject links up with Dr. Fremont-Smith's point, because according to my information it seems that the use of structures is conducive to a higher speed in myelinization, which would, of course, mean that environmental pressure, which causes certain structures to be used at a higher rate, would influence maturation.

TANNER:

I am very interested in what you have to say. As I understand you, the use of a tract causes myelinization or accelerates myelinization. I would very much like to know what the evidence for this is, and whether the neurologists here think it is true or not.

GREY WALTER:

No, this is not true. There is no evidence that the use of an organ, or of the nervous system, accelerates growth.

HARGREAVES:

Can you retard it by the deprivation of experience?

GREY WALTER:

Nothing is known about that, as far as I'm aware.

LORENZ:

I think that there is a behaviouristic parallel though. GROHMANN (1939), of Vienna, assessed by a very nice quantitative method the maturation curve of flight. He did this by putting standard perches at definite distances from the pigeon-cote, and then he standardized the distance the young pigeon would fly after fledging. Then he got a curve for the distance at stated times after fledging. He took always two pigeons of one brood, and put them in longitudinal boxes where they could not open their wings (this is not anti-genetical, because the pigeon is a cave breeder, and breeds in cavities too small for the young birds to get exercise). Now one bird of a brood was put in a separate box, the other was left free, and then the boxed bird was liberated two days after the fledging of the normal one, and so on. Now the result was this: the imprisoned bird jumped with a bounce up to the normal curve and then went on following the normal curve. This happened to the extent that the bird which was liberated after its brother had reached the end-point of the curve, which is circling in the air, came out of the box and circled immediately, and a bird kept captive much longer got into a frenzy of flying after being liberated and then had such a hangover that it wounded its wings and could not fly for weeks. It had muscular atrophy, and it is very interesting that muscular atrophy always sets in at a time when a bird would normally move its wings. A bird does not get inactivity atrophy as long as it is in the nest. Then Grohmann did the opposite experiment; he took the control bird to its perch and made it beat its wings. He took it out, put it on his finger, quickly lowered the perch—the bird would flutter. He subjected these experimental birds to a standard time of fluttering every day. The result was that their normal flight development was retarded in proportion to the forced flying movement they

52

did. From this I do not conclude that such a thing as acceleration of maturation is impossible. I am quite sure that it will be possible. But I think this story illustrates what Dr. Grey Walter emphasized before.

KRAPF:

There might, of course, be some difference between what is possible in already fairly developed individuals and what is possible in a still quite undeveloped individual. In this context, I would like to refer again to MINKOWSKI'S work (1924, 1925). According to his studies there is apparently a relationship at least in the foetus between use and rate of myelinization, but I am quite prepared to accept that later on this does not take place at the same rate and quite possibly does not take place at all.

TANNER:

Even for the muscular system, which one might suppose would be an easier system to study, there is little real evidence that exercise will cause anything but a temporary hypertrophy of muscle fibres which disappears again once the exercise is stopped (TANNER, 1952). That is certainly true in the adult, and nobody knows, as far as I am aware, whether it is any different in the child, because nobody has ever done any experiments which stand up to criticism in this regard. It should certainly not be uncritically assumed that taking a child and making it do exercises for a while is going to have any effect at all, except to make the fibres somewhat bigger just while the exercising continues.

MEAD:

Dr. Tanner, I was surprised that you did not say anything to us about the individual differences in constitutional types. In connexion with this critical period, is it not possible that periods that are vulnerable may be points of refreshment with slowing down or speeding up of a variety of these systems which are growing at different rates? If we have material on children of different constitutional types and we could extrapolate points in the pattern of differential growth curves, then we might get a more abstract statement of criticalness.

TANNER:

I hope you will raise that point later on because I should like later to say something about constitutional differences. There is also

53

one point of importance about a difficulty which fundamentally perplexes the whole field, at least on the physical side. We study the height of the child—I have shown you some curves; they are very regular. We study parts of the height measurement and find that at one stage the neck is growing very fast, at another the middle of the trunk is growing very fast, a little later the legs are growing very fast, and so on. Now bring it down to smaller elements. These, of course, we cannot study, so that we cannot really determine whether our regular curves are made up of sudden tiny, localized spurts. As far as the curve of stature is concerned I doubt whether it is, but if we think of the growth of the brain, in the foetus or at other times, then we get a little bit nearer the point, because it may be there that you get a little bit growing fast and all the rest staying still. I am not saying this does happen, but if it did we could not at present detect it.

The other thing that perplexes the field is that for the development of the brain we must have longitudinal data because of differences between individuals. Now you cannot have longitudinal data on the histo-chemistry of the brain, because once you have done the histo-chemistry of the brain of a child, the child no longer exists, so what are we going to do? In animals we can create to some extent identical individuals by breeding isogenic strains of animals and bringing them all up in the same environment. The only trouble with this approach is that the processes that are beautifully demonstrated in some species may not be present in others, particularly man. For example, the whole sequence and timing and effects of puberty in the human is vastly different from puberty in rats. The chimpanzee is two-thirds of the way to the human from the rat in this regard, and the only thing, it seems to me, is to get hold of a lot of chimpanzees to get as near the human as possible, and I know this is very expensive.

GREY WALTER:

I was going to ask Dr. Tanner exactly this question about the scale of measurements: what is the scale on which one plots results? Clearly, if you look at the mitotic figures in the individual cells, you see ample and classical evidence of the abruptness of growth. The cell remains very much the same for a long time and suddenly, in the space of hours, the mitotic spindles part and the whole thing almost explodes into two cells, so that, at some scale, one does find very sudden changes and abrupt development of functions. In the case of a relatively simple process, such as mitotic division in the normal growth of the bodily cells, one would not expect to find anything very abrupt, because the mechanism is statistically homogeneous. In other

54

words, you have a large number of muscle, bone, skin, and so on, cells, all doing very much the same sort of thing and distributed in homogeneous physical patterns. When, however, you come to study mechanisms of adaptation and behaviour, such as Dr. Lorenz studied and such as we study in the brain, there you are studying a relatively intricate mechanism made up of non-homogeneous statistical components, and in such assemblies you do find evidence of abrupt change; even a motor-car either does go or does not go, although the different parts of it may be statistically smooth or stationary. I think this question of the scale on which things are studied is a very important one for us to consider.

BOWLBY:

I would like to ask a very elementary question about the development of the central nervous system. Is it probable that on the whole the lower centres develop before the higher centres—for instance, is it probable that the mid-brain is functional before the cortex, or don't we know even that?

TANNER:

I think we don't know, and I think probably, if you will excuse my saying so, you are lumping together too much when you ask the question that way. Some parts of the mid-brain must function quite early but, as I said before, the part of the mid-brain somewhere near the tuber cinereum which functions to kick off the adolescence mechanism doesn't mature till very late. I want to ask Dr. Grey Walter, is this part of the brain the last one of all to mature? It would be very interesting if what happened was that human reproduction was held up until the brain was really completely matured. The question arises as to why we should have this very late puberty anyway. I presume the evolutionary answer is that before we breed we want to be as bright as possible in order the ensure the survival of the child.

GREY WALTER:

I quite agree with you that the idea of 'levels' of mid-brain and so on is really much too ingenuous.

LORENZ:

I think that the work of W. R. Hess is extremely interesting in regard to what happens in the mid-brain. We know from Hess's experiments that very persistent and highly differentiated motor mechanisms, behaviour patterns, are localized there. These may be activated by hormones dependent on gland maturation and at the same time be dependent on the nervous system. You can induce mother behaviour in a common barnyard cock by injecting it with prolactin because he has the nervous mechanism for brooding young. But you cannot do it in the White Leghorn, because in the central nervous system of the White Leghorn brooding has evidently suffered a defect mutation; brooding cannot be produced either in the hen or in the cock. A similar question is interesting in regard to the behaviour of your true pubertas praecox, and I should be very interested in having details of their behaviour, whether they were girl-conscious, whether they courted beautiful girls, and so on.

TANNER:

I am afraid I cannot answer that very well. It is about a couple of years since I read one of the papers. All I can remember is that the little boy of two years old showed a marked preference for some women over others.

LORENZ:

Were they pretty?

TANNER:

No, it was a more basic phenomenon, if you will pardon my calling it so. It was said in this paper that he did not pursue women who had passed the menopause, but he did become very difficult in the street because if he saw someone under forty in a nice pair of silk stockings he would make a dash for them and rub himself against them, and this got quite embarrassing. But he did not go at all for young, prepubescent girls. Neither did he ever make sexual advances towards his mother. This patient was in the Royal Berkshire Hospital, and I may add that he was studied only by ordinary doctors with both the advantages and disadvantages that that implies. There were no psychologists around, so that the study is not influenced by preconceptions of a psychological nature.

GREY WALTER:

We had a prepubertal case, a child of six who showed very good taste with the nurses. He knew the pretty nurses extremely well.

TANNER:

Well, that shows the difference between two and six, which is just
what we are after.

ZAZZO:

I should like to put three questions to Dr. Tanner. The first is as
follows: is the present state of our knowledge of allometry and of
non-parallel growth rates sufficient to enable us to understand the
critical phases and stages of growth? In other words, despite the fact
that there is a slow, continuous progression, as Dr. Tanner reminded
us, are there for the human species rearrangements in the balance
of the constituents and allometries which enable us to understand
or at least to guess the explanation of the stages of growth, and to
describe the critical phases? For us psychologists it would be important to see if any co-ordination is possible between critical phases
found by developmental biology and critical phases which we
observe in psychology.

My second question is much more limited. What is your opinion
of the frequent statement that the age of sexual maturity in girls is
earlier than in boys, since the appearance of menstruation is earlier
than that of spermatozoa? Can we consider that as an established
fact? Much research over the last forty years has tended to prove the
contrary. Is this current belief not due simply to the fact that girls
start on the phase of accelerated growth before boys? This is important for the understanding of adolescence on the psychological level.

My third question deals with the lowering of the age of puberty,
which seems to have been occurring during the last fifty years, that is
since it has been possible to obtain reliable data. Is the variation in
age of puberty with different social environments considered by
Dr. Tanner to be a well established fact, explainable by nutritional
factors? In other words, what connexion can we establish, in a general
way, between the evolution of the organism and environmental
influences, 'environment' being very widely interpreted?

TANNER:

I will take the questions in the order in which they were asked. As I
understand it, your first question implied that the study of allometry
in the physical side of development gives some background for the
suggestion that there are critical phases during growth. When allometry was first thought of by Huxley and Teissier and others, they
imagined that by plotting the growth of one dimension against
another, both in logarithms, they produced a curve with a sudden

57

sharp change of direction in it. Later work has shown this notion to be quite fallacious, at least for mammals. The sharp change of direction resulted only from drawing various straight lines through points which really show a gradual and continuous curvature (TANNER, 1951). Any idea that critical phases may exist because of that formulation of allometry is ill-founded and incorrect. That answers the question without becoming technical, which I am very willing to do if we have the time.

Now the second question—the difference in age of sexual maturity between girls and boys—first, is it established that girls begin puberty earlier than boys? Yes. Definitely, clearly, no question. About two years on average. It varies between individuals of course. There are some girls who enter puberty after some boys. There are some interesting data that suggests that those girls who develop late become relatively more masculine in physique and those boys who develop early become relatively more feminine (BAYLEY, 1943). I don't think this is entirely established, but it is reasonable, and it is a subject which would stand looking into. So much for the spurt in physical growth. However, if I understood Dr. Zazzo correctly, he is more concerned with the attainment of actual reproductive maturity in the strict biological sense, that is, spermatogenesis, copulatory behaviour, the ability to produce children. The evidence here is not so complete. I *would* imagine girls are capable of breeding earlier than boys: on the other hand, there is a well-documented period of adolescent sterility. The course of puberty is this: there is an increased velocity of growth in stature and in all the physical dimensions, and shortly after the peak velocity has been reached and the speed is slackening to zero, menstruation begins (see Fig. 5). This relationship is remarkably constant. The uterus grows fairly late and gradually becomes functional, and as growth in height begins to finish, menstruation begins. Now, despite the uterus getting to the stage of bleeding, the early cycles, which are often not so regular as the later ones, may be anovulatory, and due only to oestrogen withdrawal, and this may go on for perhaps a year, eighteen months, two years. There is some physiological evidence for this and also a good deal of anthropological evidence that repeated intercourse at that time does not lead to pregnancy. It may well be that there is a similar period in boys. There is no evidence about this as far as I know, but it seems a reasonable thing to assume. That's as far as I can go towards answering your question on the facts we have at present.

Now for the third question: is the age of puberty related to environmental factors and social class? Yes, it can be related to environmental factors; for instance, adolescence was retarded in parts of Europe where the food supply was diminished by the war. There is no

FIG. 5

RELATION OF PEAK VELOCITIES IN HEIGHT-GROWTH FOR EARLY, AVERAGE AND LATE MATURING GIRLS TO TIME OF MENARCHE. M1, M2, AND M3 SHOW AVERAGE TIME OF MENARCHE FOR EACH GROUP

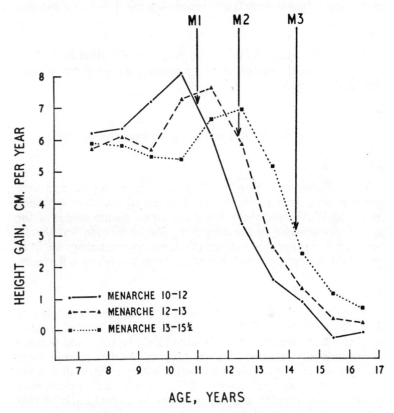

After Tanner (1953); data from Simmons and Greulich (1943)

question that malnutrition can postpone it. I am not sure whether there is any literature which distinguishes clearly between different social classes and whether any class effect could be related to things other than malnutrition, or whether indeed it could be related to genetics. As to other environmental factors such as climate, it has often been said that puberty is earlier in the tropics. But the data on which that statement was based are very poor. There has been one good study by ELLIS (1950) recently, which showed that puberty occurred at very much the same time in Nigeria as in Western

Europe. It was shown in California that different racial groups had menarche at different times, but this may be chiefly due to genetical factors (Ito, 1942). The differences were not in any case very large. So this question cannot be answered certainly, but short of malnutrition it seems that if there is any social class effect, it isn't a big one.

MEAD:

Would you include the work that PELLER (1940) did on the effects of starvation in the mother during pregnancy on delayed menstruation in the daughters?

TANNER:

I don't know that work; I would like to have the reference.

MEAD:

These studies were based on Viennese girls whose mothers were pregnant with them during the worst period of starvation in Vienna in World War I, and there was a consistent postponement of the age of menstruation in the daughters. The implication was that in handling first-generation data on ethnic groups we perhaps ought to go back a generation in order to trace the causes of any differences.

TANNER:

Or rather to the foetus. I regard this with a certain amount of doubtfulness because most of the data say that semi-starved foetuses such as we are assuming to exist would only be small and perhaps developmentally retarded at birth. Most of the data (though these data are not cast-iron stuff at all) would rather indicate that if the children were later well nourished they would catch up on their growth curves rapidly, and certainly not be thrown back all that long time during growth, as you imply.

MEAD:

There were other concomitants also. There were pelvic distortions, sometimes prolonged amenorrhoea after puberty, and difficulty in childbirth.

CAROTHERS:

It has been commonly written and commonly assumed in the past that puberty was early in the tropics, but this was largely based on estimates of age. The African never knows his age and these estimates

60

were grossly faulty. They are not quite so faulty at the age of puberty but at later ages it is easy to be ten years out, and the age is nearly always under-estimated.

KRAPF:

With regard to the matter of the onset of menarche in South America, what I have been able to find out from gynaecologists' reports about the matter is against any differences between the temperate zones and the tropical zones.

The Behaviour of New-born Anencephalics
with various Degrees of Anencephaly

MONNIER:

We have made a prolonged study of the scheme of integration of the motor functions by the central nervous system. Various methods can be used. The best way is to study the development of the motor paths in the embryo, foetus, and newborn, a method initiated by Monakov and Minkowski at Zürich and experimentally perfected by Windle at Chicago. Phylogeny and ontogeny supply us with concordant data which enable us to reconstitute the scheme of integration (Aufbauplan) of the motor functions provided that these data are analysed and interpreted according to functional criteria (MONNIER, 1946). If we admit as a criterion of integration the synthesis of the elementary mechanisms in a function adapted to an aim, we can say that the scheme of integration advances by stages at well defined times. We have distinguished the following stages:

1. Integration of motor functions in respiration and nutrition, functions of mime and vocal expression, protective functions with predominance of flexion mechanisms and functions of prehension (end of foetal life, and birth);

2. Functions of active orientation of head and eyes (two to three months);

3. Functions of lifting the head (two to three months), the trunk (five to six months), the legs, retaining position (seven to ten months);

4. Functions of progression, locomotion, and regulation of equilibrium (eleven to fourteen months);

5. Articulate language (fifteen to twenty-four months);

6. Technical manual dexterity characteristic of working man (adolescence).

Although it is always possible to study experimentally in the animal the correlations between the stages of development of motor functions and the stages of differentiation of anatomical functions, which give us information on the integrating function of the differentiated mechanisms, the same cannot be done with man. This is why the newborn anencephalics, with their rudimentary bulbo-spinal, ponto-bulbo-spinal or meso-ponto-bulbo-spinal brains afford us an exceptional opportunity of defining the correlation between a stage in the organization of motor functions and the corresponding stage in the morphological development of the nervous system. The film will show the motor paths of ponto-bulbo-spinal anencephalics (rhombencephalic anencephaly), then those of a meso-rhombencephalic anencephalic and finally those of Gamper's anencephalic with a well developed mesencephalon. At the same time anatomical sections of the brain stem will be shown, illustrating the degree of development of the nervous integrating mechanisms.

(a) Rhombencephalic Anencephalus

We have been able to observe four anencephalics whose brain was limited to the pons, medulla oblongata, and cord. In such cases the vegetative functions are very poorly regulated. The blood supply to the peripheral area is insufficient and respiration is irregular. Ingestion of food is badly co-ordinated, especially sucking. The temperature is very labile (poikilothermy) and the infant can hardly survive more than one or two days. There was no spontaneous activity and no periodicity of states of wakefulness and sleep. Motor activity consists mainly of defence behaviour by flexion with intense protective reflexes to noxious tactile stimulation or to acoustic or vestibular stimulation. Integration at this stage is characterized by poor localization of reflex responses, a tendency to irradiation, bilateralism, and even generalization of response (mass reflex). Stimulation of the sole of the foot, the malleolus, or the Achilles tendon produces, not a Babinski phenomenon confined to the big toe, but a triple retraction of the leg on the side stimulated, often also of the other side, and sometimes even a reaction of the upper limbs accompanied by clonic trembling of hands and arms. Reflexes of flexion posture and prehension reactions are highly developed. Rudimentary balancing reactions are observed with extension of the arms and flexion of the head, as in Moro's reflex. Although conditions for development of mental activity do not perhaps exist it can at least be said that mechanisms for protection against noxious stimuli and prehension to counteract the dangerous effect of weight are accompanied by expression phenomena capable of interpreting certain rudimentary affective states. The mechanisms responsible for these primordial integrations are the reticular formations of the medulla oblongata and the pons (Tegmentum pontis), with the posterior cords and the cranial nerves V to XII (MONNIER and WILLI, 1947).

63

FIG. 6

ANENCEPHALIC NEWBORNS AT VARIOUS STAGES OF ANENCEPHALY

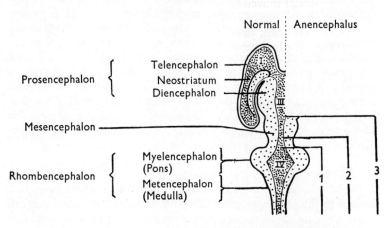

Normal : Anencephalus

Prosencephalon {
    Telencephalon
    Neostriatum
    Diencephalon
}

Mesencephalon

Rhombencephalon {
    Myelencephalon (Pons)
    Metencephalon (Medulla)
}

1. *Rhombencephalic Anencephalus*
   Monnier & Willi 1947

2. *Meso-rhombencephalic Anencephalus*
   Monnier & Willi 1953

3. *Mesencephalic Anencephalus*
   Gamper 1926

(b) *Meso-rhombencephalic Anencephalic*

I had the opportunity of observing with H. Willi an anencephalic whose brain was limited to the caudal area of the mesencephalon (isthmus) together with the pons, medulla oblongata, and cord. It was possible to keep the newborn alive for fifty-seven days. It showed good circulation, irregular and sometimes periodic respiration, poikilothermy and mediocre regulation of blood sugar. Spontaneous activity was limited to a few movements of the face and lips. The infant lay on one side with arms and legs flexed. It had the advantage over the type previously described of having a more physiological posture during sleep. The hands were prone and legs supine. It slept most of the time and showed little movement—only lazily or by fits and starts—when stimulated. The head sometimes moved slowly from one side to the other.

The somatic-motor integrated functions consisted mainly of defensive flexion reflexes released by exteroceptive tactile, thermic or chemical stimuli, more or less noxious. Very intense stimuli provoked a generalized defence reflex (mass reflex). Grasping mechanisms were well developed in both hands and feet; they could be clearly observed during trophotropic activities, such as sleep and feeding. Functions of mime and vocal expression were well developed: contortions of the trunk, vermicular movements of the head and limbs, sometimes certain facial expressions of affective pleasure reactions with stretching, extension of the arms, yawning and sighing. Passive extension of the leg induced, for example, a Moro reflex, with deflection of the head, extension of the arms, especially the right arm, opening of the mouth, and sighing. As to vocal reactions, they were limited to a sort of hiccough and stridor. The functions of extension and of lifting against weight remained rudimentary: reactions of extension and abduction of the arms (stage 1 of Moro's reflex) with lifting of the trunk. As regards functions of active orientation of the head in space, they were limited to mechanisms of buccal prehension (prehension of fingers or bottle with lips, lifting of the head under the influence of proprioceptive excitation from the stretched nape of the neck or from the vestibular apparatus). The lifting of the trunk in sitting position by passive extension of the legs can also be considered an elementary lifting mechanism.

In this type of anencephalic we were able to observe in the course of weeks the transformation of an inadequate reaction (turning of the head towards a noxious stimulus: prick of a needle) into an adequate flight reaction. This adequate reaction appeared seven weeks after birth; it was at times so intense that it even took the place of buccal prehension behaviour; the mouth moved away from the finger presented instead of seizing it (MONNIER and WILLI, 1953).

(c) Mesencephalic Anencephalic

In the anencephalic of pure mesencephalic type, described by GAMPER (1926), all the vegetative functions are well regulated, especially respiration and circulation. There is a distinct alternation between periods of sleep and waking activity. General spontaneous activity is more intense (movements of the tongue, contortions). Locomotor paths are highly developed; they consist mainly of reflexes of crossed extension, automatically released, and very clear successive induction phenomena in sitting position (epileptoid trembling). The functions of facial and vocal expression are better elaborated: smiles and tears. The Moro reaction, induced by a puff of cold air, is shown again by extension of the arms, but also by deflexion of the head, with a yawning reaction, whereas in the rhombencephalic anencephalics we had mostly a head-flexion reaction. The functions of protection and defence are well developed. Extension and lifting functions are definitely better developed than in the preceding anencephalic types. The same is true of the tonic neck reflexes, the reflexes of lifting of head and trunk, and the reactions to vestibular

C

stimulation of rotatory or linear acceleration. This is also the case with all the functions of orientation of the head and upper body in space. The paths of oral prehension are so well developed that they produce in the anencephalic an effect of an automaton, which always directs its mouth towards the finger that touches it. Here too one can say that the development and maturation are characterized by greater spontaneous activity, mainly pre-locomotor, by better differentiated functions of facial expression, giving the impression of affective reactions, better elaborated functions of lifting and motor orientation and especially by a closer and more adequate adaptation of reactions to objective (GAMPER, 1926).

Dr. Monnier then showed a film illustrating these descriptions.

MONNIER:

I would like now to discuss the question of reactive patterns changing with the development of the nervous system. My film showed a meso-rhombencephalic anencephalus turning the head toward a source of nocive stimulation (prick of a needle) during the first six weeks of life, and then turning the head away from the stimulus. This latter protective reaction could be elicited chiefly from the seventh week after birth. Ipsiversive and contraversive patterns of head turning were probably both integrated in the brain at birth, but the threshold of the two systems was different: low threshold for ipsiversive turning during the first weeks (tegmental reaction), higher threshold for contraversive turning (protective reaction). The threshold of the latter decreases only seven weeks after birth, as a sign of greater maturation of the brain.

FREMONT-SMITH:

What is the reaction in the normal infant?

MONNIER:

Always away from the stimulus.

GREY WALTER:

I beg to doubt that. There is a great difference in different children's response to stimuli in different parts of the body. If you study the same children with different strengths of stimuli you get very different responses. It is a matter of balance between the different muscles, and is very often a matter of chance, excluding the effect of well-established reflexes. It depends on the precise state of development of the motor-groups. Have you studied different strengths of stimuli?

66

When I said: always away from the stimulus, I meant, of course, a nocive stimulus; the prick of a needle. In normal newborns we got an ipsiversive turning of the face and mouth on a slight stimulation of the lips.

I should like now to define growth and maturation as a process which locates, which circumscribes a reaction, instead of spreading it. Diffusion and generalization are expressions of an immature nervous system. During growth the reaction becomes more adequate, better adapted to its purpose. I gave as an example the meso-rhomben-cephalic anencephalus, which showed a better adaptation of the head reaction to various stimuli seven weeks after birth; head turning away from the nocive stimulus. In this regard, we have to consider the notion of threshold. We know in the tegmentum of the brain stem there are pre-configured systems for ipsiversive and contraversive head turning. These systems must have at different times different thresholds. During the first six weeks, we elicited chiefly ipsiversive patterns; during the second month, as maturation of the brain progressed, the contraversive reaction of the head, away from the nocive stimulus, became more prominent. There was even a kind of rivalry between ipsiversive responses (turning of the head with sucking) and contraversive responses (flight reaction). It was sometimes even difficult to feed the baby, since the flight reaction of the head was too strong, so that the nurse could not get near the lips with the bottle. This rivalry was typical for the transition state.

What other conclusions can we draw from our observations and from the film, in relation to the problems of psychobiological development? We may say that in the lowest rhombencephalic type of anencephaly, the protective patterns of flexion type are predominant. The surface of the body is reduced in order to escape nocive stimuli. At a higher integrative level (meso-rhombencephalic type) some elementary mechanisms of standing and righting postures develop. On the other hand, the mime changes with maturation; it becomes more elaborate, sighing appears with contortions of the body, which have sometimes an expression of pleasure or displeasure. We do not know, of course, if a psychological experience occurs behind these various expressions.

GREY WALTER:

May I ask Dr. Monnier a question about the conditions during the experiments that were shown in the film? I, too, am particularly interested in the reversal of the behaviour of the child or creature from what one might call a positive to a negative tropism. This effect, as you know, can easily be imitated in a model. It requires only a simple set of arrangements to exhibit and mimic this particular development, but the effect produced both in the flesh and in the metal depends a great deal on the experience of the individual, whether man or machine. For example, in an ordinary healthy baby one may see a reversal of attitude or of behaviour, from the positive attraction to the breast or the bottle—sucking movements—to a withdrawal when the stomach is full either of milk or of wind. I am sure most of us with children have suffered from this difficulty of trying to get enough milk into the child; at a certain point there comes the avoiding reaction which perhaps may develop in the adult into a highly organized negative shaking of the head. It would be interesting to know in your film the state of the stomach of the child during these two experiments; that is, whether you are quite sure that the child is equally well fed or has an equal amount of wind in his stomach during both experiments, because one would expect that after a certain length of time, varying in the normal child from a few weeks to a month, this reversal would occur as a result simply of the presence of a distended stomach. That is, the endogenous stimuli in the belly can reverse, in fact, the whole action of the body.

MONNIER:

I am not able to make comments on the influence of the stomach and of hunger on the responses of our anencephalic newborns.

GREY WALTER:

The difficulties of feeding are found in quite normal children. I wonder whether you had any evidence of the presence of wind in the stomach. Did you X-ray the stomach to see if there was much gas?

MONNIER:

No.

FREMONT-SMITH:

Isn't your question partly answered, Dr. Grey Walter, in the fact that the ipsiversive reaction occurred nearly every time the child was tested in the early period, and the contraversive nearly every time he was tested in the later period, and therefore it would seem surprising if there was always an excess of wind in one period and not in the other. I might add that I have seen an infant up to the second and third, maybe fourth, day having difficulty in getting breast milk, being unsuccessful, and finally exhibiting a negative reaction so that

68

he couldn't be got to accept the nipple. Presumably a normal child will still feel hungry, although I don't know how much air he has swallowed.

PIAGET:

At the beginning of his interesting communication Dr. Monnier said that he did not consider that growth could be determined by generalization because generalization is a primitive stage which comes before differentiation. I think there is some ambiguity, not in what Dr. Monnier said, but in the discussions in general, particularly in the explanations given by Pavlov's followers of the formation of language by conditioned reflex. Actually this term generalization can be taken in two ways, which appear to me to be very different and which must be carefully distinguished if we do not want to become involved in confusion associated with the definitions of psycho-biological terms.

The word 'generalization' can be first taken in the sense used by the reflexologists as being a level of initial non-differentiation. Generalization, in the sense of a reflex, is a level where reactions are not yet differentiated or specific. I would call this type of generalization 'automatic generalization'.

But there is a second kind of generalization which plays an important role in growth and in the development of intellectual functions, which I would call 'intentional generalization'. Contrary to automatic generalization it depends very much on differentiation; the two are in fact interdependent.

I will give an example. One of my children at about four and a half months, an age when he was beginning to take hold of objects within his visual field, in the early stages of co-ordination between vision and prehension, started to take hold of a cord hanging from the canopy of his cot. When he took hold of the cord it shook all the dolls which we had hung from the edge of the canopy and this immediately gave rise to a circular reaction, a plan of action which he kept on repeating. In this case the plan gave rise to generalizations but these were accompanied by very clear differentiation. When a new doll was hung from the canopy you could see the child looking for the cord and pulling it while looking at the doll, but if a doll was held in front of him he did not look for the cord, he had other reactions. Later on I tried the experiment of hanging an object not from the canopy but from a long rod about two yards away from the child. I made it swing. The child looked at this with great interest and smiled, but the moment the movement stopped he looked for the cord because of the hanging object. Here we have a generalization which is a sign of development, a generalization based on differentiation and discrimination, an active and intentional generalization which should not be confused with automatic generalization.

If it is a question of automatic generalization, then I am in full agreement with Dr. Monnier, but not if it is a matter of intentional generalization.

I am insisting on this distinction because in Pavlovian discussion on the formation of language based on conditioned reflexes the great difficulty is to explain the generalization inherent in the use of words, nouns and concepts. Very often there is a change from the first meaning to the second and from the second to the first. I repeat that according to the second meaning generalization is a very clear sign of development of everything connected with cognitive functions.

KRAPF:

I wonder what one would possibly derive from considering the newborn's ipsilateral and contralateral reaction movements of the head in relation to the genesis of object relations. We have apparently a changeover from what we might call the ipsilateral reaction to the contralateral reaction, and at a certain time we even had, according to this film, some sort of conflict situation between ipsilateral and contralateral tendencies. Now I hesitate to give a psychological interpretation to the ipsilateral reaction, but I think we cannot go far wrong if we consider the contralateral reaction as a flight reaction from something unpleasant. If one considers the matter from this point of view, it would seem to me that it bears out an idea as to the genesis of the concept of object. It would seem reasonable that in the beginning the newborn has no concept of object at all; he considers the object part of himself. It seems to me that in all likelihood the genesis of the concept of object is related to the first experience of objects which are not dominated by him or belonging to him, that is to say, to introduce a term of Melanie Klein's, bad objects: objects which are opposed to the newborn and which, therefore, for the first time put him up against the necessity of considering that there are certain things in this world which are hostile and against which the better choice is a reaction of flight. I felt that Dr. Monnier's film showed very clearly not only how the ipsilateral embracing of the object expressed the all-belonging quality, but also how the contralateral reaction, the first awakening of the concept of the hostile object, arose, and how the two entered into conflict, which in all likelihood is one of the first conflicts which the newborn experiences. This I feel might be an interesting aspect of the problem of neurotic conflict later on in life which can be derived from the

70

purely physiological considerations and builds a bridge towards psychological and psychoanalytical concepts of this phase of development.

MONNIER:

I do not know if we are entitled to bring primitive ipsiversive patterns in relation with the psychological concept of all-belonging behaviour and the contraversive pattern with the concept of hostile rejecting behaviour. Of course, in our anencephalic newborns, the finger is not recognized as an object. It is just a source of stimulation. We must ask Professor Piaget at what time the notion of an object develops.

PIAGET:

That depends on the criterion you use for the idea of object. If you take as criterion the search for an object which has disappeared from the perceptive field; for example, if you put a watch in front of a baby and just at the moment when he is about to take hold of it you cover it with a cloth, the reaction remains negative until about six or seven months. It is only between eight and ten months that we find the search for an object which has disappeared behind a screen. Before this behaviour is organized, very interesting intermediate stages can be observed where the object is not yet localized. Thus, if you put a baby between two pillows, one on the left and one on the right, and you place a watch under the right pillow (you do this at the time when the baby is beginning to search behind a screen) the baby lifts up the right pillow and takes the watch. Then in front of his eyes you put the watch under the left pillow. I have seen infants of eight or nine months at the moment the watch disappears looking again on the right where the action was successful the first time. Therefore there is not yet permanence or localization of the object. Consequently if you take as criterion an object which is localizable outside the perceptive field only towards the end of the first year do you get search for an object that has disappeared.

INHELDER:

In the light of present experience it seems impossible to fix on an exact time, say four and a half months, for the sensori-motor co-ordination necessary for prehension of the object. There is always a certain learning in the act of taking hold of an object even when the object is within the child's visual field.

71

PIAGET:

This happened at different ages in my three children. In the first it was at four and half months, in the second at six months and a few days, in the third at three months and a few days. With the third I had carried out a series of experiments on imitating hand movements which seem to me to have played a part in this early reaction.

HARGREAVES:

I want to pose the question of the Spitz smiling reaction. It seems to me that is the first evidence of the perception of objects. What is Dr. Bowlby's view about that?

BOWLBY:

I think we have to distinguish between responding to a perceptual stimulus as an Innate Releasing Mechanism does, and the ability to conceive of an object persisting even when it isn't being perceived and responded to. I should have thought these were quite different things, and that Spitz was talking about the I.R.M. response principally, and that his work indicates that it isn't until after six months that an infant develops the notion of a persisting object.

ZAZZO:

I think the smiling reaction is a very complex phenomenon. The origins of imitation are still rather mysterious. Eight years ago I observed a fact which I consider almost inexplicable. I noticed in my son, who was then twenty days old, the imitation of putting out the tongue. At first I thought it was a mistake, that it was I who had imitated the child and not the child who had imitated me. I tried this experiment again several times. I took a film of it and later I was able to examine six infants in whom this imitation also appeared between the twentieth and thirtieth day, then disappeared, and reappeared at the age of about three months. I have formulated some hypotheses on this subject but they seem to me not very sound. I tell you about this fact because I should like to know if any of you have noted such early signs of imitation.

PIAGET:

Is the imitation which appears at three months lasting?

ZAZZO:

It is lasting on condition, of course, that it is cultivated. You hold the child, he is close to your face, he concentrates on your mouth.

He starts putting out his tongue when you do; he smiles when you smile; he starts again when you start again. The imitation of protrusion of the tongue then again becomes contemporaneous with the smiling response. But there is that very early imitation at the age of twenty days which is strange and which perhaps challenges our over-intellectual theories on imitation.

LORENZ:

The athetotic movements which are seen in prematures are very reminiscent of stretching movements with young. Stretching, like many other instinctive activities, has a very definite gradation of intensities and, at the highest culmination of intensity, it is always accompanied by yawning. That this very same thing occurred during the athetotic movements of your anencephalic in the film seems very important to me. Furthermore, your friend Professor Gamper, in the titles of the film, always uses a word which quite simply means stretching, so evidently he himself had no doubt about the fundamental identity of stretching and athetotic movements. In the adult, matters seem to be somewhat different. I have seen lots of patients with lesions of the pallidum and consequent athetotic movements, but the impression that there was a similarity between these movements and stretching never occurred to me. But it did instantly when I first saw the athetosis of a premature. And this impression was very strongly accentuated by your anencephalic yawning while doing athetotic movements. The beginning of it was definitely athetotic and the end was in yawning.

There is one other point on which I wanted to utter an opinion. I agree with Dr. Monnier's interpretation that two mechanisms were in conflict, that this creature actually did the 'oral prehension' reaction and at the same time the flight reaction too. I think that this interpretation is quite correct because conflicts are not in any way dependent upon the presence of higher nervous functions. You get true conflict on the level of the medullary preparation. It is the conflict between two postural automatisms. Instinctive actions or instinctive activities of any kind primarily overlap. It is not the general rule that they are mutually inhibitive. They are mutually inhibitive only in special cases where overlapping would be harmful. Flight reaction must not be overlapped by any eating reaction. If an animal running away did a mixture between running away and eating it would be very bad for him. The overlapping of sexual and aggressive reactions in fishes, which we are investigating just now, is so common that you find the greatest difficulty in ascertaining which movements are motivated by the sexual instinct and which are motivated by the aggressive

73

instincts. Judging by all we know, the factors which keep the several instinctive activities apart and prevent them from going off simultaneously, in a 'cacophony of movement', as Tinbergen expresses himself, or, more simply, in a fit, lie in the afferent control. There is no doubt that the greater part of motor mechanisms are localized farther to the caudal end of the brain than are the controlling afferent mechanisms. In the anencephalus, devoid of all but the most caudal parts of the brain, an uncontrollable overlap of motor activities is therefore only to be expected.

MONNIER:

I think that we must distinguish the athetosis of the trunk from the athetosis of the extremities. The latter appears chiefly when the inhibitory action of the striatum, and more precisely the action of the caudate nucleus, is abolished, as a consequence of extensive lesions. The lower centres of the brain stem deprived of the striatal control are then released and show an increased activity, in the form of athetoid movements of the face, fingers, and toes. Athetosis of the trunk develops in a similar way in the rhombencephalic anencephalus, when integrated structures of the tegmentum and of the reticular formations of the pons and medulla are released from the diencephalic control. The athetoid stretching of the spine and neck, with yawning and worm-like contortions of the body, are mechanisms which must be integrated in the tegmentum of the midbrain and pons, as well as in the reticular formation of the medulla.

As for the question of conflict between ipsiversive and contraversive patterns, I agree entirely with Dr. Lorenz. Both patterns must have at the same time a different, well-integrated anatomical substrate, with different thresholds; the excitability of each substrate may vary according to the degree of maturation and to the various endogenous conditions. A conflict situation occurs because the afferent controls are limited to spino-bulbar systems, in the rhombencephalic anencephalus, whereas in normal newborns cerebellar diencephalic and cortical controls, with their afferents, are still acting.

Criteria of the Stages of
Mental Development

INHELDER:

I find myself in a most unenviable position. To begin with, I have been asked to expound Piaget's conception in front of Piaget himself. The conception of mental development as it appears in the works of M. Piaget is somewhat disconcerting, not because of the facts but because of the terminology. M. Piaget, who is a zoologist by training, an epistemologist by vocation and a logician by method, employs a terminology as yet not much used in psychology (PIAGET, 1951a, 1951b, 1952). He expresses himself mainly in terms of *structures*, which by definition are systems of mental operations obeying definite laws of composition such as, for example, the mathematical laws of group and lattice. According to a number of cyberneticists structures are as much physiological as mental. It seems to me necessary to keep in mind this triple orientation—biological, epistemological and logico-mathematical—which is continually reflected in Piaget's vocabulary, in order to find one's way easily among the Geneva studies. But once these characteristics are appreciated the data and laws deriving from them become clear and are easily verified.

The general subject of this meeting is a determination of the criteria of the stages of development. How can we define a stage of development from the psychological point of view? The schools of Freud, Wallon, and Piaget have adopted different but complementary points of view. I should like to expound briefly that of M. Piaget.

The stages are defined by two main criteria:

(*a*) the process of formation or genesis;

(*b*) the complete form or final equilibrium.

The equilibrium of a stage while marking the completion of one period marks at the same time the beginning of a new period of transformation.

75

M. Piaget has been able to demonstrate three types of structures:

(1) sensori-motor 'group' structures;

(2) concrete operation *'groupement'* structures;

(3) combined 'group' and 'lattice' formal structures.

I will define each of these structures while describing them.

1. The structure consisting of a group of sensori-motor operations appears in the period of infancy and prepares for the stage of childhood. It is achieved at about one and a half years and is characterized by a system or group of reversible actions. The term 'reversible' is taken not in its medical but in its mathematical sense. Thus at one and a half years the baby is usually capable of making detours and of retracing his steps: in other words, of carrying out what Poincaré has called a 'group of displacements'. However, these actions are carried out by successive movements and not yet with the help of simultaneous representation.

2. The structure of concrete groupement begins in early childhood and reaches its equilibrium during later childhood. Actually it comes to full achievement between seven and eleven years. The concrete groupements which are carried out mentally permit the simultaneous, and not merely successive, evocation of a displacement or transformation and its inverse. Thus, for example, when a child transforms a ball of plasticine into a sausage or a cake (Fig. 7*) he can from seven years onwards mentally cancel this transformation and thus arrive at the conservation of matter. At about ten years he shows himself capable of carrying out the same reversible reasoning in connexion with conservation of weight and at about eleven years with conservation of volume. In each of these reasonings an actual transformation is cancelled by an inverse mental operation, thus leading to conservation. However, the child, unlike the adolescent, can only carry out one operative groupement after the other, not two simultaneously.

3. The structure of combined groups and lattices of formal thought marks the peak of adolescence. This structure develops between eleven and fourteen years and reaches its equilibrium at about fifteen years. The groups of formal operations integrate the partial groupements in a structured whole. The adolescent carries out a group of formal operations of the lattice type when he makes combinatorial analyses. At about fifteen years adolescents can make up a mixture of a number of chemical solutions not merely by chance but through combinations, associating each of the elements with all the others of the system. This reveals a new structure. Similarly, the adolescent can carry out a number of formal operations with a reciprocal

* I wish to thank Mr. Vinh Bang for the accompanying illustrations.

FIG. 7
CONSERVATION OF MATTER

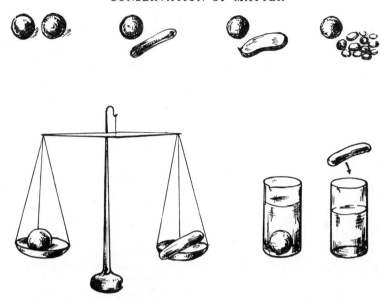

and a negative corresponding to each, thus showing a group structure. The concept of proportion which the adolescent applies in the field of geometry and physics depends also on the group. The structure of formal operations thus shows an unlimited degree of reversibility and mobility.

Genesis

Having defined the structures we can now describe the stages of development as processes of formation leading to structures of equilibrium. I will limit myself to giving a few brief indications and examples.

The first stage stretches from zero to one and a half years approximately. This first period of life can be characterized by the genesis of the sensori-motor stage of intelligence and is achieved with the formation of the sensori-motor group. This consists of a combination of reversible actions such as displacements in space. Six substages mark the gradual progress of development during this first period of life, with a gradual extension and increasing mobility of the 'schemata' of behaviour.*

---

* Piaget calls schema a piece of behaviour which can be repeated and co-ordinated with others.

77

(1) 0–1 month: Reflex exercises.

(2) 1–4½ months: Primary circular reactions (formation of motor habits and perceptions).

(3) 4½–9 months: Secondary circular reactions (formation of intentional acts and prehension).

(4) 9–11/12 months: Co-ordination of schemata (ends and means) and constancy of the object.

(5) 11/12–18 months: Invention of new means (sensori-motor intelligence).

(6) 18 months: Internalization of the sensori-motor schemata and achievement of the group of displacements (detours).

The second stage is characterized by a period of formation and a period of equilibration. The period of formation is from one and a half to seven years and the period of equilibration from seven to eleven years.*

The formation period is characterized by the genesis of representative intelligence. Within this long period of formation can be distinguished two phases without clear demarcation.

The first is determined by the formation of symbolic thought leading to representation. Actually the change from sensori-motor action in the infant to mental representation in the child is due to the symbolic function which differentiates the significant from the significate. Everyone knows of the child's first attempt to represent events by symbolic play, drawing, and language.

The second phase is determined by the formation of concrete operations. Mental actions (internalized actions accompanied by representation) are irreversible before being grouped in reversible systems. Up to the age of six years the whole intellectual behaviour of the child is still determined by the irreversibility of mental actions.

* Since every equilibration phase is at the same time (in respect of the later phase) a preparatory phase, the phase seven to eleven years can be considered equally well as the phase of equilibration of the structures prepared between two and seven years and as the preparatory phase for the structures which are completed between eleven and fifteen years. Therefore we should speak of the stage from two to eleven years and another from seven to fifteen years, because structures follow each other with no definite break, since each new structure integrates the preceding ones and is prepared by them. The break at seven or eleven years is simply a question of convention or convenience. Here we use the following convention: stage I from zero to one and a half years; stage II from one and a half to eleven years with formation or genesis from one and a half to seven years and equilibration from seven to eleven years; stage III from eleven to fifteen years with final equilibrium reached at about fourteen to fifteen years. The levels of equilibration for concrete operations (particularly at seven years and eight to ten years) are numerous precisely because these operations are not yet formal, that is to say they are not yet entirely detached from their contents but constitute a progressive structuration of these various contents.

FIG. 8

NUMERICAL CORRESPONDENCE

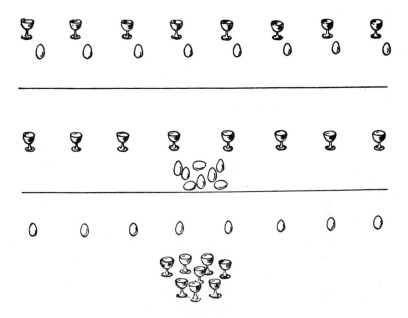

I will quote as an example the behaviour of two boys, Vincent and Marco, who at regular six-monthly intervals were willing to undergo a psychological combined with an electro-encephalographic examination. We wished to complement our cross-sectional studies undertaken upon a large number of subjects by some longitudinal studies. The psychological behaviour of Marco at the age of five years six months and of Vincent at the age of six years is in fact marked by irreversibility in their reasoning. Here is a sample of the experiments which the two boys were submitted to.

For the first test (PIAGET and SZEMINSKA, 1941) a certain number of egg-cups and eggs are used (Fig. 8). The two boys had not the slightest difficulty in choosing from a basket as many eggs as there were egg-cups on the table. By means of an operation of a one-to-one and reciprocal correspondence they were able to place an egg each time opposite an egg-cup and so on. However, when the experimenter destroyed this perceptual correspondence by spacing out the eggs and putting the egg-cups close together or vice versa the children denied the existence of conservation of number and estimated the number of eggs as a function of the space occupied.

FIG. 9
CONSERVATION OF LIQUIDS

In a second test (PIAGET and SZEMINSKA, 1941) a liquid has to be poured from a tall, narrow glass into a low, wide one or else from a big glass into several little ones (Fig. 9) (for children we make believe it is a fruit juice we want to pour). Although they had themselves poured the liquid, the two boys believed that its quantity increased or decreased. The direct action of pouring could not be reversed mentally. In the same way the two boys were incapable of understanding the reciprocal compensation of dimensions (tall × narrow = wide × low).

FIG. 10
CONSERVATION OF LENGTH

For the third test (PIAGET, INHELDER and SZEMINSKA, 1948b) two rods of the same length are used. One of them is displaced parallel to the other (Fig. 10). Once again the two boys, centering their attention on the displacement of the rod, through lack of reversibility, thought it became first longer and then shorter than the other.

In the fourth test (PIAGET, INHELDER and SZEMINSKA, 1948b) two surfaces are used which represent fields on which two cows are

FIG. 11
CONSERVATION OF SURFACE

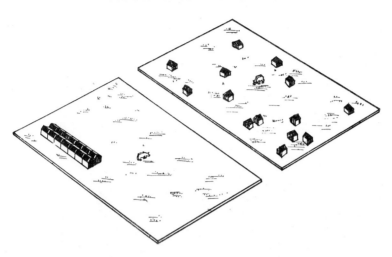

pasturing (Fig. 11). On each of the fields simultaneously we put a first house, then a second house and so on up to fourteen; only on one of the fields the houses are put touching each other whereas on the other the houses are spread out over the whole field. Now the problem is: Are the unoccupied areas of equal size. In the language of the child we ask: 'Have the two cows still got the same amount of grass to eat?' Here again it is because of lack of reversibility in their mental actions that the children are incapable of seeing the equality of the remaining surfaces.

For the fifth test (PIAGET, INHELDER and SZEMINSKA, 1948) a lake is represented with islands of different sizes on which the child has to build houses of the same volume 'with the same space inside' (Fig. 12). For the young children there is no question yet of making three-dimensional measurements. What interests us is to know whether or not they can think of compensating unequal dimensions. The two boys invariably constructed all the houses of the same height whatever the area of the base.

An absence of reversibility goes along with a certain rigidity in the systems of reference. This is why during the sixth test (PIAGET and INHELDER, 1948) Vincent and Marco were not yet able to imagine the water level as being horizontal in inclined flasks (Fig. 13).

In respect of a seventh test (PIAGET and INHELDER, 1941), and an eighth (INHELDER, unpublished), the two children had difficulty, which is characteristic for their age, in arranging objects in series

81

FIG. 12
CONSERVATION OF VOLUME

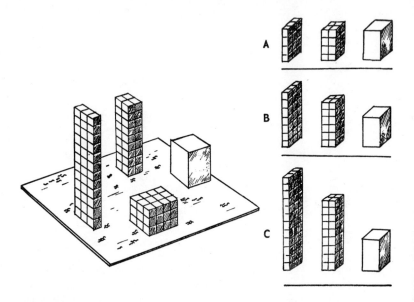

according to their size, or in classifying them according to two or three criteria at once.

In short, in these few tests, and in others, the two children were capable of carrying out mental actions but not yet mental operations, operations being by definition reversible mental actions.

After a slow continuous evolution the change from irreversibility to reversibility often occurs abruptly for a particular problem. Concrete operations as a whole, however, only very gradually impinge upon reality; the age of seven years marks only the beginning of reversibility.

The change from irreversibility to the first forms of reversibility occurred quite suddenly in Marco. After an interval of six months, that is to say between six years and six-and-a-half years, Marco's behaviour when confronted with the same experiments was completely altered. By means of a system of reversible operations he was able at six and a half years to understand certain invariances which he had denied at the age of six years. In the same way he was able to carry out operations of arrangement in series and of classification. The same change was more gradual but not less striking in Vincent's case.

FIG. 13
SYSTEM OF REFERENCE

The balanced structure consisting of a groupement of concrete operations not only marks the conclusion of early childhood but serves as a basis for further development. Here can be distinguished different substages. At the age of seven years on the average the child is able to carry out logico-arithmetical operations (classifications, arrangements in series, and one-to-one correspondences) but it is a year later that the time-space operations are achieved (Euclidean co-ordinates, projective concepts and simultaneity). Thus up to about eleven years there develops gradually a system of concrete operations which will later serve as a basis for formal operations.

The third stage is characterized by the formation of formal operations which reach their state of equilibrium at about fourteen to fifteen years. At eleven years the pre-adolescent is already capable of deducing by means of hypotheses and not simply from concrete facts. His reasoning frees itself from the concrete. But only at about fourteen to fifteen years does this new form of intelligence attain a balanced structure governed by laws of groups and lattices.

In fact two boys, Philippe at the age of fourteen, and Udrea at the age of fifteen and a half, showed themselves capable of carrying out combinatorial and proportional operations, whereas a year earlier confronted with the same experiment they only proceeded by trial and error without reaching an exact solution to the problems. In the experiment mentioned earlier, developed with the help of Dr. G. Noelting (INHELDER, unpublished) on colouring obtained by mixture of different chemical solutions, the two boys proceeded through a systematic combination of the elements presented. They combined the five colourless solutions in different orders: $1 + 2, 1 + 3, 1 + 4, 1 + 5$; then $1 + 2 + 3$ and so on, with two, three, four, and five elements until they were able not only to obtain the colouring asked for but to discover the part played by a neutral and a reversing element.

In the projection experiment developed with the help of Mr. Vinh Bang (INHELDER, unpublished) (Fig. 14) the two boys managed, at fourteen and fifteen years but not earlier, to produce a single shadow

FIG. 14
LIGHT PROJECTION

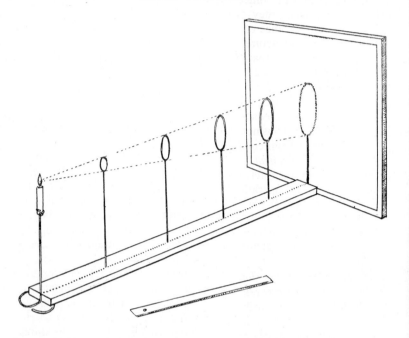

on the screen by means of a series of rings of different sizes placed at different distances, discovering, without previous teaching at school, that the size of the shadow is proportional to the diameters of the rings and inversely proportional to the distances from the source of light.

The formal type of reasoning of adolescents is thus disclosed, not only through verbal expression, but also by the way they organize an experiment and furnish a proof. The age of fourteen to fifteen years seems characteristic of this last form of equilibrium which brings about the completion of formal operations.

Criteria of Stages

In conclusion I would like to specify the criteria of the stages.

1. *The stages of development are defined by structured wholes* and not by any isolated pieces of behaviour.

The concrete groupement structure allows not only the solution of particular concrete problems but all the elementary types of classification, arrangement in series, and conservation of number. The appearance of a structured whole allows us to generalize from one particular piece of behaviour to others of the same type. Unlike the tests modelled on the Binet-Simon tests which do not allow of any generalization since they proceed by summation of successes and failures, the appearance of an operational groupement allows us to identify a mental structure.

But there is more than that: structured wholes go beyond the operations actually carried out and are the base for a whole system of possible operations. We have seen that when confronted with the problem of combining chemical solutions the adolescent at a fifteen-year level proceeds to use a combinatorial method without any previous teaching. Thus not only does he recall the operations already carried out but he can construct a system of possible operations.

2. *The passage from an inferior stage to a superior stage is equivalent to an integration:* the inferior becomes part of a superior. It is easy to show that concrete operations serve as a base for the formal operations of which they are part. The combinatorial method, for example, is based on changes of order which are possible during childhood and later develop into combinatorial operations. Proportions themselves are operations applied to operations, or operations to the power two.

3. *The order of succession of stages is constant* but the age at which the structures appear is relative to the environment, which can either provoke or impede their appearance. The genetic development seems to follow a general law of the same type as the laws of organic growth. However, may I emphasize this: the age of realization cannot be fixed absolutely; it is always relative to the environment. The influence of the environment can act in many ways—at one time through the content to be constructed, at another by the possibilities of learning, or again by the social interchange itself.

The content to be structured: a group of objects may be more or less easy to classify according to their particular perceptual qualities.

Learning: it has been found that certain spatial representations are made easier by sensori-motor explorations.

Social interchange: certain comparative studies have shown that in an environment of free interchange and discussion magical representations decline rapidly in favour of rational representations, whereas they persist much longer in an authoritative environment.

These observations as a whole show the age margin which must be allowed for in our stages. Even if the intellectual development follows a constant order its manifestations are subject to fluctuation.

In summary we could say that the criteria of stages as shown by M. Piaget are based on structured wholes which follow one another in a constant order according to a law of integration.

85

The genetic conception of M. Piaget opens a number of new perspectives:

(1) The operational pattern of psychological structures may perhaps facilitate correlation with the neurological (cybernetic) patterns.

(2) Since the development of cognitive functions cannot be dissociated from that of affective functions, it will perhaps be possible to demonstrate their parallelism. M. Piaget has already shown the relation between the intellectual operation and social co-operation, as well as the interdependence of the pre-logic of childhood and moral realism.

(3) The establishment of a scale of development based on balanced structures will enable us to identify the level of operations in a child and not only individual successes and failures.

(4) The study of structured wholes is, however, insufficient if it is not complemented by research in differential psychology (sex, race, social environment).

FREMONT-SMITH:

Thank you very much. I watched Professor Piaget's face very carefully and he seemed calm and peaceful and at times even delighted. Mlle Inhelder's presentation is now open to discussion.

GREY WALTER:

I have been, in England and in my particular milieu, one of the most enthusiastic proponents of M. Piaget. I have tried to convey the ideas which have been developed here to my colleagues in physiology, with varying success, and I should like to put to you directly a question which is always put to me when I am trying to convince my colleagues that this type of behavioural analysis has validity in connexion with physiological problems. It is this: could you tell us very roughly how many children you studied, from what groups they were drawn, and whether you have subjected your quantitative results to any of the standard statistical analyses?

INHELDER:

I am not able to quote from memory the exact number of subjects examined in each of our studies. For the studies dealing with experimental reasoning in children and adolescents we examined individually more than 1,500 subjects from five to sixteen years. In some studies the examination of 100 children was enough to give us interesting indications, whereas for others 200 to 500 were necessary.

Moreover we are now taking up again with our students those studies which gave us the most significant results for the diagnosis

86

of mental development. We are working on a large scale and trying to study for particular age-groups the relations between our various results.

GREY WALTER:

What I would like to have is, for example, a set of distribution curves showing the range of the variation of these various behaviour standards with age, comparable with the curves for reading ability or arithmetical ability or the other factors which more conventional psychologists are accustomed to plot.

INHELDER:

One of our students is now preparing a thesis for a doctorate on this subject and he is studying the distribution of the results as a function of age.

TANNER:

All this work reminds me very much of the sequence of ossification occurring in children. Obviously, this is a large jump in analogy. Nevertheless, something similar does happen. The sequences of ossification are held to even if the child's development is slowed up. If I understand Mlle Inhelder and Professor Piaget correctly, one of the most cogent arguments for the existence of their developmental stages is that the sequence of them remains the same even if as a whole they are retarded or advanced. This is exactly the same with ossification centres, and this seems to me a powerful argument in favour of the existence of the mental stages, and of their neurological bases.

I want also to ask a question. Some children are advanced physically during the period of growth, and we have several ways of measuring the degree of advancement, of which two, I think, are of chief interest in this context. One is the state of the ossification centres—the 'bone age', and the other is the state of development of the teeth. At the present time my colleagues and I are doing a study in which we hope to relate these two things—to discover whether a child that is dentally advanced is also skeletally advanced. In general I am fairly sure that the two measures are not related to the same thing, though there may be a small correlation between them. The head grows rather differently from the rest of the skeleton, and the teeth are part of the head. Now does advancement or retardation in the sequence of mental tests relate to advancement or retardation in the teeth, or in the skeleton, or in neither?

INHELDER:

In the present state of our research I am unable to reply to that.

ZAZZO:

It seems to me that the main interest of the Geneva work lies in the establishment of the sequence and the explanation of the passage from one stage to another. This is a contribution of considerable importance to psychology. However, one problem arises, that of the curve of growth, and of the significance of the more or less rapid passages from one stage to another. Mlle Inhelder moreover stated the problem very clearly in her work on mental deficiency and she has already formulated several hypotheses. The problem I should like to underline is one of method. You said that the age at which the structures are realized is very variable and you give as the main reason the influence of environment. This is obviously one of the causes. I wonder, however, if there are not others. It has been noted for a long time that tests of mosaic or multiple-variety type enable us to determine the mental level with greater precision. One wonders whether Piaget tests should not be used in conjunction with other tests dealing only with an isolated aspect of behaviour. In all these tests one notes a surprising unrepeatability of results which arises, no doubt, from the educational conditions, diversity of environment and perhaps also from the conditions of the experiment. There are extraordinary variations related to the test situation, the experimental situation, and, in a general way, affective conditions. There is no doubt that this type of test is the most subject to affective fluctuations linked with experience. I think, therefore, that the difficulty of establishing a precise age for your stages comes not only from the fact that there is a wide dispersion but also in certain cases that an isolated activity does not enable us to obtain the same results as when a mosaic-type test is used. I should like to know what Mlle Inhelder and Professor Piaget think on this last point.

INHELDER:

I agree with M. Zazzo that there is a certain dispersion and even a certain lability in intellectual behaviour. Nevertheless, I am always struck by the fact that among developing children the dispersion within a stage is relatively small compared with the wide differences between behaviour in one stage or another, between one mental structure and another.

I am not so pessimistic as you as regards the unreliability of the results due to fluctuations in affectivity. It is above all important to encourage each child to do his very best by creating an atmosphere favourable to the examination.

ZAZZO:

It seems that with these two types of test, the mosaic test and the Piaget test, we have this alternative: with the first type, we may determine a very precise age, within three or four months, but without knowing anything that lies behind it from the point of view of intellectual mechanism; with the second type of test, we may understand the intellectual mechanisms very well but not be able to fix an intellectual level. In the present state of affairs it does not seem possible by means of your tests to establish any kind of prognosis of development.

INHELDER:

I am entirely in agreement with you. In the present state of our research we are not able to say: 'such and such a child is exactly at the level of six years nine months'. However, I wonder if the compensations operating in mosaic-type tests are any more than compensations of a statistical order and whether they reveal the essential characteristics of an age level? That is another question.

PIAGET:

I should like to make a remark to the two previous speakers. The object of these studies, initially, was not to establish a scale of development and to obtain precise determinations of age as regards stages. It was a question of trying to understand the intellectual mechanism used in the solution of problems and of determining the mechanism of reasoning. For that we used a method which is not standardized, a clinical method, a method of free conversation with the child. We encouraged each child, as far as possible, in a way which was not comparable to that used with the preceding child. That is why, personally, I am always very suspicious of statistics on our results. Not that I dislike statistics; I worked on biometrics enthusiastically when I was a zoologist, but to make statistical tables on children when each was questioned differently appears to me very much open to criticism as regards the results of the dispersion. It would be very easy to make all this into a test-scale, but it would not have the value of a standardized piece of work like that which Mlle Inhelder's co-workers are undertaking now, for example. In reply to M. Zazzo, I think that by taking the operatorial mechanism for a particular level one attains something more general than the mechanism of compensations in a mosaic test. I think that Mlle Inhelder has somewhat exaggerated the differences of age, the variations with environment, in order to be the 'Devil's advocate'. In actual fact, I have personally been quite surprised by the first results of Mlle Inhelder's students who are now carrying out a standardization in the form of tests. The regularity is greater than I should have thought judging by my clinical conversations with the children. I do not despair of obtaining a scale which will perhaps not be exact within three months but which, from the very fact that it will give a structured whole, will reveal more than would a system of compensations such as the mosaic-tests.

RÉMOND:

I should like to know if you have attempted to check the validity of your deductions by the 'educational artefact'. I will explain what I mean. A child from a known environment who has received the instruction normal to this environment is submitted to a course of training which might facilitate for him the acquisition of these stages. Have you tried to put yourself in conditions which are different from those of the children who are usually around you? In this connexion perhaps Dr. Mead could tell us if among children of a so-called primitive population, that is at least not having had a western education, one would find the same stages and the same ages defined by these stages. Taking the case of Negroes, for example, should we not find that the acquisition of these stages in American Negroes receiving the same education as the white people was normal, whereas on the contrary there would be a marked retardation among certain African peoples who have a very different educational system?

INHELDER:

I have not been able to experiment by varying systematically the educational factor or going so far as to carry out the experiment in a different cultural environment. My personal experience, apart from work on normal children, is confined solely to children whose schooling has been irregular, children who were refugees in Switzerland during the war. I noted that certain of these children at first contact gave a response which seemed to be at a level inferior to that which one could expect from them. However, after a quarter of an hour of experimenting and conversation these same children reached a higher level. In a certain sense they had caught up on their pedagogic retardation whereas the true mentally defective are never able to do this. Therefore it does not seem to me impossible that in our cultural environment the method of clinical interrogation by means of concrete experiments should enable us to disclose the potential level of an individual. But I base this on only a few observations and cannot draw any generalization from it.

PIAGET:

I would like to give a second reply to Dr. Rémond. Let us take the last of the stages mentioned, the attainment of the formal level. There we have a whole structure which is characterized at first by the appearance of the logic of propositions, and if we study the lattices intervening in these propositional operations we find a correlation with proportions and combinatorial operations. From the point of view of the educational artefact it is surprising to note that proportions are taught, but combinatorial operations, at least in Geneva, are never taught in school. However, children invent these combinations by themselves. They find out not the formula, of course, but a complete method giving all the combinations for a certain number of variables. Here there are two operations which derive from the same structured whole, one of which is taught in school and the other not. They are, however, contemporaneous. It is striking that the school should have to wait till the age of fifteen before teaching proportions. I am certain that if teachers had been able to appreciate the concept of proportion in a more concrete manner they would have taught it already at eight years. If teachers have delayed this teaching until twelve years they have done so with good reason.

MEAD:

Before I can answer Dr. Rémond's question, I should like to ask Mlle Inhelder if I understood two or three of the points. Do I understand that you were working here only with sequences? Surely you have a lower limit below which you do not expect a given stage to appear? I would like to know how much possible spread you think occurs in development; do you conceive of some children reaching the six-year-old expectation at two, or at three or at five? Do you think of others not reaching it until ten?

The other question is the relationship to what we usually call intelligence. Do you expect a child with an IQ of 70 to show these stages in a rudimentary form, or do you assume that it will not reach stage 2 or stage 3 at all?

INHELDER:

As to the first question, I can only reply in a superficial way, letting you see later, perhaps, the necessary documents. In one of the experiments on conservation solved by 75 per cent of the children at the age of six and a half, I did not find a single success until exactly five years and no failure after seven and a half. I was dealing, of course, with 'normal' children examined in day nurseries and in infant and primary schools of the town of Geneva. For other experiments the dispersion may be slightly greater or slightly less.

As to the second question, I have had the opportunity of examining retarded children and mentally defective children with IQ's of 70 and less. Among these children the true mental defectives, after a period of slow development, were able, at the age of physiological maturity, to pass the threshold of concrete operation structures (seven to ten years) but were never able to attain even the lower threshold of formal structures (eleven to twelve years). The imbeciles never reached the threshold of concrete operations. However, the IQ of 70 obtained by means of mosaic-type tests does not appear to me to be an absolute norm. I have found a few rare children who, despite an IQ of 70, were able to catch up on their retardation and to give in our tests results of a higher level. The IQ of 70 can in certain cases mask either a normal process unfolding slowly or a pathological process tending towards an early halt.

MEAD:

I am going to have to answer Dr. Rémond first on theoretical grounds rather than from observations. Stated as Mlle Inhelder stated it, this framework of stages seems to me to be at such a level of abstraction that it will probably be applicable to every people we know anything about. The sort of cultural variations that one would expect to find would be of this order. The Arapesh, a tribe in New Guinea, are people who only count to twenty-four, and after that say 'a lot'—they say one, two, two and one, one dog, one dog and one, one dog and two, one dog and two and one, two dogs—after six dogs they get bored. Now among such a people only the very brilliant are likely to use the same thinking as Piaget stage three, and it would take a considerable amount of extra education, and we don't know how much, to elicit from the average the same amount of facility in stage three that one would find here in this country. On the other hand, in another people not a hundred miles away in New Guinea and of the same general racial type who can count to thousands in their heads, can do the most complicated mathematical arrangements, and are exceedingly interested in adjustment to reality, I would expect many more individuals of average intelligence able to function as in stage three. Now, when I tried to apply Professor Piaget's formulation of twenty-five years ago, it did not work because the formulation was far more concretely expressed than this formulation now. And when I tried to take magical thinking, the kind of animistic thought imputed to young children, and test it out among my second New Guinea tribe, then I found no correspondence. They were a tribe that had emphasized relationship to reality and factual reporting so intensively that the other type of thinking did not appear in children.

I think we need to distinguish between the cultural evocation of the lines of thought called primary process and secondary process thinking, and the way in which the sequence of development of these types of thinking is correlated with growth. I expect to find such an investigation cross-culturally useful, though at times it may be very difficult for a European to recognize the forms of thinking found in these different cultures.

The thing I don't quite understand, though, is the relationship of this formulation to the formulation of the child's relationship to reality, and the attribution of magical and animistic thinking to young children. That is, how do the two aspects of culture integrate or criss-cross?

INHELDER:

I can only make a statement concerning the environment in which I have worked. In fact we observe an inter-penetration of the pre-logical structures on the one hand with the animistic and realistic forms of childhood beliefs on the other hand. The appearance of the first structures of logical thought coincides with that of rational causality in the child. In our environment it seems that there is synchronism between these two processes.

PIAGET:

I think that in order to make comparisons between very different social environments, as Dr. Mead has done, it is necessary to find a system of tests as far as possible independent of language. All the tests which I used formerly had the drawback of being essentially connected with language. This is what I would call my pre-operational period. But if you take our tests on space, here is a field where one can find all the operations which can be presented relatively independently of language by a system of drawings, by comparison between a given concrete situation and drawings among which the subject can choose the true and the false. One should find something in common between different civilizations or cultures in the spatial field. These spatial operations are not, however, separate operations: one can find a whole series of groupements and other operations applied to space. As long as no systematic comparison has been made between different cultural environments with these spatial tests one has great difficulty in separating the part played by language, with all its cultural significance, and the part played by operations. It seems to me this still remains to be done.

GREY WALTER:

We had an interesting experience with the application of the Piaget methods in the clinic. It is an anecdote rather than a report of the experiment, but it is of interest in relation to whether or not certain stages of development can be concealed or evoked by treatment or circumstance. We had some adult psychiatric patients who displayed extreme immaturity, with retardation in their E.E.G.'s and other physiological peculiarities, and we attempted to relate this finding with the stage of thinking. We did a series of tests which we based entirely on Piaget principles, and found, in fact, that patients who were in a severely disturbed psychopathic state had 'retarded' E.E.G.'s, and were very primitive in their behaviour, were not in stage three as they should have been, being adults, but in stage two of their development.

FREMONT-SMITH:

Had they never been normal?

GREY WALTER:

Yes, they had been normal people. They were aged between twenty-five and thirty and they had been perfectly capable up to a certain point, but they had regressed apparently back to a state where they could not do tests equivalent to simultaneous equations; they couldn't make reciprocal reversible relationships even in very simple tests. Some of them were treated and some got better and we could observe, in fact, a correspondence between the electroencephalographic changes and re-maturation and reacquisition of the capacity for formal reciprocal thought for the solution of simultaneous equations. Now we have just applied exactly the same test to a population of delinquent children. The application of Piaget-type tests to a delinquent population aroused such an intense emotional response in the subjects that the people responsible for the children suggested we should abandon the tests forthwith.

RÉMOND:

What were these tests?

GREY WALTER:

They were very much the same as those Mlle Inhelder was describing. We put water in glasses, we dropped a stone in the water, and so on. A particular study was made of the question of causality—we said, Why do you think the stone sinks?—and they said, 'Good God, if you think I'm such a fool as that . . .'—but they didn't answer.

ZAZZO:

As regards the question put by Dr. Mead, I think it is extremely difficult to separate the parts played by education and by heredity in development because the comparisons that we can make must always be carried out, even in primitive societies, in a human environment where there is language. Moreover, it appears that cultural and genetic factors are not additive. Their relationships are certainly much more complex. When reading M. Piaget's works I always wondered to what extent evolution and culture derive by a kind of maieutic process from hidden psychological aptitudes. In this respect, I would recall certain current jokes or certain well-established facts. It is said that the child of eighteen months is at the chimpanzee age and that at seven or nine he is at the Aristotle age.

You know of certain cases of wild children brought up by animals, notably the famous case of the wolf-child studied by GESELL (1941). The report published on the story of little Kamala is very interesting. At the time she entered the orphanage Kamala, who seemed to be about six or seven years, showed no human behaviour. She was re-educated under fairly strict control and at fourteen years, when she died from a uraemic crisis, she had reached the stage of language. This is a fascinating problem. It is obvious that when she was discovered in the jungle Kamala had not reached Piaget's second stage and yet other examinations showed that neurologically she was normal.

LORENZ:

I am sorry but I must lodge a passionate resistance against Amala and Kamala. I'll take my oath, and I want to drop dead this minute, if these children have really been raised by animals, and if you try to get hold of Gesell—as I did—he doesn't want to talk about it. Mr. Singh and Mr. Zingg, I am sorry to say, are people to whom the German saying applies, 'Wer einmal lügt, dem glaubt man nicht, und wenn er auch die Wahrheit spricht'.

If somebody assures me that a child raised by wolves has green luminous eyes, then I don't believe a word he says any more. A friend of mine has caught them out in another untruthfulness. In ZINGG's book (1941) he proudly refers to an English scientist who, according to him, also refused to believe at first, but later humbly apologized. My friend, Dr. W. H. Thorpe, F.R.S., sought out that man, whose name I have forgotten, to ask him why he apologized and what had made him change his opinion. That poor fellow went wild with passion; it turned out that he had never apologized at all and did not believe a word of the whole story.

Now let me put before you a few of my arguments why I don't believe it. Supposing you have a wolf bitch who has lost her litter—if she had lost her litter there would be some chance of her caring for a child. She will grab that child and carry it to her lair, and then she will throw herself down and make herself ready to be sucked. That is all she does. She has no possibility of helping the child to find her teats. The child must be at an age where it doesn't yet grasp, because Amala and Kamala are reported to have eaten from the earth without using their hands (which a dog *does* by the way, it *does* use its hands in gnawing the bone, which Amala and Kamala surprisingly didn't, because neither Zingg nor Singh knew that dogs did). Then supposing that that child, by some incredible accident, happens by rolling about to find the teats, or that the she-wolf, by rolling about also, happens to bring her teats in contact with the child and raise that child, the she-wolf would suckle that child for two months, and then cease suckling it and feed it on regurgitated carrion. You must remember that she has to start at an age when the child still does not grasp or walk. And now I ask the paediatricians who are here what child taken by the she-wolf—let's be very generous and say at four months of age—suckled two months, and then fed by bitch-vomited carrion—what child would stand that?

MEAD:

Are all these details on the behaviour of wolves based on Indian wolves?

LORENZ:

Well, those are slightly shorter than the European ones, but otherwise they are the same.

MEAD:

And we have well authenticated details on their nursing and feeding?

LORENZ:

Oh, yes.

INTERVAL ·

LORENZ:

I have a rather long-winded question. It has to be long-winded in order to make my point clear. I am somewhat a heretic in regard to Gestalt psychology and it is my contention that Gestalt, in its most highly developed and most complicated forms, is nothing else but a phenomenon of constancy. When I see this paper in white colour, this perception is done by a very complicated apparatus working absolutely like a computer, subconsciously, and inaccessible to self-observation. This apparatus takes into consideration all other objects within the visual field, and assumes, as a working hypothesis which may not always be correct, that all these objects are reflecting light and colours, with no preference for any particular colour of the spectrum. On this assumption, the colour-constancy computer determines the relation between the colour of the impinging illumination and the colour reflected by the paper. This relation is, within certain limits, a constant, and this constant is characteristic of the object. This paper reflects, indiscriminately, all the colours of the illumination prevailing in this room; in other words, this paper is white. If the basic assumption of the colour-constancy computer is wrong, if the objects within the visual field do not reflect different wavelengths impartially, but some more than others, the conclusions necessarily are erroneous too. If the greater part of the visual field is filled by red objects, the computer assumes that it is the illumination which is red and concludes that a paper indiscriminately reflecting all colours of the spectrum, a white paper, must reflect green light in preference to red, in other words, that this paper *is* green. This miscalculation, logical in itself and only based on an erroneous premise, is the cause of what is known as the simultaneous contrast of colours.

Now consider what complicated operations the computer underlying our perception of form is able to make. They amount to the highest operations of stereometry. When I turn my pipe before my eyes its image assumes, on my retina, an infinite variety of different forms. Yet the form-constancy computer correctly interprets all these changes of form in the retinal image as movements of the object, and I perceive the form of this object as being perfectly constant. This amazing performance is even independent of the perception of depth! If I cast the shadow of the pipe on a screen, its rotation is still clearly perceptible, only the sense in which it turns has become ambiguous. Now let's go one step further and see how much more complicated

D
97

the function of our perception of form and movement can be. Suppose that my pipe, while I turn it around, should suddenly waggle its stem. I should notice it instantly—and wouldn't I be surprised! Suppose a duck, swimming before me on a pond, turns around; its image would be foreshortened, yet it would not appear shorter and fatter. Now suppose that that duck, while turning, fluffs out its feathers, so that it really would become relatively shorter and fatter. Even in this case, which seems confusing even in the telling, the two computers of form constancy and movement perception still succeed in keeping change of form and movement apart, though they have only the retinal image on which to base their computations. Our perception has not the slightest difficulty in interpreting the changes in the retinal image which are due to movements as movements, and those which are due to changes of form as changes of form. Now just hold this in mind for a moment and consider how complicated the apparatus underlying all these discriminations must be.

In phylogeny, it often happens that an apparatus, devised for quite definite and narrow ends, may prove useful in a quite different and much more generalized way of application. The human hand, evolved exclusively in the service of climbing, is the most commonplace example of such a change of function. Something very similar has happened to Gestalt perception. Maybe it is quite useful to remind English-speaking scientists, that the word Gestalt primarily is very nearly synonymous with form. And in phylogeny Gestalt perception has quite indubitably evolved out of the function of the form-constancy computer. Or, maybe, it is more correct to say it evolved out of all the constancy computers collaborating to build up our perceptual world. All these computers are objectivating in the most literal sense of the word. That is to say they always tend to determine qualities which are constant in and characteristic of the object. And that is all that they are reporting to the subject. The form-constancy computer does not report the accidental form which the retinal image happens to have at the moment, but quite directly the real, stereometric form of the object. This disregard for all concrete, but accidental, data of stimulation, the coming-down to constants essential for the object in question is very characteristic of all the constancy computers underlying our perception of things. That is what I mean by saying that they are objectivating. There is no doubt that all these objectivating functions have evolved phylogenetically in the service and under the necessity of recognizing individual objects or, to use a term coined by Karl Bühler, in the service of 'Ding-Konstanz'. But, as the human hand could be turned to new functions, the ability inherent in all constancy computers to extract essentials enables the organism to achieve something which comes

98

very near to the formation of abstract conceptions. It not only enables me to recognize my chow Susi independently of accidental circumstances by extracting her constant and essential individual characters. That process of 'extraction of essentials' can go one step further: without any change in the physiological—or, if you like, cybernetical—mechanism, my Gestalt perception is also able to extract essentials which are not only constant in and characteristic of that individual chow bitch, but of all dogs. It is able to disregard accidentals which are characteristic only of the individual, and to recognize one mutual, unconfusable Gestalt-quality of dogginess in this chow, as well as in the butcher's mastiff or my old aunt's peke. There cannot be any doubt that this direct perception of supra-individual Gestalt qualities is functionally closely akin to the formation of real abstract concepts. Very probably it always plays a considerable part in true abstraction and constitutes its indispensable basis. Cyberneticists tell me that an analogous possibility for an unexpected change of function has been found in calculating machines, too. A machine constructed exclusively for the purpose of calculating compound interest surprised its own constructor by being able to do differential calculus. The function of this 'abstraction-computer' is, after all, not more miraculous than that of the form-constancy computer enabling me to see the identical pipe in all those varying retinal images.

Wherever animals achieve something like a generic notion and whenever small children correctly apply generic names, they do so with the help of the 'abstracting' function of Gestalt perception. This is also the reason why little children often form generic conceptions with most unexpected contents. I knew a baby whose parents were quite desperate because that child 'couldn't tell the difference between a dog and a horse', because it said bow-wow to a dog and it said bow-wow to a horse and when confronted with a rabbit it said bow-wow too, but not when confronted with a goose or any other bird. It was clear at once that bow-wow simply meant 'mammal'. My friend Verlaine, in Liège, found that monkeys could, in a similar way, also achieve 'abstract' conceptions. An old and wise Javanese monkey could be trained to recognize birds, mammals, reptiles, and insects in coloured pictures and, at last, Verlaine taught him to make the difference between live creatures and dead things in general. This monkey's performance was so very extraordinary that some critics, among them my friend Otto Koehler, suspected that it did not react to the pictures that were shown to it at all, but to some signs unconsciously given by its master, just as the well-known 'talking' dogs and horses do. But I do not believe this at all, after having seen that monkey at work. With 'talking' dogs, it is always quite evident to

99

the knowledgeable observer that the animal does not pay any particular attention to the problem with which it is presented, for instance, to the characters or numbers that it is supposed to read, but evidently concentrates upon its master's face from which the signs guiding its performance really emanate. But that old monkey sat down in a frenzy of concentration with the picture in its hands, looking at it intently, and sometimes actually turning his back on the examiner. And after that he gave the correct solution in a statistically significant number of cases.

If you ask my personal opinion I am ready to assert that I quite believe in this monkey's ability to abstract, by the direct means of Gestalt perception, the 'conceptions' of mammals, bird, reptile, and so on. And one of my reasons for believing it is that my daughter, at the age of five, could do something much more difficult. In my own bird collection there were only two representatives of the order of Rails, or *Rallidae*. These two were the Coot and the Moorhen, both aquatic birds, adapted to swimming and therefore externally similar to ducks. On this statistically very misleading basis of induction, my little daughter's Gestalt computer enabled her to recognize any representative of the order of *Rallidae*. We examined her in the Vienna zoo, then containing a very rich collection. The Rail birds were kept together with other birds and distributed over a great number of different cages. Furthermore, you must know that the order in question contains a lot of species which are, in body proportions and general appearance, as different from each other as could be. There are long-legged forms looking much like herons, duck-like aquatic species, and some dry-land forms that look exactly like gallinaceous birds, for instance, like quails or partridges. Nevertheless, my daughter picked out the right birds without a single error and without any suggestive questioning on my part. On the contrary, I tried to mislead her, showing her cages in which there were no Rails at all, but some externally similar birds, asking her in a voice suggesting that there must be some, but she flatly asserted there weren't any! When I asked her how she recognized the Rails for what they were, she could only say, 'Well, they are just like a moorhen . . .'.

Now the question to which I am leading up, and which is directed particularly at Mlle Inhelder, is this: I believe that among your intelligence tests for children there are some which investigate the child's ability to abstract, to generalize. Do you ever, in such tests, find any correlation between a person's power of abstraction and his or her particularly ability to perceive complicated Gestalts? If what I suspect is correct, you ought to get in this respect a particularly big variability in tests of generalizing power, because it is well known

100

that the ability to see Gestalts as wholes is very different in different men and different types of men, and if there really is a strong causal connexion between Gestalt perception and generalization there should be a very large variation in the behaviour of children in the generalization tests.

INHELDER:

In this question we return to the form of reasoning and the content to be structured; the faculty of abstraction does not correspond to an operation which would appear at seven years whatever the object or the situation. Although a child of seven years may manage to classify red boxes and oppose them to the class of blue boxes, and may be able to classify big boxes and oppose them to the class of little boxes, I cannot tell without previous experience whether he would be able as easily to form a class of primroses and to oppose it to the class of non-primrose flowers. In the same way the hierarchical pigeon-holing of animal classes (in our experiment it is a matter of ducks, birds, and animals) can be greatly facilitated when we oppose a non-animal class (chairs, books, etc.) to the animal class.

The moment when the classification operations appear depends not only on the operational capacity as such but also, though in a lesser degree, on the content on which it operates. Obviously this is only a partial reply to your question.

PIAGET:

Dr. Lorenz spoke of a case where the common Gestalt encourages abstraction, whereas in most of our tests we try to put the perceptive configuration in conflict with the operation. That is why we have difficulty in replying to you.

LORENZ:

Yes, in order to reply to my question it would be necessary to carry out tests where the Gestalt is absolutely useless.

PIAGET:

Without wishing to detract from your daughter I would say that a common Gestalt encourages abstraction and then we are not certain of being in the presence of what we call an operation.

GREY WALTER:

It can be shown that a machine or animal that can extract invariants in the form of Gestalten, or patterns, is automatically capable of learning. A machine or animal that has been designed, or has evolved, so that it can learn can automatically at the same time extract Gestalten. This is a first principle of cybernetic design which has been developed only quite recently as a theorem.

LORENZ:

I am very excited about this cybernetic fact. Learning facts like that makes it worth while attending conferences! I may somewhat lessen my excitement by stating that WOLFGANG KÖHLER (1940) knew one side of this and said that no animal can acquire knowledge of a stimulus situation as a signal releasing a conditioned reaction if it is not within the scope of its Gestalt perception. This works only one way, though, and it seems tremendously important if it can be shown that, conversely, a machine that can perceive Gestalt is automatically able to learn.

MEAD:

This is a very good illustration, I think, of an intervention of cultural factors. The two illustrations of Dr. Lorenz are perfect examples. In the one case you have the small child who recognizes a mammal, and his parents are distressed, so they say 'No, that's a dog, bow-wow here', and they break the abstraction down to a concrete level. On the other hand, Dr. Lorenz's child, having grown up in a home where abstraction was valued, does the same thing and it is valued. We have a good many instances of this happening. The fourth word my child said was an abstraction. She said the word 'baby' for her reflection, a doll, a photograph, and a carving. Because we were interested in linguistics and were interested in concept formation we saw what she had done and we said it back, so it had some chance. So in your concrete cultures, in languages where there is a word for 'snow in the air' and another for 'snow on the ground' and another for 'snow that's crisp' and another for 'snow that's soft', undoubtedly the child at two sees snow and says 'That's snow' and is told 'No, you don't see snow, there's no such thing, it's this thing and this thing and this thing'. Then, when we come to the adult in various societies, we see one people very able to abstract and another people very handicapped in that respect.

LORENZ:

I think culture influences Gestalt perceptions even more because you have to look at something very often until the Gestalt jumps out at you. For example, the regularities contained in Eastern music are imperceptible to our Gestalt perception which is attuned to the eight-tone octave and won't respond to the scale of the Asiatics, and

102

to us Asiatic music seems at first to be just chaotic. I doubt very strongly whether a grown-up person who is not particularly musically gifted is able to learn to feel the Gestalt and thus the beauty of Chinese music, and it would be an interesting experiment for Gestalt psychologists to see at what age you are still plastic enough to learn to do so.

MEAD:

Let me come back to the theoretical point which you raised. The people who appear to us to see least are the Australian Aborigines, who apparently relate themselves to their environment much more by touch and by smell than by seeing. Australia has an extraordinarily monotonous landscape. The drawings of the Aborigines are always diagrammatic; they are not pictorial representations. But take Aboriginal children now and show them perspective and they get drunk. They get into an absolute ecstasy when they first encounter perspective, and small ten-year-olds will light up and say 'I see, you've painted it the way it looks, not the way it really is'.

CAROTHERS:

It seems to me that in our Western European world the reality is essentially one of spatial and mechanical relations. The most striking thing one sees in Africans who have lived in the country and are not familiar with a European background is their utter incapability of dealing with spatial relations. I have tried to test Africans with blocks of wood, coloured on different sides: a cube-imitation test, a very simple thing for Europeans, even perhaps at about the age of eight; but the African adult, on average, is quite incapable of dealing with this, and I finally came to the conclusion that most of the people I examined did not realize that, when they turned a cube round, the various sides maintained a constant relationship to each other. This is for us a very simple thing, and these Africans were in many ways intelligent, capable of dealing with their own environment extremely well, but in this skill, which is acquired by us I suppose in playing with toys, they are feeble-minded by our standards. Reality for them is not a world of spatial relations, but a world of spirits, and our mechanical world is much less real to them.

MEAD:

I think it is important to distinguish between the word 'reality' as it is usually used in psycho-analysis or therapeutically, when you say you have to face reality—which includes your mother-in-law, the marriage systems, the secret police, or whatever happens to be

103

around in your country—and reality in the sense that Dr. Lorenz was using it, when he said that the function of this mechanism was to inform the animal of the actual state of the object. Unless we keep those two things absolutely clear, we are going to get into a great deal of trouble. To date, I have seen no evidence anywhere of any people with an inability to interpret whether an object is moving or not (that is to function as Dr. Lorenz was describing) unless superimposed there is a theory of spirits, which then gives a new interpretation. But this is quite different from the original capacity to perceive. My interpretation, on the basis of the testing I have done with different primitive people, would be that there is something in Dr. Carothers' test which evokes an alternative interpretation in the African. After all, when the African turns his boat around he knows all about the sides. When he is dealing with any object in his own environment, he knows just what he appears not to know in that test situation. We have to think of culture as mediating between the actual nature of the object, reported in Dr. Lorenz's sense, and the final interpretation as to whether it is a ghost or a devil, or whether it was there or wasn't there.

CAROTHERS:

I think it is true to say that hearing plays a much more vivid part in the African's life than vision. He is familiar with the sounds of the wind in the trees, the running of water, the noises of the animals, and the speech of his relations and his friends. He is not nearly so insistently introduced to visual aspects of the world as European children are—reading, writing, playing with toys and blocks of wood. It seems to me that all these auditory stimuli are of a very emotional type. They are always relevant to the person. No matter what sound one hears it is always something that is of immediate interest, and even the human word as spoken is far more emotional, and of far more intense personal interest, than the written word. That is likely to play a part in the African's approach to life and to emphasize his subjectivity and his tendency to egotism and his lack of detachment. The visual world is also far more continuous and always reminds one of the fact that each event depends on previous events, that things do not happen haphazardly; whereas in the world of sound things are discontinuous and cause and effect are far less obvious.

PIAGET:

From the discussion which has just taken place I understood that everyone agreed that according to the different social or cultural

104

environment variations in mental development occur as a function of education, emotional forces, etc. Nevertheless it seemed to me that Dr. Mead and Dr. Lorenz postulated a sort of constancy of Gestalt in the immediate sensorial universe, throughout the world. I personally have some doubt on the subject. I do not think that all the Gestalten are the same for both child and adult. I will give an example from the constancies referred to by Dr. Lorenz when he was explaining his ideas on Gestalt.

We carried out some research on the depth evaluation of real and apparent (projective) size. As regards Euclidian or real size we found that the constancy was lower in the child—as was demonstrated long ago by the psychologists of the Vienna school. The child undervalues depth. At about ten or eleven years he attains approximately the level of real constancy. The adult overestimates depth. There is an over-constancy in the adult and this over-constancy is the rule. Many psychologists had demonstrated this, but with a certain constraint, passing over this phenomenon like a cat on hot bricks because it cannot be reconciled with Gestalt.

Now if apparent size is studied, that is, the way an object at four yards appears compared with an object at one yard, for instance, it is found that the adult has considerable difficulty in evaluating this projective size. He makes an error of about 50 per cent, and even more. In the case of a child of about seven years one has great difficulty in getting him to understand the question, but once he has understood it his perceptive evaluation is better than the adult's. His estimate of the apparent size is in some cases 100 per cent. In adults we have only found one case where the evaluation is as good as the young child's, and he was a landscape painter. Apart from this exception adults have a very inferior power of evaluation compared with children.

There is a large number of phenomena of this kind, which shows that Gestalt, propounded as a simple, universal explanation, appears to be a myth from the point of view of genetic psychology. Of course, I readily admit that these phenomena depend not only on age but also on culture, and I think that even from the sensorial point of view wide differences are found.

MEAD:

Some of you probably know of the experiments of AMES (1952) and the room he has constructed so as to give an illusion of being rectangular when actually it is extremely distorted. You go in and then you are given a stick and told to touch first this part of it, then that part of it; and it takes a long time for the motor experience

105

to correct this visual illusion. In this little house there are two windows of the same size, so constructed that when you look at people looking through them one person looks almost twice the size of the other. If we took members of this group into this experimental situation, if there were two of you behind the windows and one of us looking, we would get the illusion completely and accept the fact that the whole situation had been set up for it. But with a child looking at its parents, or a wife looking at her husband, the distortion does not operate and they see them with the whole perception corrected, so that there is not only the deceptive constancy of the adult but the constancy that is given by the emotional situation. (We are not quite sure what husbands see in wives, because the experimenters have a theory which relates to dependence and they maintain their theory by not having husbands looking at wives.)

LORENZ:

If a husband sees his wife the right size then at the same moment he ought to see the house askew.

ODIER:

I might relate an experience with a boy. He saw his father and mother coming up an avenue and he said to me, 'Isn't it funny, why is daddy so small and mummy so big?' Actually the mother was an inch or two shorter than her husband. The child, who was passing through the Oedipus phase, had an emotional tendency to diminish the size, i.e. the value, of his father. I think this is an illusion, a kind of 'disgestaltism', frequently found in psychoanalysis.

I would like to make another remark in connexion with Mlle Inhelder's very interesting communication and M. Piaget's remarks. Many of you commonly speak of tests, but I think a distinction could be made between an actual test and what we might call an inquiry. The way Mlle Inhelder and her students go about getting children to undergo testing seems to me different from the cold and automatic way testers apply tests just as they are to all children without discrimination. As I understand it, Mlle Inhelder prepares the ground; with each child she tries to create some relationship with an affective component by explaining things to him and playing with him. In psychoanalysis we would say that Mlle Inhelder attempts to create a positive transference. Now I have ascertained that in certain cases a negative transference is established and this affects the result of the test.

I will quote you an actual case which borders on the anecdotal. I had occasion to supervise the work of a child psychoanalyst. She was treating an anxious boy of seven or eight who had been tested with the communicating vessel test by one of the Institut Rousseau students. This test consists in showing a child two communicating vessels. One of the vessels is screened and the water-level is varied. The child is then asked various questions to reveal the extent of his acquisition of the concepts of dynamics, volume, and horizontality. The child gives all kinds of interesting replies of an animistic or magical type, saying that the water is growing, etc. Well, this child finished by telling the psychoanalyst that he had been careful not to say what he thought. He had imagined that the tester wanted to know whether he had wet his bed.

I have seen another case where a test included filling flasks with water and emptying them. The little boy was suspicious. He made a negative transference and replied all wrong because he thought the young lady—as he called her—wanted to know whether he had masturbated. Naturally in this case the result was falsified.

These examples clearly show that two different factors must be distinguished in these tests and that a so-called intellectual test must not have an affective base, and inversely an affective test must not be carried out on an intellectual plane.

CAROTHERS:

I want to ask Mlle Inhelder if she envisages these steps in mental development as definite steps with a pause in between, or does she envisage the mental development as continuous and these steps simply as milestones of measurement?

INHELDER:

The evolution appears to be continuous; however, in this continuous process there seem to be decisive periods: for example, at about seven years, which appear as accelerations. It all happens as if a slow preparation suddenly culminated in an achievement.

FOURTH DISCUSSION

Comparative Behaviourology

LORENZ:

If you pull a chair away from a man sitting on it and balancing crockery, he will put out his hands and let the crockery drop. This is due to a reflex. I am convinced that the thing called a reflex exists, but I am also convinced that it is very far indeed from being the only basic function of the central nervous system, as many physiologists still believe. Someone once said that today's truth is tomorrow's error. Otto Koehler very wittily and very profoundly replied, 'No, today's truth is tomorrow's special case'.

Most accepted 'truths' about the reflex are such special cases. None of us knows what is really happening within the central nervous system. Permit me to talk in parables. Supposing there is an automatic machine on the railway station. You put in a coin, then there is a mysterious buzz and out pops a package of cigarettes. The machine is the central nervous system, the coin is the stimulus and the cigarettes are behaviour. The buzz represents everything recorded by electrophysiology, and is the only hint we get as to what may be happening inside.

Now let us, for the moment, forget all we think we know about the approved 'truths' concerning the reflex. Let us regard the central nervous system as such an automatic machine whose insides are quite unknown to us. Let us study its different types of performance, its different types of reaction to stimulation, and also its spontaneous activities, and let us classify them from the point of view of the stimulation impinging on the central nervous system and of the activities elicited by these stimuli. One of the most common types of central nervous performance is as follows. A continuous and rather amorphous stream of excitation comes in through afferent nerves and the output is a very well co-ordinated rhythmic sequence of motor impulses. Many instinctive movements, particularly those of loco-motion, belong to this type. Or one single impulse is sent in and a series of rhythmic impulses constitute the response as, for instance,

108

in the case of a clonus. Among literally hundreds of such combinations between the impinging stimulation and the resulting efferent impulses, there is one case in which there is a direct correspondence between stimulation and efferent impulse, that is to say one stimulus elicits one efferent impulse, thus creating the extremely misleading impression that the central nervous system has not done anything but pass on a stimulus from one neuron to another; the prototype of what is called a reflex. This kind of central nervous response is neither common nor widely spread in the zoological system. On the contrary, the most typical and classical form of reflex, on which the whole conception was based, has evolved very late in phylogeny, as it only exists in animals with a pyramidal system.

Once we have recognized it as one special case amongst hundreds of different ones, there is not the faintest reason to believe that all central nervous performances are based on 'the reflex' as a primary functional element; yet with some physiologists, you will find it extremely difficult to overcome this opinion!

If we put the typical reflex—one stimulus, one efferent impulse— at one end of the diagram which classifies central nervous performances by their input and output, we find, at its other end, a number of functions which are independent of impinging afferent stimulation. This endogenous or automatic production of impulses may result in the output of a continuous stream of simply amorphous excitation, as has been shown by HOLST (1939, SCHOEN and HOLST 1950) for the sensory cells in the macula utriculi in the labyrinth of fishes, and termed 'autostaxis'. Or it may result in sending out very complicated and highly co-ordinated rhythmical series of motor impulses. Holst not only deafferented, but totally isolated the central nervous system of the earthworm, and found that it still persisted in sending out rhythmical co-ordinated impulses. These impulses proceed in waves from the rear part of the front end and are indubitably identical with those normally eliciting the creeping movement of the worm. When this was doubted by some critics, Holst proceeded to isolate only part of the nervous system and to leave part of it in connexion with several segments of the worm. Then the action currents conducted from the isolated part to a series of galvanometers went beautifully and convincingly in step with the contractions of the intact segments. This type of central nervous activity, producing, without any afferent stimulation or control, rhythmical and co-ordinated movements, was called 'autorhythmia' by Holst. Pure autorhythmia is, in the animal kingdom, about as rare as pure reflex activity, but it is indubitably a much more primitive phenomenon. It is very probable that all locomotion in protozoans is closely akin to autorhythmia, and Bethe has shown conclusively that the contractions of the umbrella of some jellyfish are autorhythmic. But in some more highly differentiated types of jellyfish, the *Scyphomedusae*, the autorhythmia of the velum has been gradully superseded by a typical reflex mechanism. These animals developed static organs called marginal bodies which primarily served a righting response by stimulating a stronger contraction on the lower rim of the umbrella whenever the animal was tilted to one side. But gradually, in a manner which need not concern us here, the reflex mechanism of this righting response has replaced and superseded the autorhythmia of the velum. Thus the jellyfishes, meek animals though they are, may serve as a warning to the physiologist never to generalize rashly. The umbrellaing movement of a primitive *Hydromedusa* not only looks exactly like that of a *Scyphomedusa*, but actually is the 'same' movement ontogenetically and phylogenetically. Yet the one is caused by the purest type of autorhythmia that we know and the second by the purest type of reflex that we know. I confess, however, that it gives me some satisfaction to remind you of the fact that autorhythmia is certainly the more primitive and the older of the two.

I deemed this excursion into neurophysiology necessary in order to explain why ethologists absolutely refuse to accept the current explanation that all instinctive activities are 'chains of reflexes'. No complex instinctive movement has, as yet, been really analysed down to its neurological components. Yet there is overwhelming evidence that true autorhythmia plays the most important part in the causation of the typical spontaneity of all instinctive activity. This assumption supplies us with a most convincing explanation of a very great number of facts concerning instinctive movement, while the same facts remain totally unintelligible on the basis of the chain reflex theory. And the fact that all instinctive activities are fundamentally spontaneous and therefore akin to autorhythmia is relevant for what I want to say to you about what we call the innate releasing mechanism (I.R.M.). As long as the elaborate and well co-ordinated sequence of movements constituting an instinctive activity was regarded as a chain of reflexes, its beginning did not obtrude itself as a problem: it was just the first one among other reflexes and the existence of a neural mechanism of a peculiar character did not become apparent. But as soon as it became evident that the elementary nervous functions underlying instinctive movements were much more akin to autorhythmia than to reflex activity, a new problem put itself very directly. If the instinctive activity is generating impulses continuously—as there is plenty of evidence that it does—and prevented from causing incessant movement only by the inhibiting function of higher centres, how is this inhibition removed at the right moment and in the biologically adequate situation in which the instinctive activity must be

110

discharged? We know that the ventral chord of the earthworm generates the impulses of creeping incessantly, yet the intact earthworm creeps only when it ought to.

There is no contradicting the assertion that the 'trigger-mechanism' removing the central inhibition which, most of the time, prevents instinctive activities from 'going off *in vacuo*' is nothing else than an 'unconditioned reflex' in the original sense of I. P. Pavlov. Yet this assertion does not solve the real problem, which actually lies in the selectivity of the releasing mechanism. This central problem only becomes apparent in the more complicated forms of the I.R.M., not in the simple cases that Pavlov's classical examples provide. When a dog secretes two different kinds of saliva on having meat extract put in his mouth in one case and sand in the other, the difference between the two reactions is easily explained by the fact that the meat extract stimulates chemical receptors and the sand tactile ones. But take the following case as a contrast. A young totally inexperienced jackdaw instantly reacts by doing 'social grooming', i.e. preening the other's feathers, if another assumes the 'friendly' or submissive attitude which consists in turning away the beak and fluffing the feathers at the back of the head. But if the other bird instead of fluffing the feathers of the head fluffs those of the back, and instead of turning the bill away turns it towards the approaching youngster, the latter will instantly 'recognize' this attitude for that of a threat, and react either by retreating or by a counter-threat, according to its relative strength and courage. To anybody not believing in vitalistic miracles, these two different ways of reacting to two stimulus situations which, after all, are only different in regard to the retinal images received of the submissive and the aggressive jackdaw, must be a source of deep wonder. We have to postulate an innate perceptual structure which acts as a sort of filter letting through only sharply defined combinations of sensory data. Thus the problem does not lie in the question of whether this performance is due to an unconditioned response or not; it lies, so to say, in the afferent side of the reflex arc.

If we do not know what an innate releasing mechanism (I.R.M.) really is, we know quite a lot already about its function. A lot of investigators, chiefly Tinbergen and his school, have concentrated on the I.R.M., so that at present it really is the best known element of innate behaviour. I cannot give you here even a short survey of everything we think we have brought to light about the function of the I.R.M.; I only want to emphasize a few points.

(*A*) An I.R.M. never responds selectively to a complicated Gestalt, but exclusively to extremely simple key stimuli. These may be relational properties, but always such simple ones that the relation in question can be stated in very few words. For example, the I.R.M.

111

which, in the young herring gull, elicits begging activity, responds to the following stimuli emanating from the parent bird's bill:

(*a*) The narrowness of the lower mandible which, in feeding, is turned with its sharp under edge towards the baby bird.

(*b*) The red colour of a round spot on the lower mandible of the parent bird.

(*c*) The contrast of this spot against the paler coloration of the bill.

(*d*) The downward tilt of the bill.

(*e*) Its jerking movements while the parent bird is regurgitating food.

The general form and colour pattern of the parent's head, bill, eyes, etc., are quite irrelevant for the releasing power of the situation.

(*B*) If, as in most cases, an I.R.M. responds to more than one key-stimulus, the effect of stimulation is exactly in proportion to the sum of the efficacies of the several key stimuli impinging at the moment. This rule, termed the 'law of heterogeneous summation', constitutes a very striking difference between the learned response to Gestalt qualities and the innate reaction of key stimuli. Furthermore, I want to draw your attention to the fact that this very limitation of an I.R.M.'s functions, particularly the limitation of their complexity, is just what one would postulate from a purely mechanistic, or, if you like, cybernetic point of view. It is quite to be expected that a 'receiving set' reacting selectively to a few and very pregnant key stimuli is easier to construct than one which reacts to a diffuse complex quality of an elaborate Gestalt. Indeed, the very simplicity of the I.R.M. is a reason for analytical optimism! Though our ideas about what the I.R.M. really may be neurophysiologically are purely conjectural, I think that the construction of a cybernetic machine of similar functions and limitations would be very illuminating.

As our ideas about that peculiar stimulus-selecting apparatus which we call the I.R.M. are largely founded on our observations about what it cannot do, it will not seem surprising to you that the pathology of the I.R.M. is also one of the major sources of our knowledge about it. After all it is the approved method of neurophysiology to study the pathological defects of a function in order to gain insight into its normal causal structure. Another reason for enlarging a bit on the pathology of the I.R.M. on this occasion lies in the fact that it might have some bearing on some phenomena of delinquency in human social behaviour.

One basic fact which is extremely characteristic of the normal function of all I.R.M.s must be stated first of all: in all cases in which a pathological disintegration of an I.R.M. is found, the activity normally released by that I.R.M. does not, by any means, become

112

unreleasable, but, on the contrary, more easy to release. This fact very strongly enhances the I.R.M.'s character of a 'filter' of stimuli: the more that 'filter' is broken up, the greater becomes the range of stimuli which are able to pass through it and to release the reaction in question; in other words, the less becomes the selectivity of the response.

There are three different factors which regularly lead to a disintegration of the I.R.M. and to a corresponding loss of its selectivity:

(A) Any, even a very slight, disturbance in the general state of health of an animal.

(B) The domestication of a species.

(C) The hybridization of two species with slightly different I.R.M.s.

Let me first give you an example of (A). The red-backed shrike (*Lanius collurio* L.) has an instinctive movement to impale insects and other prey on thorns, in order to store food. In young birds of that species, reared by me in isolation, I found that the innate movements of impaling were not innately directed towards a thorn. They tried to impale a mealworm or a small piece of meat indiscriminately everywhere; on their perches, on the bars of their cage, etc., without giving the slightest attention to the very adequate artificial thorns with which I had supplied them. Only when, by pure trial and error, they happened to execute the innate movement pattern of impaling on one of these thorns, the full success of the instinctive movement evidently acted as a reinforcement to direct the impaling activity to the adequate object, and they learned with extreme rapidity. Naturally, my conclusion was that the red-backed shrike had no I.R.M. directing its impaling activity to the thorn, but that it had to learn its proper use by individual experience. This, however, proved to be quite erroneous. Kramer, of Wilhelmshaven, reared young shrikes in order to study their migration activities. Just because an easy opportunity offered itself, he repeated my experiments on the impaling activity—with exactly the same results. But one year later he improved his rearing technique, feeding the young birds on a large proportion of live silkworms. And when he repeated our experiments with these birds which were in just slightly better condition than all those previously used, he found that they had an innate reaction to the thorn! At the very first experiment they took the mealworm in their bill, looked about for an adequate thorn, recognized it instantly when they saw one, went straight for it and, without the least evidence of trial and error, impaled their worm on the thorn, just as if they had done so hundreds of times.

Now an example of (B). In the wild ancestor of our domestic chicken, the jungle fowl or bankiva, the mother hen refuses to

113

brood any chick which has not got the typical wild colour pattern of down on its head and its back. Some bankiva hens instantly kill any black chick. In domestic hens one finds all possible gradations between this extreme selectivity of the I.R.M. releasing the brooding activities, and an entire lack of selectivity. Most barnyard hens are insusceptible to all the possible colour patterns in chicks, but some will refuse to brood ducklings or goslings; highbred races, like cochins or brahmas, will brood practically anything alive and approximately of the right size—young ferrets, for instance.

Now to come to (C), the loss of selectivity of the I.R.M. in hybrids: some hybrids of bahama pintail and chestnut-breasted teal that had been reared normally, in company with their brothers and sisters, did not react sexually either to each other or to any birds of the two parent species, but all of them, both males and females, courted a huge white-spotted domestic duck, about four times their own size. Similarly, Heinroth found that some goose hybrids persisted in courting swans. Though these are just a few isolated observations, they tend to show that loss of selectivity of the I.R.M. stimuli may result in the choice of the *strongest* stimuli available.

Finally I want to mention one peculiarity of the I.R.M. which, though not pathological in itself, may lead to phenomena closely akin to the pathological. In most I.R.M.s, the stimulus-receiving set is tuned to the quality rather than to the quantity and intensity of the natural key stimuli. Therefore most key stimuli can be exaggerated. In the jewel fish, *Hemischromis bimaculatus*, the dark ruby-red colouring of the male's throat is one of the key stimuli releasing fighting activities in a rival. By illuminating our fighting arena with ruby light, thus intensifying their colour, we can make jewel fish males 'see red' and fight each other more intensely than under normal conditions. If more than one of the key stimuli emanating from a certain object can be thus exaggerated, it is possible to construct a model which by far surpasses the releasing effect of the natural object. In the oyster-catcher, for instance, the I.R.M. which responds to the egg and elicits incubation activities is dependent, among other key stimuli, on the size, the colour, and the contrasting spots of the egg. A real oyster-catcher egg is the same size as a bantam's, its colour is bluish grey with slightly darker grey spots. If one presents an incubating oyster-catcher with an egg nearly as large as an ostrich's, of bright blue colour and with deep black spots, thus exaggerating the intensity of the key stimuli mentioned, the bird becomes absolutely fascinated, leaves its own clutch and passionately tries to incubate the giant egg, though this is physically impossible, the bird being hardly able even to stand astride the model. A very intelligent American journalist, on seeing Tinbergen's film showing this behaviour, exclaimed: 'Why, that's the cover-girl!' This witty remark is scientifically quite correct. Much of what we call 'vice' in human behaviour does not consist in anything else but the search for supra-normal key stimuli. The vice of gluttony offers very convincing examples, and quite proper ones at that.

Imprinting

There is one particular type of I.R.M. whose function is closely linked with a particular type of conditioning. I think it may be of interest to you, because this interaction between I.R.M. and learning is limited to a strictly defined phase in the organism's ontogenetic development. These I.R.M.s are of an extreme simplicity and therefore their selectivity is slight. But this lack of selectivity is compensated by the limitation of the time during which the I.R.M. is effective. During that short period, the I.R.M. succeeds, under natural circumstances, in establishing a conditioned response to its object. The resulting response then is far more selective than any I.R.M., as all learned responses always are. Let me give an example. The I.R.M.s eliciting, in a newly hatched greylag gosling, the activity of following its mother respond to an amazingly wide range of key stimuli. Any object between the sizes of a bantam hen and a big row-boat, which moves and emits noises of a wide variation of pitch, can release the following response of a newborn greylag. If a man moves and talks in the presence of such a little gosling, the latter will look at him very intently, give its greeting response, and, after a few repetitions, follow him unconditionally, just as it would normally follow its mother. Obviously this combination of a simple I.R.M. and consequent conditioning is entirely effective under natural conditions. The cases in which the mother goose is not the first moving and sound-emitting object perceived by the gosling are, of course, so extremely rare as to be of no account.

Now the particular kind of conditioning that takes place in the process just described differs from other types of learning in a number of very characteristic points which I want to summarize:

(*a*) It is limited to a very definite and often extremely short phase of ontogeny.

(*b*) It is, in the typical cases, quite irreversible.

(*c*) It takes place quite independently of whether the activity released by the stimulus situation is, at the time being, functional or not.

Mainly because of its irreversibility we have called this particular type of conditioning *imprinting*. The last of these three points is very important, because you cannot get any other conditioned response when the unconditioned response is not yet functional. That is what makes us believe that imprinting is something which takes place in the perceptive sector only, because the efferent sector of the reaction-arc need not be present at all.

There are two points about imprinting which seem important in this connexion. First I want to call your attention to a very enigmatic fact. The gosling in the classical imprinting experiment of Heinroth does not become imprinted to the particular man whom it sees at first, but to Man, with a capital, as a species. It can learn to know its keeper, later on, by a common learning process, but the irreversible imprint refers to the species and not the individual. We have no explanation of this at all.

Secondly, I want to emphasize that most probably there are all imaginable types of conditioning, forming gradations between true imprinting and the more common types of learning. What we call imprinting is a type we found at first in jackdaws and greylag geese. It is one extreme type of learning, and there may be all sorts of gradations. We know already from the work of Eckhardt Hess that, for instance, depth perception is acquired in a way very similar to imprinting, and if you prevent a chick from acquiring it during the first days, it cannot do so afterwards. That is not a fixation of a simple activity to its objects, but it is like imprinting in being confined to a very short phase of the ontogenetic development of the individual. I mention this only in order to emphasize that there may be all sorts of gradations; that is one example of extreme imprinting in some respects and not in others. There may be a superposition and interlocking of imprinting and learning. Such intercalations, though superficially tending to veil the irreversibility of imprinting, really afford its most convincing proof. The budgerigar, to give you a good example of this, is a bird which learns easily to accept substitute objects for its sexual activities. You have probably seen budgerigars in cages court a celluloid doll, etc. We imprinted the sexual activities of two budgerigars, a male and a female, to the human species— which it is quite easy to do by rearing the bird in isolation during a certain period. Then we deprived them of all human company and kept them together in a lonely garret where they were fed and watered through chutes. After a time they learned to use each other for substitute objects, courted and copulated quite normally and even reared two broods with full success. Now after the third brood had hatched, we did the crucial experiment which simply consisted in my going into that garret. Both birds instantly went into a frenzy of sexual excitement which was directed entirely towards my person. The impression of this reunion with what the birds 'considered' their own species was so lasting that they absolutely refused to have any-thing to do with each other for a long time and let their brood of

116

young die of hunger. Now consider that these birds had many times successfully copulated with each other, while all their attempts to copulate with the imprinted object of their passion necessarily had always remained unsuccessful and unsatisfying. Nevertheless they persisted in their object-fixation, if I may call it thus! Though imprinting has been found in its typical form in birds and insects rather than in mammals, I really do believe it to be fundamentally akin to those very lasting object-fixations of human beings, chiefly because these fixations also seem to be dependent on early childhood impressions and seem also to be largely irreversible. Some psychiatrists and psychoanalysts here I believe share this opinion, at least as a working hypothesis.

I now will proceed to show you a short film illustrating some of my points. The first part of the film shows the behaviour of a flock of young goslings imprinted to man, in comparison with another flock, imprinted to its own species, and the second part shows reproductive activity.

Dr. Lorenz' film illustrated the following response, reaction to warning call, unmixing of the two differently imprinted flocks, following response on the wing, greeting reaction, pair formation, copulation activities, and neck-dipping.

RÉMOND:

Dr. Lorenz started his introduction by speaking of reflexes and seemed to say that actually reflexes do not exist. . . .

LORENZ:

No, excuse me. I said that the reflex is a special case of response of the central nervous system, which exists in its classical form in certain animals capable of a high degree of differentiation.

RÉMOND:

How would you call the retracting movement of an oyster when touched with the prongs of a fork?

LORENZ:

That is just the point: I would not give it a name at all, before knowing what it is physiologically! All functions of the central nervous system ought to be termed in a way containing as little hypothesis as possible. The thing to do is to give a purely descriptive term corresponding to what we know about incoming stimulation

117

and outgoing activity. In your example of the oyster the input is very probably a single wave of excitation and the output consists in a long-lasting increase of muscular tonus—most muscular contractions of molluscs are tonic. This physiological process is certainly 'a reaction', but very different indeed from a 'reflex'. This word always calls up the mental picture of the classic diagram of the cross section of the cord with the short reflex arc coming in at the posterior root and going out by the anterior root.

RÉMOND:

Then you limit the definition of reflex to this set-up?

LORENZ:

More exactly to the function of this set-up, which consists of a single wave of efferent excitation responding to a single wave of afferent excitation. This is certainly a reflex, but it is very rare in animal behaviour. The only examples I can give are those I have already quoted. Autorhythmia, as in the creeping movement of the earthworm, is as rare as the other, and between these two extremes there are thousands of kinds of function of the nervous system.

RÉMOND:

You spoke of autorhythmia as if it were exceptional, but is not this property in fact one of the most general of the nervous system, at least from the electroencephalographic point of view? It has been found in the most elementary structures. Thus, it was demonstrated long ago by ADRIAN (1931) in the optic ganglion of the *Dysticus marginalis*. He was able to show that even when isolated this ganglion was in continuous activity. When it is connected to the eye, or what replaces the eye in this animal, this activity ceases immediately light arrives. Autorhythmia is a kind of negative to activity.

GREY WALTER:

It is the lack of electrical activity, of physiological activity, isn't it?

RÉMOND:

Certainly. That is exactly what I was coming to.

LORENZ:

I actually had intended to cite the sensory cells of the mucous membrane of the olfactory tract as an example, whose particular

118

function also is something extremely queer and rare. When the output of the central nervous system is arhythmic but continues independently of afferent excitation, this function is termed 'autostaxis'. This autostaxis of the olfactory sensory cells can change into different autorhythmias, according to the smell which impinges on it. The moment a smell impinges on these olfactory cells, they begin to fire rhythmically in variable rhythms and each of these different rhythms is characteristic of one particular smell. Adrian can look at the curve of electrical activity given out by those cells and is able to say what kind of smell is impinging on the mucous membrane of the rabbit (ADRIAN and LUDWIG, 1938). That is an immense achievement. Of course, the reflex on the one hand, and the autostaxis and autorhythmias on the other hand, are joined to each other by a number of gradations: for instance, my pupil PRECHTL (1952b) showed that the gripping reflex of the human child is apt to be a rhythmic movement in the first postnatal period. After stimulation it occurs several times. Only with the growth of the afferent control, the unnecessary and even detrimental sequence of movements is cut out and one single movement is left. The same is true of what PRECHTL and SCHLEIDT (1951) call the 'search automatisms' in young mammals and human babies. These have an autorhythmic movement of searching for the teat by turning their head to and fro. Now if you analyse this function, you find a very exceptional connexion between an automatism and an I.R.M. In the typical cases, the automatism is blocked all the time, until released by an I.R.M. which removes the block. Here, it is the other way round. The searching automatism is going on all the time, as long as the little animal is awake. It only ceases when a very definite stimulus situation is attained. In the cat, the responsible key stimuli emanate from the hairless area round the mother's nipple. As soon as the kitten finds this, its searching automatism is blocked. In other words, the I.R.M. puts on a block, instead of removing it as it does in most other cases. In the kitten, as well as in the human baby, it often happens that the I.R.M. responding to the nipple fails to inhibit the to and fro movement of the head at once, but does so with a slight delay, so that the little creature seems to look for the teat in the wrong place, which gives an effect very similar to the superposition of flight reaction and prehensile reaction which we saw in Dr. Monnier's film.

What is called the 'prehensile reflex' in the human baby, is nothing other than the search automatism brought under a strict control of afferent functions. These release the automatism on a slight touch of the corner of the mouth, allow it just one sideways stroke, and stop it at once when the nipple is found. The ontogenetic development of the 'prehensile reflex' out of the 'search automatism' has been thoroughly demonstrated by Prechtl. And yet you may call it a reflex! For very possibly a reflex, even in its purest form, is nothing but an autorhythmic process brought under the rein of afferent control to such an extent that it is just de-blocked, allowed to discharge just one stroke of excitation, and instantly blocked again. That, of course, is only theory. I only want to repeat that I neither assert that 'there is no such thing as a reflex', nor do I believe that autorhythmia 'explains everything', but that there are lots of other types of central nervous functions, just as important as these two, and that it is sheer prejudice to assume that one of these many different performances is 'the' elementary function of the central nervous system.

Now, apropos of the film, allow me just a few words on a curious phenomenon which we found in the reaction of the goslings to our imitation of the mother's warning call. It invariably was strongest at the first experiment and tended to fade very rapidly indeed with each repetition. Attempts to reinforce it were quite unsuccessful. The fading could not be prevented by letting even very strongly frightening stimuli impinge on the goslings immediately after the warning call. And even after a very long period of rest, the former intensity of the reaction does not become re-established. This is one of the chief problems which we are trying to solve at the moment.

RÉMOND:

A similar reaction in man is an absolutely natural and physiological phenomenon which occurs even during sleep. If you take as a reference the existence of a cerebral electric reaction to stimulation during sleep, you find that on repetition of a known stimulation the response very rapidly weakens until it subsides completely. If the nature of the stimulus is modified somewhat the reaction reappears, but it fades away again. On returning to the first stimulation after a certain time, it is again found efficacious. It seems that this is a very general property of the nervous system, which is on the alert only for what is new and unexpected; but as soon as there has been some kind of apprenticeship—and this apprenticeship does not necessitate a conscious vigilance—it economizes part or all of the reaction. This does not mean to say that vigilance is lost, since the least modification in stimulus causes reappearance of the reaction.

LORENZ:

I am very glad that Dr. Rémond brought up this question, which I did not make clear. Of course, these are phenomena which the physiologists have called adaptation; a rather unhappy term, because this type of adaptation has nothing to do with adaptation in the biological sense. Processes of physiological 'adaptation' may be biologically adaptive, or they may not. In order to make clear what I meant by special cases of 'adaptation', I had better describe the experiment of ROBERT HINDE (1953). Hinde found an I.R.M., whose effect he could quantify very well, the mobbing activity of the chaffinch. Chaffinches, like other small birds, react to owls by giving their warning call, approaching the owl to a certain distance, and then following it about uttering their warning calls all the time, executing certain movements of characteristic excitement, actually displacement activities. The activity goes on for a measurable time, after which they quieten down. Hinde originally wanted to analyse the I.R.M. eliciting the mobbing reaction of the chaffinch, but what he discovered was something much more important. The reaction depended on a very simple set of key stimuli, as most I.R.M.s do. The owl dummy only has to be round, it has to have eyes in a certain place, and so on. Now he quantified the number of of sideways movements and the number of 'pink, pink, pink!' elicited by a standard dummy, until the reaction quietened down. The average of the number of sideways movements and the number of 'pinks' he found in virgin birds was taken as 100 per cent.

Then he found that in a second trial on the same day he got about 30 per cent of that, and in a third trial he got about 10 per cent, and then, finally, 1 per cent. After a certain period of quiescence of one or several days he again got about 50 per cent and after a period of quiescence of six months he came up to 62 per cent, and that was all. Now we have no doubt that the reaction of the chaffinch to the owl has survival value. It was very surprising to us that this reaction is devalued by half if this unlucky bird happens to meet an owl once who who isn't hungry and is for several hours in that region. If this is so the reaction loses its biological usefulness altogether. Hinde thought that perhaps reinforcement was necessary. This was already a measure of desperation, because it is obvious that if the reaction was dependent on the bird getting nearly caught or actually pinched by the owl— which would be the only manner of reinforcing it—the reaction would be of little use to the bird. Well, he didn't succeed any more than I did in reinforcing the goslings' reaction to the warning call. We found that quite generally this 'fading' of reactions to I.R.M.s takes place whenever we elicit them with *dummies*. We strongly suspect that there must be something wrong with our experiments. What I propose to do now is this. Next year, I will take one of my greylag geese who is now two years old, and I will incubate and rear the young. Then I shall make the mother-goose warn, which I can easily do by presenting her with one of our eagles, or with a stuffed cat, or stuffed stoat, on a wire. The mother warns her flock twice. I shall have also a flock imprinted to me. I shall warn my flock exactly the number of times the mother does. I shall go on doing this and then we'll see if there is some difference in the fading between my goslings and those of the mother, because what I suspect is that in some way, with this rather crude model, you supply a key which doesn't quite fit, and in some way spoils the lock.

On the other hand, the phenomenon of adaptation is intriguing us in a very different manner. There is, in the reaction to the key stimuli constituting the I.R.M., a phenomenon of 'adaptation' which is most important. PRECHTL (1953) did a simple experiment with chaffinches in their nest which have a gaping reaction that is very nearly a 'reflex'. It can be elicited (*a*) by the slight trembling of the nest when the parent bird alights, and (*b*) by the call-note of the parent bird. These two stimuli are about equally effective quantitatively. Now you can stimulate gaping by shaking the nest and get about five or six reactions after which the bird doesn't react any more. Then you give the auditory stimulus and get six reactions more. If you invert the sequence of the stimuli, the numbers of responses remain virtually the same, which shows that neither of the stimuli is *a priori* more effective than the other, but that each of them becomes less effective with the number of repetitions. This 'blunting' of the reaction to one particular key stimulus (I prefer the word 'blunting' or, in German 'Abstumpfung' to the ambiguous term 'adaptation') is a phenomenon which we have hitherto neglected. It is a very important source of error in all attempts to quantify the exhaustion of the efferent side, of the instinctive movement itself. Also, it is a source of error in the quantification of the efficacy of the single key stimuli, as compared with each other. One cannot test one key stimulus without blunting the response to it, and therefore any new stimulus, tested after some other, appears to be relatively stronger than it really is. Furthermore, there is one queer thing about this blunting or adaptation which we cannot explain at all: if, in the experiment with the gaping baby chaffinch, the reaction to one of the two key stimuli is totally exhausted before the second stimulus is brought into play, the total of responses elicited by both amounts to an average of eleven. But if, on the other hand, the change of stimuli is effected before the first one has become completely blunted, and then a second change, back to the first stimulus, is made before the second one has become ineffective, and so on, back and forth, a total of forty-eight reactions can be released on the average.

FREMONT-SMITH:

Suppose that the chaffinches who could react to either of two stimuli got them both at once, what would happen then?

122

LORENZ:

You would get a reaction of high intensity which might last considerably longer than the reaction to one of them. But you get a smaller number of reactions than by changing the stimuli.

GREY WALTER:

In the case of the goslings whose reaction to warning of the owl's presence appears to fade, is there any evidence that if you allow your real or model hawk to catch one of the goslings the fading becomes less? In other words, does the experience of a catastrophe to a flock act as a reinforcement—does that tend to keep the response up or is there no such interaction?

LORENZ:

We are not quite able to answer this. We did rather mild and not very thorough experiments by just letting the hawk swoop a bit and we didn't get any influence from that. Prechtl didn't get any influence by feeding his birds after gaping, which would have been a reinforcement. I think that when an instinctive movement does lead up to a definite consummatory act, then the consummatory act tends to act as a quite definite reinforcement; there is no instance of fading in that type of I.R.M. Fading only occurs in another type of instinctive activity, in which there is no definite consummatory act.

Dr. Rémond spoke about a little change in the stimulus allowing the full reaction to occur again. In this regard SEITZ (1940) could get the whole courtship activity of the male astatotilapia, up to fertilizing the egg, with dummy experiments. (The last step is elicited by olfactory stimulation emanating from the eggs, and he couldn't get that because the plasticine dummy didn't lay eggs.) When he painted the dummy a slightly different colour the reaction returned after fading and the curve of response rose quickly, but also was lowered more quickly. After repeated change of dummy the fish learnt that even a new dummy wouldn't be any good. He was 'disillusioned' as to dummies. But this 'disillusionment' is certainly not identical with fading.

FREMONT-SMITH:

Bronk showed, if I remember correctly, that the response of an isolated sympathetic nervous ganglion to one type of input would depend upon whether or not it had received previously a different type of input along the same or along another nerve. One could even say of the isolated sympathetic ganglion that its response to a given stimulus depended upon its past history. It seems to me that there must be a continuing effect of some sort in these cases also, a residual that has been left in.

GREY WALTER:

The whole nervous system is designed to deal with a complex environment in which what matters is not that something particular occurs but that something is related to many other things. The isolated peripheral nerve fibre is a special case in which this is not true, because the isolated peripheral nerve fibre is purely a communication system, not an analysing system; but the moment you get into the spinal cord, the importance of coincidence and the importance of time-relations between stimuli becomes obvious.

FREMONT-SMITH:

Isn't that also true in the isolated nerve fibre?

GREY WALTER:

It is not quite true, it's rather doubtful, I think. By mutilation you can make a nerve fibre regress to something a little bit more unspecialized; for instance, by cutting the ends and joining two together you can make an artificial synapse, but this is really a very special case of experimental interference.

LORENZ:

I should like to mention the experiment of BIRUKOV (1952), of Freiburg. He tried to exhaust righting reactions in frogs. Righting reactions have a tremendous amount of energy at their disposal and take an immense time to get tired. He found that on a wobbling surface the righting reaction tired after several thousand attempts. When the frog was tired, and didn't right itself any more, a change of axis of tilt of only a few minutes of angle resulted in awakening the reaction again. Only then it got tired sooner, and the smaller the change in angle the sooner it tired.

BOWLBY:

There are two questions I want to ask, the first regarding the notions of 'fading' and 'disillusionment'. Is it true that these are two separate processes? You mentioned the 'fading' that can occur when I.R.M.s are elicited with dummies and you used the analogy of the key that doesn't quite fit and spoils the lock. In the second illustration, when you used the word 'disillusionment', you said that the consummatory act reinforces the response and that a certain fish learnt that dummies were no good. If you take that fish back to a real female, are its copulatory activities diminished?

LORENZ:

Well, we haven't done that, but to our isolated fish the female would have been nothing but another very new dummy and I should predict that he would react strongly and come to copulation with the female and this ultimate 'success' would reinforce the reactions to it. He would give the reaction again and again with her. But I agree that fading in I.R.M.-elicited activity without consummatory action is something different from the fading which is brought about by non-reinforcement, because in the cases in which the satisfaction of the consummatory act is lacking, the 'extinguishing' of the response is due to true learning.

RÉMOND:

I should like to ask Dr. Lorenz whether the warning reaction given by the mother goose to her young when she sees the eagle depends on experience or whether it is absolutely spontaneous the first time an eagle goes by. And would the effect on the goslings be different if a duck or a goose went by instead of an eagle when the warning call is given?

LORENZ:

Well, I am afraid I must answer this question very extensively, in order to prevent generalization. I will answer it for the goose first. In the goose, the reaction to the eagle is purely innate, and the most curious thing is that the little geese look at the eagle when the mother is warning, but do not react to it afterwards on their own account. They do not learn by being warned, nor later remember it. It is not necessary, because they keep together with their mother. If you try to make experiments on a hand-reared goose it does not react to the eagle at all until it is fully fledged, and then it suddenly, at about nine weeks, begins to react to the eagle with an immense intensity, irrespective of whether it has seen eagles before. The I.R.M. of the eagle in the goose is extremely simple. An 'eagle' is anything which (a) is depicted against the sky as a background, (b) does not beat its wings, and (c) moves slowly. A goose will give the full eagle-reaction to a black feather drifting slowly in the breeze, or a pigeon gliding slowly against a strong head wind without beating its wings. You see all the geese giving full eagle-reaction to the pigeon, and when the pigeon gives a few wing-beats all the geese give an immense relief displacement-shaking and are quiet again. One funny thing takes place, which is just the opposite of imprinting. My first goose, Martina, had no experience of being warned by parents and didn't react to aeroplanes which were flying there all the time. She did not seem to notice the aeroplanes until her I.R.M. was mature, and then she suddenly got awfully afraid of them. But after a time she quietened down again, and got adapted to the aeroplanes flying over her.

Now let's take another bird, the jackdaw. It has no innate reaction to enemies at all. One single case of hearing the warning call of the mother forms the full association between the object at which the mother warns and the reaction. Again, in a turkey, the I.R.M. of the bird of prey is much more complicated: form plays a role in it. If you make a dummy that has a short process on one side and a long process on the other side, and you draw the dummy across the sky on a string with the short process pointing forward, then the reaction is the reaction to the hawk, and if you point the long process forward, then it is a goose, and there is no reaction because a goose is not dangerous. KRÄTZIG (1940) showed that grouse have two different reactions to two different birds of prey. They reacted to an eagle dummy by taking to wing and towering, and they reacted to a falcon dummy by taking cover. Krätzig has been reproved for doing too few experiments, but the whole point is that you cannot do many experiments because you get a conditioned reaction very quickly. When Tinbergen and I were experimenting on geese, one day, I came into the garden; Tinbergen had prepared our dummies, and as I came into the garden he said, 'We aren't going to experiment today'. I said, 'Why not?' He said, 'I'll show you'. In order to attach our dummies to the piece of metal that slid on the wire it was necessary to climb the tree, and Tinbergen and I used to climb it by throwing our legs over a certain branch. Tinbergen went to quite another tree and threw his leg over its lowest branch—and all the geese looked up to the sky and went to cover. And that is why for I.R.M. experiments you ought to have a new animal for each trial.

MEAD:

Dr. Lorenz, you mentioned three conditions under which diminution of I.R.M.s might occur: hybridization, domestication, and ill-health. Can you differentiate among them in the sorts of damage done? It seems to be conceivable that ill-health might diminish the strength of the response to each of a series of stimuli, and that you might get a quantitative but non-selective diminution, whereas in another case the diminution might be selective. I will give you an illustration of what I mean. In Bali I was in a village which turned out to be an

126

area of acute hypothyroidism; every single aspect of the culture had been simplified, but without loss of pattern. Instead of putting a hundred items in an offering they put twenty-five in, but they kept the essential elements—showing the difference between the diminution that you get with hypothyroidism and that which you get with neuroses.

LORENZ:

The question is very fascinating and I do not know whether I can answer it out of hand. There is in the reaction to the I.R.M. a loss of selectivity and that may result in making the release of the reaction easier.

MEAD:

A kind of vulgarization?

LORENZ:

Exactly! This would result in a person being sooner content with an object. That object need only possess a few of the releasing characters which act as key stimuli to the normal, undisintegrated I.R.M., and a lot of others may simply be dropped out without impairing the object's releasing value. And you have no idea how very aptly the word you have just chosen, vulgarization, describes the situation. If you compare, for instance, the sexual behaviour of a wild greylag with that of a domestic goose in which the whole elaborate courtship ceremonies have become irrelevant, and in which any goose and any gander that are put together during the mating season will proceed to copulate without any more ado, you cannot help feeling that the behaviour of the barnyard goose is grossly vulgar. But I'd better tell you, in some more detail, the sequence of the disintegration of an I.R.M. in domestic hens which Heinroth studied extensively.

He found that the first key-stimuli which became independent were those of colouring. In the usual domestic hen that you find with peasants, a hybrid race of fowl, he found no hen that minded whether her chicks were black or white. In Phoenix hens, the long-tailed type, he found a good proportion of hens that would kill black chicks, and did not mind white chicks. In bankivas he found hens that would kill everything that was not wild colour. My friend Otto Koenig, in Vienna, tried to repeat those experiments with bankiva hens of rather doubtful origin to see if those things drop out in a few generations— we do not know how fast domestication occurs—and he did not find a single one that would kill a black chick, whereas there is no doubt that Heinroth's did kill black chicks. (A nice point is that they do not mind and are quite ready to mate with a black cock.) You find barnyard hens who will refuse to brood ducks and even kill the duck in the egg when they hear the first cheeps. Yet Orpingtons and Rhode Islands will take goslings and ducklings, so long as they are downy: they won't take a naked bird. If you let them hatch a raven or a cormorant, which are about the largest birds whose newly-hatched young are quite naked, they will kill them. Then there are Brahmas that will brood anything up to kittens. It's a nice sequence, isn't it, how the characters drop out singly.

TANNER:

All these things Dr. Lorenz has been describing make one think that there are circumscribed mechanisms in the central nervous system which should be relatively easily susceptible to anatomical and physiological delimitation. Has, in fact, any work of this sort been done? Presumably there are centres where the energy for the I.R.M.s builds up. Where are they?

LORENZ:

I am not quite in agreement with the hypothesis that they must be circumscribed, for one reason: you must keep in mind that where reaction to form is concerned, as, for instance, in the turkey cock, the whole thing must somehow go through a Gestalt perception, an apparatus certainly very widely distributed inside the central nervous system. That does not apply to all I.R.M.s and, of course, there are all gradations including the case where one sensory organ only is required to elicit one response. If you have a cricket, where the female has a hearing apparatus with a range of only a few tones in pitch, and which is only meant to receive the mating call of the male (which releases a positive reaction causing it actually to jump into the loud-speaker in the celebrated experiment) there the question of selectivity does not arise; but when the jackdaw reacts in one way with a submissive attitude and in another way with an aggressive attitude, then the whole thing must be shunted somewhere over the remotest projections of the cortical visual apparatus.

TANNER:

I was thinking more of the effector end of the mechanism. After the Gestalt has been received, brought in over certainly many pathways, one would imagine that these then converge on some distinct anatomical structure which would be the power structure of the I.R.M.

LORENZ:

Some results of Professor Hess tempt one to think that in his excitation experiments he gets a place at least very near to the input on the receptor side (HESS and BRÜGGER, 1943). In most of Professor Hess's experiments he got an entirely coherent, integrated sort of behaviour. If he stimulated the 'fighting centre', the cat behaved entirely as if there really was a rival. In such cases one would suspect that the excitation influenced a centre very high up in the hierarchy of the central nervous system, or even that it was the afferent side of the response that was stimulated. Such a cat behaves exactly as if it had an hallucination of another cat fighting it. But the interesting point is that Hess could get different levels of the hierarchic system of this instinct at will. When he let a very slight stimulation impinge at the more cranial point, he got a slight threshold-lowering of fighting-reactions. The cat would not yet attack *in vacuo*, but it would bite Hess's assistant whom it would not have bitten without that stimulation. In other words, slight stimulation at that more central point would put the cat into 'fighting mood'; if the stimulus was increased the cat would attack substitute objects which were still less similar to a rival cat; and so on, up to 'explosive' fighting *in vacuo*. But if Hess stimulated at a point situated a few millimetres farther to the caudal end of the brain, the cat, as a whole, was not put into a fighting mood. It got no threshold-lowering, went on purring peacefully, allowed itself to be scratched by the assistant, and then, on stronger stimulation, it would quite suddenly discharge disjointed fighting movement, like scratching and spitting, only to go on purring in the next moment. All this fits in with Tinbergen's theory of the hierarchic organization of instinct so beautifully that it is almost too good to be true (TINBERGEN, 1951). If you ask me where to look for the localization of an I.R.M., I should say: the I.R.M. joins on to the effector side of the response in those places where Professor Hess got his most generalized instinctive behaviour patterns.

HARGREAVES:

We need, I think, to know whether there are any characteristic differences between mammals and birds in this field of ethology. We talked of loss of I.R.M.s. I want to know if there is any way of putting them back. That is to say, has anybody created in animals new I.R.M.s that didn't exist before?

LORENZ:

Birds and fishes were the first objects in which we found these things. A systematic study of mammals and insects in this regard is in

E   129

its initial stages, but these initial stages allow us to state that it is quite surprising how these elementary mechanisms repeat themselves in animals as widely different as a rodent, a bird, a fish, an insect, and a cephalopod. Thorpe has found imprinting in insects which is absolutely comparable to that to be found in birds; the only thing about which we are still very doubtful is imprinting in mammals. Most mammals, except monkeys and man, are animals with a large olfactory region in their brain, and in these macrosmatic animals it is difficult to experiment because you can't control your stimuli—you don't smell yourself. There is the olfactory type of mammal and the visual type, and that is why the ethology of monkeys and of man is so surprisingly convergent with what we find in fishes, and very unlike that of olfactory animals. Nevertheless, we get more similar reactions than we expected, with the exception of imprinting. There are some instances where sexual activity in ruminating animals is optically released, and in these few cases it seems that true imprinting also occurs. All known observations concern sheep and cattle, but I am sorry to say none of them is very conclusive.

FREMONT-SMITH:

I would like to close, if I might, with an anecdote which perhaps will relate, in a light way, the bird to the child. This observation was made by my son when he was about fourteen, on some cardinal birds. He had a bird-station just at the right photographic distance from our back window, and a young cardinal came to the station and began to eat the seed quite vigorously. Then his father flew down to the bird-station, and immediately this little bird crouched, dropped his crest, lowered all his feathers, put his head up in a begging reaction, and would not eat anything on the bird-station unless fed by the father. When the father flew away, he roused, became himself again, stood up straight. This was repeated several times, and my wife and I also saw it. What I wonder is whether we can say that this was a regression to a dependent attitude in the presence of the father.

LORENZ:

Well, I don't think so. I rather think it is just the overruling of the still stronger feeding reaction over the weaker one. I can duplicate that observation by one on young shrikes, exactly the same individuals on which I did the impaling experiments. These shrikes were fully fledged but were still fed mainly by begging. When there is anyone in the room the shrikes are prone to go on begging for a very long time, even when they are already quite able to eat. Now I went for a motorcycle tour for four days, and during these four days those young

130

shrikes were left alone by themselves in my room. They fed themselves perfectly and they were absolutely healthy, sleek, and fat when I came back. I had important work to do, and sat at my desk and the shrikes were sitting in their cage begging at me, and I said, 'Confound you, you have shown me that you can eat for four days, I am not going to feed you any more'. In the afternoon I saw that the shrikes became seedy and sad and saw that they hadn't eaten one bit, because their begging reaction actually prevented them from feeding themselves, and they would have died of hunger because I was sitting in the room, though they would thrive perfectly when I wasn't. I think that's the chief explanation, and a more economical one, of the phenomenon.

FIFTH DISCUSSION

Electroencephalographic Development
of Children

GREY WALTER:

When a child is born it exchanges a physiological for a social environment. It is about some of the aspects of the child coupled with the social machinery that I want to talk.

I am going to leave out of my remarks nearly all matters of technology. For the most part these can be found in the literature (WALTER, in HILL and PARR, 1950; WALTER, 1953). I am also going to take for granted that the information, such as it is, on adult neurophysiology is accessible, though it may not be known to us all, and I am going to assert where I could, in fact, prove. You will have to take my word for much of what I shall have to say, and possibly in the discussions I can amplify some of my statements.

First of all about the general difficulties of studying children. My wife and I have spent some years examining children from many points of view—electrophysiological, psychological, ethological— and we have constantly come up against the difficulty of assessing the nature of the population we are studying. Is it, or is it not, a select population? If one is going to study normal children of school or preschool age, these children are necessarily drawn from schools, families, and friends who are willing for them to be studied; and that eliminates children whose parents are not willing—parents who have, perhaps, some quite natural superstitious distrust of science and scientists, and particularly of neurological institutes and mental hospitals. This eliminates a certain group of the population so that, when I tell you that this is a normal child or these are normal children, you must weight what I say with that previous knowledge. These are children with no neurological or psychiatric complaints, but they are inevitably selected for their willingness or their parents' willingness for them to be studied.

The next difficulty which we have in considering children is that

132

development of the individual physiology and psychology is coupled reciprocally with social influences. For example, many delinquent children come from unhappy and broken homes, but if you inspect those homes in detail you find that they also contain genetically pathological specimens. There are brothers or sisters who are mentally affected or insane, there is a father who is alcoholic, a mother who is a prostitute. The separation of social family factors from genetical and ontogenetic ones at the present time I believe to be impossible.

Then, a question of pure technology which I must mention. I hope that many of you who are not physiologists or electroencephalographers will be tempted to read encephalographic and electrophysiological literature, but I do beg you in reading it to be extremely sceptical of the results, particularly from the technical standpoint; to bear in mind that the sort of information we collect from our machines is very liable to deceive us, that only the most refined, sophisticated and flexible techniques of recording and interpreting are likely to be of value. If one goes through the literature on child electroencephalography, one finds very little that, in the last analysis, one can accept as fact. The methods of recording, the methods of display, the methods of transformation, of analysis, of statistical checks—all these are subject to very serious criticism, so that the assertions I am going to make about infantile and juvenile physiology are based mainly on my own work, merely because I do know at least exactly what the limits of accuracy and interpretation of that are. Beyond that, I would not like to go. The accuracy of even the simplest experiments, as you will see in a moment, is very limited.

As you examine younger and younger children, the first feature which you find is a gradual increase in the general amplitude and profusion of electrical activity, and at the same time a progressive decrease in its frequency. The electrical waves from the head, recorded in the conventional manner, get larger and larger and slower and slower as you go down the age-scale. If you put electrodes on the belly of a pregnant woman, you can record before birth the electrical activities of the foetal brain, and these bear out the extrapolated child data: the brain activity of the foetus is, on the whole, very slow, irregular, and poorly synchronized. It can only be observed in snatches, because the foetus is always moving, so that there will be a few seconds when you get nice clean records, then suddenly there will be a sort of convulsion, the child will turn over and the head will have gone.

If we follow our child through its first months of life, we find the slow activity, swelling, waxing, waning, and in some stages of sleep and repose giving place to certain features well known in the adult, the spindles, 14 c/s oscillations characteristic of adult sleep. One then begins to notice what to me is one of the most fascinating features in the whole of this work, the enormous differences between individuals still in the normal range, a range so wide that I myself hesitate to be in any way dogmatic about what the normal E.E.G. is. If one looks for the meaning of these slow rhythms in children one sees that they are associated with the search for peace, if you like to call it that— the repose and inactivity of the child. As the child begins to get older, spends longer periods awake, pays more attention to its sur- roundings, makes apparently volitional movements and gives overt expression to affective states, one observes a decline in the slow rhythms. Often one hemisphere will start first to show suppression of this activity—sometimes it is the left, sometimes the right. At a very early age, sometimes as young as two or three months, long periods occur during which the slow activity is minimal, particularly when the child is attentive and being played with by its mother or performing some relatively complicated act.

Now I am going to follow the various E.E.G. components up through the years and discuss what they seem to mean—supposing the components can be considered as individual phenomena. (It is quite possible, of course, that we are dealing with a number of phenomena which have only a superficial resemblance.) Imagine us taking records longitudinally in children and following the develop- ment of the slow activity through to adult life. As the child gets older these slow rhythms—the *delta activity*—become more intermittent and in general they decline to a small figure of scarcely perceptible size some time between the second and tenth year. The situation is that illustrated in Fig. 15. At the top of the figure we have a chart showing the prominence of the various components of the E.E.G.—I use the word 'prominence' advisedly: it is a measure of both ampli- tude and abundance of activity together as a product. The data have been obtained by automatic analysis of many hundreds of records; the lines at the top and bottom of the delta band show the range of individual variations. If one plots from 100 to 75 as being the birth range, the variation becomes so wide at the age of about three that you can have one child showing almost no delta activity, and another showing as much as a newborn.

Exceptionally this delta activity can persist until the age of eighteen or twenty. We have made a special study of this type of activity in delinquent children compared with normal children (HODGE, WALTER and WALTER, 1953), and we have been bold enough to suggest a term to describe the psychological features which statisti- cally and experimentally are associated with the presence in the brain of these diffuse, rather poorly synchronized, slow rhythms. This term

FIG. 15

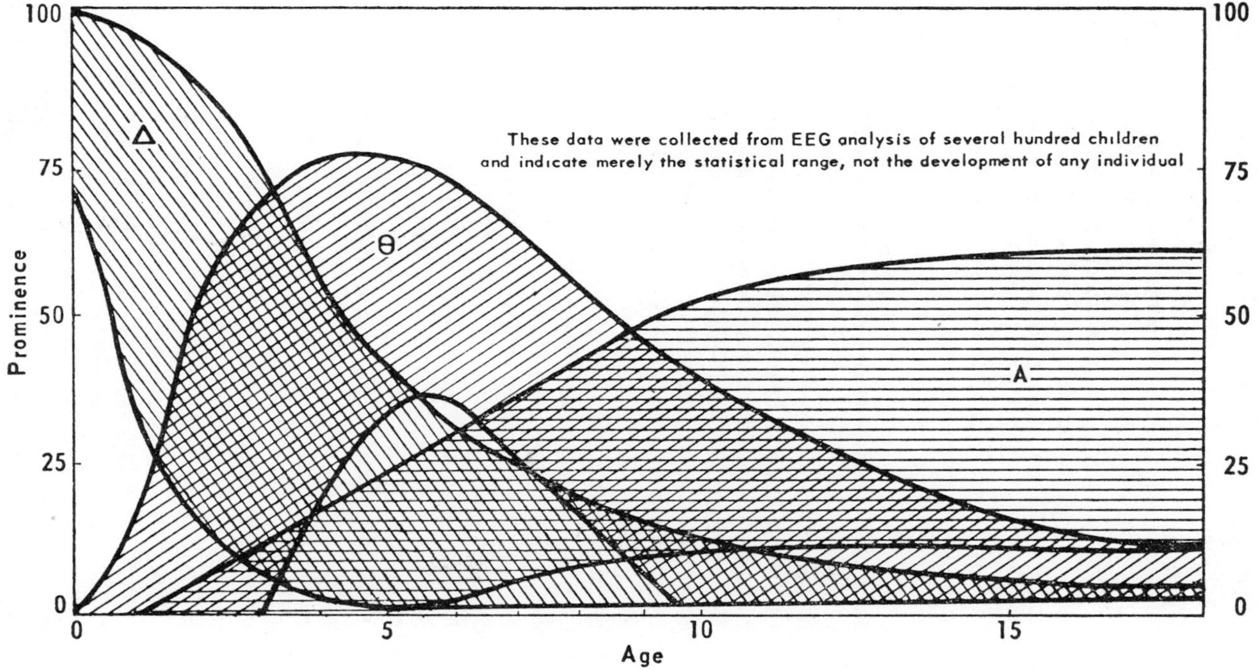
100
75
50
25
0
Prominence
Δ
θ
A
These data were collected from EEG analysis of several hundred children
and indicate merely the statistical range, not the development of any individual
0
5
10
15
Age

is *ductility*, which means, of course, the ability to be drawn out without breaking, for the personality to be deformed and moulded into shape without cracking or taking a permanent set. Ductility was observed first in delinquent children, where we found the presence of slow activity associated with something that shocked me as a physiologist. It was not associated with childishness in the general sense, or with stupidity or intelligence, but with a relatively *good* attitude as judged by psychiatrists and schoolmasters—a good attitude to the children's mother, to their fellow schoolchildren and to their leisure. This was discovered by statistical analysis.

As a physiologist I found this notion of a physiological basis for affection and spare-time occupations almost too good to be true. I was brought up in a very sceptical school of physiology where the study of the brain was considered rather disreputable, and normal psychological functions as completely outside the field of physiological investigation. But here one has a very firm statistical association between a measurable, quantitative, physiological phenomenon and a very complex and a very sentimental aspect of the child's life: the relation to his mother, to his spare time, and to his fellows. If the attitude were bad, if he were a naughty boy or a backward boy, then one would have accepted the relation as a phenomenon of immaturity in the nervous system, or inefficiency of brain metabolism, or what you like. But these slow rhythm boys were the boys who had a *good* attitude, they were the nice boys, docile, manageable, easily-led; in other words, ductile children. In the delinquent population they were the sheep who followed the leader. We have tragic evidence that children with this character very easily find themselves inextricably stuck once they get into a criminal society. They may be pushed in any direction, and naturally tend to drift down the social gradients. The consequences of certain mixtures of different types of this sort can be disastrous. Perhaps one of the most useful things we can do is to see how this work can be applied to such serious social problems as crime and delinquency.

Slow electrical activity is common in adults in sleep, and I should like to put to you the hypothesis that the presence of slow electrical activity of diffuse nature (not associated, of course, with organic disturbance) is the external objective representation of mechanisms in the brain which are directed towards defence of the brain. We all know that in the brain the three mechanisms which in the rest of the body defend against the consequences of injury are totally lacking. If you break your arm you feel pain; as a result of it the arm is immobilized and, even without the help of the surgeon, a better chance is obtained of the bone healing. In the brain you feel no pain. Secondly, you have no lymphatic drainage in the brain to drain away infected organisms or damaged cells. Thirdly, there is no regeneration of tissue; the brain-cell once destroyed is never replaced. So the brain is in a vulnerable condition. It is enclosed in a hard box, but once that box is penetrated, or something happens in the brain system which is dangerous or undesirable, there are apparently no defences. I would suggest that the slow rhythms represent the one defence. The brain has either to shut off from excessive action a part of itself tnat is damaged or, in a normal person, to rock to rest those mechanisms of the central nervous function which are either exhausted or have attained a wrong set in the adaptive process. One can show that any complicated mechanism which has its design not predetermined, but which determines for itself its own design, must have built into it quite elaborate mechanisms for what we call 'failure-to-safety': that is, arrangements which ensure that should something go wrong, should some undesirable state occur, the mechanism shuts down as a whole and does not go too far wrong. I suggest that these slow rhythms are a sign of this functioning, as a 'failure-to-safety', of some of the brain mechanisms.

The methods of studying these slow rhythms, particularly in children, from say two to twelve years old, are very important technically because the waves can be evoked and suppressed. Fig. 16 shows two records taken from children both aged twelve. The upper one is an example of a record from an entirely normal child. The presence of the slow activity shows in the record, and the analysis peaks indicate the total quantity of slow activity during each period of ten seconds. The lower record is from another perfectly healthy, happy, normal child, but he displays in the periods of rest large regular slow rhythms at about 3 c/s, as well as an alpha rhythm at 9 c/s. Whenever that child is stimulated by anything whatever, by sound, by a word, or even by an idea, the slow activity is suppressed. During this particular recording a flickering light was intermittently turned on, as shown in the bottom trace. Whenever the child was stimulated in this way, the slow activity ceased. This is a particularly old child to show such very rhythmic slow activity, and he was in fact very highly ductile. He was a charming child; any suggestion you made he would fall in with, any advice you gave him would be taken. His intelligence was quite adequate to take care of any normal problems, but he was easily led, and easily led astray.

The next feature of children's brain rhythms which seems to be particularly important is the appearance and significance of the *theta rhythms*. These rhythms have a different frequency and a different time-scale. They are sometimes easily seen in the record, but sometimes they are variable and subtle, and apt to be mixed up with other rhythms. In Fig. 15 the large band marked theta represents the

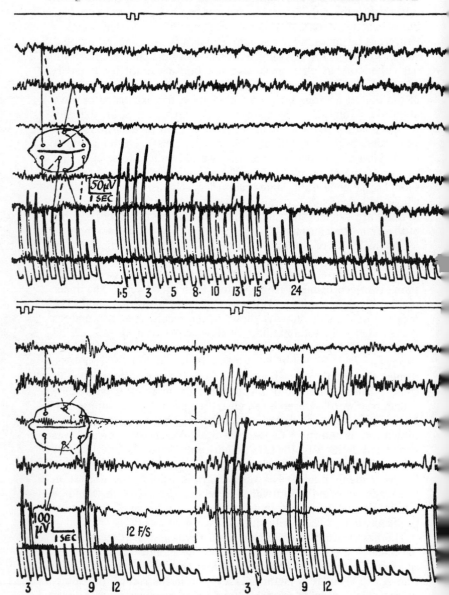

FIG. 16
E.E.G. RECORDS FROM TWO CHILDREN BOTH AGED TWELVE

The upper record shows a characteristic but rather juvenile medley of rhythms in all areas. The lower is an example of an unusually large and responsive delta rhythm at 3 c/s suppressed during the exposures to flicker.

This type of record is associated with a high 'ductility'

FIG. 17
NUMBER OF TEMPER OUTBURSTS WITH AGE

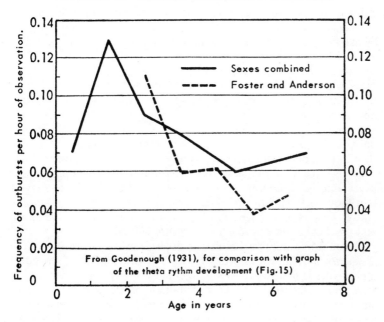

growth-range of the theta rhythms in a normal juvenile population. The range is again extremely wide. Fig. 17 is a graph of the frequency of temper outbursts with age in children, taken from the work of GOODENOUGH (1931). There is an astonishing correspondence between the frequency with which temper is lost in children, and the appearance of theta activity. The period of maximum rate of temper outburst coincides not with the maximum height, statistically, of the theta activity, but with the maximum rate of change of theta activity. This period of most likely temper outburst is a period when the theta rhythm is changing most and is the period when it is first taking control of the organism, when it first becomes the most prominent rhythm of all. We have observed this experimentally as well, quite independently. One finds, in fact, that if a child of two or three is happy and content then the record may have little or no theta activity even with the most refined methods of analysis. The moment the child gets annoyed—and, of course, a child can be annoyed by an enormous variety of situations or stimuli which to adults are quite neutral—then one sees a burst of theta activity. This burst may long outlast the stimulus period. It may be a matter of hours, even in some cases of days, before the effect of a certain disagreeable stimulus has worn off. The first experimental situation in which we observed this was the following: we were taking records from normal children and in the younger children of two or three we found it quite difficult to get them to co-operate well enough for our purposes. We used to give them a sweet on a stick to suck, but for the purposes of the recording itself we had to remove the sweet in order not to confuse the electrical activity of the jaw-muscles with that of the brain. The moment the sweet was removed there was always this burst of theta activity. In the adult we found it more easy to evoke a theta rhythm by withdrawal of a pleasant stimulus than by annoyance. Real deep-seated annoyance is an almost impossible thing to contrive in the laboratory, but you can give somebody a pleasant stimulus and interrupt it, and then in the adult you get a burst of this childish frustration rhythm.

I suggested that the slow delta rhythms represent a search for peace and the equilibration of the organism: I would like to suggest that these theta rhythms represent a search for pleasure as a specific entity. This should, I feel, link up in some way with a psychiatric and psychoanalytic approach to pleasure and pain.

I should like now to discuss the appearance and meaning of the *alpha rhythms*, shown also in Fig. 15. The distribution of the adult alpha types is first seen at about age nine to eleven; in other words, it is about this age that the distribution of alpha types becomes similar to that seen in the adult. I have to describe the situation in this somewhat roundabout way because of the individual variations. There are people who show no alpha rhythms at all, and there are those in whom the alpha rhythm is persistent throughout almost all their waking life whether their eyes are open or shut, whether they are reading, or anything else. Apparently the type of alpha rhythm relates to the type and vividness and persistence of imagery. If the delta rhythms represent a search for 'peace', and the theta rhythms a search for 'pleasure', I suggest that the alpha rhythms represent a search for 'pattern'. There are certain people who, when they close their eyes and relax, are not at rest. The moment the eyes are shut, a picture-show starts. These pictures—I speak from experience—are not in any sense obsessional, but they are quite vivid and can be turned on or off and manipulated as one chooses. In other people this does not happen. The time at which a juvenile population starts to divide into these types is about the age of nine or ten, which coincides with the time when reading ability increases considerably.

The curves in Fig. 15 are simple statistical displays, garnered from a large population and shaken down by statistical methods into a fairly smooth curve; but if you follow an individual child through these phases you get an entirely different picture. Then there is nothing like a smooth curve. For some months the delta activity may

140

go on showing occasional spindles; then quite suddenly one day you get a burst of theta rhythm as the child wants something but does not cry; the first time the child is deprived, annoyed, frustrated, and does not burst into tears.

The individual records show abrupt changes and also violent vacillations from one world to another, just like a switch which is hovering between contacts and, just while it is closing, chatters for a few days or hours and then shuts irrevocably. This is an observation which, if confirmed and worked out in detail, is very important for general ideas about living animals. The notion of the occurrence in the nervous system of the possibility of abrupt change helps us not only to understand, but to predict, the behaviour of organisms in a way which no other process possibly can. It means that you have a machine which can work within a perfectly well-defined framework of rules and which, if the representative point of that machine gets beyond a certain area, does not break down. There is suddenly a tick-tack-tock and a different set of rules is put up. The brain has a capacity for resetting itself, for setting up its own wiring, which, of course, confounds the Cartesian dualists, who admit that you can make a machine to imitate any property of the human being, but not a machine to imitate the human being itself. I don't say whether you can or whether you can't, but what I do say is that you would have to make a machine that would reset its own contacts according to experience and the chances of survival. Many such machines would fail, but the machines that did survive would be self-adjusting machines, machines which could re-orientate their internal connexions according to what had been found satisfactory on a statistical basis. Such machines would not be logical computers, but computers of similarities and differences, of relations of patterns of environment and behaviour, readjusting themselves according to what had been found to work.

Fig. 18A is a record which demonstrates some of the features I have described. It is from a girl of sixteen who was taking part in a test situation which involved her feeling, blindfolded, with her left forefinger the outline of a groove in a block of plaster, which was in the form of a large letter H. With her right hand she was supposed to draw just what she felt, whether she recognized the design or not. On the top line of the record is her speech, her pulse, and her breathing: on the second line the resistance of her skin, the activity of her neck muscles, and the pressure of her pulse: on the third line the E.E.G. from the right and left occipital regions and then the position of the right and left hands. At the point H the H-block was inserted and she immediately began to feel and explore the groove, and began, rather badly, to draw the outline with her right hand. The

141

FIG. 18A

RECORD OF TEN VARIABLES DURING THE PERFORMANCE WITH THE EYES SHUT OF A STEREOGNOSTIC TASK BY A GIRL OF 16

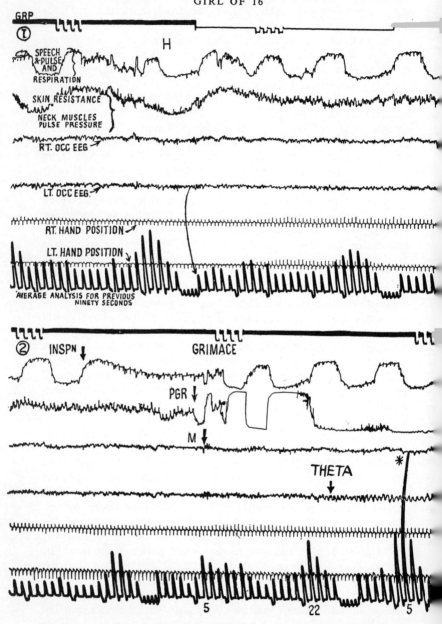

The first record covers the start of the task and shows rather irregular breathing and complete suppression of alpha activity. The second record is a continuation of the first and shows a sudden sigh, a grimace, a violent drop in skin resistance, acceleration of the pulse, tensing of the neck and then a sudden increase in theta activity, all associated with a feeling of annoyance and frustration.

FIG. 18 B

Showing the persistence and final subsidence of the theta activity as breathing, skin resistance and tension return to normal.

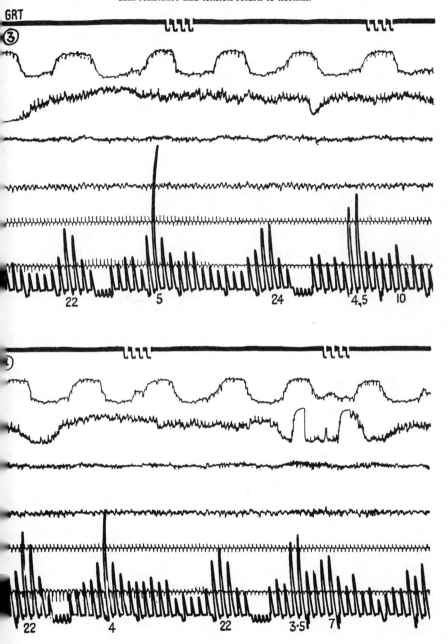

E.E.G. shows no dominant rhythm—her whole mind is active, working out this problem—then a little later she gave a great sigh, and grimaced, and later still, her muscles tensed, and the theta rhythm appeared, in that order. First came the breathing, then the grimace, the tensing of neck muscles, a drop in the skin resistance, acceleration of pulse, and, finally, the theta rhythm. At this point she made the remark, 'How far do I go?' She was worried about what she was supposed to do: the instructions given were quite vague; she had felt accurately the upright of the H and the cross-bar, but she hadn't found the other line. Then she got really annoyed that she hadn't got good instructions—she was a schoolgirl and used to being told exactly what to do.

Fig. 18B shows the further development of her theta activity. These are records taken continuously and you see that after the affective display you get a big peak which is the amount of activity at 5 c/s during than ten-second period. During that time the girl felt really frustrated, and didn't know what to do; as you see, her left hand is moving up and down, repetitively, constantly searching, and the right hand is not moving very much. The theta rhythm gradually, after a time, got smaller and smaller, and finally died away. Then there was another change in skin resistance and she returned to her normal state. Because of this frustration, she was quite incapable of solving this problem, one which every child that we have seen so far has been able to do. Her intelligence was quite high enough, but she got herself into a frustrating situation, and even at this age of sixteen developed an entirely infantile response of theta rhythm which was the essence of frustration for her, and which was the signal not to finish or solve the problem, but to get out of it, to regress to an emotional display. Then after the affective discharge, skin-resistance changes, the theta rhythm, the desire to get out of it all, you see her suppressing this display and making up her mind to be a good girl. She was a good schoolgirl from a good school, and we were nice people and she was not going to lose her temper on this silly problem. After she had got over this she solved other problems quite well. It is very characteristic during testing, as you know, in children of this age, that they may make several silly mistakes in the ordinary intelligence test, and then later on solve problems up to their age level perfectly well: this is just that kind of emotional instability that one sees at that age.

Fig. 19 has to do with another aspect of personality; the extent to which the alpha rhythms vary from time to time in the individual. This suggests the notion of *versatility* as a personality parameter which is at least measurable. Some brains keep the same tenor of activity hour after hour, even from minute to minute, from second to

FIG. 19
EXAMPLE OF TYPE OF RECORD MADE TO ASSESS 'VERSATILITY'

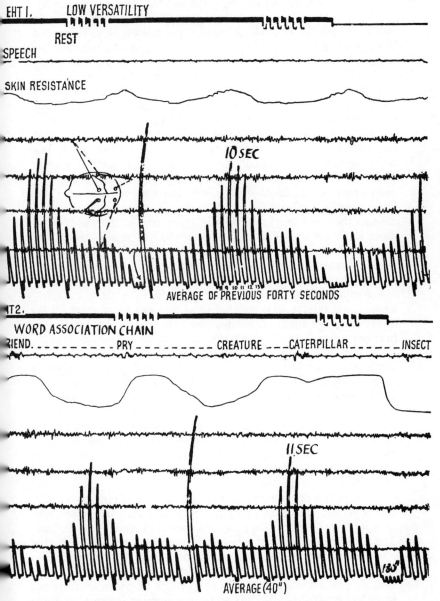

Above. The frequency analysis averaged over forty seconds during rest. There was little variation from epoch to epoch in the profile of the spectrum. *Below.* The conditions during the word-association chain test. The range of ideas was limited and each link was associated with a fall in skin resistance. The E.E.G. analysis shows a slight shift to the right in the modal peak but the profile as a whole is little altered.

second. They have a small repertoire; little versatility, The other sort of brain may not be any better, in the sense of having a higher IQ, but is one which is constantly changing. This is something we can measure quantitatively and automatically and objectively. The record of Fig. 19 is an example. In it a girl, under a test situation, has her speech recorded at the top and her skin resistance below. The group of upright lines is the frequency analysis averaged over the previous forty seconds of activity. You see the profile of one spectrum is very much like the profile of all the others: this was a child with low versatility. The lower record shows the effect upon the same girl of the task of forming a word association chain beginning with the word egg. The record was taken toward the end of her association. At this point she had got to 'friend', 'pry', 'creature', 'caterpillar', 'insect'. The E.E.G. analysis shows a very similar profile to the resting one, except that the mode of the analysis, the highest point, is 11 c/s instead of 10 c/s. You may notice also that for each of the association changes there is a large drop in skin resistance. At the word 'caterpillar' she has managed to get out of the affective trap of 'friend, pry, creature'. You can see a slight tendency to produce theta activity which is suppressed, because she got on to the notion of caterpillar, and the chain was terminated just there.

Investigations of this sort on children have so far given fairly unequivocal results, showing that versatility can be measured from a very early age and, as far as we have seen, a child that is versatile in respect of one sort of rhythm will also be versatile in other respects, suggesting that this is a characteristic of the nervous system which can be measured and extrapolated with some safety. Versatility may have some connexion with the sort of things people like to do and particularly with the way people join up in groups. Two versatile people don't generally get on very well together; there is too much criss-crossing of ideas, the association is explosive and unstable. A versatile person and a non-versatile person get on very well together, because the versatile one will feed the other with ideas. The electrophysiology of these social groups seems to me one of the most fascinating things that one can study.

I have put before you these notions of ductility, of temper-keeping, and of versatility as personality factors. Now I am going to consider another factor which I suppose one could call *stability* or *balance*. This notion is related to the Pavlovian analysis of behaviour. Pavlov identified a character which he called balance in his animals and in his human subjects. This is important also in brain physiology, because one can show that the way in which an organism responds to violent stress varies all the way from a 'freezing reaction' of doing nothing at all, to a violent and sustained oscillation.

146

FIG. 20

WAVE-AND-SPIKE DISCHARGE EVOKED IN A YOUNG
DELINQUENT BY FLICKER AT ABOUT 20 FLASHES
PER SECOND

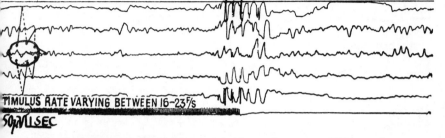

This discharge was accompanied by a transient lapse of awareness. This type of record is associated with considerable 'instability' and is commonest in epileptics

In Fig. 20 you see the record of a neurologically normal child who was a delinquent. He was at this time sixteen, and two years later he was convicted of a capital offence. He was one of the ductile type and he was also unstable. He had run away from home and required firm institutional control. This record is the response to a series of flickering light stimuli, which produce a gradually increasing fast discharge and then a large slow discharge. The whole brain is excited into an almost convulsive state by this simple flickering light. This is a response which one can elicit from about one in thirty of the normal population and is associated with the type of behaviour one sees in very young children. It is inappropriate, exaggerated behaviour. It is found in the sort of person who commits not a motiveless crime, but who instead of shouting at somebody or insulting them, knocks them down. If you get a combination of a lad with high versatility and normal E.E.G., and a boy like this with a high ductility and high instability, then almost always crime results, often murder.

In Fig. 21 we have a similar sort of picture. This is a record of a normal girl aged twenty, but here the stress has been made very difficult to bear for anybody, by making the stimulus itself depend upon the brain activity. The brain activity is made to operate a trigger circuit which provides the stimulus to reaffect the brain activity, and a feedback oscillatory system can be set up. Most brains are equipped to deal with this, which very likely occurs in the normal course of events. I suggest that it is one of the functions of the slow activity of the brain to deal with precisely this situation. Here we see the activity in the left occipital region arranged to provide the stimulus which is shown on the bottom trace. This bottom trace

147

FIG. 21

WAVE-AND-SPIKE PATTERN SIMILAR TO THAT IN FIG. 20

but less extensive and protracted, evoked in a normal adult by feedback
flicker, the left occipital rhythms being made to generate a flash-stimulus.

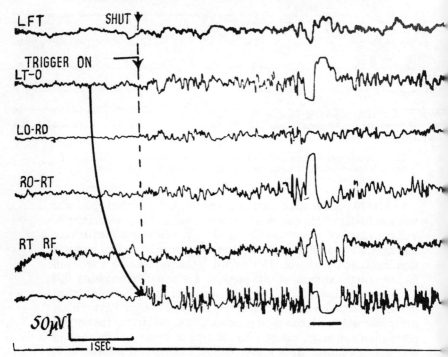

LFT

SHUT

TRIGGER ON
LT-O

LO-RO

RO-RT

RT RF

50μV

1SEC

The large slow wave (underlined) interrupts the reflexive mechanism, but the
subject complained of feeling 'light-headed' whenever it occurred. The effect
faded after about 15 repetitions.

copies the occipital one, and adds to it the stimulus, the sharp upward
deflections indicating flashes of light which produce in this normal
girl a violent discharge over the whole brain, leading up suddenly
at the marked point to a series of very sharp discharges. Then these
are cancelled in a large slow surge. The feedback chain is broken and
this is what I mean by failure-to-safety. This may result in unconsciousness, and most people in this situation feel a bit 'swimmy'.
This was the first time that this person had had this experience. If
you repeat it, the effect no longer happens in a normal person. About
a dozen experiences of this sort produces a gradual fading of both
the fast and the slow response; in other words, the brain adapts itself
in such a way that the retroactive networks are no longer established.

I believe failure-to-safety to be an important aspect of *petit-mal*. The reason why the wave and spike of *petit-mal* persists and recurs is that the brain does not reset its switches so as to avoid the retroactive arrangement. The mechanisms one sees at work here, I think, are those responsible in the brain for the four selective operations which are essential for the preliminary stages of learning. I think that these basic processes originate in the reticular system of the brain and are connected particularly with the estimation by the central nervous system of to what extent a set of signals are significantly associated. We are slowly collecting evidence for the view that the various operations necessary for learning develop at different rates in different children at different times; one may get, for example, a very mature and high selectivity in a child with no *constructivity* at all. The child has a very good discrimination and yet cannot retain in its mind a notion that two things are related. Conversely, a child may have a very highly developed constructive ability and yet be completely unselective.

PIAGET:

You said that there was a certain correspondence in electroencephalography with our stages, but I must admit that I have not quite grasped where this correspondence lies and should like to have some details.

GREY WALTER:

It is very difficult to describe briefly what this correspondence is, and our own experiments are very far from complete. In stage I (of early infancy) wherein Mlle Inhelder distinguishes six different epochs, transitions from the second to third epoch, from the primary circular to the secondary circular reaction, seem to be related to the way in which the slow delta activity is interspersed with faster activity. The change from epoch three to four, from the secondary circular reaction stage to the co-ordination of patterns, where you get for the first time a real goal-seeking mechanism, seems to be associated with the time at which the electrical responses are not directly evoked sensory effects but appear in the temporal and frontal lobes as an abstraction of the stimulus. At this stage, instead of a response to flashes of light being merely in the visual area there will appear in the temporal or frontal lobes transient interwoven crystals of electrical energy which maintain for seconds or minutes the abstract form of the stimulus. The age at which this first happens is quite critical. Before this the signal reaches the sensory area, the child sees,

149

but it doesn't know the meaning of what it sees; then quite suddenly it does see the meaning. This is, of course, related to the ability to read and understand.

These experiments are rather tedious to do because they must be longitudinal; cross-sectional surveys are very misleading in this matter. If any of us are going to go on with this sort of work it's going to cost a great deal of money, because we have got to follow many children for years, examining them in enormous detail by methods that are quantitative, objective, and above all unobtrusive, because in making these experiments it is essential that one should not inject into the child the sort of thing one wants. It may be very difficult to work out a technique whereby you are not coupled too closely to your system, not yourself part of it, influencing it all the time.

MEAD:

Don't you need really to develop children that think that the whole of this measuring situation is part of life?

GREY WALTER:

Yes, of course, just like going to school.

TANNER:

I have a small point of criticism about your relating the curves of growth of keeping the temper from one set of data (Fig. 17), and electroencephalographic frequency from another (Fig. 15). I feel very dubious about relating two cross-sectional-type curves in that way. If the data are not taken on the same child followed longitudinally, the appearance of correlation may come about owing simply to general changes with age, though the correlation between the two variables in any given child may still be very small.

GREY WALTER:

That is a most reasonable criticism. In Figs. 15 and 17, I agree entirely that such relations can be quite meretricious. But we had already established experimentally a relation between theta activity and bad temper; the similarity between the two curves struck me as a particularly happy coincidence since the data were culled from quite independent sources, while our experiments with teasing children may have been spoiled by some sort of unintentional collusion.

MELIN:

I should like to know if Dr. Grey Walter can mention some sort of a pathological condition in a child which more permanently changes its electroencephalogram to a slow record and if this is accompanied by the related psychological manifestations.

Another question: we have seen how different emotions can influence the E.E.G., for example, how an angry child will show a changed type of activity. I have myself been doing some work in this field and found out how anxiety can influence the records and increase the amount of theta and also delta waves in the record. My question is: Can a child exposed to constant anxiety have its electroencephalogram permanently changed?

GREY WALTER:

I can't give an unequivocal answer: it is rather difficult to get children who have been through a traumatic psychological experience and arrange to observe them long enough and carefully enough to detect these changes and measure them; however, we have had the opportunity to see a few children as inpatients in whom just such changes have been observed. There was, for example, a boy of about twelve who had one of those peculiar psychometric documentations in which the results of various tests seem to be incompatible. The most striking feature about him was his inability to read. He was a very intelligent boy by non-verbal tests, with an IQ of about 130. His E.E.G. showed terrific profusion of alpha rhythms of all types. He had absolutely no visual imagination; but he had been taught to read visually. At the same time as these alpha rhythms he had a lot of theta activity and a lot of delta activity; he had an E.E.G. which would be more or less normal for a child of three. During the fortnight he was admitted, the E.E.G. record was completely transformed; his alpha rhythms became moderately responsive, theta and delta activity disappeared. His whole attitude to the problem of reading and the extraction of concepts from the mnemonic marks on paper was completely transformed by a process of non-visual tuition and separation from his family. Five years ago I should have said that records like this were unalterable. At one time I supported the statements of Lennox, in America, who said that the E.E.G. is an hereditary trait (LENNOX, GIBBS and GIBBS, 1945), but experiments we have done since that time have considerably modified my ideas. I have seen in E.E.G. records and in the psychological state of a child both regression as a result of injury followed by recovery, and also transformation from infantile behaviour and an infantile record, to a completely adult appearance as a result of quite mild psychotherapeutic treatment or the mere passage of time.

I have been fascinated by Dr. Grey Walter's communication and should like to ask him two questions:

(1) Does the troubled stage you speak of occur before six years: that is to say, does it precede the first appearance of the alpha rhythm or does it come at about twelve years when the alpha rhythm becomes more regular and stable?

(2) Do you interpret the theta rhythm as indicative of stabilization of behaviour with attainment of control over self or as a phenomenon showing the adaptive reaction of a particularly emotive child? Dr. Monnier and I have examined a child of six years who showed a great deal of theta rhythm and we wondered what was the reason for this rhythm. Is it a question of a pronounced reaction to emotivity or of a stabilization of rhythm natural to this age?

GREY WALTER:

Was this spontaneous or deliberately evoked?

MONNIER:

It was spontaneous, but very much increased by hyperventilation. Why do you consider now the amount of theta rhythm as an expression of controlled temper rather than as the expression of affective bursts or increased emotionality as you described it previously?

GREY WALTER:

This is a change in my own point of view, based on what I have seen. The theta activity is associated with the practical need to control temper; in other words, in the child you speak of, you have a child who has a bad temper, and because of that, he has to control that temper, and it is the effort to control it which seems to be associated with theta activity. But there is something else underneath which we must study in great detail, and that is the possession of a bad temper, whether or not you can control it.

In answer to Mlle Inhelder's first question about the appearance of the alpha rhythms, it seems that rhythms of alpha frequency may appear well before six, in the back of the head; responsiveness to visual activity starts considerably before six in some children. You can sometimes find signs of alpha rhythms even in babies of a few months, but at the phase at which it appears and becomes responsive, there occurs usually a considerable vacillation in the child's behaviour. He will suddenly be able to read frightfully well, and then the next day he can't read at all. Or one day he will play with his toys and bricks like a baby, and then quite suddenly he will go on to draw a picture.

BOWLBY:

This notion of ductility has puzzled me quite a bit since I first heard about it. What occurred to me was that the good child is not necessarily a normal child. Normal children are difficult, especially in certain situations, when they have their emotional and instinctual responses aroused in regard to special people, particularly parents. I wonder whether these ductile children haven't got some of their major social responses knocked out. One knows, of course, that that does happen to children in hospital. They are very difficult for a bit, then, after a few days or a week or two, they 'settle down' and are good. And everyone says, 'Isn't it nice, they are good'. They are being ductile, but they are also being very abnormal in the sense that, as people·remark, 'They forget their mothers'. I was interested in the notion that the delta waves are related to a search for peace, because that is how one conceives of the separated young child: he gives up wanting his mother. To want and not get her is much too turbulent and awkward an affair so he 'forgets' her: he then becomes ductile— he has found a sort of peace.

LORENZ:

Dr. Sylvia Klimpfinger found in hospitalized children who were torn from their mothers, and who were exposed to a quick change of nurses, that they tried to form personal contacts with the new nurse, in a much weaker way the second time, in a still weaker way the third time, and then they gave it up. These children subsequently showed very different behaviour and could be divided into two types. One type was all over everybody, and the other type behaved like a chow dog that has lost its master—they became autistic. All of them showed a very great instability in their interests. They couldn't be kept at the same play for any appreciable period. They behaved then, especially the autistic ones, very much like delinquent children, with a general weakness of emotional reactions. These children who had their early reaction-to-mother knocked out were so similar to children who, either genetically or partially genetically, had a weakness of emotional and social reactions, that you could not tell them apart.

GREY WALTER:

The point against the explanation of ductility that Dr. Bowlby suggests is that statistically the children who had the most prominent

153

slow activity were those who had preserved most nearly intact a good attitude towards their mother: they wrote letters to her, they asked to see her, went back to stay with her during holidays, and so on, and during their leisure time they were the most socially active; they made models, they played games, and they were good company to their fellows; in fact their social orientation was most nearly normal. They were not those who rejected the mother-figure or had become hardened.

FREMONT-SMITH:

Was this information based on an average of a questionnaire answer?

GREY WALTER:

The isolation of this factor was based on the statistical results of an inventory of psychological and sociological inquiries.

FREMONT-SMITH:

Perhaps one would need to have a group of the typical ones examined more intensively. I think you might find that their relationship to their mothers was not as appeared in the statistical results.

GREY WALTER:.

Yes, that might be so. These studies were made about three years ago; since then we have made a few more intensive studies and a few longitudinal studies, and as far as we can tell this still holds true: they are the children who have not rejected their mothers, who still keep in touch with them. One interesting thing we found was that the boys' attitude to their mothers was not necessarily associated with the mothers' attitude to the boys. The mother might be completely indifferent to the child, but the child would still be fond of the mother. That is not true of the father relationship. The relationship of the father to the child and the child to the father was reciprocal. If the father liked the boy, the boy liked the father.

BOWLBY:

I think that the extraordinary differences in the behaviour of these people in different social situations is most perplexing. In one situation they behave very satisfactorily and then, when they get into another situation, they go into quite a different gear. I am thinking of a well-known murderer who was head-boy of a delinquent school. He

154

was obviously an exceedingly psychopathic boy, but in that particular environment he could function as a social being; whereas in another situation where other stimuli reached him, such as sexual stimuli and love-object stimuli, his behaviour was quite different—he murdered his girl-friends.

GREY WALTER:

I wonder whether this ductility question isn't a matter of simplification of the response pattern. Perhaps the response of these children is not less normal, but less in quantity than that of a non-ductile child?

TANNER:

What is the relation between this measure of ductility and measures of suggestibility such as the Eysenck sway test?

GREY WALTER:

I don't think the psychologists used that particular test, but they did use a number of others and it looked as though certain aspects of suggestibility (the results, for example, of the Düss test) would relate significantly to ductility.

MEAD:

There are characters we call in jargon 'working idiots' in New Guinea and Melanesia. The only idiotic thing about them is that they work; they are people who will do things just because you ask them to. They are not economically forced to do this. They are not stupid, and they are quite well recognized through quite a large cultural range. This is against Dr. Bowlby's explanation as compared to a genetic one, because they occur in societies of such extraordinarily different mother-child patterning. People regard them as a resource. My suspicion would be, from the distribution in New Guinea, that there is a genetical element.

FREMONT-SMITH:

They might not be really parallel to ductile children.

CAROTHERS:

I have three questions. The first is, that I understand that the alpha rhythm has its main centre, as far as the cortex is concerned, in the occipital area: I was wondering if the theta was similarly associated with any particular part of the brain? The second question is: is there any relation between the type of rhythm and whether the subject tends to use auditory or visual imagery? The third question is, in view of the difficulty of comparing unsophisticated people with sophisticated, and the difficulty of making the African calm and at ease in a test situation which is very frightening for him, would there be any advantage in comparing these people in sleep? Does sleep vary during life in any constant pattern as one grows older?

GREY WALTER:

The distribution and geometry of the alpha rhythms are extremely variable, but certainly they are oriented longitudinally over the back of the head rather than laterally at the side. There is a relationship between the distribution of the alpha rhythms (which are always plural) and the way the information coming into the brain is distributed and relayed around the surface of it. Now compare that to the theta geometry. There are many sorts of rhythms in the theta, but the most prominent one is at right angles to the alpha field; the alpha rhythm is fore-and-aft at the back, the theta rhythm athwart the head at the side, mainly in the temporal and parietal regions. In certain parts of the brain these two interlace. At a certain age of the child you may have alpha and theta activity going on at the same time. The part of the brain where we see sensory signals first abstracted, or given meaning, is the part where this interlacing is usually most intricate, where the texture is most elaborate. You get a sort of tartan of these spontaneous rhythms, and it is where this tartan is first formed that you get the most highly abstracted and elaborated and preserved pattern of incoming signals. In other words, it looks—on a completely superficial and possibly mistaken view—as though the pattern-seeking and pleasure-seeking mechanisms were interlaced in some way, like the threads in a sewing machine.

In relation to the question of examining Africans or any people with a different background, this is obviously most important, because, in order to compare two populations and get any idea at all of what an African's brain is like, one has to make an extremely elaborate analysis of the whole situation, to see how he looks at it. In other words, you must be an African or train an African to study his own people; it seems to me that is the only way we can do it. One simple example of that: most people in laboratories wear white coats; for most children a white coat is a danger-sign. The result is that if a child in our laboratory is examined by somebody in a white coat you may get one sort of a record. If he is examined by someone in a green coat you may get an entirely different record.

To go on with my answer to Dr. Carothers, I don't know very much about rhythm and imagery in Africans. In an English population, about 70 per cent of the population have a mixed imagery type: they can turn on any type of imagery they need, more or less, within reason; about 15 per cent can only use visual imagery, they tend to be obsessed by visual images, and can't do much else; and about 15 per cent cannot produce a visual image if you pay them.

CAROTHERS:

The other question was about sleep.

GREY WALTER:

Sophisticated and unsophisticated people studied in sleep. The sleep pattern as it is described in textbooks is not much like the real sleep patterns, which are much less rigid. There is enormous personal variation in pattern, but there are certain features that do occur very commonly. Always at some stage you get slow rhythms, always you get spindles. The first stage is usually a theta stage, which is a 'floating' stage when you feel your body disappears and you are floating—that is usually the time when the afferents are cut off from the body—but the alterations of these phases, and the amount of time occupied by each one during diurnal or nocturnal sleep, is an enormously personal factor. It seems to be set at a very early age and to maintain itself throughout life. You can predict to a certain extent from the examination of a child's sleep record the sort of sleep he will have when he grows up—apart from emotional disturbances and so on; and even then you can predict, to a certain extent, from this very early infantile characteristic what effect such disturbances will have on a person's sleep. We don't know whether there is any ethnic variation in these characters, or if the situation is different in peoples who can sleep very easily. Nor do we know whether sleep patterns are susceptible to conditioning. We know from Pavlov that sleep can be conditioned; it is one of the standard effects of delayed and trace reflexes. But even when tried out in dogs it is found to be characteristic of the individual dog, and to be one of Pavlov's typological criteria.

CAROTHERS:

But is there no close parallel between the degree of development during waking life of the individual and the rhythms in sleep during the same period of life?

GREY WALTER:

You mean as a general rule throughout? No, you may get the sleep variations and the adult variations behaving quite differently. I don't say there aren't some correspondences, but superficially considered the two things are different mechanisms. That is probably simply because we haven't used the right sort of stimuli in waking life.

KRAPF:

To what extent do you believe that the different electroencephalographic patterns could be related to Rorschach studies? Just lately, in Yale, they have developed differential patterns of the Rorschach in different ages of childhood (AMES, 1952) and it struck me there might be a parallel, for instance, between form and percent alpha or maybe the Erlebnistypus and the delta pattern and so on. I feel that this might give us an interesting slant on our problem.

GREY WALTER:

We have data on a number of cases. There was a boy who had a number of fits whose Rorschach was grossly abnormal when first seen. His E.E.G. also was highly pathological, immature, and retarded, and showed some epileptic features as well. He was then given anti-convulsant drugs, which controlled the seizures quite well. Three months later he was seen, at the age of about eleven years and three months. The Rorschach was repeated, which, of course, was a doubtful thing to do, and there was complete transformation to normal. His E.E.G. also was then normal. We thought this might be due to the drugs, so we took him in as an in-patient, withdrew his drugs for two weeks, and though he did have one seizure, his whole personality remained quite stable. So in that case within the space of three months we were able to see a complete transformation from an immature, quite pathological, child with an abnormal Rorschach, abnormal behaviour and abnormal E.E.G., to an integrated, almost adult person.

REMOND:

I should like to say a word on the question of choosing longitudinal or cross-sectional series. It is true that statistical population studies found in the literature are mainly cross-sectional studies. Today it is considered that longitudinal studies, even when much more restricted, are of much greater interest. Personally I consider that certain cross-sectional studies would continue to offer great advantages where very homogeneous groups are used.

At present I have the opportunity of examining a group of 200 persons. They are cadet pilots of twenty to twenty-four years who have been medically examined and have the physical and intellectual aptitudes qualifying them to become pilots. They form, then, a very homogeneous group. We insisted on getting this group because the Air Ministry in Paris asked us to define the criteria of E.E.G. normality for acceptance or rejection of cadet pilots. For a long time we refused to take such a responsibility, but during a recent experiment, when we were studying the effect of stimulation on the electro-encephalogram in an attempt to find proofs for the existence of an epilepsy of which there was little evidence, we noticed that the threshold above which these cadet pilots responded to stimulation seemed much lower than that which had seemed to us to be normal up to then. The study of about fifty individuals taken at random and from different age-groups had in fact given us a vague statistical idea of what was the normal threshold.

These very low thresholds of stimulation seemed very curious and we wondered why these individuals were, in relation to our previous work, pre-epileptics. Our psychologist friends, having considered the problem, then suggested that our subjects had wanted to become fighter pilots because they had this particular characteristic which we considered as being pre-epileptic.

Recently when we began to examine a new group of 200 cadet pilots we were surprised to discover again, even from the first ten, that the average electroencephalogram and the average reactions to various sensory stimulations were very different from what we had thought up to then to be the normal aspect for that age. We found with this group an abundance of slow waves in the parieto-occipital regions and a notable quantity of rapid rhythms in the anterior regions. These rather special characteristics make us say: take care, this is perhaps an abnormal individual. If we took his epileptogenic threshold we should no doubt find it very low; if we examine him thoroughly we may find traces of a past pathological attack, although the history has allowed us to think there has been none.

Given the very homogeneous constitution of this group, which is a selected group, the common characteristics we shall find among these persons will be far more valuable and significant to us than if we had carried out this study on a cross-section of the population of the same age, but taken at random.

If I might add another conclusion I would say that this cross-sectional study will cost less than a longitudinal study on say 10 per cent of the same subjects. This study will become more valuable when it is compared with other studies of very homogeneous groups such as we have already begun to consider. Thus we are going to be sent a group of French railway employees chosen to be engine drivers. Naturally, we always choose individuals without, or with very little, neurological history, and I think that we can thus obtain some guiding points for discussions, I will not say on the normality of an individual but on the aggregate of his special characteristics.

ZAZZO:

I agree with Dr. Rémond, but I think two things should be specified: on the one hand, the necessity of constituting a valid sample, and on the other, for a study in genesis, the need to proceed longitudinally.

I do not think Dr. Rémond's arguments give a full reply to the problem of choice between transverse cross-sections and the longitudinal method, since the example he has furnished concerns adults and the problem for him is to choose a significant group among these adults. I therefore think that the question remains open and that although in some cases the cross-sectional method may suffice, in others it may be very dangerous. Thus, if we study girls of thirteen the cross-sectional method is meaningless, because some will be pubescent and others not. In this case the cross-sectional method cannot be used. Therefore I think it is necessary to distinguish between the two questions, that of the constitution of the sample and that of the choice between the longitudinal method and the cross-section method. The question of sampling always comes in but it can be differently solved according to the method chosen.

RÉMOND:

I should nevertheless like to say that the first series in which we were interested comes within the bounds of this group's study because the growth of the subjects is not finished. I think the end of growth comes at about twenty-five years. However it may be from other points of view, as regards electroencephalography this group was shown to be relatively infantile. We do not think that these characteristics are any more evident among younger children. Moreover, this group will help us define one of the particular aspects of the end of growth or development.

Stages of Psychological Development
of the Child

ZAZZO:

I intend to comment briefly on the report drafted by Professor Wallon, thus coming back to the stages of early childhood, especially to the first year. After that I will go over the stages in the period of schooling; then I will take two sectors of behaviour, the evolution of graphic ability and the evolution of language, and refer very simply to the main stages, as they have been defined by a large number of authors. Then I will conclude with some considerations on method which seem to me common to psychology and all the branches of biology.

I have been asked to prepare a report on the work of the Wallon School and also on some of the work of Gesell, whose pupil I was. It seems to me already significant that Mademoiselle Inhelder and myself should have been asked to give an account of certain psychologies—I am purposely using the term in the plural: the psychologies of Wallon, Piaget, and Gesell. It seems that there is not a science of psychology, but a group of systems. We can, however, ascertain by reviewing psychological literature that there are extensive data on which to base an objective science. It is, therefore, not lack of established facts which leads us to speak of psychologies in the plural. Because of the nature of psychological facts, and perhaps certain biological facts too, organization and interpretation are constantly necessary and these established facts, if they are to be used, require a system in the present state of our knowledge.

Motor Development in Early Childhood (according to Professor HENRI WALLON, 1925, 1946, 1947, 1949)

There are two ways of presenting the motor development of the child. The first is to give a description of the child's reactions in the chronological order of their appearance and in relation to their physiological context as well as to the circumstances of the moment.

F

This is the basic method; but it calls for much detail and can lead to confusion owing to possible anticipations or frequent overlapping between manifestations differing in significance. The second is the functional method which groups these manifestations according to their nature. It is synthetic and more interpretative, but also more distinct and explicit. It is the method adopted here.

(1) *Automatisms of Posture*

Co-ordinated reactions of the head, the limbs, and the trunk in response to certain exciting causes can be observed from the foetal period onwards. Such, for example, are the labyrinthine and cervical reflexes described by Magnus and de Kleyn. They are easily demonstrated in premature infants and also, under favourable conditions, in those born at term, by rapid displacement of the body upwards, downwards or horizontally, or by change in the orientation of the head relative to the trunk. They soon disappear. It would seem, nevertheless, that this series is connected with the reactions consisting in adjusting differently the segments of the body to each other and to exterior supports. To begin with there is the reaction acquired during the first few weeks: the active lifting of the head and its lateral displacement by means of the muscles of the nape of the neck. After that comes a whole series of readjustments arising from the child's contact with the ground in attempts to sit down, to stay on all fours, to stand up and finally walk. The difference between these reactions and the reflexes of Magnus and de Kleyn is that instead of being purely passive they are the result of active ventures into the outer world. It is the same difference as exists between intra-uterine life and life in free space. The automatic and unreasoning character of the first reflexes can be found again in the sudden emergencies of physical danger; they are components of actions with a fixed object.

(2) *Tonic Activity, Attitudes, and Means of Expression*

It is difficult to distinguish at birth between the spasms arising from tonic activity and actual movements. Cries, and the accompanying gestures—particularly stiffening of the trunk, opisthotonos, and sudden tensing and relaxing in the arms—appear to be definitely more spasmodic. The motor discharges in the lower limbs have the more dynamic character of pedalling. Perhaps there is a period where tonic and clonic activity are still poorly differentiated; this could no doubt be discovered through electrical examination of the muscular apparatus. It is, however, tonic activity, both of the visceral muscles (respiratory, laryngeal, and gastro-intestinal) and of the skeletal muscles, that corresponds to the effects noted. Its proper field is that of attitudes and expression; in other words, that which is of greatest use to the child, since only by these means can he obtain and solicit from his surroundings the help which is essential. The visible effects of his needs, his discomforts, and his sufferings soon link up, by means of conditioned-reflex mechanisms, with the tutelary effects which they have caused, and eventually become a means of arousing them. Towards six months the expressive manifestations of the child are so finely graded that all the major varieties of emotion can be distinguished. Vocal intonations precede language. The voice, the medium of speech, is a tonic activity. The attitudes which result essentially from tonic activity establish contact between the individual and the corresponding situation, underline the meaning of this situation and contain already its image.

(3) *Circular Activity*

There comes a period where the resultant effects of gestures tend to make them more specific, for example, the hand which enters the visual field and obscures the view, or the sound produced by certain muscular contractions of the vocal organs. This association must mark the moment when the fields of kinaesthetic, visual and auditory etc., imagery fuse together. Then what Thorndike calls the law of effect, or what Baldwin had described as circular reaction, comes into play. It is an important factor in the psychomotor development of the child. The effect obtained excites the movements which have produced it, and inversely. All kinds of learning processes follow (vocal noises and language phonemes, autopalpation and recognition of body activity, etc.). This period belongs to the second half of the first year.

(4) *Movements Towards External Objectives*

The first meetings with external objects seem to cause only reflexes without relation to the objects themselves. For example, the hand which closes over whatever touches the palm does not show prehension but rather a clinging contraction which is closer to the actions of holding on or climbing than those of picking, seizing, or grasping. The period when the child becomes capable of reacting to an object as such appears towards eight or ten months. It is the period of 'near space' (W. Stern), a period of exteroceptive and exterofective exploration, of catabolic elaborations rather than anabolic, such as those which could be called autoplastic and which are directed towards the construction of the individual, not only of his organic basis but also of everything which can give him shape and form.

Motor activity can develop in two different orientations which are, moreover, interdependent: one, whose source lies in the sphere of

163

attitudes, that is to say in tonic activity, but whose later developments can use all the other forms of motor activity or mental activity (imitation, for example); the other could be said to be extraverted, seeking its effects in the outer world, but requiring the first in order to become precise and consolidated. A large number of activities can be considered alternately from one or the other point of view; for example, motor habits, according to whether they are related to their object or to their learning.

(5) *Motor Stages and Syndromes*

The successive stages of motor development, which moreover overlap each other, can then be distinguished as the *affective-motor* stage, the *sensori-motor* stage, and the *objective-motor* stage, which could also be called the projective stage, since the perception of an object calls for a total projection of activity, the perceptive or conceptual settings remaining indistinct or inert. In every motor act, however, intervene neurological components, which can be more or less retarded or deficient, one or the other. As a result certain functional deficiencies or fragilities occur, which lead to different syndromes or motor types, each in connexion with the corresponding psychic dispositions.

The regulation of tonus can be affected in different ways. Some children in the larval state, and depending on the occasion, show the stiffness which is observed in Parkinson's disease. In others, of a quite different psychic type, the hypertony is shown by contractions of the face or the body such as occur in certain pallidal lesions. They are mobile and can eventually give way to generalized muscular relaxation.

There also exist cases which closely resemble cerebellar asynergy. Another syndrome comprises muscular instability accompanied by tremblings and very slight irregular displacements of the head, shoulders, trunk, and limbs, which if enlarged would give a picture of chorea and which I have called for that reason subchoreic instability.

Finally, there are various syndromes which appear to refer directly to the functions of the cortex. It seems possible to localize two of them fairly accurately. One of them is basic to apraxia. It concerns the global comprehension of the motor act and its carrying out according to well arranged phases. The other affects that field of psychic activity which is closely related to attitude and particularly with those reactions which can be aroused in us by the presence of another person and which I have called reactions of bearing. The syndrome would be one of prefrontal inadequacy.

This brief outline has, of course, not taken into account the many details whose description here would lead to useful conclusions or confirmations. It is only intended to give the main lines of the functional plan with which psychomotor activity complies.

I will not dwell on Professor Wallon's system. I shall simply try to show where the PIAGET (1951)-WALLON (1947) controversy lies as regards these ideas.

Personally I do not believe that the opposition between Piaget and Wallon, which some have wished to establish and maintain, exists. I have the impression that they have each put themselves in a different perspective and have considered things according to their own temperaments. Moreover they illustrate very well how, starting from the same established facts, divergent interpretations can be evolved, which are not, however, necessarily in opposition.

The two aspects which seem to me different are the following:

Firstly, with PIAGET (1936, 1947), as far as the infantile stage is concerned, the interest is focused mainly on the genesis of sensorimotor intelligence. For him the essential is to get a grasp of the very first elements in this genesis, even before the appearance of sensorimotor intelligence. He searches for the most fugitive signs in the very first weeks of life.

Wallon, on the other hand, is preoccupied with something entirely different. He studies by his own dialectical method how, starting from the same organic sources, very different types of behaviour separate out. Thus, deriving from the motor activity he observes between the ages of three and six months, he finds motricity orienting in two different directions. The first is an aspect of motricity which is in a sense made of tonic material and constitutes a starting-point for affectivity and for syncretic affective sociability. The second orientation is the sensori-motor sequences, those circular reactions which will be the starting-point for the idea of object and for representation. Wallon attempts to show how these two aspects of human behaviour, starting from the same organic sources, finally determine each other.

The second difference, or at least apparent difference, between the two systems concerns just this idea of syncretic sociability. This is where PIAGET (1926) and WALLON (1951) have been most strongly placed in opposition to each other by those who in my opinion have schematized both.

Generally Piaget is schematized thus: the child starts from a sort of autism—moreover a relationship is established between Piaget's autism and psychoanalytic autism—and gradually the child becomes a social being. So, starting from an egocentric state—and even, going farther back in childhood, one might speak of a sort of solipsism—from which the child at about six years socializes himself until at about twelve years he achieves the feeling and idea of reciprocity.

According to Wallon there can be no question of autism in early childhood—unless, of course, the term is redefined. Wallon insists on the extreme sociability of the small child and says that probably at about six months the child is the most sociable of beings, having that syncretic sociability which he has defined. Then evolution will not be from a state of autism, of withdrawal into oneself—which by the way Piaget never said—to a social state: progress will start from a state of non-differentiation, a state of communion with the mother, and will gradually reach a definition of interdependence between self and others. At the same time as this evolution is taking place on the affective plane, sociability is taking on another aspect: it is becoming more intellectual, while continuing to retain this affective, emotive basis, which can be found still even in the adult.

There is, therefore, no opposition between these two authors, but they treat different functional levels of sociability. Personally I regret that the words 'autism' and 'egocentrism', used by Piaget with all sorts of precautions, should have given rise among careless readers to false interpretations.

Main Stages of Development from Three to Eighteen Years

I should now like to pass on to the second part of my communication, that is to the evolution of the child between three and eighteen years. Rather than giving a complete and dogmatic exposition of this problem I will refer to certain stages which we might discuss.

I shall now abandon the frame of reference used by Wallon the neuropsychiatrist and neuropsychologist and use one which contains nothing scientific: scholastic organization as it exists in most of our countries. Whatever your opinion on the value of scholastic programmes and pedagogic methods, you will no doubt admit that the school must take into account, at least approximately, the child's possibilities, and that the main scholastic stages schematically interpret a sort of implicit psychology. Moreover, historically the question of mental age originated from the question of school age. Age differentiation became useful only when compulsory education was instituted in most of our countries. The identification of the stages and forms of intelligence became more precise with the diversification of studies as formulated, for example, in the British Education Act of 1944 and the French 'Plan de Réforme' of 1947, known by the names of its chief promoters, Langevin and Wallon.

To come back to the scholastic stages, let us see how the psychologists have defined their significance and their limits.

Between three and six years there is a pre-school stage in almost every country. Attendance is optional, and there is not so much instruction as education—at least that is so in theory.

From six to twelve years comes the stage of primary schooling, which consists in the acquisition of the basic intellectual automatisms reading, writing, and counting.

From twelve to about eighteen comes the stage of so-called secondary schooling which culminates in the matriculation (baccalauréat) type of examination.

Beyond eighteen years comes the post-school educational stage or university studies.

It is interesting to note that these ages, three, six, twelve, eighteen years are the same in most countries with a variation of about one year. It is also interesting to consider that reformers, when demanding an extension of schooling beyond twelve years, no doubt take into account reasons of a social nature. They want to democratize the school, open the school to the whole of the population and give equal opportunities to all children. But according to the most recent demands for reform, we see that another argument is invoked: in actual fact the intellectual evolution of the child is not finished at twelve years, and to achieve a harmonious development of the individual instruction should be prolonged until fourteen or sixteen years, perhaps even to eighteen years. It is instructive in that respect to read the 'whereas' clauses of the British and French plans for reform.

School practice has not only prolonged the limit of studies but has also determined the sub-divisions within the main primary and secondary stages. By and large a sub-division is marked at nine years, when the mechanisms of fluent reading and writing have already been acquired (end of elementary course according to French terminology). Another sub-division is made at about fifteen to sixteen years, as shown, for example, in the two stages of American secondary education (junior high school and senior high school) and the two stages of the French grammar school (orientation stage and determination stage).

It seems then that the school in our different countries has marked the following stages: three, six, nine, twelve, fifteen, and eighteen years. It is to be noted that there is some kind of concordance of psychological studies with these different stages.

As for three years, for a long time psychologists have marked this as a period of crisis and of socialization accompanied, moreover, by an attitude of opposition. The child experiences a certain confusion and uneasiness and yet new possibilities of the beginning of a collective life are appearing. The nursery school or kindergarten answers the needs of this age.

At six years an emotional stability is seen to appear in the child. The child enters the phase called by psychoanalysts the latency period which, according to other authors, is a period of objective interests. One fact we can definitely establish is that the child becomes capable of fixing his attention and concentrating for fifteen or twenty minutes on exercises he would have found very boring previously. Dr. Grey Walter mentioned the same phenomenon in his communication: at about this age the E.E.G. takes on a fairly characteristic form. The alpha waves are dominant. We have been able to ascertain by using a very old test, the crossing-out test, that the child of five years is quite incapable of this effort. For about ten years we have been using a rather special technique which consists in giving two degrees of difficulty in this crossing-out test: in the first, one sign has to be crossed out; in the second, two signs have to be crossed out. Thus the reactions of a child faced with two degrees of difficulty can be compared. At five years the child is incapable of carrying out this test. He abandons it very quickly. At six years the task becomes possible; 60 to 70 per cent of the children are capable of performing it. At seven years the adult formula is already established. At six years the formula for behaviour is very characteristic: the child's activity, although well adapted when he has to discriminate a single sign, tends to become disorganized when there are two signs.

From the age of seven years the adult formulation is reached, though naturally with a difference in speed. I think that this shows an essential phenomenon: the possibility of concentrating on tasks which do not involve the immediate interest of action. The child is capable of sustaining his interest in order to act on an intellectual plane.

At about twelve years a very remarkable fact is noted: the most diverse psychological methods are unanimous in describing this age as a sort of culmination. Beyond twelve to thirteen years the tests are hardly discriminatory, or rather they are no longer discriminatory as tests of development. It would seem that individual differentiations are then more apparent than differentiations due to age. We all know of the work carried out during the First World War where it appeared that the mental age of the recruit, the ordinary soldier, was twelve years. This does not mean that our armies were composed of mental defectives; it means that the age of twelve marks the culmination of a certain type of development. The same conclusions are reached in Piaget's work, which shows that the principles of conservation have been acquired on all levels by this age.

However, we certainly have the impression that evolution continues beyond twelve years. How does it continue? It is a fascinating problem from the physiological, neurophysiological, psychological, and social points of view. Unfortunately our documentation on this subject is much less sound than that on the child of zero to twelve years.

Much has been written on adolescence but in my opinion very little of it is valid in the field of psychology. One notes that the adolescent as described in psychological works may be the adolescent of a certain epoch and particularly of a certain social milieu, that is to say the milieu of school children and grammar-school pupils. Does this very romantic picture of the adolescent, with this profound crisis, this personal upheaval, correspond to reality? I do not believe so. Of course this type of adolescent exists; I have certainly met it in the grammar schools.

We have carried out certain comparative studies on adolescents in different environments, some already working in factories, and others continuing their studies. It is most surprising to discover that among those who have already entered a social life a hostile attitude towards the family is very seldom met, whereas this attitude is at its maximum among grammar-school pupils of the same age with the same material conditions, that is to say, having as much pocket money as the young worker. It is not, therefore, the fact of having money which explains the attitude of these young people, it is the fact of earning it or receiving it. Moreover, a much earlier autonomy is found in the young worker than in the young grammar-school pupil. Obviously this is not sufficient to give a valid differential picture because, even if we find here that the worker has superiority over the grammar-school pupil, on the other hand, the grammar-school pupil has the superiority in that he becomes aware of cultural realities.

Our knowledge of the adolescent is still very imperfect. Perhaps what we understand best is what is revealed on the intellectual plane by the possibility, for a boy or girl of fifteen to sixteen, of attaining on the practical or theoretical level a hypothetico-deductive attitude. What does this signify? I will make a very shaky hypothesis: at about twelve to thirteen years all the fundamental mechanisms have been acquired. Beyond that the cultural element comes into play much more than the developmental elements, although evolution continues on a physiological level, but the mechanisms already acquired at twelve to thirteen years still need to be made flexible, through exercise. In this connexion SIMON (1939) said that it was not sufficient to have intelligence, it was necessary to know how to use it. Perhaps it is just after twelve years that this intelligence begins to be used in different directions. I mean by that that psychologists are perhaps wrong in looking only for the limit of intelligence. The age of twelve to thirteen years marks perhaps a new departure. Intelligence is nothing if it is not creative and intelligence can only be effective if it goes back to certain affective sources. Now it is perhaps during this period from fourteen to eighteen years that the human being, coming into contact with new social, human, and affective realities, manages to give a deep, concrete sense to all the perceptive-intellectual mechanisms which he has acquired during the scholastic period.

In short, I wished to underline our lack of certainty about this period of adolescence, on which much has been written. This study has been perverted because not enough account has been taken of the cultural and social dimensions which give direction to adolescence and without which this period cannot be defined. I think that beyond twelve years cultural factors are of such importance that it is necessary to proceed by a differential means in order to reach significant results.

Evolution of Graphic Ability and Language in the Child

I will now pass on to a statement on two series of behaviour: evolution of graphic ability and evolution of language. For these examples we shall return to early childhood. I apologize again for the schematic nature of this sequence but it is only intended to serve as a basis for discussion.

On the subject of the evolution of graphic ability (AJURIAGUERRA et al., 1949) I should like to stress the fact that it seems to me to be of capital importance and that it starts at about the age of eighteen months. The child then becomes capable of copying a vertical or horizontal line, but he can only copy the line right next to the model line. We frequently observe this phenomenon of 'sticking close' in the child's first graphic images. This tendency seems to last up to two or two and a half years.

At three years, the child becomes capable of copying a few capital letters but he copies as he draws; the cursive movement of writing appears about six months later. The child very early has a different attitude to drawing from writing.

At four years he is capable of copying words but he puts them anywhere on the paper. At the beginning he writes at the bottom of the page and at about six years, under the influence of instruction, he begins to write at the top on the left.

At five years he can copy phrases and becomes capable of writing a few words spontaneously, but with many inversions in letter order.

At six years we have observed a very interesting phenomenon: the appearance of the human profile turned towards the left. This phenomenon has given rise to quite a number of interpretations. In any case on the intellectual plane this shows fairly considerable progress.

Up to five to six years graphic ability is determined by motor ability. The dominant hand develops less rapidly than the other with a retardation of one stage. I should like to recall here the law propounded by GESELL (1945), the law of reciprocal overlapping, according to which the definitive formula on the motor plane is not

170

established gradually in the child but by means of a play of alternation. These alternations, according to Gesell, are the sign of a deeper alternation due to myelinization.

Beyond six years the intellectual and affective factors are decisively added to the motor factors in the evolution of writing and drawing. A number of authors have studied the psychology of drawing, notably LUQUET (1913), who distinguished different stages as, for example, the passage from what he calls intellectual realism—a stage where the child draws with an effect of transparency and of skew—to visual realism, which is attained at about nine or ten years.

At nine years orientation of graphism towards the left is noted (sinistrogyration) not only in writing, but also in drawing. This originates as a motor effect and attains a sensory form.

In this connexion I carried out the following experiment (ZAZZO, 1950). A child is given some very diverse figures and is asked to discover profiles in these pictures, which are shown very rapidly. At seven to eight years there is no difference, he finds as many on one side as on the other. At nine years almost all children see only the profiles which are turned to the left. We wanted to confirm this law in adults and we found the same phenomenon.

In short this perceptive organization, this sensory evaluation, appears at nine years, and from nine years on the same percentage is found as among adults. I make one reservation, but at the moment I cannot give any definite interpretation of it: during adolescence, between twelve and fifteen years, an extraordinary reversal of these proportions is observed. I do not, however, think that there is a perceptive disorganization at this age. During this period the right profile takes precedence. Is this a sign of a tendency to opposition, a disruption on the perceptive plane due to emotive factors? I cannot say. I pass this question over to the competence of those who are more directly concerned with the problem of affectivity.

I will carry on then with the history of graphism. Among the various observations that have been made I find stages and ages which appear to me particularly significant. With the appearance of organized graphism, the first stage which I consider to be important is the disappearance of this graphic confusion which expresses on the graphic-motor plane one of the fundamental characteristics of childhood—non-differentiation. This stage comes at about two and a half years.

Still another important stage is that at six and a half years when the child is capable of well-organized drawing and attempts to write.

Another important age is that of nine to ten years. At this age, when the profile experience occurs and where it is no longer the hand which is responsible but the eye that guides the hand, the child is

171

found capable of dissociating himself from motor conditions and dominating them. There is an organization of a perceptive field, a sort of perceptive Gestalt, whose genesis we have already seen; there were first neuromotor determinations, then towards nine years demands of a sensory nature which dominated motivity. It is at this age that a child's drawing attains conformity to appearance. It is also at this age that he attempts to read and write fluently. I think that the convergence of these facts is highly significant.

Beyond ten years the story continues but the cultural factors markedly dominate developmental ones. It is no doubt necessary that intelligence should continue to evolve for the child to be capable of giving chromatic relief to perspective, but it is obvious that education is a most important factor and that a person who has received no instruction cannot produce perspective even if psychologically and physiologically he is capable of doing so.

It is interesting to note that all the comparisons that have been made on children of different cultures show the same evolution up to ten years. One of our colleagues, PRUDHOMMEAU (1951) applied drawing tests to different ethnic groups, Eskimos and others. Exactly the same stages of evolution were found. No difference has been found between French children and children of other nationalities that we have been able to examine.

I will now pass on to the problem of language. It would be very interesting to define the common points by comparison of these different lines of behaviour.

In the first two months, there is wailing and emotive crying.

From three months onwards we get babbling and warbling, and certain utterances gradually take on an expressive character. According to PICHON (1947) this is pre-verbalism which has, moreover, been confirmed by most of the English and German authors and has been fixed at the age of about six months.

Then comes the stage which certain authors have called the stage of pure comprehension: a child understands but cannot yet express himself.

The first word appears towards the end of the first year, but it is very difficult to fix a date for the first significant word. There is much discordance among authors on this point and by saying that the ages are considered to vary between nine and fourteen months I will not have added anything very interesting to the discussion.

Are there any natural words which are found in all cultural milieux? The word 'Mama' has been suggested and the negation 'no', which marks a movement of refusal of food. One thing is certain, that is that at nine months (possibly a little before) a child is capable of imitating certain syllables. The child has the lip movements which are

172

structured into sounds or phonemes. Is the 'Mama' a continuation of sucking? This is possible. Has this word a definite significance? I am quite certain that it has not. Of course an association is gradually built up between the mother and this 'Mama'. Under normal conditions it is always reinforced because the father and mother watch out for the appearance of the first word, but when it is not reinforced the word does not take on this significance.

I carried out an experiment which might seem inhuman to you. With my first son, who is now eighteen, I did not confirm the 'Papa' and 'Mama' so that the child has never called us 'Papa' and 'Mama'. Even to the present day he calls us by our Christian names and this horrifies many of our friends. We admit that this is inconvenient. Moreover, we have seen that this experiment may be dangerous because when the child became aware of it for the first time, at the age of three, he had a shock because the teachers were horrified and tried to force him to call us 'mother' and 'father'. This he always resisted. The later children say 'Daddy' and 'Mummy'.

After twenty months the first phrase appears. Although it is difficult to establish exactly when the first word comes, which is not very important in the evolution of the child, the first phrase, on the other hand, seems to me highly important and in direct relation with the general intellectual development of the child. Mentally deficient children will say the first word at about the same time as normal children, but, on the other hand, their first phrase is always delayed. We still have to define what is the first phrase. Most authors agree in considering that there is a phrase when the child is capable of uniting two words in a language. It is then that the true regulating function of language appears: the child filters his phonemes and emotive cries through a web of tenses and begins to organize them.

From two years onwards the number of grammatical possibilities increases with an extraordinary rapidity. Functional normalizations start with the third year. Here again we find this a significant age. Prepositions, declensions, inflexions, tenses, genders, and number appear and there is a change from pre-grammatical language—what might be called Pidgin English (*petit nègre*)—to organized language.

By three years pronouns, past tense, and plurals have been acquired.

By six years, language is almost complete on the verbal plane. We should notice here a certain time-lag: at five years the child can use all tenses and can even use the subjunctive properly if it has been used in his hearing.

There are wide individual variations in the attainment of these functional standards. Naturally, if certain tenses are not used in the hearing of the child, he will not use them either; but he is capable of imitating them and a person who imitates shows by doing so that he is capable of understanding a situation. At five years, then, acquisition is practically complete. Later we shall find that there is a re-apprenticeship when it comes to written language; this is a new functional level and is of considerable interest because with written language symbolism in the second degree appears. Spoken language is already a symbolism because the word symbolizes the thing. Written language symbolizes verbal language which already itself symbolizes the thing.

It would have been interesting, in order to understand the mechanism of language evolution better, to consider the sequences within the different grammatical categories; but we have not enough time. I will simply recall that 'no' appears before 'yes' and I think this is so for all languages. This is no doubt due to the fact that 'no' has a much greater affective value than 'yes'. Adjectives appear before adverbs, and adverbs of place before adverbs of time. 'Why'—at least in French, though possibly not in all languages—appears before 'how'. 'Me', which is more affective, appears before 'I'. The question of the acquisition of pronouns is worth a study in itself, since it is with the mechanism of pronouns that the child expresses which stage of decentralization he has reached, because the pronoun changes according to the person who is speaking. This is a fundamental acquisition. Here again it is necessary to distinguish between languages because this acquisition varies with the language structure.

It would be worth comparing this language evolution with the different stages of grapho-motricity and with other sectors of behaviour. I think, in fact, that it is up to the psychologist not to isolate one sector but to see how the progressive differentiations occur and to discover, despite possible overlappings, certain functional levels.

We have tried to compare the different aspects of child behaviour which could show the attainment of awareness of self (Zazzo, 1948). I will only indicate one aspect of our studies, which was the first chronologically. We studied the evolution of language in a young child, particularly of personal pronouns as related to the recognition of his own image in three different situations: in the mirror, on photos, and in films. From this study we obtained some very interesting data. Recognition in the mirror, on photos, and in films is very much delayed when the precaution is taken, in the case of the mirror, of not giving the child any suggestive help or any intensive training. We find that the recognition does not occur until two years and two or three months. It is also found that the recognition of self and of others is interdependent—the recognition of others coming, however, slightly earlier—and this is so for the three situations. With the mirror it is very clear. I have noticed that although the child is no doubt looking at himself in the mirror he concentrates on the image of the other person because he knows the other person whereas he has never seen himself. There are games in front of the mirror where the child looks behind the mirror as an animal would. Then at about two years we have noticed there is a kind of disorganization as if a sudden state of awareness of self had caused an affective upset. A few weeks afterwards the child recognizes himself in the mirror (at about two years, two months). Up to the end of the third year he displays a certain anxiety and at the same time a certain pleasure in looking at himself. At about two years, ten months this disappears; the image has become familiar and no longer causes uneasiness. However, at two years he recognizes other people on photographs but does not recognize himself until at least six months later.

As for films, he recognizes the situations in which the film was taken; he recognizes the beach or the room where he was, but he does not recognize himself. At two years he recognizes other people without hesitation but he himself is a child whom he does not know. When he does recognize himself at about two and a half years, he uses rather a strange form of speech, as if there were a duplication between himself and the image. He says 'there are Johns' or 'there is a John'. He speaks of himself in the third person.

These phenomena have been confirmed with other children. They always occur during the third year though the exact age varies, and the recognition of other people always comes before the recognition of self.

Now this follows very closely the evolution of language. It is at about three years that the use of 'I' appears without hesitation and is used grammatically. Before that there are no doubt syncretic 'I's'—he says 'I don't know'—but the 'I' is only properly distinguished at about two years ten months. On the other hand, the grammatical and possessive forms 'me', 'you', and 'your' appear simultaneously. The personality crisis with opposition and negativism appears in more or less crude forms between two and a half and three years.

HARGREAVES:

Is there any difference between the recognition age for black and white photographs, which are an artificial convention, and colour photographs?

ZAZZO:

I have not carried out any systematic experiments. I have tried with colour films and the results appear to be about the same, but I cannot give a definite reply here.

Conclusions

Now I should like to draw some conclusions on the laws of child evolution and make some observations on method.

To come back to Gesell—whose work I have drawn upon several times during this communication, without naming him—growth is a unifying concept. From the beginning GESELL (1929, 1945) rejects dualism which, according to him, would make us incapable of properly understanding the liaison between the physiological sub-stratum and behaviour. This can be seen, moreover, in the structure of his tests, where there is no duality, but in any case a differentiation occurs in proportion to age. This is a law of psychological evolution and also of neuro-physiological evolution.

The first general law then would be a law of differentiation and of progressive integration apparent on all levels.

Firstly there is differentiation between various intellectual activities. The studies of PIÉRON (1949) and of his pupils (FESSARD, 1931; MONNIN, 1933), which dealt with scholastic and professional orienta-tion, came to the following conclusions: the correlations between different forms of intelligence are very high at about six to seven years and become gradually lower as the child grows. There are both differentiation and integration at the same time.

On the affective plane as well, we find during childhood a differen-tiation occurring between self and others, a differentiation which is, at the same time, an interdependence, and which the Piaget school calls reciprocity.

Thus on all planes, differentiation and integration lead the child to finer and more flexible adaptations and to an autonomy which is not an isolation but is, on the contrary, an interdependence and an organization. One could formulate this law in a very sketchy way by using the terms of child psychologists as follows: the child evolves from syncretism and from non-differentiation to a synthetic activity or on the motor plane to synergies and re-organizations of movement.

GREY WALTER:

Dr. Zazzo mentioned the behaviour of children when confronted with a mirror and its use as a test for self-recognition. Now in some of our machines we have demonstrated, quite accidentally, precisely the same type of behaviour. There are certain simple machines which display a characteristic mode of action when they are presented with their own reflections in a looking-glass. It is quite unique, an always-and-only response, so that it is diagnostic, in a zoological sense, of self-recognition. These same machines, when confronted by one another, again display a unique but different behaviour diagnostic of

176

social recognition; they build up a society which has characteristic modes which can then be interrupted by a common stimulus. The social organization can be broken down into a competitive complex, possibly with the destruction of all the machines. These two behaviour modes of recognition of self and of society can be analysed into quite straightforward cybernetic ciphers. One can describe these processes as being reflexive—I use that word deliberately—and the appearance of them depends upon certain well-defined or definable mechanisms appearing within each individual machine. One can say that if these mechanisms appear, reflexive behaviour will start, it will have its diagnostic characters, and if observing from outside one would say: 'this is a recognition of self', or: 'at this stage a recognition of society appears'. I think this sort of application of cybernetics to these problems can be enormously fertile. It doesn't deny anything (and that's a very important point) but it can affirm a great deal.

I would like to ask Dr. Zazzo one rather trivial question. The use of the term reflexive was quite deliberate on my part—as far as I know it is my own particular use of this word; I don't use retroactive, or feedback, but reflexive. Now does Dr. Zazzo know whether the attitude to self in the child—the time at which it develops, the way it develops, the form it takes—is related at all to the linguistics of the child? In English you tell the child to say 'I wash' or 'I am washing', in French you have to say 'Je me lave'—I wash myself. That is a reflexive verb and in French the reflexive is used a great deal more than the passive.

LORENZ:

In Russian you haven't got a passive, you just use the reflexive.

GREY WALTER:

It often seems quite ridiculous to English people to talk in French about an inanimate object doing things to itself, finding itself, etc. Now, have you any evidence that that affects the way in which a child develops its attitude to itself?

ZAZZO:

At the age when the child recognizes himself in front of the mirror his language is not yet sufficiently well organized for one to be able to see a transformation occurring in the reflexive verbs. From the linguistic point of view we cannot have any indication because these verbs do not exist for the child at that age, that is at about two years two months. On the other hand, we have been struck by the fact that the child begins at this period to use personal and possessive pronouns and 'me' and 'you' simultaneously. This reply is not very satisfactory because the reflexion you speak of cannot appear.

Your comparison with machines is very interesting, and raises all kinds of problems. How far is the analogy legitimate? In the case of machines, would there not rather be an analogy with mimicry, a reciprocal imitation? What appears to me to be characteristic in the child's behaviour in front of the mirror is his uneasiness. There is a sudden awareness, a hesitation; he sees another and starts to be aware of himself. It is only after several months that this uneasiness disappears and he looks at his image naturally. I see in this uneasiness the mark of a sudden awareness of self which could not have any analogy with the example you gave.

LORENZ:

The disturbance and anxiety of the child when it recognizes itself in the mirror is perhaps based on the fact that somehow the child feels 'Well, I am here, I cannot be there too'. It is really a very difficult thing to understand that my being here doesn't exclude my being there, though it doesn't seem so for adults. But birds do not know, and neither do dogs, that one subject cannot be in two places at once. That's very surprising to us, because to us it is self-evident that an individual object which is here cannot be there. But I know of two chance observations, one in dogs, and one in my pet greylag goose Martina, which show quite clearly that this self-evidence doesn't exist for the animal. I was coming back from a long canoe trip with Martina, and I was dressing and Martina was preening, after a long paddling tour on the Danube. Suddenly Martina gave her flight call and prepared to take off, which was very disagreeable to me, because I wanted to go home and didn't want to lose her. She called again and again, her social call, which was at that time directed exclusively to me, and then I saw what she was seeing. She saw myself, a man in an identical canoe on the other side of the Danube—a fat fellow with a beard. I instantly realized what she was thinking, and tried attracting her attention, saying 'Hullo, here I am' but I couldn't prevent her from taking off. She flew over the Danube and landed in front of that man, and then she recognized that it wasn't me, and go so frightened that she rocketed like a firework, and came back to me for protection, then greeted me violently and threatened in the direction of that man.

The second instance is a dog which Heinroth had when a student, a kind of Griffon bitch. Heinroth had a girl friend, and when he went for a rendezvous, the dog knew it, and smelt every lady that looked approximately like her in order to greet her when she saw her. Now when she had come, and the dog had greeted her, this didn't prevent the dog from looking for other girls resembling her. She wanted another individual of the same kind.

MEAD:

I have a rather detailed study of a child working toward this recognition with films, because I have persistently shown my child films of herself, and I started quite early to watch what happened. She went through the stage that Dr. Zazzo described, in which she would call the child in the film first 'the baby' and then 'that Catherine', which was different from 'this Catherine', and then came the moment when she sorted the thing out. Watching a picture of herself swimming, she was standing with her hand on her doll's perambulator and she looked at the picture and said 'That's Catherine, I'm swimming, that's Catherine swimming', and then she shook the doll carriage, then took up the swimming position, and then said, '*I'm* shaking the doll carriage, that's Catherine swimming. I'm shaking the doll carriage', and made the time distinction. This was at about two years and nine months.

ZAZZO:

I should like to spotlight this phenomenon by means of a reverse phenomenon of a pathological kind. I think what is essential here is the formation of the image of the body itself with visual, postural, etc., elements: an image which, in my opinion, is closely associated with the genesis of awareness of self. In certain kinds of pathology disintegration is often the reverse phenomenon of doubling, of positive or negative autoscopy. I am thinking of the case of Guy de Maupassant. The sick man loses his image, or, on the other hand, he may have an hallucination. He sees his own image appearing in front of him. This is a phenomenon which has been frequently underlined in psychiatric literature—and also in other literature. It is a theme which is used, for example, in *The Student of Prague*. We have then two sides to this phenomenon: the establishment of the image of self which is absolutely necessary for the awareness of self, and in certain pathological cases a disintegration where the individual sees himself; one might even allude here to Socrates' demon.

INHELDER:

I have followed with great pleasure M. Zazzo's communication, which testifies to a most discriminating and conciliatory attitude. M. Zazzo said that the Wallon school is often placed in opposition to the Piaget school. I think, as he does, that this opposition is partly the result of a false interpretation of their ideas given by the pupils of these two teachers. However, M. Zazzo knows as well as I that these two creators of systems can discuss their ideas in all cordiality and friendship, of course, but it is evident that every creator of ideas experiences some difficulty in putting himself precisely in the place of another because above all he defends his own creation. We, the followers, have not the same reasons for being aggressive or egocentric. We are quite naturally drawn to look for means of unification rather than of separation.

I should now like to take up again certain distinctions established by M. Zazzo between the two trends of thought and to add to them briefly.

Firstly, there is a difference in the points of view and the problems raised: M. Wallon raises the question of the origins of all psychological behaviour. This orientation of mind is shown by the titles of some of his works: *Les Origines du caractère chez l'enfant* (*The origins of character in the child*) (1933); *Les Origines de la pensée chez l'enfant* (*The origins of thought in the child*) (1945). M. Piaget is more interested in the end of evolution. He studies *La Génèse du nombre* (*The genesis of number*) (PIAGET and SZEMINSKA, 1941); *Le Développement de la notion du temps* (*The development of the concept of time*) (PIAGET, 1946a); etc. (PIAGET, 1946b).

Next there is a difference in method: M. Wallon seeks, above all, to study the complexity and the clash—frequently tumultuous—of the many factors arising during a phase of development or the passage from one phase to the next. M. Piaget attempts rather to determine the most general comprehensive laws which he interprets as laws of equilibrium. The fact that these methods are complementary is shown in the choice of the facts studied.

The results themselves are complementary. I consider that M. Wallon has made an important discovery which M. Zazzo has perhaps not emphasized sufficiently, that is, the positive role of emotion (WALLON, 1942). Emotion is often supposed to play the negative role of a disturbing agent. Now, M. Wallon has demonstrated the very positive role played by emotion in mental development, facilitating even the formation of thought. M. Piaget, on the other hand, has neglected the emotive aspect of behaviour; he does not deny it, but he has not dwelt upon it because he has attempted above all to determine and circumscribe the structures of adaptation to reality.

Let us now come to the controversy on egocentrism which M. Zazzo underlined. You perhaps know that the discovery of egocentrism on the one hand made the reputation of M. PIAGET (1923) and on the other hand appeared as an obstacle to the understanding of his later work. Personally, I think that the term 'egocentrism' is not particularly suitable. Actually, M. Piaget has attempted to make it more precise. At present I think he would uphold the following point of view: the social does not exist in itself but as a series of social exchanges maintained by the child with his environment. M. Wallon expressed something analogous by using (as did Claparède and Piaget) the term 'syncretism' which clearly expresses the initial state of fusion existing between the ego and the non-ego. Perhaps M. Piaget did not manage to make himself understood when he called the first social exchanges egocentric relations, establishing an analogy with autism in Bleuler's sense, but it seems to me that the essential point is to show how this first form of exchange is gradually modified until relations of reciprocity and co-operation are achieved. Lack of co-operation due to incapability of seeing things from another's point of view does not in the least preclude fusion with another or imitation of the model. Confusion with its intervening mechanisms of projection and identification is, in fact, an obstacle to true co-operation. Thus, here again it is not actually a question of discord, but rather of complementary interpretation of the same facts.

At the moment I can only see one point on which there might be divergence: the passage from sensori-motor activity to the activity of thought (and we should have to go deeper in our research to discover how much is fact and how much is interpretation).

According to M. Piaget there is a continuous transition between the sensori-motor behaviour of the infant and thought as it develops during early childhood. M. Piaget tries to show through precise experiments (among others, stereognostic tests: PIAGET and INHELDER, 1948) that thought has motor origins. Mental representation is prepared by a whole number of sensori-motor explorations (the mental image being partly shaped by previous tactile explorations). On the other hand, M. WALLON (1942) insists on the opposition between these two phases of mental life. According to him, thought incorporates into itself new elements through contributions from language and social life in general, but this is a matter of hypotheses requiring verification.

Finally, it is interesting to note that Wallon and Piaget seem to have travelled in opposite directions. Each of them has modified the orientation of his research. M. Piaget began by studying the child in his social manifestations, such as verbal exchange. This led up to the study of the child's sensori-motor activities, which M. Piaget is trying to relate to the nervous structures themselves. M. WALLON (1925), taking the opposite path, centred his early work on motor development, whereas now he is concentrating more particularly on the conditioning of the child by the social environment.

This again is a question of complementary evolution and not a taking-up of unshakeable positions.

SEVENTH DISCUSSION

Psychoanalytic Instinct Theory

BOWLBY:

For my remarks I have selected out of the whole field of psycho-analysis the topic of instinct because I feel that instinct is the central core of psychoanalysis, and that the study of instinct distinguishes psychoanalysis from other branches of psychology, which commonly study other aspects of the human organism. Psychoanalysis regards a great deal of psychiatric illness as being due to a disorganization of instinctual life. I share that view, and I think that by looking at it that way we may prevent much mental illness.

Freud made several attempts to formulate a theory of instinct. Both his main formulations were in terms of a dichotomy:

(a) The sexual and the ego instincts (*circa* 1910).

(b) The life and death instincts (*circa* 1920).

A further important proposition was that the goal of the organism was to obtain pleasure and avoid pain. Freud himself did not feel very satisfied with his work in this field and in 1915 remarked that it would probably prove necessary for psychologists to look to biology for an adequate theory of instinct. As it happens, in the same paper he outlined a theory of instinct almost identical in principle with that of modern ethology. He conceived of instinct as having a *source* in somatic process, an *impetus* or force, an *aim*—that of 'abolishing the condition of stimulation in the source of the instinct'—and an *object*, namely 'that in and through which it can achieve its aim'.

Psychoanalysts have varied a great deal in regard to which of Freud's theories they have adopted. In Great Britain, under the influence of MELANIE KLEIN (1948), there has been an emphasis on the object-seeking nature of instinct. FAIRBAIRN (1952) has supported this view and argued explicitly against the pleasure-pain theory.

Freud also called attention to the fact that human beings are organisms which at times are driven by forces within themselves which they cannot easily control. We *fall* in love, we *lose* our tempers, we panic, we are possessed by forces which seem alien to ourselves; and, of course, there is the primitive theory of mental illness that people are possessed by a devil. It is these phenomena that I want to discuss and, just to give them a little more concreteness, I shall illustrate what I have in mind by referring to a couple of patients whom I have seen very recently. One is an adult of about forty, a woman with a severe degree of illness, tremendous phobias, great hatreds, deep depressions, who is subacutely murderous and suicidal. I have been treating her now for two and half years and her relations to me are characteristically ambivalent. I have experienced long sessions when she was shrieking at me for two or three hours without a break. There have been other occasions when her endearments have been on the same scale. I recall that when I came here in June last, on the one hand she was very sad that I should leave her, but, on the other hand, as she told me afterwards, she hoped I would drown myself in the lake—and she meant it. The thing that has struck me so particularly about her is that one day she can be friendly and cordial and we have what I call a sober session, and the next day she rants and raves at me as though we had never had any other relationship. Another feature about her is that she is terrified of friendly relations. She is 'happy' only when she is on angry terms with someone; her sense of stability is better when there is mutual anger. Obviously the problem is, why is she like this? My own view is that this is the result of the relations which she had with her mother when she was small, having been extremely unhappy and chaotic, but, naturally, I can't prove this. What one has *now* is a first-hand and mammoth demonstration of ambivalence: in her case this historical reconstruction must remain very treacherous and unreliable.

The other patient is a little girl of eight. She was rather an attractive, neat, pretty little girl. I asked her whether she knew why she had come to the clinic, and she said, 'Well, I have tempers, but I am learning to control them'. We talked a bit about her tempers, and we got on to her day-dreams; she imagined various things to herself. Sometimes she sees faces on trees—nasty faces—but she turns them into nice faces. Then it appears 'the nasty faces—they want to kill my mother'. From this I had no doubt that *she* wanted to kill her mother —or rather, a bit of her wanted to kill her mother. It's a good family, her mother is a decent woman, but she has tried to smack the tempers out of this child. As a result the child not only wants to murder her mother but these impulses are split off from the rest of her personality.

Now, I give those two illustrations just to show the nature of the problem which we are trying to solve.

I want to remark on three or four psychological processes which may be relevant, and in doing so I shall speak in a hybrid, bastard language which I have come to use, which derives from both psycho-analysis and ethology. Why do some people develop strong impulses to kill, and why do they actually kill others on occasion? More importantly, since they usually don't kill others—why don't they? That takes us into the field of super-ego development. It has seemed to me for a long time that the controlling force, conscience or whatever we call it in the human being, has an instinctive root. It seems to me that ethology, as I understand it, gives good grounds for thinking this is so; I am referring to Lorenz's observation that the wolves' attacking impulse is inhibited by certain behaviour in other wolves.

Amongst the instincts that psychoanalysts are concerned with are the instinct of flight, the instinct of attack, the following response,* which is of great importance in the study of the young mammal, and, of course, sexual instincts. Now, a very difficult problem is, *why do these instinctive responses become dislocated in infancy*? It appears that the instinctive life of the human being can become dislocated and that it is in infancy and early childhood that dislocation is particularly apt to occur. It would appear that in the early months of life the infant responds to sign-stimuli which are isolated in the sense that the infant doesn't know that they belong to an 'object' in the Piaget sense of the term. Spitz' work on the smiling response (SPITZ and WOLF, 1946) suggests that the infant responds in a friendly way to a particular sort of sign-stimulus; presumably his rejecting responses are evoked by something else. MELANIE KLEIN (1948) has developed the idea of the 'good' object and the 'bad' object; I think she may be using the word 'object' here to mean an isolated sign-stimulus. She has further developed the notion that there comes a point in infant development where the 'good' and the 'bad' object fuse; this I suppose is the same thing that Professor Piaget describes as the 'formation of the object'. It would appear from the psychoanalytic work that the 'formation of the object' is interfered with if there are very powerful and contradictory impulses evoked by the sign stimuli emanating from that object. Certainly, with the first patient that I referred to, the most striking thing about her is this split, the extra-ordinary independence of her hatred for me and of her affection for me. I can be for her either extremely 'good' or extremely 'bad' but, as an ordinary person, I hardly exist.

The next problem is, if these things become dislocated in infancy *why does the dislocation persist* and affect not only the responses

---

* The term used by ethologists to describe the young animal's instinct to attach himself to and to follow some other creature, usually the mother. Though it is still a controversial matter, the ethological evidence seems to me to point to its being an instinctive drive in its own right in the human child.

immediately concerned—the following response, let's say, to the mother—but the person's sexual responses and adult love, and even the parental responses of a mother to her own child? In birds at least, these different instinctual responses are curiously independent. Each one comes along, is imprinted to its object, and then another comes along. That doesn't tally with the human, because what psychoanalysts have observed is that in humans there is a horrid continuity, in humans the responses are *not* independent. Of course, one possible explanation may lie in the extraordinary fact (which may well prove a key for psychoanalysis) that a response can be imprinted long before it becomes operative. It may be that human sexual responses are imprinted in early childhood and not later.

A second notion of the ethologists which strikes one is that each instinctual response waxes and then wanes. Each response, ontogenetically speaking, has its own time at the wicket, but in certain circumstances, it would appear that the batsman can refuse to leave the crease! For instance, it looks as though the following response which waxes in the early months of life reaches its peak in the second and third years, and then wanes—and it looks as though that response can, in certain circumstances, persist into adult life.

A third clue to the solution of this problem may lie in the fact that sexual responses can make use of certain components of the parent-child response. It is known that in certain species of bird the male's behaviour towards the female is similar to that of the parent feeding the chick, and the female's behaviour is similar to that of the chick being fed (ARMSTRONG, 1942). If there are certain components in human sexual response which are derived from parent-child responses (which seems clearly to be true) it would not be surprising if problems that had started in the one situation should be carried over to the other.

However, there are other areas that we haven't explored at this conference which may be relevant to this problem, in particular the special properties of responses learnt under stress. The two characteristics of such responses that strike me as being interesting are first that the response is often, in terms of adaptation, an irrelevant response, and, second, that once learnt it has an extraordinarily persistent quality. It looks as though the infant under stress can learn 'silly' responses and the adult under stress can revert to such.

I look upon research on the effects of separating the young child from his mother as being the study of the following response in health and disease, with particular reference to its ontogeny. We ask: in what circumstances is it evoked; in what circumstances does it persist; in what circumstances is it never evoked; in what circumstances is it cut out, or repressed, to use the psychoanalytical term?

Further, what part do hereditary differences between individual children play in these things? These are our research problems.

Further, we are convinced that in research of this kind nothing but longitudinal studies can help us, because we have to have the details of the child's experience, which often cannot be obtained retrospectively even a month or two afterwards. We must observe the child at the time he is having the experience.

Let me conclude by giving you a list of propositions to which most British psychoanalysts would now subscribe (some would add many other propositions):

(1) The dysfunction present in most people with 'emotional disorders' lies in their incapacity to make satisfying relations with other people and in particular with those who occupy the role of love objects to them (e.g. parent, sexual object, child, etc.).

(2) The reason for their incapacity is that the love object arouses powerful and conflicting instincts, e.g. instincts to love and cherish and instincts to hurt or kill.

(3) The disturbed person is unable to tolerate these contradictory instincts so that one or more are divorced from consciousness. One or more are also likely to be inhibited in some degree, though the drive to action persists (or, perhaps more accurately, remains liable to be re-awakened). Such repressed but active instincts manifest themselves in various symptoms and are experienced by the subject as tension, anxiety, and depression.

(4) Such powerful and intolerable conflicts rarely if ever occur for the first time in the relations of the older child or adult towards his love objects. When present in an older person, they are the developmental successors of similar conflicts which were present in his relations to his first love objects, e.g. his mother or his father.

(5) There are special features in the immature human being, especially in the first two or three years, which lead him (*a*) to be particularly prone to strong and contradictory impulses and (*b*) to be unable to sustain their pressure, with the result that processes such as repression, inhibition, displacement, projection, etc., occur readily. This is presumably due to physiological machinery for organization and integration being inadequate.

(6) There is much debate as to why some individuals develop conflicts on a greater scale than others and why some individuals appear capable of sustaining these conflicts in consciousness and others cannot do so. All agree that the child's experiences of satisfaction or frustration in his relation to his parents are of some importance in determining the strength and development of his impulses. Some give much weight to postulated differences in hereditary endowment; some give less.

(7) There is a tremendous literature on the reasons why particular symptoms are developed by particular patients. Few of the theories advanced are entirely satisfactory; some are very unsatisfactory.

(8) There is agreement that the efficacy of therapeutic measures depends far less on their ability to understand and deal with symptoms than on their ability to deal with the primary conflicts in object relations. The technique used is to permit these conflicts to develop within the therapeutic relationship (which they do in some fashion spontaneously) and to help the patient experience the impulses in relation to the analyst, whom he sees and feels as both a satisfying and a frustrating object. When these conflicting impulses are experienced together within a relationship of trust, there tends to be a restructuring of the instinctual life, permitting less conflictful and therefore more satisfying relationships.

ODIER:

I might give you some ideas on the value of affective factors, not only in neurosis but also in the development of the child and the social life of the adult.

Freud and Piaget go up and down the same stream on opposite banks. Each remains on his own side, so they cannot meet. My main idea in my work is to throw bridges between the two banks and my object is to reconstitute the organic and functional unity of child development. On the one hand, there are interesting but partial theories, on the other is the child himself as he develops according to very complex laws.

There is a need, then, firstly to study this development in all its aspects, and secondly to attempt to establish syntheses between the respective data of all the studies confined to one or other aspects of this problem, but I will limit myself to underlining a few points which seem important to me.

As you know, Freud postulated three or four successive theories of instinct which are different and seem to me contradictory. It is these continual contradictions that have helped to disconcert not only biologists but also psychologists and philosophers. This fundamental confusion is constantly reflected in psychoanalytic jargon, and the reader is always constrained to examine texts most critically in order to know exactly what is the subject and on what plane the psycho-analyst is working. Thus, in psychoanalytic works the word 'libido' is used in at least five different senses, without the distinction being clearly indicated. It sometimes expresses sexual pleasure and some-times the sexual act, and all kinds of behaviour driving the individual to obtain this satisfaction, etc.

There is, then, in these texts a source of confusion between the energy being used, libido or aggressivity, and the instinctual act which this energy is supposed to determine. Thus, according to Freud, instinct is an internal movement from the disagreeable toward the agreeable, from the painful toward the pleasant*; but then, according to this conception, too much insistence is laid on the causal factor and not enough on the intentional factor (it is precisely the latter, if I have understood the situation properly, which escapes the ethologists). Hence these interminable controversies between causalism and finalism of instincts. Now on this subject we can sum up Freud's thought as follows: an instinct is at the same time a cause, an object, and an aim. Here again it is necessary to distinguish between two very different things. According to a first theory the instinct is defined by a tendency to reproduce a previous state which is a state of relaxation or repose. The insistence then is on the actual energetic mechanism of this re-establishment of a previous state, which is a pleasant state, in order to suppress the present state, which is one of tension. Behaviour is then determined by the tension factor, and we have here an energetic conception.

In other texts, however, behaviour is no longer determined by this regulating, almost cybernetic, mechanism, but by the painful, disagreeable nature of the state of tension. In fact, Freud showed that the final state after the relaxation is subjectively less painful than the initial state, hence his famous theory of the pleasure principle.

In short, his first description corresponds to a very strict psychophysiological conception; his second is a purely psychological approach on a subjective basis, that is to say based on sensations of pleasure or displeasure. The relation between these two forms of phenomena often remains obscure. This no doubt arises from the fact that psycho-analysis is at the same time objective and subjective.

Another subject which seems to me to contain some ambiguity is the problem of the specificity of the object. According to certain theories exterior objects are never releasers of behaviour. They are not the actual cause of instinctive acts. They are rather the effect of a series of selective pieces of behaviour conditioned through heredity and used by the instincts to obtain their satisfaction in the exterior world. Thus instinct as a primary phenomenon is released by internal vegetative, hormonal, diencephalic, or cortical organic excitations. In short, drives or instincts are not initially fixed on specific objects. This has been demonstrated by some remarkable studies on ants (BRUN, 1920). Entirely inadequate ('empty') anti-biological reactions

* This psychic process is invariably started off by a painful tension and is directed towards the final result of a lowering of this tension, that is to say, suppressing pain and producing pleasure (FREUD, 1920).

188

can be released in ants. I would recall also Dr. Lorenz's experiments on the starling.

It seems, then, that two separate things have been confused in psychoanalysis: the hereditary predisposition to a certain action and the instruments used by instinct either during its phylogeny or during its ontogeny.

Child psychologists, when explaining the search for an object, do not necessarily resort to inwardly determined primary and secondary mechanisms. It seems that from the beginning these mechanisms are intimately linked and that the passage from one to the other is reversible. Thus one finds situations where the object itself can release the instinctive acts and affective reactions which define the first social link, this specific object being the protective mother. This is what is found, for example, in the 'smiling response' which takes on an elective character. Certain babies respond to their mother's smile only. The very interesting problem of the specificity of the object is called in question by ethologists who show that an object is not initially specific. In Dr. Lorenz's films we have seen geese and ducks following him with obvious love as if he were the father or mother. At the moment of imprinting, then, the specificity of the object is lasting and irreversible.

Does the same thing happen in the child? Here is the great difficulty of establishing links between ethology and physiology on the one hand and child psychology on the other. I think that mother-fixation under normal conditions is specific. No other object can replace the mother without producing disturbances which are sometimes very serious and can lead to the anxiety which is called 'the feeling of insecurity'. My work on what I have called 'the neurosis of neglect' (ODIER, 1950) is centred on the origin, nature, and development of this feeling of insecurity in the child and the disturbances caused by it. It seemed to me that emotional reactions played an essential role in the etiology of the 'affects' and that very interesting results could be obtained by analysing in detail not only the instinctive causes of conflict between the libido and aggressivity but by analysing the affectivity itself, and by describing the phenomena not in terms of instinctive causality but in terms of structure.

Affectivity, like thought, has a whole history. Affectivity presents very interesting structures which evolve and are entirely transformed when the Oedipus complex appears, when the child acquires an entirely new conception of social relations based on dualism. In other words, he relinquishes his egocentric position: he can pass from this well-known affective participation, where there is confusion between himself and his mother, to a realization of a new conception, which for boys is identification with the father as an object. The child begins to feel intuitively that he himself is a subject; he can begin to consider things as subjective. In these entirely new relations the child can be the subject who experiences feelings which are either very ambivalent for his father or loving for his mother, and at the same time he may reverse the situation. It is at this moment that the reversibility of affective relations begins in so far as he can consider himself as the object and his father or mother as the subject. This is a very great problem. Psychoanalytic work has perhaps contributed to spread a certain confusion in public opinion. The Oedipus complex is considered as an instigator of disorder, as a necessary cause of neurosis. In my opinion the Oedipus complex is, on the contrary, a sign of health and of normal evolution. It is therefore necessary to explain to parents that it is a critical stage in development, but of a nature to ensure equilibrium in the child.

This meeting seems to me a fine demonstration of an effort towards synthesis between the biological and psychological planes. I have, however, the impression that the dominant tendency is that of biological reduction, that is, a tendency to carry the actual psychological processes to a level of mechanisms and instincts. But there is another method, the reverse method, which consists in passing not from the more complex to the simpler, but from the simpler to the more complex. By attempting to simplify the complex too much, one bypasses problems raised by the more complex. We now know, thanks to the work of Wallon, Piaget, and others, that the actual psychic processes obey not a causality—which is always very hypothetical—but a legality, a set of rules or laws which it would be interesting to examine.

What is lacking is a link between the two planes in order to avoid what I call the 'jumping method', where one jumps from the biological plane to the psychological plane without always being aware of the jump, and neglecting the whole territory over which one has jumped. It is precisely on an intermediary plane, which I call emotional or affective, that one can investigate what becomes of the instincts spoken of by Dr. Lorenz and others. What is the fate of all this instinctive life? It is transformed into an affective life which leads us to a superior level of intellectual life. It is the affective life which links instinctive and intellectual life. This study of the intermediary plane would lead us to our problem: the development, not only psycho-biological but also bio-psychological, of the child, and would put us on the level of actual experience.

LORENZ:

Many psychological problems have a physiological origin, and there is not a single psychological or philosophical thought which

190

has not its correlate in the physiological sphere. Now, I should like to see the link between psychoanalysis, as seen introspectively and psychologically only, and the physiological processes. We are concerned with the psychobiological problem. I should like to see the same thing first with one eye, then with the other. Moreover, this is what we must do if we wish to advance.

GREY WALTER:

It is very hard to keep the subject to children and there are several things I want to ask now. First, about the characteristics of the imprinting mechanism, and the I.R.M. that doesn't require a reward or reinforcement, in relation to the psychoanalytic approach to instincts; this seems to me to be of extreme importance. With regard to reward, I should just like to mention an important difference in conditioning between appetitive reflexes and defensive reflexes. In the appetitive conditioned reflex, whether in the flesh or the metal, a reward is necessary—this is the classical association of Pavlov. In the defensive reflex a reward is not necessary at all. A defensive reflex may be self-maintained. In a machine made to imitate a defensive reflex I can show that a single experience may suffice, so that thereafter the conditioned response perpetuates itself. The avoidance of 'pain' or 'displeasure' is enough to make the response perpetuate itself as though it were imprinted, though it is not an imprinting in Dr. Lorenz' sense; it can be shown to depend on the same mechanisms of selection and association that operate in ordinary conditioning.

LORENZ:

Especially if the experience is traumatic.

GREY WALTER:

Especially if it is traumatic. This seems to me to be a very important possible source of error and perhaps also, as so often in these paradoxes, a source of enlightenment, because we may have here the bridge between the conditioned response with associative learning and the type of imprinting which you describe. I should like, as I say, to enlarge on the mechanism of this conditioning process as applied to children and as applied to brain physiology, because I think there is a big field here to study in an objective fashion. It is our ambition to define and describe the instinctive processes in man in terms of quite objective physiological mechanisms in the brain. I think that the study of these learning processes might be extremely profitable to discuss even at this stage.

Another point, which was raised repeatedly by Dr. Bowlby, is the question of affect and what we might call, for the sake of argument, 'reason'; the experience of a number of events, and the sorting out from this experience of what matters. From the physiological standpoint, all behaviour is always a mingling of reason and affect. I have never seen an animal—a mammal, at any rate—behave without physiological signs both of logico-statistical behaviour and of affect. One can show this in measurements and I think a division of: 'this is reason and this is affect', 'you've forgotten affect', 'you've forgotten reason' has no basis in the truth of what happens. I think that certainly anyone who neglects one or the other is wrong; and even if we think we are neglecting one, we are not doing so. Perhaps the psychoanalyst could say why we like to divide things so that we say: I feel one thing in my head and another thing in my heart. I think this pseudo-anatomy is a clumsy, archaic device for indicating the relative proportion of autonomic participation in a behaviour pattern. These are arbitrary and dangerous divisions, and I urge that we should try to insist upon this recognition of the unity of physiological function.

KRAPF:

I think that Dr. Odier has put his finger today on one aspect of our discussion which is particularly close to our subject-matter when he introduced those two polar conceptions of causalism and finalism, because there it would seem to me that what he and Dr. Bowlby said links up with what we heard from Dr. Zazzo and from Mlle Inhelder, about the psychobiological development of the child conceived in terms of the socialization phenomenon. I would like to take up something which has been said by Dr. Bowlby, that conscience has an instinctive root. Obviously conscience is a phenomenon of socialization, and I would be in full accord with him if he said that conscience had *also* an instinctive root, because it is questionable whether the genesis of its function can really be referred exclusively to an instinctual origin. This leads us into the central problem of the super-ego. When Freud defined the super-ego for the first time, he did not immediately introduce the term super-ego, he spoke of an ego-ideal, and later on he changed over more and more to the term 'super-ego', and 'ego-ideal' gradually disappeared. But many years ago Dr. ODIER (1926, 1943) wrote a paper in which he suggested that conscience had in fact two roots, one which could be described as 'super-ego', roughly identical with Freud's 'ego-ideal', and the other, which he called the 'super-id', with deep instinctive roots, which would have been associated with the super-ego of Freud's second conception. Now, it would seem to me that Freud's second super-ego, Dr. Odier's super-id, would be what Dr. Bowlby had in mind when he said that conscience had an instinctive root. It seems to me there is another factor in what we usually describe as conscience which has a finalistic structure, and this corresponds to Freud's ego-ideal and Dr. Odier's super-ego. In fact, I believe that this difference has ramifications even into such finer psychological points as the moment when the super-ego is born. Is it true that the super-ego is purely the heir of the Oedipus complex, as Freud supposed, or is it developed at a much earlier stage, as Melanie Klein says, or are there two forces in the determination of behaviour, one which is causal, and tied to instinct, and the other finalistic and defined as motive? I would very much like to hear what Dr. Lorenz has to say about this: whether there might be a difference between man and animals, the animal perhaps being finally directed in a biological sense, but not in the sense of a conscious finality.

ODIER:

Concerning Dr. Krapf's remarks, I should have liked to speak of the super-ego and the structure of the super-ego mechanisms which are manifested in the very frequent symptoms of what is called auto-punishment. In his famous *Memoirs* of 1923 Freud exposed his concept of the super-ego, but he did not differentiate between various expressions: the super-ego such as we find it in neuroses, the ego-ideal, the conscious moral conscience, if I may say so—because it would be frightful nonsense to speak of unconscious moral conscience—and finally the ideal of the ego. It is on this subject that I published the study (ODIER, 1943) alluded to by Dr. Krapf to show that in fact four different things were concerned. A distinction must be made between what I call pseudo-morality of neurosis and a new form of morality linked with motivations from moral conscience which itself is linked with what I have called choice or adoption of norms because our moral life always has a normative character whatever the value or the nature of the norms we adopt.

KRAPF:

This can be envisaged as a socializing process, can it not?

ODIER:

Yes. We must evaluate certain aims which determine and stimulate our work and our interests, etc. Now this process of evaluating aims is very little understood. To my knowledge no work on the subject

G   193

exists, although it is at the centre of social life and the evolution of the human being.

Another point on which I should like to give some details is that of the difference which I thought I had noted between our results and the data of the ethological school. What do we find in animals? A lack of selectivity. They can follow anybody as long as the imprinting occurs sufficiently early. Among infants, on the other hand, there is an excess of selectivity. The fact that many children have a mother-fixation is determined by a factor which has certainly escaped the physiologists and ethologists and which nevertheless plays a fairly big part in human life. This factor is the need for security which is conditioned by the need for love. What, for example, do you think of the concept which has been called the instinct of security? I think that this raises a big problem. In my opinion the hypothesis that such an instinct exists is useless because I think that the need for security is the consequence of a series of experiences in the child. In certain states the child experiences very agreeable feelings and in other situations, on the contrary, he feels anxiety. Hence his need of re-establishing the feeling of security by elective mother-fixation.

Generalizing, then, from this point of view, one might say that the infant experiences two kinds of feelings which it is difficult to find in the animal: on the one hand fear of his instincts, which is why he represses them so energetically, and notably fear of his sadism (the English school now postulates the congenital nature of sadism, children being supposed to be born with a strong sadistic tendency); on the other hand, there is the fear of the exterior world, the fear of frustrations and menaces. This fear leads him to see in the exterior world hostile forces which he attempts to explain to himself by magical thought, animism, etc., by all those forms of thought so well described by Piaget. Many children, in fact, see in the exterior world a baleful influence which constantly menaces their equilibrium and their life: they therefore attempt to defend themselves by tightening the exclusive link with a specific object—the beneficial protecting object—the mother. From this arises the very common conception in affective life of 'all or nothing'. And this certainly is an inevitable source of deep frustrations and great deceptions.

LORENZ:

If you will pardon my saying so, I think that in the discussion of the last few minutes there has been a horrid mix-up regarding causality and finality and regarding the subjective and objective side of behaviour. I will start on finality. I should assert that 'finalism' is as much a nonsense as 'causalism'. Let me explain in a parable. I am driving along in my old car, with the finality of giving a most important lecture. I am enjoying the wonderful finality of the construction of my car, how beautifully all its constructive details are calculated to help humanity to be enlightened by my lecture—it's the finalists who are apt to be so assuming, because I am not. Now, suddenly my old car says 'hp! hp! hp! hp! hp!' and stops.

And now I'll find out something fundamental. I'll find that finality is not a force. It cannot be used for traction. It is causality that is pushing along my car—and everything else on this planet and all others. The fact that my intended lecture is of the utmost importance for the salvation of humanity—in other words, the value of the goal—does not help me three whoops in hell. The only 'factor' which can direct my activities in the right direction is the insight into the causality of the defect. It may enable me to screw out the jet of the carburettor and blow out the drop of water that caused my motor to peter out.

Let's take another example. The finality 'factor' won't help a man in whose appendix a cherry stone has got stuck, but the youngest pupil in the surgical clinic can help him, if he has insight into the cause of the illness. And that is exactly why medicine, the queen of all applied sciences, is forever occupied with the unravelling of the causes of all illnesses. It seems to me very futile to quarrel about whether the question of causality or the question of finality is more important. Neither is of any importance without the other. The investigation of causality would be quite senseless if humanity were not striving for goals. And humanity striving for goals would be powerless if it had no knowledge of causality, which gives it power to change, at its will, sequences of natural events. This relation between the final and the causal question must be grasped; it is perfectly simple. Yet finalistic behaviour students persist in accusing ethologists of being blind to the finality of things, and they do so in spite of the fact that we actually begin most investigations with a quest for finality. When I see a queer organ in a new animal, I do not start with any 'causing' investigation, how the animal got to have that organ, but I start with the question, What is this organ for? And even in putting this question, we must not forget that the whole conception of finality can only be applied to processes moving in a certain direction, which certain processes in the universe do. We must not forget that the finality of adaptation in the organic world is an arrow of direction which we have fixed to the process post factum, and we don't see the many abortive trials of nature, the whole vast quantity of animals and plants that have become extinct.

Now as to finality in behaviour, I think I will have to explain something very commonplace which concerns appetitive behaviour

195

and the consummatory act: one of those commonplaces which are so incredibly difficult to see. An animal's behaviour is directed; it is purposive, and EDWARD CHASE TOLMAN (1949) has given a very good objective definition of purposive behaviour. Purposive behaviour is characterized by the fact that the same constant end or goal is achieved in the animal by variable adaptive behaviour. Now all finalists, most prominent among them McDOUGALL'S (1933) school of purposive psychology, had assumed, more or less *a priori*, that the end or goal for which the organism is striving is nothing else than finality itself, in other words, the survival value or the biological effect of behaviour. For a school of thought which regarded Instinct (with a capital I) as a 'directive factor', it was entirely consistent to assume this. The great discovery of Wallace Craig was simply this: the organism as a subject does not strive for the biological effect of its instinctive activities, but only for the discharge of these activities for their own sake. It seems utterly commonplace that I do not go to luncheon because I purposely want to get fatter, but because I like eating and shall become most dissatisfied if I do not get food. Also it seems a rather rude and crude *reductio ad absurdum* to state that the young man does not try to impress the beautiful maiden with the direct aim of becoming, as soon as possible, the father of a lustily squalling baby, but for very different reasons. I think that in judging and describing animal behaviour, we cannot be strict enough in keeping apart the survival value of behaviour and the subjective end which the animal or man is striving for. We are quite justified in saying 'this animal is striving for an end'. If a dog wants to kill the rabbits in a rabbit-hutch and first tries to dig a hole under the rabbit-hutch and then tries to jump under it, and then finally gnaws a hole into the hutch, then that's variation with constant end.

Well, so much about finalism and causalism. There ought not to be one single biological investigation which doesn't take both viewpoints into account.

BOWLBY:

It is interesting that Freud made this distinction in his 1915 paper on instinct (FREUD, 1915). And this notion is, I think, crucial to the whole Freudian theory of instinct—that the aim of the instinct has nothing directly to do with survival.

HARGREAVES:

I was much impressed that Dr. Lorenz' wording is almost the same as Freud's; instinct has the aim of 'abolishing the condition of stimulation in the source of the instinct'.

LORENZ:

Dr. Odier said that the selectivity of the human child in regard to its mother should be so much greater than the selectivity of an animal directed by I.R.M.s. Now I am going to ask him how does he know? Has he ever tried to offer a simplified or otherwise different substitute mother to a newborn child without previous experience? And, of course, nobody would dare to make the experiment, to try a chimpanzee mother and let her foster a human child. And I can tell you what would happen: she would drop it very soon. I am not prepared to accept the statement that the human child's reactions are so selective. On the contrary, it is our general experience that the I.R.M.s of the higher animals are much less selective than those of the lower animals, because more scope is left for learning.

HARGREAVES:

It seems to me that both the statements are true because the Spitz smiling response is very unselective. It is not a smiling at any particular person: it is the smiling at an oval object with two black dots on it which is moving. But within a comparatively short time—I think about a month—the response is given only to the mother.

LORENZ:

The greylag goose gets imprinted to man within ten hours, and it will know its mother within about forty-eight hours, and not respond to any other goose. It is very curious for the narrowness and specialization of its Gestalt perception that the little goose finds it much easier to learn the difference between the individual facial expressions of two geese, than between two human beings. One of my students, Margret Zimmer, and I each reared flocks of geese this year. We consented to 'peck' at each other's children, and even with this reinforcement it took the goslings about three weeks to differentiate clearly, to know the two of us apart. Miss Zimmer is rather a petite blonde girl of twenty-four and, well, you know me! Yet it took three weeks until her geese wouldn't follow me any more and mine wouldn't follow her, while you never see any attempt of a little goose to follow another goose except its mother after two or at the utmost three days. As to Dr. Odier's question of 'l'instinct de sécurité', my answer must refer to the difference between McDougall and the purposive psychologists, and us. The purposive psychologists who were prepared to answer the question 'why' with 'so that' had naturally no compunction at all about giving instincts names according to their ends and creating as many instincts as there were ends, whereas our concepts of instinct are based on physiological mechanisms. As to the instinct of security—well, the goal of security may be reached by any number of neural mechanisms which all contribute to that end.

I want to add one point to a question of Dr. Bowlby's which interested me very much because it is our chief object of investigation just at present: that is the overlapping and interacting of two simultaneous instincts. We thought formerly that instincts in animals were mutually exclusive. JULIAN HUXLEY (1914), speaking in parables, said that man resembled a ship with many captains on the bridge fighting all the time between themselves, while an animal was a ship which was also governed by a number of captains, but when one captain popped up in command on the bridge, the others had to go below. I have quoted that again and again because I believed it myself. But it is not true in the least. One excuse for thinking it was our choice of examples. We were quite justified in seeking the most simple examples, just as Mendel searched for the monohybrid type, but in reality we find that these mutually exclusive, unmixed instincts are about as rare as hybrids heterozygous only in one gene. Everything can overlap with everything, and the result is very often a quite crude superposition of movement just as two automatisms can be superimposed on each other in one muscle contraction, so you can have two instinctive movements superimposed. In my film of the courtship of the mallard duck, you will see a very beautiful example of superimposed instinctive activities. A female mallard is trying, simultaneously, to execute the movements of inviting her male to copulation and inciting him to drive away another drake who comes disturbingly near. At first you see her doing the two movements—both are movements of head and neck—alternatively, and then the two rhythms begin to attract each other by what HOLST (1936) calls 'Magnet-Effekt', until both movements fall into step and form the queerest superposition.

Our assumption is that superposition is the most primitive form of interaction between two instincts, and that mutual inhibition is only due to a secondary mechanism which evolved later. It is, of course, very necessary that the instinct of escaping blocks all others, or that sexual instinct prevents fighting or killing the mate, etc. It also may be regarded as an argument for our assumption that in pathological cases, in which the inhibiting and dividing superstructure gets defective, there occurs a mixture and superposition of instinctive movements which normally never occur simultaneously. If you get down to the epileptic fits, where all superstructure is suddenly struck away, you get a cacophony of pretty well all the endogenous movements that the human has—escape activities, sucking activities, etc. But your description of that woman who hated, Dr. Bowlby, and at the

198

same time was affectionate to you, strongly reminded me of what some fish will do, which primarily are aggressive, but in which the aggression has to be inhibited in order to let the pair take care of the brood together; this inhibition mechanism is very fragile and very easily broken down, and you suddenly get an awful fight between the couple.

The Cross-Cultural Approach to Child Development Problems

Films presented by Dr. Lorenz and Dr. Mead*

MEAD:

I want to emphasize two or three things on method first. The approach I will be talking from is based entirely on the study of a whole community whose place in a series of communities constituting a closed culture is known. There may be seven or there may be seventy villages, but before one selects a village one knows its size, its composition, its relationship generally to the whole of the pattern. I make the choice of a village that is itself as closed as it is possible to get (which depends on the society), that is clearly demarcated and contains a functioning whole ranging from grand-parents to babies. I don't study any village of more than 500 persons, and I prefer a smaller one. I study the whole community so that I know the positions and relationships of everybody in it. If I concentrate then on particular children or particular families, I know their place in the whole structure. If I concentrate on particular pieces of behaviour, such as that of the pre-school child or of infants, it is against the picture of the whole. It is as if you threw a light on the whole tribe and then a brighter light on a smaller group, and a brighter light still on a still smaller group. For instance, I have a thousand photos and ten thousand feet of film of one of the babies in a Balinese village;

* Films presented by Dr. Mead: *Bathing Babies in Three Cultures*, a comparison of the interplay between mother and child in three different settings—bathing in the Sepik River in New Guinea, in a modern American bathroom, and in a mountain village of Bali in Indonesia. Part of *Character Formation in Different Cultures*, a series of films produced by Gregory Bateson and Margaret Mead, on the basis of field work in Bali and New Guinea, showing the relationships between the way in which infants and children learn their culture and other aspects of behaviour, particularly dance, trance, and other forms of dramatic behaviour (New York University Film Library).

of many other babies I have perhaps only fifty photographs. By using photographs and film as well as notes, we preserve all the things that we don't know enough about to look at, and all the things that are going on simultaneously so that one could not possibly write them all down. It is possible with these new techniques to carry many more unanalysed variables than ever we could before.

It seems to me that we are working here in this group with two problems. The first: trying to define the nature of maturation for human beings. What are the minimum points below which it is not possible to learn certain things? What is the whole pattern of chronological maturation and the degree of individual differences? Do these individual differences fall within a normal curve of distribution, or are there extreme temperamental discontinuities that are innate? My expectation is that in the end we shall decide that there are a large number of innate individual differences in every society; we have no reliable method at the moment of measuring any sort of constitutional differences that are cross-cultural. My impression after working intensively in seven primitive societies is that the range of temperament in them is about the same as it is in our own society. The range of intelligence is usually narrower, but that is very largely a question of the small size of the group, and the fact that most of the defectives do not live, so that you have less at the lower limit; and your chances of a genius are enormously reduced when you are working with a people of whom there may be fifteen hundred in all.

Now the other problem we have to deal with is the role of culture in patterning the growing individual. When the anthropologist works with one of these communities he first makes a cross-sectional picture of the adult culture—the finished mature behaviour, the institutional patterns, the language. Then he studies the way individuals are inducted into the society and learn the culture. I would expect that when we get to the point of being able to specify the pattern by which the individual learns the culture and the pattern which is represented cross-sectionally in the adult you would recognize them as very highly identical patterns. This would only be so, of course, in a static society which is not changing, where the adults have been inducted in just the same way as their children are being inducted. But in a society such as the Iatmul of New Guinea, where the grandparents have been held by the arm in exactly the same way as the baby is held today, so that every member of the society of every age has experienced the same infantile situation, you expect the old adult to represent the entire growth sequence and growth experience, and to represent it to the young individual.

We can make distinctions between societies where children are reared by their grandparents, and societies where they are reared by their parents. In societies where they are reared by their parents, it looks as though they develop more curiosity and more adventurousness, and they are less conventional. In societies where they are reared by grandparents, they learn as babies what it is like to be old, and accept it. A third possibility is where children are reared almost entirely by other children, carried around by little girls and boys or just by little girls; this has certain characteristics in common with rearing by peasant nurses in that it keeps the child much closer to its own bodily processes than when the rearing is done by an adult.

We assume that the cross-cultural differences of mother-child behaviour between New Guinea, Bali, and modern America and all that they represent in terms of technology, attitude toward life, posture, gesture, etc., are learned behaviour; that there is nothing in the Balinese that prevents them from becoming as awkward as Europeans. Within one generation of rearing in Europe of Balinese babies, you would expect to lose the lovely weaving of the fingers. I have had one experience of an American child in Samoa, where the dancing is not as beautiful but is somewhat of the same order. At two he could dance beautifully in the Samoan style. He came back to the United States at three, and at ten he was as awkward as any American child. The whole thing had probably not been eradicated but driven underground, and when I spoke Samoan to him he sniggered as if I were saying something pornographic. He has an IQ of 160 but a deficiency in written English, and when I analysed his English it had Samoan grammatical locutions underlying it. This rather dramatizes the points that children from quite different environments can learn these things as infants and also that these things are all learned. The Balinese hand is like a monkey's hand. In America, when I stand in a line and shake hands with college students, about one in two hundred has a hand that is like a Balinese hand, and if I ask the girl what she hopes to do, most probably she answers, 'I am going to be a dancer'.

On the other hand, if we look at the often exceedingly elaborate ritual styles, we find that each culture has picked out the innate potentialities of part of the human race and, because of our great capacity to learn, has devised ways of teaching the other members of the culture to do that particular thing. There is a good deal of evidence (of the sort that underlies the writings of Jungian students) that there are a limited number of these characteristics that recur sufficiently often so that we will have repeats of psychological patterns in many different parts of the world where we cannot prove any historical connexion. Myths (which as nearly as we can tell are quite independently evolved by different peoples) are an example. They cannot simply be referred to childhood experience, because some peoples don't have them. One people will develop them and another will not. There is a possibility of recurrence in every society of types sufficiently alike to account for these similarities, and then each society takes one or more for its model. For example, sometimes a society will pick one temperament for a man and another for a woman. Another society will pick the male and female of the same temperament, and another society will distort one sex greatly in order to bring them into accord not only with the temperament, but with the sex of another group. In very complex societies, such as modern England or France or the U.S.A., we have, of course, class typing by learning, and we have occupational typing. We have our Bohemias and our Greenwich Villages, which are socially selected mechanisms for people who find one way of life more acceptable than another. In primitive societies the range is very narrow, and everybody who is going to stay alive has to be fitted into a tighter pattern.

Every human culture has to be learnable and usable by everybody who is going to survive in that society. You can have a society that keeps only half the babies alive; there are very many who do. You can have a society that says that people who are born deaf aren't going to talk, and they are put in an outcast position. But if you take the position that is developing in the Western world, that the people who are born deaf are going to talk, you may then have to try to modify your linguistic usages so that people who are deaf *can* talk. In a society which has a language that makes lip reading difficult, and which also has a large number of deaf people, one would expect that in time the language would be modified. If you insisted on Braille and had a large number of blind people, then you would have to work out a machine that would recognize the letters, or you would have to alter your script to make it more adaptable to Braille. This is just an extreme example of the point that everything that is learned has to be learnable by every ordinary human being in the society, in addition to being exceptionally congenial to some temperaments. If we all sat here and thought what kind of language we would make up if we wanted to make one up, our ideas would differ, but if we wanted to use the language, it would have to be modified so as to be learnable to every person here. In a sense every culture is a model of every other culture and contains all these possibilities, which is why an adult can move from one country to another and continue to operate. The place where we can conventionalize that is language. Man has known for thousands of years that he could learn the language of another group. We haven't conventionalized the rest of our cultures to the same degree, so many people will go into another society and learn nothing but the language (not even the postures and gestures that go with it). But if we take language as a model, it seems that any human being who has thoroughly learned his own culture and learned that cultures can be learned, can learn another as an adult. And that learning is of a totally different character from the learning as a child.

HARGREAVES:

What about the sub-cultures of occupational groups?

MEAD:

Well, they can be learned if you learn that you can learn them. People in the natural sciences are generally taught that other people can't learn them. The scientists say: 'They will never understand; they can't count.' In a class society, the members of the lower class are taught that they can never learn to be members of the upper class, and if they are taught that well enough the class society will last for a very long time. So when one says that every culture is learnable by every member of every other culture, the statement contains all of this 'learning to learn' in it. HEBB (1949) discusses in his *Organization of Behavior* the probability ·that first learning is of a very different order from adult learning. Even if so, however, each culture contains the record of that first learning in its adult institutions and patterns.

I want to say something about the application of some of Gesell's work cross-culturally. The book *Growth and Culture* that Frances Macgregor and I collaborated on was an *ex post facto* attempt to do this (MEAD and MACGREGOR, 1951). I had not been very much interested in Gesell's work until in 1945 I saw what Frances Ilg was doing with it, with her enormous capacity to assess kinaesthetic and motor development. We worked with four thousand photographs of eight Balinese children on whom we had accurate age records. (And they were the only infants on whom, in two years' field work, I had been able to get *both* dates of birth *and* long sequences of photographs—this in a society that keeps accurate dates for the first seven months of life! I wish everyone who has comments to make on material in primitive societies would bear this in mind—that it took two years to get sequences on eight children whose date of birth we knew with absolute certainty.) We worked with these photographs along with the whole Gesell group, spreading the photographs out in various simple categories and letting the Gesell people pick out from our children the things that struck them as completely deviant. Then we took their categories and studied them. The general finding was that the gross chronological stages were identical in the two cultures. It has been my general feeling (working always with approximations and very few real ages) that the sort of thing that Professor Piaget's and Professor Wallon's school are agreeing on in periods from five to seven or the period about twelve is reproducible cross-culturally.

204

What we found was this sort of difference. The Balinese child's hands and fingers are very delicate. The lovely type of precision that one gets with the Balinese is an earlier development than our type of prehension and is accompanied by very poor thumb-forefinger opposition. When the child picks things up it opposes its thumb to the second and third finger and not to the first and tends to bring the fingers down to the thumb rather than bringing the thumb toward them. The sort of thing that we think of as using the thumb is under-developed, and there is a high development of the ulnar side of the hand. Prehension gradually develops, and the children pick things up with the third, fourth, and fifth fingers, and there is an emphasis that gives a tilt to the handling of things. In the same way, the development from crawling to sitting differs somewhat. American children go through a long period of either hitching or crawling, walking on all fours, then they stand, and much later learn to squat. The Balinese child is not permitted to crawl very much and is always being picked up because crawling is behaving like an animal. It goes from sitting to squatting to standing. The squatting is a much deeper and broader posture and as nearly as we can tell is an effect of being carried on the hip but not having to grasp because of the sling, so that the child just spreads. The mother just hangs the baby up on her; or there may be a child-nurse who plays violent running games with a baby in a sling around her neck. The child has to learn to adapt to this. If it didn't, it would have its neck broken, and conceivably an occasional baby does get its neck broken. So apparently a combina-tion of the cultural attitude about animality which the Balinese are apt to stress (one tries to keep one's animality under control) and the method of carrying babies produces a posture which is a different kind of squat from ours.

FREMONT-SMITH:

Are there vipers or any other dangers to crawling?

MEAD:

No, these are urban people. The prohibition is directly related to the feeling about animality and incest. People who have committed the crimes that are most disapproved of, bestiality and incest, are made to crawl on the ground like pigs, eat from a pig's trough, and wear a pig's yoke on their necks, in expiation for their behaviour, before they are banished from the high gods and condemned to the vicinity of the cemetery for ever.

I want to stress, for a minute, the interaction between the mother and the child that we get in these living societies, that gets left out here when one keeps talking about 'the child does this', and 'the child does that'. A Balinese baby is limp and soft, but at the same time capable of performing quite elaborate acts even so young. The teaching is kinaesthetic (you get behind the child and you teach him by manipulating his body) or it is visual—never verbal. The Balinese are incapable of learning anything verbally. They are incapable of carrying out the Binet-Simon Grade III instructions. The Gesell phrasing of it is that the child keeps the neonatal flexibility that we see in very young babies. You get the same kind of weaving flexibility; you see it in Spitz's films on regressed, neglected hospitalized babies—the wandering hands with each finger going off on its own. The hand postures are exceedingly asymmetrical. In Bali any part of the body can go into trance. The little finger can go into trance and so can the whole hand. There is catalepsy of parts, and there are ceremonial trances in which the hand goes into trance but the rest of the man doesn't. The assumption is that you have here a mother who expects her baby to be limp, who embodies in every movement she makes in her handling of the baby an expectation that the baby will continue to be neonatally flexible. The baby, then being flexible, again reactivates the mother's expectation of flexibility, and the two things interact. If you could give a baby of this sort to a Western mother, you would alter her behaviour to some extent, especially if she were an experienced mother and could feel the surprise in the baby. On the other hand, if you gave an American child of nine months to a Balinese mother, it would probably learn a good proportion of this behaviour. My suspicion would be that the one girl in two hundred that I encounter in a group of American students whose hand feels Balinese has some hereditary predisposition that is like the hereditary style that the Balinese have made into a whole culture that is learnable, and learnable at different stages.

I want to make one remark about thumb-sucking, because I think it fits into what Professor Lorenz was talking about in connexion with I.R.M.s. One of the most astonishing results is that we have never found thumb-sucking in genuinely primitive babies that haven't had any Western-type public-health nurses around. Even in societies with enormous oral emphasis where they suck everything else—their wrists, their lips, their knees—they never suck their thumbs. That does not mean a thumb never goes into the mouth, but a typical thumb-sucking position with the thumb deeply in the mouth is absent. The only explanation of this that I can suggest is the kind of suckling the child receives as a very young infant. Just once in my experience have I seen a baby put its thumb in its mouth in the thumb-sucking position—at about two hours after birth, when there was no one there to suckle it.

FREMONT-SMITH:

There is evidence that thumb-sucking probably takes place in utero. Swallowing of the amniotic fluid certainly takes place and the thumb is in a very convenient position for getting into the mouth. At Caesarian operation the thumb has been observed to be in the mouth.

STRUTHERS:

One sees newborn babies as they come from the delivery room, before they get to the nursery, who are sucking their thumbs.

MEAD:

I am suggesting that thumb-sucking represents some sort of later phase of deprivation, that if a baby does not have enough breast-sucking at a given period it will take to it again, but properly breast-fed babies are babies that are fed a great deal and fed when they are hungry and without that long period of wait at birth. The thumb-sucking is absent in every group where the baby is fed by somebody within an hour of birth.

I would like to close with one other general point. We have a great deal of evidence from clinical material that man is capable of receiving exceedingly specific irreversible impressions. The sort of thing that is called in technical slang 'a lech' has the type of specificity that is extraordinarily suggestive of some phenomenon related to imprinting. A 'lech' is the sort of sexual demand that makes a man go to a brothel because he wants something exceedingly complicated. He must have a woman in a white dress with a red sash with spots of ink on it, or something. Usually his demands contain elements which are uncongenial to almost all wives. It is the sort of thing that the brothel seizes on.

We also have evidence that human beings are capable of making self-selection of foods that are right for their own growth; experiments have been done on rats that show that a rat, confronted with prepared substances which never existed in human history in a pure form, can pick from among them a better diet than a scientist can choose for the rat's particular needs (RICHTER et al., 1948).

HARGREAVES:

But it has been suggested that it is a learning process. The first try makes you feel better than the others and therefore you concentrate on this.

MEAD:

What I meant is that this is a potentiality, whether it is completely innate or learnt.

FREMONT-SMITH:

It needs one thing to be added to that, which rather dramatizes it. The rat when pregnant will shift to a diet that is appropriate when the infant rat is born, and it shifts again when the weaning takes place. And when the adrenal cortices have been removed the rat readjusts the diet promptly, taking in enough salt to keep himself alive from a salt solution which is available alongside the fresh water, and which he ignored previously. A similar thing is true of the rat made diabetic. The rat shows an extraordinary capacity to adapt himself to his bodily needs in a way which is very hard to conceive of being learnt. Of course, it has survival value and in that sense may make him feel better.

MEAD:

We know that human beings will do some of these things. There are cases of children without an adrenal cortex who could not yet speak, who have learnt to eat salt. There is a very particular case of that, an instance in which an adrenal-deficient child had learnt to eat salt while the mother was sick and the mother did not know of this. The child was taken to hospital, had no way of finding the salt, had no way of saying that it needed the salt, and it died.

Now the difference between building a diet which will keep most people alive comfortably and properly fed, and creating a situation within which each person can self-select the exact items which he needs, represents one of the dilemmas which society has always dealt with. It looks as if it is wiser to create a more generalized pattern and have people learn. This can be generalized to the point where we do not coerce individual idiosyncrasies, where it is possible, for instance, for children to refuse to eat something. In some societies children are forced to eat things and some of them probably die because of it. American share-cropper children are forced to eat fat; they rebel violently but unsuccessfully and that gives them an inability to learn to eat meat later on. Something has evidently been forced upon them that is nutritionally so bad that it creates a learning defect. In every culture you see a compromise between the finding of a pattern within which all individuals can survive (though with different degrees of free activity), and the insistence on a pattern that is lethal or destructive or deforming to some individuals.

LORENZ:

I would like to ask a question. First, I think that we ought to ask whether the special requirement in rats leads to the choice of that unknqwn food factor at the first time, or whether it is found by trial and error (which I strongly suspect). I think that the answer is enormously important, because we know of cases where there is a most specialized I.R.M. present for such a special need, for instance, the I.R.M. for chalk in birds. Its optimal object simply consists in something hard and white, but just not too hard to be nibbled. Anything which fits that I.R.M. would be eaten by birds in need of chalk and I have killed valuable birds by giving them calcium carbide, which I mistook for chalk. It just shows that there may be an I.R.M. which is never used in the wild bird.

Now I can go on with what I have to say. Different people say that there was a tremendous resemblance between Dr. Mead's film on babies and mine on birds. Now I want to give a warning; you saw a similarity but you did not see the same thing. You saw something analogous, but on a very different level. In both films you saw behaviour patterns which have evolved historically. But in one case they evolved in the palaeogenetic history and in the other in the cultural history. Both ways of evolving differ from history in the common sense of the word in being much slower and much more conservative. This forms a link between the two, and it is this conservatism in how you court, or how you hold your child's hand, or how you dance, and so on, that is responsible for the tremendous similarity, because it produces ritualization. In my opinion, the analogy between ritual dances and ritualized instinctive activities lies in two points: first, activities which primarily had mechanical function, like sowing, or reaping food, etc., have been in turn made into something with an entirely different symbolic function. Second, several independent movements, joined on to each other by an adaptation to the plastic needs of the situation, have been welded together into one rigid form, which, by that very process of welding, achieve autonomy, as one pattern of behaviour.

MEAD:

I agree with the welding point, but I would question the slowness of the process. In an unpublished study on hand postures in court-ship (in the biological sense rather than the social), among young people in Louisville, Kentucky, Ray Birdwhistell distinguished over twelve ritualized pieces of behaviour in the way the average college boy in Louisville holds a girl's hand. They are stylized and ritualized and not articulate.

209

LORENZ:

Are they not a fashion?

MEAD:

No, they are not a fashion in the sense of being articulately communicated; but I don't have any reason to believe that they are a hundred years old. They are systematically linked with so many other things in the human body; the body as a whole is a factor in the ritualization. In New Guinea we have no indication at all that some of the cultures are more than five or six generations old. They change with extraordinary rapidity and change into very different styles, with the human body as the integrator.

LORENZ:

Gesture is a convention; it has to be learned. There are innate elements in it, though. Your directing your hand towards me so that everybody understands your meaning is a convention; but it evolved historically from a series of innate movements.

HARGREAVES:

But you could not call the stiffening of the arm in anger a convention. It is a conventionalized use of something which originally arose in another situation.

MEAD:

The New Guinea temper tantrum gesture, you mean? It is absolutely characteristic of children in that part—it occurs over and over again. You can say that babies learn to do that because they see other babies doing it. You can say they do it because of the way the mother holds the arm. It can be learnt very fast though. That is an important point which I think we should go into here, because in cultures like modern America the speed of change is so great that there is very little ritualization.

GREY WALTER:

I want to ask if anything is known about the extent to which the ritualized gestures, either in birds or lower mammals, or in human culture, could be related to some complex of physiological mechanisms. These are things about which we know very little, but which are described in great detail in some of the Eastern cultures, particularly in yoga, where you get highly ritualized postures of different types which have a most remarkable effect on the autonomic system. In the Indian physiological textbooks of a few centuries ago one finds all we know about the vagus nerve, for example, described in terms of kundalini, a great snake in the body; and very precise descriptions are given of how to control this section of the autonomic system, by tucking the heels up under the genitalia and so forth. These look like merely ritual gestures, but in fact are very crafty adaptations of the human frame for a certain cultural need of yoga or trance.

LORENZ:

I wouldn't say they were ritualized; they are dictated by the needs of the body.

FREMONT-SMITH:

Is it possible in the human that imprinting, if it occurs, is of a physiologically fundamental kind so overlaid with embroidery that we practically never see the pure form of the imprinting?

LORENZ:

I hardly know how to answer—of course, imprinting is always dependent on some I.R.M. being there, and Dr. Mead was quite right to say that there is a tremendous variation in this respect. That unhappily deprives you of the only possible character by which you could recognize imprinting and the I.R.M. at all without doing experiments. I agree with what Dr. Mead has already said of the innate components of human behaviour. They must be something occurring in very many cultures—that's about all you can say. As to experiments, I must ask you not to expect too much knowledge about imprinting in man from ethologists. There is one I.R.M. definitely found in man, that is the I.R.M. to snakes. This I.R.M. is present in about 50 per cent of people and in very many people it is already less selective than in some others. It might interest you to know that the horror of mice is due to the same I.R.M. as for the snake, because of the movement without legs. Snake movement has the legless character and also a winding motion, and there are people who do not mind the winding but do mind the legless movement, and those are the women who are scared of a mouse.

TANNER:

Could you quantitate the extent of that I.R.M. in an experimental way?

LORENZ:

Well, in human beings it appears you cannot quantitate it because you cannot quantitate the inhibitions of the higher central nervous components.

TANNER:

If you could it seems to me that the genetics of it could be studied.

LORENZ:

It begins to operate at about three years—in the three-year-old child you can nearly neglect the effect of self-control.

MEAD:

You have to have people who live in an environment where they know nothing about snakes, there are no words for snakes, no dances about snakes.

LORENZ:

These were children in Viennese hospitals who certainly lived in a world where they weren't taught anything about snakes.

MEAD:

Were there mice?

LORENZ:

There were no mice.

ZAZZO:

One can distinguish between, and to a certain extent compare, different cultural ritualisms and the codification of mimicry. One example which seems fairly clear to me is that of the different stages of smiling: the smile of appeasement after food which appears immediately in the infant and which gradually takes on significance and becomes a sign, an expression. It is fairly clear that we have here a tonic, postural origin of certain signs. Now, I should like to know to what extent this explanation, which is valid for smiling and certain kinds of behaviour and some mimicry, can be validated for the organization of certain cultural rites.

MEAD:

I am not quite sure that I understand your question. You have people who reply to the smile, mothers who spend hours smiling at their babies and playing with them. In other cases, the baby spends almost the entire time held on the mother's back in a bag, where it has all the cutaneous pleasure of being next to her. When it is hungry it can be fed, but it is much less face-to-face with the mother. The Balinese regard indiscriminate smiling as the first sign of insanity, and one of their definitions of an insane person is somebody who will smile at anybody and who will respond to a smile with a smile. The only adults who smile are the type we would probably classify as hebephrenic. The Balinese are the most unresponsive people in the world. They ignore oratory. If you try oratory on them they either go home or go to sleep, but you cannot make a speech to the Balinese and be heard. Probably this comes from their continuous stimulation of little babies. They smile at them and play with them, and they don't discriminate between smiling and tears in Bali. It is just as much fun to make a baby cry as to make it smile. They just want to make it do something. At first there is an exaggeration of the elicitation of smiling responses, until the baby is seven months old. The Balinese say 'as happy as a baby at its seven-months' birthday', and it is just at the height of its smilingness, responsiveness, gaiety. But by the time the child is about two-and-a-half, it has decided to quit. It ceases to respond. The adult finally does not respond when other people want him to do so. The Balinese smiles when he wants to smile, not when other people want him to, and grief is not permitted at all except on the stage, or in a mother of a baby dying under three months. If she cries a little then, they forgive her. Otherwise, no crying, no grief at all, though on the stage the representation of grief would be recognized by a European as beautiful deep grief.

LORENZ:

So you would see an expression of grief, perfectly intelligible to us, on the stage but not in real life?

MEAD:

Yes, on the stage you mourn when you are lonely, when you are deserted, when somebody dies, and it is a beautiful thing.

INTERVAL

LORENZ:

I would like to point out that in thumb-sucking, and in relation to psychoanalysis and the neuroses something very definite and complicated comes in, which has not yet been discussed at all, and that is *displacement activities*.

HARGREAVES:

Would you give us a summary of what you mean by displacement activity?

LORENZ:

In certain situations, especially those of a conflict, or in other cases in which an activated drive is deprived of its normal outlet, there occurs a very striking phenomenon, called by TINBERGEN (1951) displacement activity. If an instinctive activity is released, activated by its normal I.R.M., and then another, conflicting, instinct is brought into play, which prevents the consummatory act from occurring, there happens something very surprising: the animal suddenly performs movements pertaining to neither of the two conflicting instincts, but to an entirely independent third one! When the fighting drive is activated in a stickleback and, at the same time, escape reactions are released, because the fish, though furious, is considerably afraid of his adversary, he will, after some vacillation between attack and retreat, suddenly start to dig in the sand, performing exactly the same instinctive movements as when building a nest. Two roosters, in the same conflict situation, begin to peck at the ground. Avocets do some displacement sleeping (the most amazing among all displacement activities), putting their bill behind the wing and, in this peaceful position, glaring furiously at each other with one eye. As you all know, humans, in conflict situations, start to scratch their head. In all displacements, it is usually a very common, primitive instinctive action which is released. Most frequent are so-called 'comfort activities', preening, scratching, yawning, etc.; perhaps you know the fits of displacement yawning in furious monkeys, especially baboons. Sucking certainly also is, among all mammals, a very archaic instinctive movement and it has been known to appear in displacement situations in apes, monkeys, and bears. I have no experience with thumb-sucking in children, but I am ready to take a bet that you will find it is a true displacement activity in moments of stress. In man and very highly organized mammals learned activities may also occur as displacement: women patting their hair, men adjusting their tie, both lighting cigarettes. Always these learned movements are highly automatized, kinaesthetically 'ground in'.

The term 'displacement activity' is, in my opinion, not a good one. It was chosen by people who did not know or care about what it means in psychoanalysis.

BOWLBY:

I want to emphasize that terminological difference; 'displacement *activity*' is where the tension belonging to one instinct is discharged by being short-circuited to another instinct activity. If we use this for the ethological concept, the term 'displacement' can continue in psychoanalytic usage to mean not hitting 'x' but hitting 'y' instead. In displacement it is the same instinct being discharged, but with a different object (see TINBERGEN, 1952).

LORENZ:

The first man to describe displacement activity was MAKKINK (1936). He talked about sparking-over activities. In all conferences about terminology I still advocate the term 'sparking-over activities' because that's exactly what they are.

I think much emphasis should be placed on the fact that there is first activation and then frustration. There is a little lack of clarity in Tinbergen's terminology because with him the word 'block' is used for the inhibition sitting on the automatism and removed by the I.R.M. But in the case of displacement activities he talks of a drive which is 'blocked', when it really ought to be 'reblocked'. An instinct must first be 'deblocked' and then 'reblocked' by a conflicting one.

MEAD:

If you have a person who when frustrated in love suddenly begins to play chess very hard, or a woman who after a love disappointment takes to eating on a large scale, would that be comparable to displacement activity?

LORENZ:

On a higher level, it may be, because if you ask me what analogy I see in psychoanalysis to displacement activities, I should say, I see it in two cases: in the neurotic symptom, and also, or at least something very like it, in sublimation.

HARGREAVES:

Do such things as displacement activity and imprinting in fact occur in mammals, and if so, under what circumstances?

LORENZ:

Well, to the question of mammals I have got a very simple answer. We don't know a thing about them, because of the purely technical difficulty of rearing mammals from immediately after birth. We have tried to, we are working on it, but while for birds there is a tremendous tradition since the time of old Pastor Brehm, who taught us how to rear birds from the egg, there is no tradition on how to rear mammals. There is hardly even adequate knowledge of the milks of different mammals. There is no mammal which I should undertake to rear except big ruminants, let's say a sheep at least, and they take up a lot of room, and we haven't done it yet. We must keep in mind that an animal who is only just living is no use to us for our experiments. You remember that shrike who showed a serious diminishing of its I.R.M.s, when it did not get the right food. You can imagine what happens when you try to rear a dog or a sheep artificially: it would not be absolutely healthy. We haven't succeeded in rearing a newly-born rodent, except a guinea-pig, at all, and guinea-pigs are domestic animals domesticated by the Aztecs and show a tremendous variation, so that they are extremely inadequate for investigation of I.R.M.s. Then I must still further emphasize the immense difference in the sensory apparatus between most current mammals and man—a mammal which is so purely optico-acoustical as man is very hard to find, except for monkeys. Of course, if I had had chimpanzees, I would have done imprinting experiments with them, and then I could tell you a lot about the I.R.M.s and the resulting mechanisms. But, unless you take primates, which we intend to do when we have room and money, I cannot answer your question. Maybe in about five years I can just tell you something about small monkeys, or lemurs, with which we intend to start.

HARGREAVES:

What about the 'Mary had a little lamb' story? It is believed among English farmers that, if the lamb's mother dies, and the lamb is hand-reared, it afterwards becomes a complete pest to human beings. It's always about the house, it follows people, and this is the origin of the story of 'Mary had a little lamb, that followed her to school'. What effect does that have on the relationship of the lamb to sheep, both as a lamb and as an adult?

LORENZ:

Once you try to evaluate animal stories, connected with people who do not know what is important and what is not important, you find that they have absolutely no value. You just can use them as hints, and at present there is one lamb known, that was brought up not by Mary, but by Hediger, in Basle, that is definitely imprinted socially to man. The imprinting has been quite irreversible, but

216

unhappily the lamb is a female, and a female sheep is very passive, and there is no indication whom she would like as a mate, so there is no telling what man or dog or god-knows-what this sheep would like to copulate with.

FREMONT-SMITH:

I think Dr. H. S. Liddell had one lamb that was reared in the home, and I believe I am right in saying that this lamb did not run with the flock.

LORENZ:

Nor does that of Hediger. We must keep in mind one aspect of social animals. The most disagreeable thing you can imagine for a social animal is a closely related species. If you have greylag geese in a flock and a flock of bean geese flies by, they just look away. That is not innate, but certainly acquired. A new goose, not personally known to the others, is a pariah. A quite definitely negative social reaction is shown in an animal which belongs to one group towards the next group.

MEAD:

Do you attribute that to continual disappointment through false recognition?

LORENZ:

It might be. I might add something about the false recognition. You know what Seitz called 'Gespenstreaktion' in fishes—their reaction to ghosts—which we might call, in a less emotional way, the reaction of the broken-down Gestalt. If you change one essential character of this quality you change the whole complex and the whole Gestalt breaks down, rather as if one important chord or simple tone changed in a melody. This is very disagreeable. There are many instances where animals react to the change of single characters with escape reactions of extreme intensity. For instance, jackdaws are very afraid of a white jackdaw, an albino; so much so that you could not get such an intense reaction in a jackdaw from any other object of the same size. The same applies to fish presented with a formalin preparation of the same species. That's about the worst thing that can happen to them. Now, if you imagine that suddenly a man who is a formalin preparation walks in at the door, it would be very frightening indeed. He would have white eyeballs, a chalk-white skin and so on—a ghost, you see. Martina, my pet goose, who was tamed

217

to me as mother, and next to me to my wife, gave a fearful escape reaction when my wife sat in the canoe in my place. She didn't notice at once, and followed the canoe, when my wife pushed off. Suddenly the goose looked up, saw my wife, and incontinently dived, and came up yards away. That is a reaction of broken-down Gestalt, and something like that may be one of the reasons why the bean-goose may be a 'ghost' to a greylag goose. In favour of this explanation is also the fact that the animal can very easily get over its fright, and get habituated to, for instance, the white jackdaw.

GREY WALTER:

This is one of the features of animal behaviour that can be very beautifully demonstrated on a neurophysiological level. If one presents a human subject with a time Gestalt, that is a time pattern which is regularly repeated, it produces very complex responses in the so-called association regions which usually die away rather quickly, after a few seconds or minutes. Now, if you change one feature in the Gestalt, so that instead of making your flashes in one regular rhythm you change to another, then the whole picture explodes, and you see on the screen an electrical explosion as it were, which is far greater than that produced by any single item. Some people say that they feel 'swimmy' or faint or light-headed—they suddenly have this shuddering feeling very much as though they had seen a ghost.

HARGREAVES:

Is this mechanism related to the kind of horror one feels at the sight of anencephalic newborns and the rejection of them by the nurses who don't want to feed them, and the mother who wants one to die?

LORENZ:

Yes, I should certainly say so. But it might be that in that horror an I.R.M. also plays a role, because the anencephalics are just the opposite of the normal baby with its protruding forehead and typical proportions. Then I might remind you that all pictures of ghosts, and all devil masks, and even the Chinese dragons, are distortions of the human form; they are not animals at all, but they are men in a reptile skin with the head proportions of a man, a man with horns and a tongue.

I want to ask Dr. Grey Walter: do you find a correlation between the degree to which the Gestalt has become familiar and the intensity of the reaction to the breaking-down of the Gestalt?

GREY WALTER:

Yes, for some people, but that raises the enormous problem of types of personality. Some people show this, others show the reverse.

LORENZ:

Yes, the Gestalt perception is very different in different people, and it is to be expected that very different changes are necessary to 'break up' the recognizable quality. But this also depends largely on personal experience with the particular Gestalt in question, with its familiarity. Some animals, for instance my ravens, resent the slightest change in a very familiar environment, and do not mind it in a less familiar one. A new pile of wood in our courtyard would frighten them away for days, but the same pile on a forest glade two miles off did not matter to them at all; they sat on it.

Now, I have been asked to talk about innate releasing mechanisms in man. I am somewhat embarrassed, and in order to make my statement tolerably convincing, I must remind you of the difference between Gestalt perception and the summatory character of all I.R.M.s, of the independence of simple single key-stimuli. The only indication we have that something is based on an I.R.M. is that it will respond to single key-stimuli, in other words, that it will respond to dummies. That the acquired reactions generally do not react to dummies is a general rule to which we have hitherto found no exception. When we first experimented with a fish, *Astatotilapia*, we thought it to be pretty nearly impossible that the animals should possess acquired reactions to the other fish, because then all we knew about fish were Tinbergen's beautiful dummy experiments, in which he could do anything with both sexes with dummies. When we started to work with *Astatotilapia*, a fish with a very beautifully patterned and colourful male, and a cryptically coloured female, we could get all the reactions of a male to a dummy male but none of the reactions to a dummy female. The fish simply refused to react even to our most elaborate imitations of a female. Then my confidence broke down and I said: Well, here we have an I.R.M. responding to a Gestalt. Only I was lucky to have in Alfred Seitz a pupil believing more than I did myself, and he said 'Well, you must rear them from the egg'. We did so. Now, when one of these fish reached adulthood, Seitz, who was a very systematic man, said, 'Now we will start with the simplest possible model', and he rolled a ball of yellow plasticine, and stuck it on a glass rod, and slowly entered the aquarium with it. If I had been forced to take a bet then, I should have taken a bet to any sum that this fish wouldn't do anything at all, so convinced was I of my having been wrong about the I.R.M. and that the isolated male would not react to the simple dummy any more than a normal male would. But what really happened was that this fish just looked at the plasticine ball, spread all its fins, trembled with emotion, and started in a frenzy of courting that ball. That was the most dramatic experiment I have ever witnessed. And the simplicity of the I.R.M. has been demonstrated again and again ever since.

FREMONT-SMITH:

Was it just the colour of the ball?

LORENZ:

No, it was just an object approaching and not flying away—one slowly approaching object. That's all the I.R.M. there is for the female in *Astatotilapia*.

MEAD:

Did you make beautiful models with all the patterns in them?

LORENZ:

At first, for the males normally reared, we had made models which we could hardly tell ourselves from real females, they were so beautiful, and we got no reaction whatever. That was with cichlids. And cichlids are, of course, much more intelligent than sticklebacks— they have a much higher level of Gestalt perception.

This preamble is all to say that, where we get reactions to dummies, we have a very good reason to suspect that there is an I.R.M. Now, in man, there are quite a number of reactions which definitely will be elicited by extremely simple dummies, and among these are all the reactions of man to the expression movements of the fellow-members of his species. Everybody knows by self-observation that if we use animal heads as dummies, and observe people in zoos, we find that morphological characters of an animal's head are invariably interpreted as if they were movements or postures of the human head and face in expressing some emotion. If the eagle is the symbol of strength and courage—actually he is less courageous than a raven—it is all because the eagle has, by virtue of the bone-covering of its eyebrows and the form and the angle of its mouth, the big eye looking foward, something of what we call the 'hero face' of the human fighting male. We cannot get away from that, and the emotional value of the eagle face is inescapable. Just as little can you escape the stupid superciliousness of the head of the camel or the llama, and that is only because the head is permanently held slightly above the horizontal, so that the nostrils are higher than the eye, because the lid of the eye comes slightly down, as a protection against the desert sun, and the nostrils are narrow slits as a protection against the desert sand. These are all morphological characters, nevertheless you cannot prevent yourself from interpreting them as human expression movements and from feeling that the camel is very stupid and supercilious. You can go on giving examples for hours and hours, for instance, in the mandarin duck, the upward curve from the corner of the eye makes you feel that it is smiling, while in the closely allied North American wood duck, the female has a white patch under the eye and that has got something of a distressed look, as if it had wept. So, we all have a lot of these reactions to dummies represented by the heads of animals. But you can go down to simplifications which go way beyond the simplification of human expression proportions. When I was a child a certain type of railway carriage in Austria, which had narrow and high windows and had a ventilation slit just above the window, had to me a·very disagreeable, frightened look because, quite understandably, these slits were interpreted as eyebrows, and the face was a long face; while the Pullman cars, which had broad windows, and a sort of line beneath, looked large and happy. HEINZ WERNER (1933), a Gestalt psychologist, thought that this kind of experience, of dynamifying experience of environment, was a genuinely primitive character of all experience as such. In my opinion, all the dynamic experiencing of environment is due to a miscarriage of an I.R.M. directed to the expression of emotion in man. We must always remember that one key-stimulus alone in the supranormal object may elicit a reaction that is qualitatively the same as the whole set of key-stimuli. This simplification may go on so far that something like the proportions are reacted to as being beautiful, even if they are realized in the most exaggerated way. Our own reaction to such supranormal proportions is shown by any fashion paper.

Something interesting about all these I.R.M.s is that all domestication characters elicit a negative emotional reaction. When the artist, from Greek sculpture onwards, tries to present something ugly, he does not represent any old distortion of the human form, but a quite definite distortion of being too short and fat and bow-legged. On the other hand, the artist can exaggerate the opposite proportions to any extent, he can paint a man with shoulders broad and legs elongated to any extent, and these exaggerations are taken in without any resistance of our sense of beauty.

MEAD:

I want to be sure that I have got this last point. Do I understand that the characters that are used to produce something unpleasant will be ones that are characteristic of domestication in animals? Short and fat?

LORENZ:

Yes, shortness of legs, bow legs, loss of muscular tonus, sagging belly, small and lustreless eyes, etc., etc. In a series of photographs representing domestic animals in comparison with their wild ancestors, it is quite amazing how extremely ugly the domestic forms appear, and they do so to everybody, not only to biologists.

But now let me proceed to what interests us most, the mother-child relationship. One of the best instances of the I.R.M., except for the snake, is our reaction to the quality of *cute*. In literary German there is no word for this, but in the Austrian and Bavarian language there is the word *herzig* which implies the verb *herzen*, to fondle. The word which most succinctly means just this and nothing else is the American slang word *cute*. Now, let's look at the properties which produce the impression of a thing being *cute*. The head must have a large neurocranium and a considerable recession of the viscero-cranium, it must have an eye which is below the middle of the whole profile. Beneath the eye there must be a fat cheek. The extremities must be short and broad. The consistency of the body ought to be that of a half-inflated football, elastic; movements that are rather clumsy elicit the reaction very strongly, and finally the whole thing must be small, and must be the miniature of something. Now, if you observe yourself and your reactions to different animals, you will find that wherever one of these qualities is present, you react with a feeling of that particular kind. In the German language, where there are many diminutives, this expresses itself in the names given to animals. All animals whose German name ends in 'chen' have at least these head proportions. If something is a miniature of something very big—an elephant, but you must know how big an elephant ought to be—then you find how sweet the baby is. You must know how long the trunk ought to be in order to interpret the trunk of the baby elephant as being much too short for an elephant. I want to stress the relational property of those key stimuli. You may even make a miniature of a pipe, and you say, 'oh, how cute'. The child is miniature. Another heterogeneous summation can be demonstrated very nicely in animals which, for instance, have not short legs, but long legs, as, for instance, foals or lambs. Nevertheless, you find that the degree of cuteness is always dependent on the number of key stimuli realized in the object. The cheek is very important and the *corpus adiposum buccae* is also very important, and its lack in monkeys does much to detract from the cuteness of little monkeys. Also a very important part is the tactile stimulus—the rounded behind of the baby, because you feel that when you carry it, and monkeys who haven't got that are distinctly repulsive. If you see chimps and young gorillas side by side (the gorilla is a ground animal and has a large gluteus maximus where it ought to), it is infinitely sweeter than the chimp who hasn't got it. Now, in order to see whether many people have got that I.R.M., we ought to do a mass experiment with thousands or millions of experimental persons. Just this experiment has already been done: it has been done by the doll industry, which, of course, sells the supranormal object best. The exaggeration of key-stimuli can be very nicely shown in the 'cupie' doll, and the 'Käthe Kruse Puppe' in German, and if you want facts on what I say, then go to Walt Disney's films and see how Walt Disney represents cute animals.

I want to say one word more on the *corpus adiposum buccae*. Many speculations have been written on its function. Some have said that it helps in sucking. Now I don't see why the monkeys, who have got a much longer snout, are able to do without it. I propose the theory that the *corpus adiposum buccae* is really a releaser. It is there for the very purpose of eliciting an I.R.M. in the adult. That is not so speculative as you may think, because quite a lot of the releasers, which have definite correlates in the male's I.R.M. to the female, are nothing but fat—fat determining body outline, in breast, hips, and so on. So that it wouldn't be so very surprising if the *corpus adiposum buccae* should be the same, especially if there is colour on it.

Now, a dig at psychoanalysts. I agree with McDougall that emotion is the subjective side of an instinct, of one particular instinct. One qualitatively isolatable emotion is subjective to one instinct. Now, I feel that I can in myself very clearly differentiate between my reactions to the key-stimuli emanating from the female and my I.R.M. reactions to the baby. I think that I can, by introspection, assert with a quite considerable degree of certainty that what I feel while fondling a lion cub, a chow puppy and a baby is qualitatively the same, and different from what I feel when sexual I.R.M.s are brought into play. I would even go one step further and assert—I would perhaps not dare to publish it, but I do dare to say it among friends— that I can introspectively recognize the workings of an I.R.M. as such. It gives you quite a particular feeling, I should say the ego is always surprised at the unexpected and independent reaction of the id—I don't know whether I quite succeed in expressing what I mean. But anyhow—what I want to emphasize is the value of introspection, of psychology in the strictest sense of the word: it can tell the objective behaviour student quite a lot about himself, and he ought to be interested in that animal, too.

Now I want to proceed to a rather passionate theme. It concerns one of the very few pure instinctive movements of man, a movement of expression. We have already spoken about our own reaction to it, of our reaction to the 'eagle-' or 'hero-'physiognomy. When you are brought into a situation in which the fighting male in you 'believes' that it must go in defence of something, then you get, as reaction, an expression movement involving the whole human body and one of the few real instinctive activities of our species. If you are an enthusiast this reaction will occur whenever you are stepping in for an idea, for something that ought to be defended, it may be your nation, it may be the old school, it may be the freedom of scientific investigation. In all these cases you behave in a very singular manner. You feel a prickle going down your back, 'ein heiliger Schauer'—and it is quite characteristic of the German language that this is holy only in German—and I am not making fun at all. Then the tonus of your musculature goes up. Your arms are slightly abducted and go forward, you make the hero face, and then you are ready to do anything, to lose yourself, to forget yourself, in the good and the bad sense of the word. You are selfless and ready to die for the society, for the super-ego which you are about to defend, and you are also ready to do something absolutely foolish. Now, I affirm that a man who has not got that back-prickling reaction is an emotional cripple, and I wouldn't like to have him for my friend. But a man who has got that reaction and doesn't know about it is a danger to humanity, because what everyone ought to know about this reaction is this: when a chimp is aroused to enthusiasm, that is to say in defence of his family, he thrusts forward the jaw, he throws outwards his arms, and he fluffs out his pelt. It is very illustrative of the extreme conservatism of instinctive reaction that in this reaction we not only fluff out a pelt but we still throw out our arms in such a way that the pelt will stick out in a direction in which it serves to make our outline bigger and more imposing when we are facing or expecting our adversary. I think that this dilemma is very characteristic of the whole of humanity and of humanity's need to know and govern its own instincts. If there are no instincts, if all instincts drop out, then you get an emotionless, feelingless model man of the *Brave New World*. If you have this reaction, but don't know about it, then you are the victim of any demagogue.

TANNER:

These matters of the evaluation of and reaction to body images have been very much on my mind for some years. There is a vast literature about the way in which animal heads and animal expressions have been used by the human to signify certain things. It was most prominent about the time of the Renaissance, the best-known work being by DELLA PORTA (1668); this is a very famous series of drawings in which different people with different aptitudes were portrayed with different animal heads and expressions. This literature also goes down to the detail of individual expressive movements, particularly in the Indian dance literature; the various gestures in the Indian dance are often referred to by animal names. It seems to me that the interpretation Dr. Lorenz put on this may very well be the correct one. I say advisedly 'may' because I do not think it is certain that these things are I.R.M.s rather than learned.

Dr. Lorenz mentioned the idea that to make a person's image into a devil's image, you change his shape by spreading him out in a particular way. I do not believe that you only do that; I think you use caricature. I believe this is a matter of the valuation of a particular physique. I have hanging in my office a very amusing cartoon by Vicky of two English politicians whom most of you will know, Cripps and Bevin, both now dead. It happened at the time this cartoon was done that a British ministry put on an exhibition to popularize certain ideas, mainly the Marshall Aid Plan for Europe, and in this exhibition they had distorting mirrors which made you fat and thin. Vicky had drawn Bevin, who was massive and nearly spherical, looking at his long-drawn-out thin image in one mirror, and Cripps, who was very slender, looking at a totally inflated image of himself in the other. Under the first mirror was written 'without aid' and under the other 'with aid'. As an illustration of D'ARCY THOMPSON's (1942) famous method of transformed co-ordinates this was amusing, but it was also instructive, I think, of a great deal more. There are barriers between people which are to do with their different physiques but are not due to I.R.M.s—rather to the valuations we put upon physique and our identification positively or negatively with different builds. People built, for example, like Bernard Shaw, are simply not regarded as human by certain others, and equally those of the Bevin build are regarded as sub-human by some of the other sort of people. One must be continually aware of the difficulties of communication across these barriers, but they may not be difficulties of an instinctual nature. If they were the devil-distortion might be expected to go in one direction only. But I doubt whether it does this and I want to ask Dr. Mead what she thinks about that in other societies. Are there places where the long, thin ones are despised, and made the prototype of the devil?

MEAD:

I would be prepared to believe that there are certain sorts of distortion in either direction which, if they were too great, would be unattractive.

225

H

LORENZ:

I saw once in the *National Geographic Magazine* a picture of a black chief with a row of about seven wives standing behind him, in the order of their favouritism. They were quite exactly in the order of their hour-glass form.

MEAD:

That would be completely reversed in Bali. The Balinese make their monstrous figures of the witch out of the most masculine and the most feminine characters you could think of. The witch has big breasts—the Balinese think they are loathsome—and she has hairy arms as well.

LORENZ:

The favourites in the picture had little breasts.

MEAD:

Yes, but there are plenty of societies where that is not true, where big breasts are the important thing, and where the tiny breast would be rejected. The Balinese reject both extreme male and extreme female characters and prefer the male and female that are—well, GEOFFREY GORER (1936) once made a crack about it and said you could not tell a Balinese male and female apart, even from the front. This is almost true. If they are clothed to the waist you cannot tell the male from the female, say at about nineteen or twenty years old, from a short distance. They devalue curves, breasts of any size or any degree of pendulousness, and hairiness or muscles on the male. They are quite capable of developing muscles, and if you turn a Balinese into a stevedore he develops perfectly good ones. But their way of life is such that they have almost no muscular development. So that you have to postulate a complex mechanism, part of which might be an I.R.M. and part of which is imprinting or learning the type which is approved in your own society—whether that type is simply the type you see in your parents, highly valued or devalued.

LORENZ:

But don't these Balinese girls have beautiful female sexual proportions?

MEAD:

They are very under-developed as females. They have very small, very high breasts. The standard Balinese figure is such that you carry the baby high, and the baby drinks from the upturned breast. In some cases you get a pendulous breast, but the mother still carries her baby up high. To say that that is a beautiful female figure is a matter of the aesthetics of any given people.

LORENZ:

Does any people prefer very big pendulous breasts?

MEAD:

Yes, there are societies in which the Balinese woman would not get married.

May I return to the point about domestication; you said that characters producing the feeling of unpleasantness are those associated with domestication. That seems to me to lay overmuch emphasis on biological factors.

LORENZ:

This is, of course, quite true, and I am quite ready to accept that this is a simplification. About domestication, it seems to me—and I refer to our explicit permission to talk suspicions—that the same holds true to a certain extent for the behaviour traits of domestication. You hardly find one domestic animal in which sexual behaviour and eating behaviour is not increased quantitatively in an enormous degree, and the more complicated forms of social behaviour, caring for young, and so on, decreased in intensity. This is so general among domestic animals that I would find it very hard to find one instance of a domestic animal that is more social than the wild one, except, of course, the dog. Now, I think that in our emotional evaluation of our own instincts we put a very great plus value on those things which in domestication tend to atrophy and to disappear, and a minus sign to those which tend to hypertrophy. Everything we call bestial and brutish is not characteristic of animals in general but quite exclusively characteristic of domestic animals. I mean, if some wild goat were to talk about the proverbial lecherousness of the domestic buck, he would say, 'Poor fellow, he has been under human influence for centuries.' I see this daily in greylag geese as compared to domestic geese. You get similarities to human beings which are surprising, and you cannot help yourself from having sympathy with those nice, restrained, non-bestial wild ones and feeling some contempt for the domesticated ones. We must keep in mind that mother-love is not more necessary to the survival of the species than the drive to copulation. Why, then, are those drives to copulation 'brutish' and why is 'maternal love' sublime? This is simply our emotional valuation of instinctive behaviour in man—and it is largely dependent on supply and demand. I am convinced that we have something very deep, innate, in our behaviour, which tends to devalue sex and eating and to value very highly mother-love, social behaviour, defence of family, and so on.

MEAD:

You can find societies which put a high value on sex and eating, and a low value on maternity, and it would be important to make a list of these atrophying and hypertrophying characteristics, and then see how they are combined in different societies. For instance, in the Marquesas, which is about the most pathological society that we know much about, women dislike having children very much and maternity, breast-feeding and care of the child are devalued. Women are reduced to 50 per cent of the men, so that every woman can have at least two husbands, whom she keeps by her sexual attraction, and maternity destroys the woman as a sexual object. Food was highly valued and cannibalism highly institutionalized. This was one of the most vulnerable societies we know anything about; it almost disappeared with European contact, in spite of a big population and a good food supply. Comparison of these points in different societies has enormous possibilities if we bear in mind that societies can organize these things in different ways.

LORENZ:

Let me ask a very special question of Dr. Mead about the Marquesas. We quite agreed on the fact that there is a supranormal object and that this supranormal object may cause imprinting in a non-desirable direction. We must not forget that in imprinting we get all the accidental characters of the object which causes imprinting linked up irreversibly with the releasing key-stimuli of the object itself. Do you think you can get sexual imprinting of young males to an unbiological cover-girl—in your 'pathological' Marquesas sense?

MEAD:

Well, Bali is on the edge of it certainly. To have a whole society in which the bulk of young males is imprinted to an inaccessible object in some way—I do not know of any extreme behaviour like that. Bali is a case where you fall in love with your not-mother, or, taking it the other way, perhaps, the attitude toward the mother is sexually inhibiting to a very marked degree. In all theatricals, the hero tries to get a beautiful girl who is not like his mother, and the tragedy is

228

that you are always trying to marry the slender, far-away, not-mother figure, and you end up married to a Balinese woman. There is a very high degree of avoidance between husband and wife. The marriage ceremonies are filled with highly ritualized jokes on the possibility that the husband may never consummate his marriage at all and never have any children, in a society which is organized to make people have children.

This is not as simple as a simple imprint at all. You have simultaneously presented to the young child the witch, embodying the fear of its mother, and the beautiful princess he would like to have but whom he can never get. This is represented over and over again in a whole series of forms, so that the child is getting treated by his mother in a witch-like fashion and sees the supranormal witch played by a very tall man with all the exaggerated characteristics, and at the same time sees his other visionary type of sexual object. The Balinese define the delights of sex as starting with the first interchange of glances and going steadily down.

LORENZ:

Now, just one thing. I want to get your reaction to this. If you compare—I hope you will forgive my using a goose and not a mammal —a wild goose, you know that the first sign of her love is just a glance at him, and when he displays, apparently she looks everywhere else except at him, but really she does look at him, but so quickly that nobody notices it except him: at least, if she doesn't look at all, he ceases the display immediately. From these first preliminaries the whole thing very gradually works up to neck dipping, to the triumph ceremony, and so on, until at last she invites copulation. Now, a pure wild greylag goose is absolutely unable to come to copulation in any other way except beginning with a glance and working up through the whole sequence of those reactions. The copulation of the domestic goose is totally independent of all these preliminaries, and when she wants to copulate she obtrudes herself to a male with three or four neck-dipping movements and then invites copulation, and that is all. Yet she differs from the wild one only in that the activities of lower intensity are skipped over or dropped out and the action of highest intensity appears without these preliminaries; the whole step-ladder of intensities leading up to it in the wild bird has become unnecessary. Now I think that I see this in human beings. There are some that will start with very hot glances, and love is likely to be immediate. The activities are the same which occur in a 'normal' woman at a very much later stage and the difference is only that the preliminaries have dropped out.

Now the question is, have you got something like these differences —of a very long ladder to copulation, or the dropping out—in your different cultures?

MEAD:

You have whole cultures that represent either type. For instance, among American Indians courtship might take four or five years. The girl never speaks to the boy, but there would be a slight exchange of glances, maybe for two years. Then at corn-husking, if she had got to the point where she wants him to do something really rather desperate—to speak to her—she might try to get from the ears of corn a pure red ear and then carry in her arms a bunch of corn, one ear of which was the red one, and as the boy went by he might say, 'That is a red ear of corn.' That would do for the next year.

Then perhaps for another year or so he would go hunting with her brother. Then when you finally get marriage you go through a very formal presentation, sending game home by her brother to her father and so on. These Indians are one of the few people we know that have a long period after marriage before copulation, and in many of these societies the girls wear a sort of chastity belt for quite a long time after marriage. Husband and wife lie awake and talk. You have enormous romanticism about the husband talking to his young bride—he has been wanting to talk to her for seven years and has not had a chance! This occurs in an area also where we have the institution of the copulation blanket, a special leather blanket which it is necessary to borrow from a chief, in order to beget a child legally and ceremonially, so that it will be the right kind of child, and where people boasted of not having children within five years of each other, or seven years of each other. It is pattern of extreme restraint and extreme romanticism combined. Then you can have societies with all the other points in which they behave just like your domestic geese. But I see one other even more important thing in what you said, and that is that very rapid culture mixture and very rapid social change have the same effect on human beings in vulgarizing the responses and destroying sequences that domestication has on animals.

LORENZ:

It is always a matter of breaking up or dissociation.

MEAD:

Of these elaborate patterns: the training of individuals in this excessively elaborate series of preliminary requirements before a mate could be chosen.

230

TANNER:

To come back to what Dr. Lorenz was saying; you could, of course, speed up the response considerably by giving a sex hormone. This is true of most mammalian species.

LORENZ:

There are two processes working in the same direction. The loss of selectivity of the I.R.M.s in the domestic goose is accompanied by a tremendous increase in hormones, which is quite clearly indicated by the fact that the domestic goose lays eggs in the first year and the greylag goose only starts laying properly in the third. On the other hand, you get considerable independence of the ceremonies from the hormones; because all these rituals do develop in the domestic goose much later in life. She starts by being absolutely promiscuous, because she is sexually mature before all her 'marriage' ceremonies are mature, and these are what keep the pair together, and make for monogamy. So that in domestic geese who do develop a 'triumph ceremony'—not all of them do—you have a stage of absolutely promiscuous life ending up in the slow development of the triumph ceremony, which matures later than normally and in the end there results a monogamous couple quite similar to the wild ones.

TANNER:

In general, I suppose, hormones don't affect the sequence of events, but they lower the threshold.

LORENZ:

Yes, they lower the threshold. They may have a big effect and they may have no effect at all, and that there is no effect on behaviour sequence can be even shown by the potential homosexuality of some birds. When you haven't got a male, the female may do with another female all the things that a male normally does, up to copulating, but while she is behaving absolutely like a male, she lays eggs, which shows that her female hormones are quite all right. We thought for a very long time that in cichlids sexual behaviour was dependent on a quite definite hormonal stage which A. A. ALLAN (1934) thought too when he wrote his paper about 'synchronization of the mating cycles'. We were quite sure that this was the case with all fish, until this year when Beatrice Oehlert found a bigamist fish who had a wife and children which had just hatched out of the eggs. He knocked down and chased away the male of another couple at the same time in another corner of the same tank and occupied his territory and his wife. Then he went to and fro and behaved in quite a different manner with his new wife and his old wife, doing nest-building and inseminating activities in one corner, going back and doing the phases of three weeks later with his first children, then going back and fanning the eggs with his second wife, and so on. This showed that he could change his reactions within seconds, quite independently of his hormonal state.

REFERENCES

ADRIAN, E. D. (1931). *J. Physiol.* **72**, 132.
ADRIAN, E. D. and LUDWIG, C. (1938). *J. Physiol.* **94**, 441.
AJURIAGUERRA, J., ZAZZO, R. and GRANJON, N. (1949). *Encéphale*, **38**, 1.
ALLAN, A. A. (1934). *Auk.*, **51**, 4.
AMES, L. B. *et al.* (1952). *Child Rorschach responses. Developmental trends two to ten years*, New York.
ARMSTRONG, R. A. (1942). *Bird display*, Cambridge.
BAYLEY, N. (1943). *Child Develpm.* **14**, 47.
BIRUKOV, G. (1952). *Z. vergl. Physiol.* **34**, 448.
BOYNTON, B. (1936). *Univ. Ia. Stud. Child Welf.* **12**, No. 4.
CONEL, J. L. (1952). In: *The biology of mental health and disease*, London (The report of the twenty-seventh Annual Conference of the Milbank Memorial Fund).
DARWIN, C. (1872). *Der Ausdruck der Gemütsberwegungen bei Menschen und Tieren*, Stuttgart.
ELLIS, R. B. W. (1950). *Brit. med. J.* **1**, 85.
FAIRBAIRN, W. R. D. (1952). *Psychoanalytic studies of the personality*, London.
FESSARD, A., MONNIN, J., PIÉRON, H. (1931). *Bul. Inst. nat. Orient. Prof.* **3**, 197.
FREUD, S. (1915). *Instincts and their vicissitudes*. In: *Collected Papers* IV, London.
GAMPER, E. (1926). *Z. ges. Neurol. Psychiat.* **104**, 49.
GESELL, A. (1929). *Infancy and human growth*, New York.
GESELL, A. (1941). *Wolf child and human child*, London.
GESELL, A. and AMATRUDA, C. S. (1946). *Embryology of Behavior*, New York.
GESELL, A. and AMES, L. B. (1945). *J. genet. Psychol.*, **66/67**, 45.
GESELL, A., THOMS, H., HARTMAN, F. B. and THOMPSON, H. (1939). *Arch. Neurol. Psychiat.*, Chicago, **41**, 755.
GOODENOUGH, F. L. (1931). *Anger in young children*, Minneapolis.
GORER, G. (1936). *Bali and Angkor*, London.
GROHMANN, J. (1939). *Z. Tierpsychol.*, **2**, 132.
HEBB, D. O. (1949). *Organization of behavior*, New York.
HEINROTH, O. (1911). *Verh. v. intern. ornith. Kongr. Berlin* 1910.
HESS, W. R. and BRÜGGER, M. (1943). *Helv. physiol. Acta*, **I**, 33.
HINDE, R. A. (1953). *Behaviour*, **5**, 1.
HODGE, R. S., WALTER, V. J. and WALTER, W. GREY (1953). *Brit. J. Delinq.* **3**, 1.
HOLST, E. VON (1936). *Pflüg. Arch. ges. Physiol.* **237**, 655.
HOLST, E. VON (1939). *Ergbn. Physiol.* **42**, 228.
HUXLEY, J. (1914). *Proc. Zool. Soc. Lond.* **84**, 491.

INHELDER, B. (1943). *Le Diagnostic du raisonnement chez les débiles mentaux*, Neuchâtel & Paris.

INHELDER, B. (1948). *Synthèse*, **7**, 58.

INHELDER, B. (1951). *XIIIème Congrès international de Psychologie*, p. 153.

ITO, P. K. (1942). *Hum. Biol.* **14**, 279.

KLEIN, M. (1948). *Contributions to psychoanalysis*, London.

KÖHLER, W. (1940). *Intelligenzprüfungen an Menschenaffen*, Berlin.

KOSKAS, R. (1949). *Enfance*, No. 1, p. 68.

KRAPF, E. E. (1950). *Schweiz. Arch. Neurol. Psychiat.* **65**, 108.

KRÄTZIG, H. (1940). *J. Orn., Lpz.* **88**, 139.

LE MARQUAND, H. S. and RUSSELL, D. S. (1934). *Roy. Berks. Hosp. Rep.* **3**, 11.

LENNOX, W. G., GIBBS, F. L. and GIBBS, F. A. (1945). *J. Hered.* **36**, 223.

LORENZ, K. (in press). *Vergleichende Verhaltenslehre*, Vienna.

LUQUET, G. H. (1913). *Les Dessins d'un enfant*, Paris.

MAKKINK, G. F. (1936). *Ardea*, **25**, 1.

MEAD, M. and MACGREGOR, F. C. (1951). *Growth and culture*, New York.

MINKOWSKI, M. (1924). *Schweiz. Arch. Neurol. Psychiat.*, **15**, 239.

MINKOWSKI, M. (1925). *Schweiz. Arch. Neurol. Psychiat.*, **16**, 133.

MONNIER, M. (1946). *Schweiz. Arch. Neurol. Psychiat.* **56**, 233; **57**, 325.

MONNIER, M. and WILLI, H. (1947). *Ann. paediat.* **169**, 289.

MONNIER, M. and WILLI, H. (1953). *Mschr. Psychiat. Neurol.*, **126**, 239, 259.

MONNIN, J. (1933). *Bul. Inst. nat. Orient. Prof.* **5**, 1.

ODIER, C. (1926) *Int. Z. Psychoan.* **12**, 275.

ODIER, C. (1943). *Les Deux Sources consciente et inconsciente de la vie morale*, Neuchâtel.

PELLER, S. (1940). *Growth*, **4**, 277.

PIAGET, J. (1923). *Le Langage et la pensée chez l'enfant*, Neuchâtel and Paris.

PIAGET. J. (1926). *Le Langage et la pensée chez l'enfant*, Geneva.

PIAGET, J. (1936). *La Naissance de l'intelligence chez l'enfant*, Geneva.

PIAGET, J. (1946a). *Le Développement de la notion du temps chez l'enfant*, Paris.

PIAGET, J. (1946b). *Les Notions de mouvement et de vitesse chez l'enfant*, Paris.

PIAGET, J. (1947). *La Psychologie de l'intelligence*, Paris.

PIAGET, J. (1951). *Cahiers Int. Sociol.* **10**, 34.

PIAGET, J. (1951a). *Traité de logique*, Paris.

PIAGET, J. (1951b). *Introduction à l'épistémologie génétique*, Paris.

PIAGET, J. (1952). *Essai sur les transformations des opérations logiques*, Paris.

PIAGET, J. and INHELDER, B. (1941). *Le Développement des quantités chez l'enfant. Conservation et atomisme*, Neuchâtel and Paris.

PIAGET, J. and INHELDER, B. (1948). *La Représentation de l'espace chez l'enfant*, Paris.

234

PIAGET, J. and INHELDER, B. (1951). *La Genèse de la notion du hasard chez l'enfant*, Paris.

PIAGET, J., INHELDER, B. and SZEMINSKA, A. (1948). *La Géométrie spontanée chez l'enfant*, Paris.

PIAGET, J. and SZEMINSKA, A. (1941). *La Genèse du nombre chez l'enfant*, Neuchâtel and Paris.

PICHON, E. (1947). *Le Développement psychique de l'enfant et de l'adolescent*, Paris.

PIERON, H. (1949). *La Psychologie différentielle*, Paris.

PORTA, G. B. DELLA (1668). *La fisionomie dell'uomo*, Venice.

PRECHTL, H. F. R. (1952a). *Experientia*, 8, 220.

PRECHTL, H. F. R. (1952b). *Naturwissenschaften*, 39, 140.

PRECHTL, H. F. R. (1953). *Behaviour*, 5, 32.

PRECHTL, H. F. R. (in preparation). *Quantitative Untersuchungen über den Greifreflex.*

PRECHTL, H. F. R. and SCHLEIDT, W. M. (1951). *Z. vergl. Physiol.* 33, 53.

PRUDHOMMEAU, M. (1947). *Le Dessin de l'enfant*, Paris.

RICHTER, C. P., HOLT, L. E. and BAVELARE, B. (1938). *Amer. J. Physiol.* 122, 734.

SCAMMON, R. E. (1930). In: Harris, J. A. *et al.*, *The measurement of man*, Minnesota.

SCHOEN, L. and HOLST, E. VON (1950). *Z. vergl. Physiol.*, 32, 552.

SEITZ, A. (1940). *Z. Tierpsychol.* 4, 40; 5, 74.

SIMMONS, K. (1944). *Monogr. Soc. Res. Child Develpm.* 9, 1.

SIMMONS, K. and GREULICH, W. W. (1943). *J. Pediat.* 22, 518.

SIMON, TH. (1939). In: Imprimerie Moderne, ed. *Centenaire de Th. Ribot*, Agen, p. 558.

SPITZ, R. A. and WOLF, K. M. (1946). *Genetic Psychology Monogr.* 34, 57.

TALBOT, N. B., WOOD, M. S., WORCESTER, J., CHRISTO, E., CAMPBELL, A. M., and ZYGMUNTOWICZ, A. S. (1951). *J. clin. Endocrin.* 11, 1224.

TANNER, J. M. (1947). *Proc. roy. Soc. Med.* 40, 301.

TANNER, J. M. (1951). *Hum. Biol.* 23, 93.

TANNER, J. M. (1952). *Amer. J. phys. Anthrop.*, *N.S.* 10, 427.

TANNER, J. M. (1953). *Lect. sci. Basis Med.* 1, 308.

THOMPSON, D'A. W. (1942). *On Growth and Form*, Cambridge.

TINBERGEN, N. (1951). *The study of instinct*, Oxford.

TINBERGEN, N. (1952). *Quart. Rev. Biol.* 27, 1.

TOLMAN, E. C. (1949). *Purposive behaviour in animals and man*, Berkeley.

WALLON, H. (1925). *L'Enfant turbulent*, Paris.

WALLON, H. (1933). *Les Origines du caractère chez l'enfant*, Paris.

WALLON, H. (1941). *L'Évolution psychologique*, Paris.

WALLON, H. (1942). *De l'acte à la pensée*, Paris.

WALLON, H. (1945). *Les Origines de la pensée*, Paris.

WALLON, H. (1946). *Egypt. J. Psychol.* 1, No. 1.

WALLON, H. (1947). *Cahiers Int. Sociol.* **2**, 3.

WALLON, H. (1949). *Les Origines du caractère chez l'enfant*, Paris (2nd editn.).

WALTER, W. GREY (1950). In: Hill, J. D. N. and Parr, G., *Electro-encephalography*, London.

WALTER, W. GREY (1953). *The living brain*, London and New York.

WERNER, H. (1933). *Einführung in die Entwicklungspsychologie*, Leipzig.

ZAZZO, R. (1942). *Psychologues et psychologies d'Amérique*, Paris.

ZAZZO, R. (1947). In: Inst. nat. Etude Travail Orient. prof. ed., *Etude objective du caractère*, Paris, p. 128.

ZAZZO, R. (1948). *Enfance*, **1**, 29.

ZAZZO, R. (1950). *Enfance*, **3**, 204.

ZINGG, R. M. (1941). *Wolf-children and feral man*, New York.

Index

239

DISCUSSIONS ON
Child Development

VOLUME TWO

*The Proceedings of the Second Meeting of the
World Health Organization Study Group
on the Psychobiological Development of the Child
London 1954*

MEMBERS OF STUDY GROUP

DR. JOHN BOWLBY

Psychoanalysis

Director, Children's Department
Tavistock Clinic, London

DR. FRANK FREMONT-SMITH

Research promotion

Chairman

Josiah Macy Jr. Foundation, New York

MLLE. BÄRBEL INHELDER

Psychology

Professeur de Psychologie de l'Enfant
Institut des Sciences de l'Education de
l'Université de Genève

DR. KONRAD Z. LORENZ

Ethology

Forschungsstelle für
Verhaltensphysiologie des Max-Planck
Institutes für Meeresbiologie
Buldern über Dulmen, West Germany

PROF. G. R. HARGREAVES

Psychiatry

Formerly Chief, Mental Health Section
World Health Organization, Geneva
Professor of Psychiatry
University of Leeds

DR. MARGARET MEAD

Cultural Anthropology

Associate Director Dept. of
Anthropology
American Museum of Natural.History
New York

DR. K. A. MELIN

Electrophysiology

Director, Clinic for Convulsive Disorders,
Stora Sköndal, Stockholm

DR. MARCEL MONNIER

Electrophysiology

Chargé de Cours de Neurophysiologie
appliquée, Université de Genève

PROFESSOR JEAN PIAGET

Psychology

Professeur de Psychologie à la Sorbonne
et à l'Université de Genève

DR. A. RÉMOND

Chargé de Recherches, Centre National
de la Recherche Scientifique, Paris

Electrophysiology

DR. R. R. STRUTHERS

Formerly Associate Director
Rockefeller Foundation, Paris

Research promotion

DR. J. M. TANNER

Formerly Senior Lecturer, Sherrington
School of Physiology, St. Thomas's
Hospital
Lecturer, Institute of Child Health
University of London

Human biology

DR. W. GREY WALTER

Director of Research
Burden Neurological Institute, Bristol

Electrophysiology

RENÉ ZAZZO

Directeur du Laboratoire de
Psychobiologie de l'Enfant
Institut des Hautes Etudes, Paris

Psychology

GUESTS

DR. DALBIR BINDRA

Department of Psychology
McGill University
Montreal, Canada

DR. D. BUCKLE

Regional Officer for Mental Health
Regional Office for Europe
World Health Organization
Geneva

PROF. HOWARD LIDDELL

Professor of Psychobiology
Cornell University
Ithaca, U.S.A.

PROF. JOHN W. M. WHITING

Laboratory of Human Development
Harvard University Graduate School of
Education, Cambridge, U.S.A.

PREFACE

Readers of the first volume of this series will know that at its first meeting the W.H.O. Study Group on the Psychobiological Development of the Child based its discussions on a series of presentations each of which covered the general views on child development of one of the various disciplines represented in the membership of the group.

At its second meeting, held in 1954, the group based its discussions on presentations related to a broad common theme—Learning, with special reference to learning under stress and to learning in the immature organism.

The meeting lasted for six working days. Half a day was devoted to the discussion of each presentation.

The topics presented included electro-mechanical models of aspects of learning (Grey Walter), the effects of perceptual deprivation in man and animals (Bindra), learning under stress in animals (Liddell), and the cross-cultural study of learning of internalized standards of behaviour (Whiting).

In addition two films provided material for discussion, the first on motor behaviour patterns in the premature human infant (Lorenz) and the second on the response of a two-year-old child to hospitalization (Bowlby). Other subjects that entered into the discussions included an account of the study of the development of abstraction in learning, by Professor Inhelder, and the measurement of opto-motor-cortical time as a parameter for studying learning, by Dr. Monnier.

The enthusiasm of the group and the ability of the Chairman, Dr. Frank Fremont-Smith, led to a week of far-reaching and vigorous discussion.

Dr. Tanner and Professor Inhelder, the editors of this series, have again undertaken the task of condensing to the dimensions of a single volume the lengthy verbatim transcript of the meeting and have carried it out with a skill that even the victims of their blue pencils admire.

G. R. HARGREAVES

Lately Chief, Mental Health Section
World Health Organization

Leeds University

CONTENTS

PLATES

Introduction

FREMONT-SMITH (Chairman):

Mesdames, Messieurs, may I call this second session to order. We are exceedingly happy that we have our three guests present with us for this meeting. We will not all go through our autobiographies as we did last time (see Vol. 1). But we do want to hear from our guests something as to their background and the interests that led them to attend this Study Group on the Psychobiological Development of the Child.

First let me remind them and all of us as to what we aim at for the mood and technique of these conferences. We are a multi-professional group, each of us trying to stretch our outlook to include some approach to or some aspect of science of which we were ignorant or only dimly aware before. We are trying to *communicate with* each other, not, as in the ordinary scientific meeting, to *make statements at* each other. The two are very different processes.

New ideas, that is, the new findings of others, are likely to produce a certain amount of anxiety, especially if they challenge our area of interest and competence. This is something which it is hard for us to accept—the idea that another scientist would make me feel anxious is rather intolerable—so what one does quite naturally is to suppress this anxiety, and as you know, anxiety suppressed does not disappear, but is transformed very quickly—into hostility. One can take it as a rule of thumb that new ideas from others, challenging our area of interest, almost spontaneously evoke hostility in us. This is why there is such difficulty in communication among scientists, and particularly across the disciplines.

The easiest reply to make to such a hostile idea, or hostility-provoking idea, is to say 'That's nonsense. That's not so, that is not in accordance with the facts'. But with a good friend the position one takes is different: by definition he is somebody who makes sense and whom one wants to communicate with. So instead of saying 'That's nonsense' we would say 'But I could not quite have understood you; I did not have the insight, explain yourself further'. In a group like this what we aim at generating is the diametrical opposite of the psychoanalyst's free-floating anxiety. We need

15

free-floating security, so that instead of having multiple swords of Damocles hovering above the group waiting to plunge we have an atmosphere in which we can say what we like when we like, and in which the ideas of others provoke interest and not hostility.

I will now ask our three guests to introduce themselves.

WHITING:

I think perhaps I should start with my education. In my undergraduate days, except for an introductory freshman's course in biology, I took nothing which anybody might possibly talk about here. I did the easiest courses in history and English literature that I could find. I was an expert poker player, however, and I was captain of the wrestling team.

As a graduate student I started out in the field of sociology at Yale and after the first year I switched over to anthropology. At this time, Edward Sapir and John Dollard were associated with the Department of Anthropology. I got interested in the problem of personality development, or culture and personality, and I read *Coming of Age in Samoa* by DR. MEAD (1928) which had a great influence on me. I became interested not only in anthropology but also in psychology, particularly psychoanalysis, and started to get training in analysis and to carry on work in that field. For my anthropological field work, I went to New Guinea, in Margaret Mead's general territory, and did a study of child training in a group up the Sepik River.

Up to this point I had hardly heard of learning theory. It seems rather strange, therefore, that I am here, presumably, to represent learning theory. I became interested in it about a year after I got my doctor's degree and worked with Hull, primarily at the Institute of Human Relations, and Miller, Sears, Marquis and Mowrer, who were all there at the time.

During this post-doctorate training, I worked on a learning theory problem which was an experimental one. I also tried to apply what I had learnt in New Guinea on child training and child development. That is, I reinterpreted my field notes and the result of this reinterpretation finally came out in a book (WHITING, 1941).

Since that time, I have worked trying to put together cultural anthropology, psychoanalysis and learning theory into a more or less coherent framework so as to understand the development of the child, that is how the child becomes an adult member of society.

After the war, I went to the Child Welfare Research Station of the State University of Iowa, where I started some research with Bob Sears. After a couple of years there, I returned to Harvard with

16

Sears and set up a laboratory with him of which I am now the Director. We continued our work in child development both with data on children in the setting in and around Harvard and from published literature on children around the world. We also sent people into the field to observe children directly.

I think I should end by begging a complete ignorance of biology, but at the other end of the spectrum, I may be joining with many of you here at the psycho- part of psychobiology.

LIDDELL:

I think all of us who continue in the experimental investigation of behaviour become of necessity evolution-minded and history-minded. It is certainly true in my own case.

First a word about the history. My own investigations derive very definitely from the British Isles. At the turn of the century Professor E. A. Schaefer, who later became Sir Edward Sharpey-Schaefer, was doing a classical investigation with his colleague, Oliver, at Edinburgh. It was a study of the effects of injecting adrenal extract into a mammalian preparation specifically to observe the effect on blood pressure. At that time, Professor Schaefer had already changed his interest from neurophysiology and neuroanatomy to the endocrine glands. He was invited to give the Lane Lectures at the University of California Medical School in San Francisco, out of which came his book, *The Endocrine Organs*. He stopped to lecture at the Ithaca Division of the Cornell Medical School, and this School was in search of a professor of physiology. Schaefer recommended Sutherland Simpson, who was his lecturer. Simpson became Professor of Physiology in our medical school in 1909, and I joined him as instructor in 1919.

My own work over these many years with sheep and goats depends upon two modest physiological facts. Firstly, in sheep and goats the inferior parathyroid glands are free in the neck and not embedded in the thyroid, and therefore the removal of the thyroid gland from a lamb or kid three weeks of age is a simple operation under local anaesthetic and parathyroid tetany does not supervene. Secondly, twinning is a frequent occurrence in both sheep and goats. Dr. Simpson put these two facts together. He wished to engage in natural history or case-history physiology—the chronic experiment. So from 1909 until his untimely death in 1925, he was devoted to his new field of endocrinology with special reference to the thyroid, trying through the chronic experiment on the thyroidectomized animal to contribute to clinical endocrinology.

My own academic history is very simple. I entered the University of Michigan, began preparation for medicine, then changed to psychology. My psychology teacher, Professor Pillsbury, had been a pupil of Edward Bradford Tichener of Cornell. I came to Cornell in 1918 as a graduate student of Professor Tichener and received the conventional instruction in structural psychology and learned how to introspect in structural terms. But Tichener conferred on me a great benefit. He saw to it that I took as a minor subject medical physiology. There I encountered Professor Simpson and in due course became his research assistant. His experiments were simple in design and long-continued in operation. He selected twins of the same sex, kids or lambs, thyroidectomized one of the pair at three weeks of age and observed both until the death of the operated animal. Since he could demonstrate most of the signs of athyroidism, he said, 'Since you are a psychologist, it would be interesting to demonstrate the blunted mentality in these thyroidectomized sheep and goats'. But what about the mentality of the sheep and goat? Has it any mentality to be blunted?

I was committed to becoming a psychologist again, because Simpson made me responsible for the animals' behaviour observed day by day in the pasture and the laboratory. Having to teach physiology, I read *Pavlov*'s work on the digestive glands and his Huxley Lecture in the *Lancet* and resolved to apply a really physiological method to this field and be done with the nonsense of psychologizing the sheep and goat. So I began to demonstrate defects in conditioned reflexes in these sluggish thyroidectomized animals, and each time the animal came to the laboratory it became a laboratory preparation and I bid it good-bye at the door; my responsibility for it was done. But it was not that simple. It became necessary to put pedometer watches on the animals to get diurnal activity in the pasture. It also became necessary to study their diurnal fluctuation of body-temperature. Then, insensibly, I came back into what I think is fairly called the field of psychology, and overcame my squeamishness about anthropomorphizing. I think one can say that in studying an animal, homology may throw light on behaviour as it does on structure. The sheep is not a man; nevertheless, we can freely empathize; we have our own view as to how we would regard the situation if we were in the animals' place; and we have taken this matter seriously. Every single procedure which we apply to our animals in the Pavlovian situation we try on ourselves, and this has led to important clues.

It might interest some of you to know my own contact with the word psychobiology. I heard this word first in 1919—I think at the American Psychological Association on a conference on nomenclature. Robert Yerkes insisted on inserting the word 'psychobiology' as an acceptable psychological term. No-one else paid any attention to it. Yerkes, however, persevered, and he is now Emeritus Professor of Psychobiology at Yale. Then the issue was confused by Professor Adolf Meyer, the Director of the Phipps Clinic at Hopkins who caused his school of psychiatry to be known as psychobiology. Adolf Meyer also supported experimental psychobiological work with animals in his clinic, where W. Horsley Gantt still continues Pavlovian conditioning.

BINDRA:

My undergraduate work was done in India at Punjab University, where I specialized in zoology and psychology. For my graduate work I went to Harvard and worked with Boring and Allport. The subject of my doctoral dissertation was hoarding behaviour of rats. After obtaining my degree in 1947, I went down to teach in a small American university in Washington, D.C. A couple of years later I joined Professor Hebb at McGill and have been there since.

My interests in psychology at the present time revolve around the theory of emotion and motivation. My research makes use of both human and animal subjects. Our general approach to all problems involves developmental (ontogenetic) and phylogenetic comparisons. I must admit that at McGill our idea of phylogenetic comparisons is that of comparisons between rat, cat, dog, chimpanzee and man, and Dr. Lorenz's discussions of sub-mammalian animals makes us feel guilty for our sins of omission.

So much for my research interests. Another side-interest that I have followed for some years is that of scientific method, and I feel that a consideration of the relation between common sense and science is particularly relevant to discussions of many psychological problems. My feeling is that psychological concepts, on the whole, are still more or less common-sense concepts and have not been developed to any degree of precision. These common-sense psychological concepts are undoubtedly very useful in everyday life and are useful in clinical practice; but they are not good enough for scientific purposes. By way of analogy, consider a layman's concept of hot and cold: it is a cold day outside or it is a warm day outside. These judgments of cold and warmth are very useful, they tell you whether or not you need to wear a coat; but any scientific treatment of cold or warmth will have to be in terms of certain dimensions such as temperature, humidity, wind velocity and things of that kind. Many psychological concepts in the area of emotion and motivation are common sense concepts, such as fear, anger, jealousy, anxiety, and I feel that unless we are able somehow to replace these

19

I

concepts by more precise ones, analogous to those of the physicist's temperature, humidity, and so on, we will probably continue to run into difficulties. This is relevant to the difficulty which has been mentioned by Dr. Rémond. It is the difficulty of relating EEG measures to psychological or behavioural concepts. The reason we are unable to relate anxiety, anger, fear, and so forth to electro-physiological measures lies partly in the vagueness of these psychological concepts. It is the psychologist's task to refine psychological concepts before asking for electro-physiological correlates of psychological events.

FIRST DISCUSSION

Presentation:
Dr. Grey Walter

GREY WALTER:

To begin with, I want to put before you the proposition that the psychobiological development of living creatures can occur in six ways:

1. Genetic evolution (mutation, selection, etc.)
2. Reflexive action (tropisms, archisms, taxias)
3. Instinct (innate releasing mechanisms, imprinting, etc.)
4. Practice (learning by repetition)
5. Learning by association (conditioned reflexes)
6. Social communication (insect up to human communities)

I do not say it can occur only in six ways, though I am rather inclined to believe this is true, and that there is no other way possible. I should like to include with 'living creatures' perhaps also 'artificial creatures', such as we shall discuss in a moment.

The first proposition which I am maintaining is that these six methods of change or development are the largest single categories we can recognize for convenience in study, though in fact we know that these six categories mingle in an extremely elaborate way. The division into six is based not on an arbitrary criterion but on the empirical one of experiment. One can detect differences between the mechanisms and recognize each by quite diagnostic traits. One of the virtues of this systematization is that it helps one to list and understand one by one the important factors in development which depend upon a nervous system.

In order to decide what the nervous system *must* be able to do apart from what it *might* be able to do, it is useful to recall the capacity of plants. Of the six methods of development that I have listed, I suggest that plants possess only the first and second, and perhaps in some cases the third. The first method of development

21

is that of *genetic evolution*. Mutation and selection are included here, and all methods which involve change of character or behaviour from individual to individual, whether or not this necessarily results in the development of a new species. Evolution of this type does not depend essentially on the nervous system.

The second category of development I have called *reflexive action*. This use of the word 'reflexive' is my own choice and in it I include both the artificial reflexes of the laboratory of classical Sherringtonian type and the tropistic, archistic and taxistic responses such as occur for example in infusoria, in insects, and also in plants. There are many examples of plants which devour and digest a variety of foodstuffs, which orientate themselves to the sun, adapt themselves to a support up which they climb and so forth. A nervous system is not essential for reflexive action but its possession does permit a much wider variety of reflexive modes than we find in plants.

In the third category labelled *instinct*, I include all the types of behaviour which Lorenz and his ethological colleagues have made, if not familiar, at least very attractive to us. I feel more and more inclined to study this type of behaviour and its physiological concomitants and I think we shall soon see the way in which this can be done. Instinct can at least be defined clearly and the sort of nervous system that is necessary and perhaps sufficient for behaviour of this type can also be to some extent defined.

The fourth heading is *practice (learning by repetition)*. This is difficult to define in detail, but perhaps I can dispose of it now by saying that change of behaviour by repetition is at once so trivial and so profound that it has almost nothing to do with the unique properties of animal behaviour. The improvement in performance which occurs when any mechanism whatever continues to work is universal in occurrence. As examples, I suggest the running-in of machinery, the erosion of a river bed by a river, the change in a billiard table after it has been played on, the change of the shape of shoes after wearing—the change induced in any one system by contact and coupling with another. In the true animal systems this type of change by repetition, which we call practice, has special characteristics and I certainly do not mean to deprecate the importance and beauty of it. But it is not a specifically organic or animal property. This is sometimes forgotten. The improvement of performance as rated in the laboratory situation is often the same as improvement of performance in any mechanism turned on for the first time and allowed to run in, and to regard this as having a special property and a special interest may, in certain circumstances, rather confuse the issue and make experiments harder to understand and more difficult also to repeat.

22

BINDRA:

In this item, learning by repetition, do you include such things as fatigue?

GREY WALTER:

No, not necessarily. In some particular case there might be evidence that the effect was a running-down rather than running-in, but these are not the same.

BINDRA:

Fatigue does refer to behavioural modification resulting from repetition. But I see that if you did include fatigue under 'change in performance with repetition' it would complicate your scheme.

GREY WALTER:

I do not include fatigue unless there is some special reason; for example unless fatigue was the result of practice, when it could be included as a running-in process. But 'fatigue' designating stocks of metabolites exhausted, say, or the failure of a membrane potential, that is not learning by repetition. That is a much more complex process.

BINDRA:

You are restricting your category to *learning* by repetition?

GREY WALTER:

It has to be a change in behaviour which occurs by repetition of an act and which also is *adaptive*, that is permits tighter coupling between organism and environment.

BINDRA:

But, then, does the shoe that fits better after use fall into this category?

GREY WALTER:

Yes. Your foot may 'learn' to fit the shoe. That would be the same process.

BINDRA:

That is learning?

23

GREY WALTER:

No. I would not call a process which involves merely practice 'learning'. Learning is a rather precious word and I should restrict it to the other types such as I am describing. ECCLES (1953) has shown that some degree of practice effect can be detected even in the spinal cord reflex system. He isolated a reflex preparation for a long period and then applied a stimulus and found improvement by repetition of the stimulus. He does regard this as learning. That practice can occur at the spinal level is an important observation, but I do not regard it as any more significant than the fact that if you allow a machine to rust and then use it again, it will be some time before it gets up to its maximum speed.

The fifth category I define as *learning by association*, of which the main example in the scientific field is generally called a conditioned reflex. A large part of my contribution will be about this. It introduces notions which I find hard to understand because I am extremely inept at devising or comprehending mathematical notations, and the algebra involved in the mathematical aspect of their study is formidably complex. For me it is easier to consider these problems in the form of a mechanical embodiment or model of the equations.

PIAGET:

May I interrupt? To make clear the difference between (4) and (5), would you agree that (4) is what one usually calls 'exercise' in French and (5) 'acquired experience'?

GREY WALTER:

No. I should say my discrimination between the two would depend upon number five including adaptation to two series of events, not one. Learning by practice, or the running-in of machines, depends simply on the repetition of a certain action which wears down resistances, obstructions and so forth and makes for smoother running. Whereas number five, as I shall show in some detail, depends upon the adaptation to a combined contingency of *two* series of events.

The sixth category, which again is defined too crudely to bear repetition outside this circle, is *social communication*—the development of creatures by means of social intercourse. Even in the lowliest animals there is some indication of social development. Insects display it to an intense degree. For social communication to occur it is far from essential to have a very complex central nervous system though whether one can reasonably imagine social plants seems to me doubtful.

These six categories are operational divisions which are based upon the possibilities of recognizing the differences between them. In any real case, however, all these factors are entangled, and it is very difficult to design an experiment in which any one of them is reasonably faithfully magnified without distorting the others, or in which all the others are removed without distorting the single factor that you want to study. Most of us here have attempted at one time or another in our experimental lives to isolate a single factor in the classical tradition of the experimental physiologist. Such is classical physiology, classical chemistry, and classical physics, but never classical psychobiology. That is our difficulty. It is no good saying; try to isolate a single variable. In isolating it we are destroying the system we are studying, and efforts to record just one factor very carefully and very accurately over a very long time are of academic interest only, and tell us more about the experimenter than about the subject.

In the application of electrophysiological methods one stumbles at the threshold over an extremely awkward barrier, that of technical description—how to display to untutored eyes changes in time and space of a dozen or two dozen variables. For us who work in electrophysiology to convey to you, not merely the nature of our studies, but also their range and reliability means that we would have to introduce you to some of the extremely tedious technical tricks which we use. We would have to confess to you the degree of our inaccuracy; to take you with us to our laboratories and say: 'This we can measure, that—not yet'. We should have to inflict upon you a shortened intense course in electrical technology. The years since the last war are an unfortunate stage in this work. In ten or twenty years we shall have as much confidence in telling you what we have seen as the astronomer describing the nature of some remote galaxy, or the spectrum of a star. He does not have to instruct us in the principles of the spectroscope or the telescope, he just has to tell us there is a galaxy which is such and such a size moving at such a velocity, and we believe him. Electrophysiologists, however, are still in the embarrassing technical stage, when we wish to participate in meetings of this sort, of having either to sell an idea in a bag, or describe very exactly what the bag is made of. I am going to do neither of these things, but if anyone would like to have more information or if, during the weekend, anyone would like to see for themselves the hardware that churns out these results, they are very welcome to come to visit us in Bristol! If you enjoy hardware we can give you a good time. But there is not the slightest reason why you should come into the ironmongery shop at all.

If one avoids this ironmongery, one comes to an alternative way

25

of describing the results obtained. From our observations and the hunches we have had in studying human beings in relation to the subject of this conference, we have built up a number of hypotheses, and I am going to asseverate that when one has a notion which purports to explain observed phenomena, one has a right to turn one's hypotheses into a model. The observation of these models has the same degree of validity as the study of animals, if you are relating your studies to human problems. In studying animals one is studying what one supposes to be a model of human behaviour, and one is perfectly at liberty to anthropomorphize—'the animal does so and so, and this is what I feel when I do the same thing'—if it makes thinking clearer and more vivid and makes the hypotheses more precise and conclusive.

The same applies to the study of a model. A model, provided it fulfils certain criteria, can be just as useful, just as helpful, and in some cases almost as charming, as the animal which it replaces. But the scientific laws one has to obey in making models are very strict. The first is the principle of parsimony; that entities must not be multiplied beyond necessity; in making a model, you must not include a single redundant part or component, you must not have a lot of frills that are not necessary. You must take away anything superfluous from the model and see if it still works and if it does then you have to think again. This can be quite a tedious process.

Here I might possibly mention some of the devices quoted as being models of human behaviour, that is, electronic computing machines. We have all heard of, and many of us have seen or used, computers of various types. I think that the tendency to use these electronic devices as models of brain activity and human behaviour is an unfortunate one, because these computers do not observe the principle of parsimony. They are enormous things with a vast quantity of redundant parts, designed particularly to do well what we do badly—addition sums and so forth—and being designed to do exactly the things which we find extremely difficult, they bear no more relation to the human brain than a hacksaw does to the human hand. Their enormous number of superfluous components rules out their interest as models of the sort of things we are talking about.

It may help us to see why the models I am going to show are different from computing machines if I discuss for a short while the nature of various systems of communication. Most computing machines operate on a binary system, the system in which there are only two possible assertions: yes and no, one and zero. A large part of mathematical computation can be handled on this basis, and many questions of logic also.

Another system which has been developed, oddly enough more

26

recently, has been particularly profitable in the hands of UTTLEY (1954), an engineer-physicist at the Radar Research Establishment in Malvern. This system is a unitary one, it can only say 'yes' and that is all. In other words, nothing does not mean 'no', it means nothing.

There is a third category which one can call the plenary system. This is really much more relevant to our problem, because it resembles more closely the sort of thing that happens in our experience. An example of a plenary system is an ordinary telephone system. If you dial a number, several things can happen. Suppose you are a burglar and you are doing what they call in England 'sounding the drum', that is you are ringing up a house to see if there is anyone at home. You dial, and if the person answers that is all you want to know and you hang up. This is, of course, a 'yes' response; but in a telephone system a number of other things may happen. You may hear the bell ring but get no answer. This tells you nothing at all except that the bell is ringing. You may get a wrong number; you may get complete silence, the number may be engaged, or there may be a fault. That is a plenary system in which 'yes' and five ways of saying 'no' exist. This is much more like our experiments. You feed your animal and the response may appear or all sorts of other things may happen instead. If the animal does not respond you do not know whether it is dead, tired, sleepy, if you have stimulated it properly, if it has already been stimulated, or if it just is not interested.

The models I have brought with me are mostly unitary systems. They are the simplest. One model, however, is a plenary system in which almost anything may happen, apart from the simplest response of 'yes'. This has rather interesting relations to logic and semantics. If you say to somebody, 'Do you understand me?', and they say, 'Yes', that conveys no information at all. If they say, 'No', that probably does. If you say, 'Can you hear me?' and they say, 'No', what information can that convey?

The next stipulation in model-making is that one must know more than one feature of the system one is going to copy. This may sound childish, but it is often forgotten. If one wants to make a model of a bicycle, one must know more than that it has two wheels. A great many things have two wheels, but not all of them are bicycles. But, if one makes a thing which has two wheels and can be ridden, the chances are it will be a bicycle. However, if you make something that can be ridden, it need not have two wheels. An important and often forgotten point about the making of hypotheses or models is that you cannot make a model of something very simple. For example, if one wants to make a model of a seesaw, well, the model of a seesaw is a seesaw.

The third very stringent requirement, of course, is that a model must be found to reproduce more than has been put into it, which is the same thing exactly as saying that a hypothesis must permit prediction. It is no good if your model does something curious which you cannot understand; it must actively develop some mode of behaviour which you had not thought of first and had not deliberately built into it and which enables you to see that the thing it is a model of must show the same unexpected behaviour.

I have not attempted to make models of the first and fourth of the methods of development which I have listed (genetic adaptation and practice adaptation) and for various reasons I do not think they are worth making at the present time.

I will carry on now with the description of the first model I want to show you, which will be available during the rest of the meeting if anybody would like to play with it. This model demonstrates purposive behaviour and the first proposition I am going to put to you is a very general one; that so-called purposive behaviour can be defined in terms of reflexive action without recourse to transcendental teleology. It is an important first principle to establish that the so-called 'purpose' which, until recently, was always regarded as an essential and intrinsic diagnostic attribute of animals does not depend on and is not diagnostic of the presence of an elaborate nervous system as such.

The second proposition I wish to make is this: that the classification by a purposive mechanism of experience as relating to 'self' or 'not-self' is bound to occur when the reflexive circuit includes an environmental operator. (An operator is an indication of how two or more terms influence one another. A multiplication sign is a simple operator which says how two numbers are to be joined. In this particular case, the operator I am referring to tells us how the organism and its environment are to be joined together.) The proposition here is that the responses which are characteristic of the organism noting its own existence are distinguishable from the responses that occur when the organism notes that something outside itself has happened.

The third proposition, which depends on the same mechanisms, is that one gets the impression of social organization; the setting-up of a social complex is bound to occur when two or more reflexive mechanisms of the type previously defined interact one with another. What I am saying is that, if you construct reflexive mechanisms, then these two things, the classification of 'self' and 'not-self', and the formation of a social organization, are bound to occur. In other words, these two processes are predictable from the purposive nature of the mechanism, and you require no more information than that the mechanism is purposive to foresee the recognition of self and not-self and the formation of a society.

This model is a unitary system and contains two elements. It is like an animal with two nerve cells, each of which is a unitary system. It either says yes, or it says nothing. It has been described in detail elsewhere (WALTER, 1953) but it is as well to remember that in a system with n elements, the possible number of modes of behaviour is $2^{(n^2-n)}$. That means if we had six neurones in our brain, or six nerve elements (which might have many neurones in each), we should have enough elements in our heads to provide us with a new sensation every tenth of a second for the whole of our lives. Such is the richness of inter-connexion. The expression is exact only when n is a large number; it is only approximately true when n is less than 10. As you can see, this is an explosive series; it is one of the interesting consequences of this type of model-making—though I realized it only after I started making these toys—that a very small number of nerve elements would provide for an extremely rich life.

I am now going to show some pictures of one or two of these unitary, two-element creatures. They are designed merely to indicate how complicated the structure of behaviour can be, even when the anatomical structure is simple. The thing to look at in all these pictures is the trace of the line of light which is the track of the creature under various conditions.

The particular creature illustrated in Fig. 1 (facing p. 64) has two receptors, one of which is sensitive to light and the other to touch. In Fig. 2 (p. 64) we see the response to light. The light is the goal that the track leads to; you see that the creature has a tropism, confined to a response to light. The choice of light in this particular model is of some importance because it is very easy to make light represent food; these models 'eat' electrons, and where there are electrons there can be light. They will chase light and where light happens to be associated with a suitable supply of electricity, there they will plug themselves in and charge their batteries should they require to do so. When nourishment is over they will leave the feeding trough and wander about in search of adventure. The specific name for this' animal is *Machina speculatrix*—the Spying Machine. They have one unit of curiosity. They are capable of investigation and will explore as long as they retain their power, only desisting when their metabolism is strained beyond bearing.

In Fig. 3A (overleaf, p. 30) we have a slight complication in the situation to which these creatures are subjected. Here the creature, starting at the bottom, catches a glimpse of the distant light, a candle

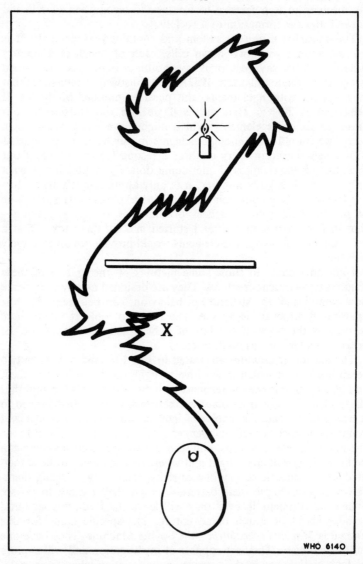

WHO 6140

on the other side of an opaque screen. The creature starts off for a moment in the direction of the light, but is very quickly baffled by the fire-screen which cuts out the light. It then makes a circle round to the left. At the point marked X an accident occurred which is characteristic of model hypotheses. To make these photographs an ordinary kitchen candle was stuck on the creature's back and at point X the creature caught sight of the reflection of its own candle in the polished fire-screen; so there it stuck, and it took some time for it to make a readaptation and concentrate on its goal. However, it finally circled around the fire-screen and got into an orbit round the attractive light. This indicates the way in which having once got a line on some possible attraction, the creature will take it up again, even after it has lost sight of the original goal. It has no power to remember, no power to adapt in the sense of the later categories I spoke of; it only contains tropistic reflexive mechanisms.

FREMONT-SMITH:

How does it keep after the light?

GREY WALTER:

If you have a scanning device, a rotating photo-cell, then once it gets on to a line it will tend to pick up that line again within a reasonable time. The same unfortunately is true of self-guided missiles. If a missile is aimed at London and interrupted by some counter-force, it is easy to make it take up the line again, after the perturbing force has been circumvented. This is characteristic of quite a simple system without storage.

In Fig. 3B (p. 32) is an arrangement in which the creature starts at the bottom of the picture and is attracted towards the candle again at the top; but in between there is a low obstacle over which it can see the light, but through which it cannot move. It has to circumvent this obstacle and its touch mechanism comes into operation. It starts off straight towards the candle, it touches the box and dodges it by a series of backing and butting movements. At the point marked by an arrow there arises by sheer accident a storage system; if A represents one element and B the other, the feedback mechanism A B A B A, etc., occurs. This has brief storage, so that if the model encounters an obstacle it will not only avoid it, but will go on doing so until it is clear of the obstacle, a consequence of the way the act is done and not of the way the machine is designed. One of the predictions of this hypothesis is that if a reflexive mechanism which is capable of two modalities or sensations is engaged in one modality, it will not, at the same time, be able to cope with the other. In other words, in this particular case it is 'more important' for the creature to circumvent a material obstacle than to chase a distant light, and the circumventing of the obstacle immediately cuts out the photo-electric responsiveness.

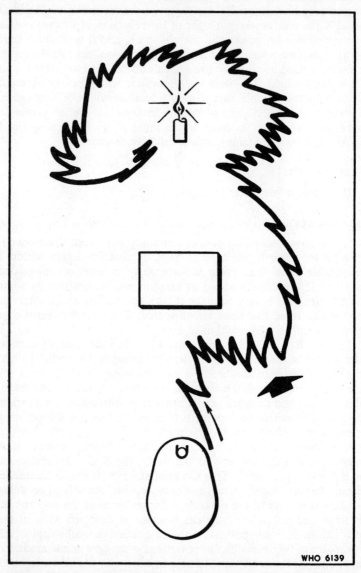

WHO 6139

The remaining pictures show situations of increasing complexity and difficulty for the model. Fig. 4, I think, brings the thing a little bit nearer to the field of biology, because here we have evidence that a system with two elements of a reflexive nature may have a tendency

32

PHOTO-CELL ---- TOUCH

FIG. 1

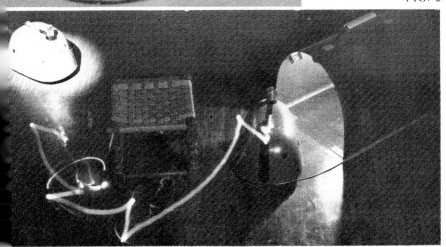

FIG. 2

8 A

I.R.M.A.

ON OFF   INF.   AGE

FIG. 11

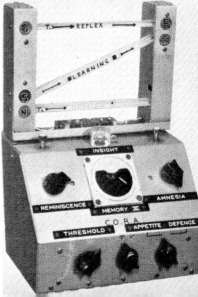

REFLEX

LEARNING

INSIGHT

REMINISCENCE   MEMORY III   AMNESIA

C.O.R.A.

THRESHOLD   APPETITE   DEFENCE

FIG. 12

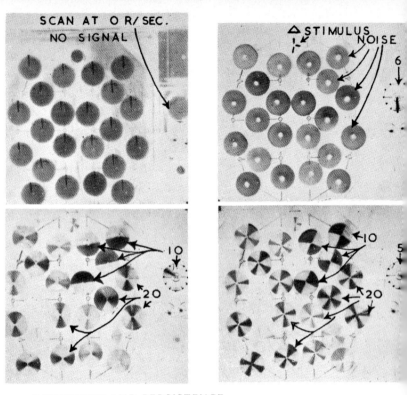

SCAN AT 0 R/SEC.
NO SIGNAL

△ STIMULUS
NOISE

6

10

20

5

10

20

DISPERSION AND PERSISTENCE

OPEN

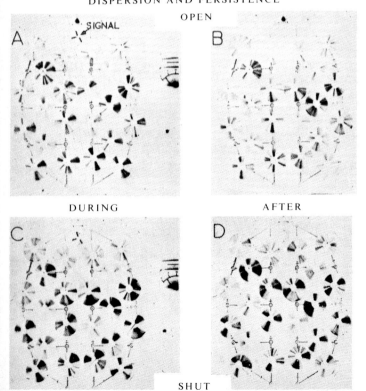

SIGNAL

A

B

FIG. 13

DURING

AFTER

C

D

SHUT

FIG. 4

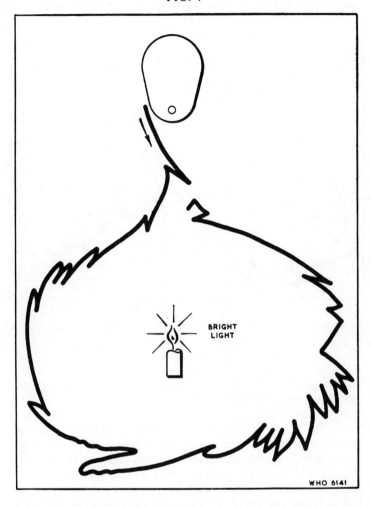

BRIGHT
LIGHT

WHO 6141

to seek an *optimum* and not a maximum. We have a very powerful attraction—a sixty-watt light bulb instead of a candle. The model starts, in this case, at the top of the picture and it chases towards the bright light source. But it reaches a point—the first squiggle—where the light becomes too bright. It then starts to circle round and maintains itself in an orbit of moderate brightness. It does not seek maximum illumination and run into the candle. An interesting point about this is that this moderation is attenuated, or even terminated,

FIG. 5

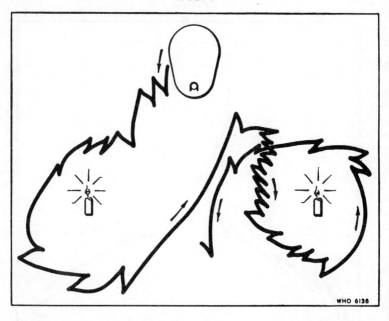

WHO 6138

by appetite. If the creature gets 'hungry'—its batteries run down and
it needs more electrons—then this extremely circumspect behaviour
in relation to powerful stimulation begins to dwindle and finally it
runs right into the light. This may have some relation to the behaviour of certain animals we know of who tend to become less moderate
as their needs become greater.

Fig. 5 has a lesson for the philosophers among us, if there are any.
This is the solution by a two-element model of what has been called
the dilemma of Buridan's Ass. The dilemma, as conventionally
stated, is that of a creature which does not possess free will, when it
is faced with two exactly equal and equidistant stimuli; it is then
not able to choose between the two alternatives and will die of hunger
before it decides which of these two alternatives to accept as a
stimulus.

This particular model has a scanning device in order to have
freedom of movement. It also has a very interesting property in that
it lives in Bergsonian and not Newtonian time. Newtonian time is
reversible; the Newtonian solar system could be run backwards and
it would be exactly the same as it is now. But Bergsonian time cannot
be run backwards; all organisms live in Bergsonian time; time for
us, as we all know, has an arrow. That arrow points to the grave;

34

FIG. 6

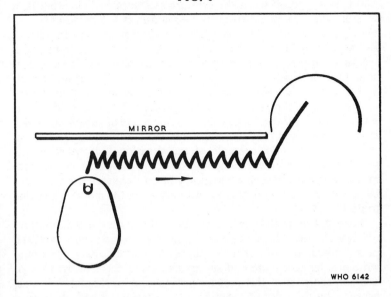

that may be deplorable, but it has one important advantage, that with it we can solve Buridan's dilemma. We have the creature again starting at the top of the picture. There are two candles which are about equidistant; they may be precisely so. The creature is released at the top and it happened to see the light on the left first. The spatial symmetry is not also symmetrical in time, so the effect of a scanning machine is to solve all dilemmas which involve symmetries in space. One of the signals must be seen first, and the one which is seen first is the one visited first. The creature explores the possibilities; when it gets close to the first light its moderation mode is invoked and it wanders across and does the same thing with the other light; it forms a figure-of-eight diagram. So our two-element model, which is essentially a reflexive mechanism richly inter-connected with a scanning device, can solve the dilemma of Buridan's ass, and would not die between sources of nourishment.

With Fig. 6 we come to some of the refinements which emerged only some time after these creatures had been made. This mode of behaviour and the next one were, quite frankly, surprising to us though, of course, we ought to have been able to predict them. Fig. 6 illustrates the situation when a creature of this type is confronted by its reflection in a mirror. It has on its nose a small pilot light, put in originally to tell us what was happening inside; it is so arranged

35

that it is turned .off when the creature sees another light; that is, it tells us when the photo-tropistic mechanism is in operation.

In this case, the light which the creature was allowed to see was its own pilot light in the mirror. In this situation, the act of 'seeing' it makes it automatically extinguish the light which it sees. The apparent stimulus light having been extinguished, it turns it on again, then off and so on, so that you get a characteristic oscillation. You can see how peculiar and regular it is by the zigzag going up the side of the mirror. This is an absolutely characteristic mode of behaviour, which is seen always and only when the creature is responding to its own reflection. This is an example of the situation I described in the second proposition, where the reflexive circuit includes an environmental operator; in such a situation you get a characteristic mode of behaviour which occurs always and only when the model is reacting to itself.

Now, put yourselves in the position of a biologist exploring an unknown island. He comes across a hard-shelled creature; when he puts a mirror in front of it, it behaves in a specific way. He would write a letter to *Nature* and say he had evidence of recognition of 'self' on the part of this mollusc, crustacean, or whatever it was, because, by the rules of scientific interpretation he had observed a 'diagnostic' character.

Let us now apply this to a society of two individuals; only two because more than two is hopelessly complex. The two are placed a little distance apart on the floor and allowed to 'play'. Remember that each of them has a pilot light in its nose; in other words, each can see the other. Remember also that in seeing the other's pilot light it turns its own off, and you have the situation in which each of the creatures is capable of seeing the other, but in doing so becomes invisible. Then you have a very interesting waltz. The two circle around one another at a respectful distance; they never quite escape, nor can they ever consummate the attraction, because the moment they actually touch, the touch mechanism is put into operation and they recoil from one another only to be re-attracted. Just to demonstrate how like they are to certain societies with which we are familiar—I turned on the feeding light during the middle of this social pattern. The immediate effect of that was to break up the social pattern and instead of co-operative pattern-weaving you got competitive straight lines.

These are all unitary systems, which are the simplest possible devices which could behave like this at all. You see here evidence of some rudimentary trace of social organization, sensitive to a stimulus which breaks up the social pattern by attracting the individuals, changing them into a hustling line of people waiting to get into the feeding-trough. Note too that in a condition in which the need for nourishment is small, the competition would be less. In other words, if these animals' batteries were very well charged, they would display moderation, would not get too near the bright light and would carry on the social routine in reasonable security, even in the presence of a bright light, with only occasional interruptions. But the moment they began to get fatigued then they would start to be fiercely and mercilessly competitive.

These pictures are designed to suggest the various possibilities in this type of study as applied to the simplest elements and rudiments of organization at the lowest level. These models illustrated so far have no memory and no power for social adaptation. They have reflexes, but no instincts. They have simply two reflexes with two receptors. They are self-maintaining, but they could not learn the best places to find food; it would be a matter of trial and error on each occasion. They are unitary, not plenary systems, and they are in every way as simple and as basic and, I hope, as easy to understand as they can be. They could not be any simpler and be of interest; if one took out one element or receptor they would lose any resemblance to a living creature.

(*Machina speculatrix* was then demonstrated.)

FREMONT-SMITH:

If we came upon this animal in the desert, how long would it take to understand it?

GREY WALTER:

Several of its generations unless you could dissect it. It is an interesting point of analysis that one cannot tell exactly what has happened inside it. You would have to kill it, work out its anatomy, dissect it and then see. It is interesting that when put in a pen with one way out it will always find its way out, by trial and error, though it has no intelligence, no insight and no cognition. One cannot predict its behaviour exactly, one can only categorically say that it will do such and such a sort of thing, one can define the end but cannot predict the means. As a corollary to that, no two creatures are exactly the same, even if one makes them as much alike as possible in components.

FREMONT-SMITH:

Why would not two behave exactly alike?

37

GREY WALTER:

They are so richly inter-connected. The slightest imperfection or variation is amplified vectorially, so you could start two at exactly the same position in relation to light and so forth and every time the scanner turned round in one it would be a micro-second sooner or later than the other's, and that would bring it to a new position and the differences would multiply cumulatively.

BOWLBY:

Why does it keep going round?

GREY WALTER:

It is looking for more lights. If you imagine a world which this thing is adapted to, and in which there are charging devices for its batteries, it would be important for it not to get stuck on one; it has a much better chance of being fed when it has several sources of food. It would wander around the room and always be near feeding sources. It is always looking for better and better light; it is never satisfied. If you made one of these things adapted to live in a tropical climate, you could make the shell of photo-electric cells and it would charge itself in the sun. It would be important for it to find a place where the sun's light was bright and steady, not between trees or houses, but a wide expanse of light; it would always seek this out and then sit and charge. At night it would have to collect dew-distilled water, so it would find two places, one where it could collect light and another where it could collect dew for its batteries; that is all it needs.

FREMONT-SMITH:

How many circuits are there in it?

GREY WALTER:

In this one there are two. The construction and circuit diagram are given in Fig. 7.

FREMONT-SMITH:

How many units are there in each circuit?

GREY WALTER:

Just one, but the systems have the capacity for inter-connexion, so that we may have either A, or B, or (A and B) or A→B or B→A or A⇌B. We have six modes of behaviour, excluding zero.

38

FIG. 7

THE ELECTRIC CIRCUIT OF *M. Speculatrix*

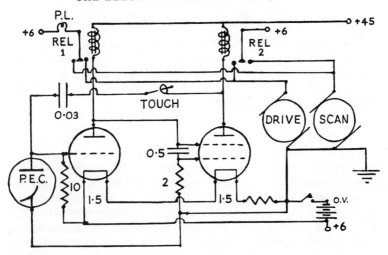

BINDRA:

What is its name?

GREY WALTER:

This one is called Olga, the beautiful spy. This spying machine was made for this type of demonstration with a transparent and rather glamorous coat, and a well-proportioned body!

BOWLBY:

It is sensitive to light and negative to touch, is it not?

GREY WALTER:

It does not see the light when it is touching something. The whole carapace is mobile and is the touch receptor.

LORENZ:

Could you explain the mechanism to us in a few words?

GREY WALTER:

Yes, quite easily. The batteries, which supply its motive power, also provide a grid bias, the voltage of which holds the valve just on.

When the batteries go down, the bias goes down and so the mode of moderation which requires both valves to work disappears.

LORENZ:

The threshold is determined by a summation between the stimulus received and the 'internal stimulus' of its present grid tension? When the grid tension is very low, even the addition of a very strong light stimulus will not be sufficient to reach the threshold of its 'turning away reaction'. Have I got this right?

GREY WALTER:

Yes. When the shell touches something the switch is closed which connects the output of the amplifier back to its input and produces a multi-vibrator circuit. The sensitivity to light is lost, and the steering-scanning motor is alternatively on full and half-power and the driving motor at the same time on half and full-power. The effect of this is to produce a turn-and-push manoeuvre. The time-constant of the feedback circuit is selected to give about one-third of the time on 'steer-hard and push-gently' and two-thirds of 'push-hard-steer-gently'. This seems to give a prompt response to the first contact with an obstacle, a reasonable chance of getting through a gap and a short after-discharge to ensure final escape. Though there is no direct attraction to light in the obstacle-avoiding state, the feedback time-constant is shorter when the photo-cell is illuminated, so that when an obstacle is met in the dark the drill is done in a leisurely fashion, but when there is an attractive light nearby the movements are more hasty.

From now on we get into very much deeper water, because we now embark on the subject of adaptation by imprinting, by instinct and by association. When Lorenz was with us in Bristol about a year ago, I said that when we next met I would have a model of imprinting to show him, and I have brought one with me. One difficulty is that the definition of imprinting, and its discrimination from other types of behaviour, is still a bit difficult. However, I have made a model which Lorenz may say is not in fact a model of imprinting at all, but it is a model of something, and it has some interesting properties.

Originally I intended to attach it to this moving toy, but the situation gets incredibly complicated when you have a model of imprinting, or, as you shall see later, of learning by association, actually moving round the room. It is as bad as bringing a small

THE 'NEURONIC' CIRCUIT OF I.R.M.A. THE HEAVILY-DRAWN LINE REPRESENTS THE CIRCUIT MAINTAINING SUB-THRESHOLD TONIC ACTIVITY AT THE INPUT CELLS IN LAYER III

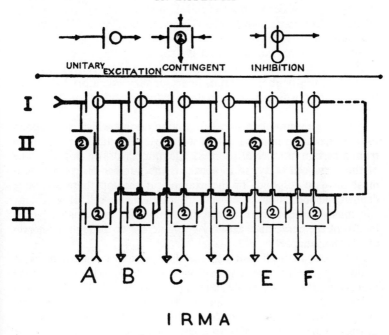

I R M A

kitten or sheep into the room and trying to explain what it is doing. So I detached the learning apparatus from the moving model and what I am going to show now are preparations rather than complete working models. Making a model of imprinting was not at all easy; it had to be simple enough to be instructive yet close enough to the original to be convincing. The model I finished with is certainly sufficient to show some of the features of instinctive responses and particularly of imprinting, but whether it could be simpler, I am not yet sure. Whether it is the only one that would work I do not know either. It is up to other people to make and play with similar arrangements, but it has two or three secondary characters which were unexpected, and which I think are interesting, for they suggest experiments to see whether in fact in any animal systems of this sort exist.

Before I show you the actual model, I think I will show you its neuronic circuit. (Figs. 8A, facing p. 32 and 8B, above.)

This model is called I.R.M.A. It consists of two networks which are arranged, for convenience, in three layers labelled I, II and III. This might conceivably be helpful in neuro-anatomical analysis, because it suggests that for instinctive, innate releasing mechanism (I.R.M.) type of behaviour one should look for a minimum of three levels, or three ganglia or layers of functioning elements. The essence of this system is that it contains one cascade chain of neurones or functional elements in layers. At the top are the conventional signs used in making up these neuronic analogues of electrical circuits. Top left is the symbol for an ordinary unitary excitatory synapse, a bar and circle, which is easier to draw than the conventional reversed arrow.

A contingent unitary synapse or junction is one which can respond to or transmit an impulse only if it receives simultaneous activation from a certain number of sources. The number drawn in the middle of the nerve-cell body, so to speak, is the number of excitations it must have to respond. In the example at the top there are three dendritic arborizations, as it were, round the nerve-cell, of which any two must be active for it to respond. Inhibition is indicated by the tendril of the nerve fibre actually going across or through the nerve-cell of the synapse.

In the circuit itself you will see that there is in heavy black, a chain of synapses all excitatory, which ends up with a very long process, an 'axon' if you like, which provides activity for all the cells in layer III. There could be an indefinite number of such elements in layer III though I have included only six. So we have a series or cascade of neurones leading to a large chunk of nerve tissue on the input side of the nervous system. The inputs are indicated by arrows. As it is a formal model, the receptors are simple push-buttons, though they could perfectly well be photo-electric cells or microphones, or whatever you please. The output to the reflex response system can be imagined as terminating in an effector. This model is so arranged that when the system is born, that is, turned on in the electrical sense, nothing whatever happens at first. But if a signal arrives from outside, that is if one of the buttons on any of these circuits is pressed, it has two effects. It activates its own circuit, which is already receiving one unit of activity through the cascade system, and requires two units. This unit of afferent activity plus the unit of 'tonic' activity succeeds in exciting the nerve-cell. This then immediately inhibits the corresponding cell in the chain in layer I, and activates the cell in layer II, and in so doing, it turns off the tonic supply from all but itself, and diverts the whole supply to itself.

This is the basic principle of the system; when it is turned on at low level, if nothing happens outside, nothing happens inside. But if you press a button, then that one immediately has a unique effect, and the effect of all the other buttons thereafter is minimal. They may still produce some reflex action, but the effect upon the total activity (which I define simply as the amount of information circulating in the nervous system) is great only if the original button is pressed. If you came into the room and did not know which stimulus had been given first, you could discover this by pressing one button after another to find which one has the exaggerated effect.

There are two interesting secondary properties of this system, which I think are relevant, because they seem to remind one of the effects which Lorenz has described. The first is that this system will be extremely sensitive to the action of very slight perturbations of its metabolism. The reason is that the provision of a number of elements in series provides for amplification of effects, such as those, for example, of a drug. Consider a drug which in a given concentration has been found to reduce the probability of passage of an impulse across a single synapse by 50 per cent.; any impulses which do get across the first synapse will also have one-half as the probability of getting across the next one; and so on. When the final response depends upon transmission through a cascade system of this kind, any agency which reduces the chance of activity to one-half will have an effect on the whole system of one-half to the power of N, where N is the number of elements in the system. The action of a drug which has the moderate effect of reducing the level 50 per cent. in a single element will reduce activity over a thousandfold in a system which has a cascade of ten.

I remember Lorenz (Vol. I) describing the case of shrikes. The effects of very slight dietary deficiencies in these birds are said to modify profoundly one or two features of their instinctive response to their prey—they fail to impale it on a thorn. The behaviour of domestic animals may in some cases differ from that of wild animals because of a change in diet which is quite unmeasurable by biochemical means. A very slight change in metabolism might produce a dramatic change in instinctive behaviour.

The other secondary effect is that if the total activity in the system rises, you are liable to reach a state where the characteristics of the system are completely reversed. That means that instead of being an imprinting model it becomes a model of fashion, it follows the latest novelty. This might be interesting in relation to growth and the critical phases of development. As you turn up the power in the model it comes to a rather delicate phase where it is not quite sure whether it is imprinted or not, and as the power gets very big the imprinted response is submerged and a wide repertoire of responses appears. This change occurs without any circuit rearrangements. I think this is an important point; in all attempts to analyse behaviour in neurophysiological terms, we should see whether the effects observed could be due only to change in magnitude.

FREMONT-SMITH:

Could you explain why a certain increase in magnitude leads to this change in behaviour?

GREY WALTER:

In this particular model, you mean? The reason is that when it is just turned on, the amount of activity available is only just sufficient to maintain the tonic activity and then to operate the chosen circuit.

FREMONT-SMITH:

That drains off all the activity?

GREY WALTER:

Yes, and when I provide more by increasing the current there is ultimately a surplus of activity which allows it at some critical stage just to hold a second response for a moment.

FREMONT-SMITH:

Can growth in this situation be represented merely by an increase in power?

GREY WALTER:

Yes, a simple increase in current in the 'tonic' network. Growth of the nervous system might well lead to an increase in the total number of impulses circulating in the nervous system. Information is a better word, perhaps. The more information there is, the less restricted the system is in its responsiveness.

MEAD:

When this becomes a creature of fashion, does the primacy of the first button completely disappear?

GREY WALTER:

Practically completely. This possibility of reversal or modification with change of size is one of the things which one has always got to consider. As the child grows older the brain physiology changes in size as well as in kind, and it is not always easy to decide whether the change one observes is a quantitative or a qualitative one.

TANNER:

I take it that what you are calling the change in size as the child grows is the change in magnitude of the power input, rather than change in number of neurones. During growth there is no increase in the number of neurones after a very early stage, but an increase in the size of each and in the concentration of substances of one sort or another within them.

GREY WALTER:

The increased number of *active* neurones may be what matters.

FREMONT-SMITH:

There are units actually active at any given time and units potentially active as well as units which are not yet even potentially active in the growing child.

GREY WALTER:

The thing I have more in mind is that, in real nervous systems that we know of, there is always some apparently 'spontaneous' activity. That corresponds in this model to the 'spontaneous currents' which flow when I turn it on. There is a battery providing the basic tonic activity, a current through the heavily drawn circuit in the diagram. A nervous system which contains neurones in this sort of circuit has the peculiar property that in early youth it allows for a very specific response to be built up, and later allows for a variety of response, without any anatomical transformation, simply perhaps with an increase in the frequency of the rhythmic activity—which does occur in growing children. This is close to my heart, because in the growth of the child's brain the most dramatic feature is the rise of frequency of the spontaneous activity, which must account for a large part of the total electrochemical energy available. It is just conceivable that some of these features might be related to a necessity in evolution for the development of infantile, instinctive, imprinting behaviour which can still become, in the vertebrate, a versatile repertoire of behaviour modes without any metamorphosis. In most insects there is a dramatic metamorphosis, in which behaviour seems to be transformed in some quite miraculous way, but in the vertebrate there is no possibility of metamorphosis, and there you may have to allow for the needs of the animal by this type of development during growth.

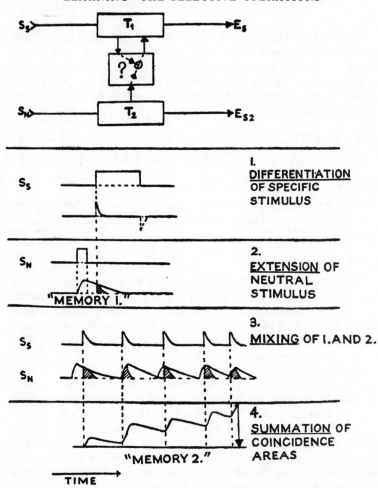

FIG. 9A

THE FIRST FOUR OF THE SEVEN OPERATIONS OF
LEARNING—THE SELECTIVE OPERATIONS

Now we come to the question of learning by association. Fig. 9, A and B shows the learning-by-association situation as I should like to represent it for my own purposes; it is not very different from those which have been suggested before. There are two transmission systems: T_1 is exactly like the one in the first model I showed you, *Machina speculatrix*: a simple reflex system, an input with a specific stimulus S_S leading to a synaptic relay, which may contain two

THE LAST THREE OF THE SEVEN OPERATIONS OF
LEARNING—THE CONSTRUCTIVE OPERATIONS

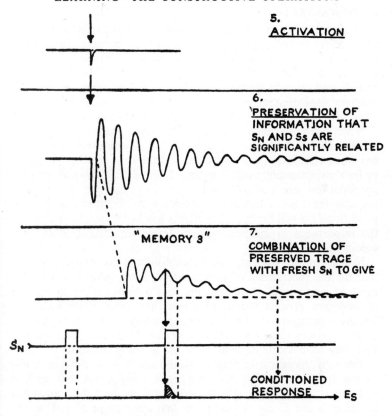

5.
ACTIVATION

6.
PRESERVATION OF
INFORMATION THAT
S_N AND S_S ARE
SIGNIFICANTLY RELATED

"MEMORY 3"

7.
COMBINATION OF
PRESERVED TRACE
WITH FRESH S_N TO GIVE

S_N

CONDITIONED
RESPONSE E_S

synapses, and having a specific effect, which I have designated E_S. The specific stimulus would be, in the Pavlovian case, food in the mouth, and the response would be the flow of saliva; or S_S might be an electric shock to the leg, E_S its withdrawal.

Below it is another transmission system of the same type, but with a stimulus neutral to the response E_S; in Pavlovian terms, the conditioned stimulus. This operates through another transmission system and of course may have a specific effect of its own, but with that we are not at the moment concerned. In the Pavlovian sense, supposing the neutral stimulus is a bell, there might be a pricking of the ears in response to the sound, but there would not be a flow of saliva. In respect of E_S it is neutral.

While it is specific in respect to E_{S2}?

Yes, as a reflex system it would have its own pathway, but it is not directly linked with the first system. But between the two we have a 'learning box' in which there is some sort of mechanism that provides for the building up of an association between neutral stimuli and specific stimuli in such a way that after regular and frequent repetition of a neutral stimulus followed by the specific one, the neutral stimulus comes to have the specific effect.

When trying to make a model of this some years ago, I got into considerable difficulties. I thought at first it would be easy to do, but when I looked at my own data, and the data of other people as to how conditioning really happens, I found that the performance specifications are complex and rigid. For example, the neutral stimulus must occur before or during the specific stimulus. It is no good ringing a bell for your dog after it has had its meat. Thus arises the importance of temporal order. There are several other such specifications.

Now as to the 'learning box' I established to my own satisfaction that for the functioning of such a system seven internal operations must be performed. It amazed me that a thing so simple as this rudimentary process requires no less than seven quite elaborate internal operations in the machine or in the brain. There may be more, of course, but I maintain there cannot be less. You will see that they have a definite relation to the learning situation.

The first operation is comparatively simple—the differentiation of the specific stimulus. The important thing about this specific stimulus is its beginning. The important thing which the animal has to detect in the giving of food is the first appearance of it. The way that is done here is to differentiate in such a way that we see only a pulse of activity at the beginning of the specific stimulus (see Fig. 9). In the case of the neutral stimulus, on the other hand, a different process must occur. The neutral stimulus must be stretched or extended, because there must be some degree of memory or storage of information of it. If, for example, the neutral stimulus is a bell just before the presentation of food, there must be something in the nervous system which stores at any rate for a short time a trace of the fact that the bell has rung.

The next operation is a rather more complex one, because it involves the mixing together of the abbreviated specific stimulus and the extended neutral one. They must be superimposed. This is represented in Fig. 9 by a series of specific stimuli, each one preceded by

48

a neutral stimulus with the areas of overlap of the two events shaded. It is those areas which are important. They are the areas of coincidence between the specific and the neutral stimuli.

That leads to a fourth operation, which is the summation of these areas. Each time a pair of events occurs together, the degree of coincidence must be recorded and stored. Here is a second type of memory. Our first type is simply a sort of after-discharge such as you find even in the spinal cord, but here we have a different sort of storage, a storage of areas of coincidence, which is a much more elaborate process, because it is not a storage of a single event, but a storage of association of events.

Note that these four operations are *selective* or *classificatory* operations. They provide for the selection of information from the outside world on the basis of contingency or coincidence. This is a very much more elaborate and interesting process than the instinctive response. This process of classification and selection is precisely equivalent to the recognition of pattern. You remember at the last meeting (see Vol. I), I mentioned that a system (whether flesh or metal) which could recognize pattern could learn and, conversely, a system which could learn must recognize pattern. Here the pattern is very simple, the pattern of contingency, of two things happening together in a regular and consistent order.

The next operation is what happens when the staircase effect reaches some threshold. When this happens it fires a detecting device which you will see indicated in the model. That then sets into operation a long-term memory. This is our third-class memory. This memory has an even more interesting character; it is the preservation of information that the neutral and specific stimuli were associated together *more often than would be expected by chance*. This is where we introduce the notion of a statistic of learning. In this selection and classification process we rely on some notion that there is a certain expectation of events and that the association of bell with food is extremely improbable to occur by chance. If they do happen together, bell-food, bell-food, bell-food, for a reasonable number of times, this is a phenomenon worth paying attention to. We recognize in this selective process and its immediate effect on behaviour what Pavlov sometimes called the 'go-and-find-out-reflex', the curiosity and the investigatory procedure which is the preliminary to all associative learning.

FREMONT-SMITH:

In the bell-food the food is something which the animal has had frequently in the past, but am I right in thinking that the bell is significant because it is new?

GREY WALTER:

Not necessarily; what is new is the association. It is not an essential condition that the dog should never have heard the bell before.

FREMONT-SMITH:

But if you had been hearing a lot of bells all along the line and getting a lot of food all along, would it not be much more difficult?

GREY WALTER:

Yes. If you make the statistics difficult to evaluate for an animal, if for example, it has heard the bell twenty-five times and had food fifteen times, then the establishment of the conditioned response depends, among other things, on how hungry it is.

The final operation is the combination of this storage or memory system with a fresh neutral stimulus to produce the conditioned response. We then get our impulse passing through the learning-box from the neutral transmission line to the specific one. Finally the modest pip on the bottom line of Fig. 9 is the conditioned response which has been produced by this elaborate procedure of statistical selection and construction and which requires these three storage systems.

It is very important from the philosophical standpoint to see in this analysis of learning that what is stored in the system is something quite unlike the original stimulus or the original response. It is a private image; it is an idea, a symbol. All that is happening in the actual model is an oscillatory discharge.

LIDDELL:

You are saying that every conditioned response is idiosyncratic or unique?

GREY WALTER:

Yes, that is one way of putting it. Fig. 10 is a neuronic diagram of the process. This is analogous to the diagram of the imprinting model, using the same conventional signs, the differentiating synapse, which is the commonest type in the nervous system, the extension or after-discharge synapse, and the summation and inhibitory synapses. For this particular analysis these four types of synaptic relay must be postulated. They are known to exist, in fact, in nervous systems and it would be rather nice if one could relate them to

50

FIG. 10

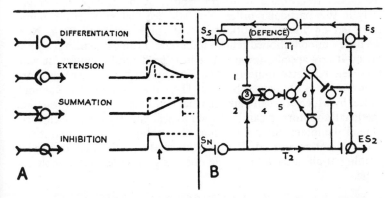

(a) Conventional signs for indicating the four types of nerve junction necessary for learning, used in Diagram (b).

(b) The simplest neurone circuit which could perform the seven operations of learning.

certain shapes and appearances of the nerve-cells. That is only possible in certain cases at the moment.

On the right we have the actual diagram of this system in terms of neurones or equivalent neurones. At the top we have the first transmission system, at the bottom the neutral stimulus, and between them the medley of neurones which are the learning-box. Our first process of differentiation is labelled (1). The second (2), the extension of the neutral stimulus, converges on the same neurone group. The effect of these two is mixed in neurone number three. The summated effects, when they reach a certain statistical threshold, activate the storage system, which I represent as simply a feedback loop.

A picture of this purely formal model is seen in Fig. 11 (facing p. 32). The display system is arranged so that I can show it to you as you would see an animal in the conditioned-reflex laboratory, but with some insight also into what is going on in its brain. There is a knob marked 'N', and when I press it a faint light comes on. This represents the neutral stimulus; it is faint because it has no significance at the moment. It can go to a number of places; it can radiate up or along. It has a very modest effect. It may have a specific action, but we are not concerned with this at the moment. Next there is the specific stimulus, with its reflex pathway, a fully-grown and perfectly conventional reflex. When I press the knob 'S', a light lights up, then another further along, its specific output. If I now press the neutral stimulus and follow it regularly by a specific one, there should gradually be built up inside

51

K

the model an estimate of the probability of things happening regularly in this particular order. You will see that at a certain point, after ten or fifteen repetitions, a little pink light will flash. Now we have our conditioned reflex established. I can extinguish it by not giving it any specific reward, but just the neutral stimulus. It will, however, reinforce quite quickly. The model has a latent memory even when it is not being operated. There is a knob labelled Reminiscence, by which you can make the memory long or short, as you like; the length of storage can be varied at will entirely for convenience. One of the interesting points about this storage system is that it will decay if not reinforced. If one establishes a reflex, and then does nothing at all, after a long time one finds the reflex has completely gone.

LIDDELL:

If you repeatedly give the neutral stimulus alone until extinction has occurred, and then press the reinforcement button by itself, can you get recovery of the response? You can with animals.

GREY WALTER:

You certainly can with a defensive reflex. In the defensive reflex, the conditioned response tends to be self-reinforcing. In Fig. 10 the defensive feedback circuit is drawn above the line T1. In this system, if you establish a defensive reflex instead of an appetitive one, it can be self-reinforcing, because every time the specific response is evoked by the neutral stimulus, it will look like a specific stimulus and have a self-reinforcing action. A defensive reflex may be self-reinforcing, or even, as it were, obsessional, and extremely difficult to destroy. In an appetitive impulse I would say it is more difficult to produce a reinforcement after extinction.

One of the odder effects with this device, which we observed by accident, is that if one uses a rhythmic storage system in this process, then the application of a rhythmic stimulus can in unfavourable circumstances evoke an imaginary response. In other words, by giving rhythmic stimuli, you can produce a conditioned reflex to something which never existed.

LIDDELL:

All animals will show these hallucinatory reactions if you work with them long enough.

GREY WALTER:

The paper by BRADY (1954) shows the establishment of a conditioned reflex to illusory colour sensations produced by stimulating the eyes with white flickering light. Under these circumstances most people see, for example, a brilliant red from time to time which is 'not there'. When a conditioned reflex to actual red light is well established, conditioned responses occur when an illusory experience of red is produced by flickering light.

Now we come to the various types of memory required for these processes. We have already noticed that there must be three types, each with its own characteristic time of build-up and decay. There is the after-discharge type of memory; the staircase building-up of summated actions; and the long-term storage of information about two things that have occurred regularly together. If one wants a permanent memory—and in most higher animals there is a very long-term storage—one requires yet a fourth type, something which carries a copy of the whole experience. I should say that eight operations are necessary for this complete theory of learning.

The question which is often asked is, 'Which, if any, of these memories or these impressions are associated with consciousness?' Very obviously the first two need not be; in fact, they should not have anything whatever to do with conscious awareness. If they were conscious activities one would be continually preoccupied with all kinds of trivial evaluations. It is conceivable that in certain psychotic conditions this may be the case. The only class of memory which could be usefully conscious in the vernacular sense is the third one, dealing with the storage of information about contingency. That could well be in some sense a real experience, an experience which you can describe and evaluate on its own terms. I do not say it must be conscious; a conditioned reflex may be established without the animal or subject being aware that anything is happening. One can learn to dilate one's pupils unconsciously, or secrete insulin or produce glycosuria without being aware of it at all.

I have done some work with a moving model equipped with one of these learning devices. The situation it had to solve was to get to its food and search around a stool in the middle of the floor. Its education consisted very simply of trying to teach it that sound meant obstacle, which in turn meant trouble. The schooling was to blow a police whistle and kick it. After it had been whistled at and kicked about a dozen times, it learned that a whistle meant trouble. We then removed the specific stimulus—the stool. The whistle was blown, and it avoided the place as if there were a stool there.

I was more ambitious. In England a police whistle has two notes which sound together and make a particularly disagreeable sound. I tried to teach it, therefore, that one note meant obstacle, and that the other note meant food. I tried to make this differential reflex by having two tuned circuits, one of which was associated with the appetitive response and the other with the avoidance response. It was arranged that one side of the whistle was blown before the machine touched an object so that it learned to avoid that, while the other side of the whistle was blown before it was supposed to see the light. The effect of giving both notes was almost always disastrous; it went right off into the darkness on the right-hand side of the room and hovered round there for five minutes in a sort of sulk. It became irresponsive to stimulation and ran round in circles.

As you would expect, there are only three ways of alleviating this condition. One of them is rest; in this case that was sufficient, it was left alone to play around in the dark until the effect of all the traumata had died down and it found its way home in the end. Another method is shock, to turn the circuits right off and start again with a clean bill. The most satisfactory method for my purpose is surgery, to dissect out the circuit.

Those are all the models I want to describe. I should like to round off my contribution with some mention of conditions sometimes referred to as 'stress' in learning. In the laboratory situations which I have described so far the experimental procedure has been carefully designed to eliminate stress and to provide for the models or for the animals as clear a statistic as possible. That, of course, is the purpose of the conditioned-reflex laboratory unless experiments are being made on conditioned neuroses. The same is true of the classroom or of this room here, where we are isolating ourselves from noise and other stimuli, so that what I am saying to you can seem to have significance which it would lose if there were a dozen other people talking together, or a band playing, or a lot of children running round the room. The function of education in learning is to emphasize, sometimes to exaggerate, the statistical significance of the stimuli which are presented. The function of the teacher or the trainer is to provide a pre-selected statistic, which he presents to the child or the animal, in such a way that it cannot evade working out the correct contingency computation.

Now I am going to go back about twenty years to describe to you some experiments which I did under the direction of Professor Rosenthal, who was one of Pavlov's pupils. He came to Cambridge in 1934, I think, to start a conditioned-reflex laboratory there, and I was seconded to him as assistant. We started the training of animals, and then Rosenthal went back to Russia for a holiday, but I was not fully trained, especially as Rosenthal spoke very little English and I spoke even less Russian, so that we got our wires crossed quite often. In the experiments we were making it was necessary to provide an absolutely regular repetition of stimuli, rewards and punishment, over a period of many months to get the animal ready for the experiments Rosenthal wanted to do. But when he left, I completely muddled what he wanted me to do, and I have put in Table 1 a condensation of the protocols of some of these experiments.

L: Light   F: Food
T: Touch   P: Pain
S: Sound   N: Nothing

CONDITIONING *IN SECLUSION*:

		L	T	S	
LF, TP, SN.	LF, TP, SN.)	F 6	0	0	$\chi^2 = 24$
LF, TP, SN.	LF, TP, SN. (	P 0	6	0	
LF, TP, SN.	LF, TP, SN. (	N 0	0	6	$P < 10^{-4}$
SIX TRIALS, NO ANOMALIES)		eighteen stimuli			

CONDITIONING *UNDER STRESS* ('NOISE'):

LF	TP	SP	LN	SN	LP	LF	TF	TP	TN	SN	LN	LF	SF	TP
TF	SP	SN	LP	LF	TN	LF	SF	TP	*LF	SN	TP*	LF	TF	TP
LF	LP	SN	TP	SF	SN	LN	LF	SN	LF	TF	LF	LP	SN	TP
SF	SN	LN	LF	TP	TN	SN	TP	SP	LF	TF	TP	SN	TN	LF
SP	SN	TP	LP	TP	LN	LF	SN	SF	TP	SN	TN	TP	SN	SP

TWENTY-FIVE TRIALS, ALL ANOMALIES   75 stimuli

	L	T	S		
F	15	5	5	25	$\chi^2 = 24$
P	5	15	5	25	
N	5	5	15	25	$P < 10^{-4}$
	—	—	—	—	
	25	25	25	75	

Table I

Condensed protocols of experiments on Conditioned Reflex formation in five dogs, which accidentally demonstrated the effect of statistical stress in promoting neurotic traits in certain types of animal.

Light is represented by L, touch by T, sound by S, food by F, pain by P, and nothing at all in the reward situation by N. The experiment which I was supposed to carry on is represented by the top table, light-food, touch-pain, sound-nothing. What mattered was that every day the dog should be shown a 60-watt bulb followed by food; he should be stimulated by touch, followed by pain, an electric shock; he hears a loud sound, followed by nothing. The sound was the hum of a fan, which was going to blow various gases into the chamber, which was the purpose of the experiment. This would be repeated regularly until the conditioned reflex was established, which it very soon was.

A record of six days of experiment is shown at the top. On each day the stimuli were presented in their correct order. There were six trials, with no anomalies and everything perfectly regular. This Table may be more interesting if you try to put yourself in the position of the animal. Supposing you want to decide for yourself, you being inside the experimental box, what the outside is like, you might draw up a χ^2 contingency table, with three rows and three columns, the columns being light, touch and sound, and the rows being food, pain and nothing. You find you have six occasions in which light was followed by food, six occasions on which touch was followed by pain and six occasions when sound was followed by nothing, and no exceptions. If you apply the χ^2 method to this, you find that the probability of this association being pure chance would be 10,000 to 1 against, though the numbers are too small to use or need the test. So you would be quite right in assuming light meant food, touch meant pain, and sound meant nothing.

When Rosenthal went back to Russia I was left with these dogs and, not realizing just what I was supposed to do, I arranged the situation as represented by the *lower* table. What happened, in effect, was that I gave these stimuli in an almost random order.

There were five dogs, and you see that in the 25 days of these experiments all the presentations were anomalous. Not a single one obeyed the law L–F, T–P, S–N. There was only one occasion when the associations were almost perfect, but even then they were not in the right order; L–F, S–N, T–P. Now if you set up the χ^2 table for these trials, you find light was followed by food on 15 occasions, and sound by nothing on 15 occasions. If you work out the probability of contingency, you find again that χ^2 is 24, and the probability of the association being random was again 10,000 to 1 against. In other words, if you were in the experimental box, it would be just as reasonable for you to infer significant association in the second case as in the first.

On this actual occasion, one of the five dogs retained a quite reasonable conditioned reflex response system, two of them became inert and unresponsive, and two became anxious and neurotic; in other words, although the situation had the same statistical value in both cases, it did not have the same effect on the animals. They were being conditioned under stress. If you like, you can call it 'noise'; there was a high level of randomness in presentation which had the effect precisely as described by Pavlov and others of producing a variety of experimental neuroses. The dogs had been selected on the basis of their typology, and the phlegmatic dogs became inert and passive; the so-called melancholic and choleric ones became agitated and anxious; and the one sanguine dog managed, even through this noise, to retain its conditioned reflex responses almost intact.

FREMONT-SMITH:

You are making the assumption that the relationship of the experimenter to the animals was either equal in all these experiments or non-existent? You can overcome completely the tendency to neurosis if there is the appropriate relationship of the animal to the experimenter or of the individual to the leader.

GREY WALTER:

I would say only in some individuals. That is a very personal characteristic in dogs and in men, though it may not be true in the simpler animals. In fact, the animal that Pavlov called a sanguine type did survive completely.

MEAD:

Did you like him best?

GREY WALTER:

Well, I do not like melancholic, fawning-type dogs. The sanguine dog was an independent sort of fox-terrier cross, and I found him much pleasanter to deal with. The melancholic ones were whippet types, the phlegmatic and choleric ones were of no known origin, rather large dogs.

FREMONT-SMITH:

Then it does turn out that the one that was stable was the one you liked best?

GREY WALTER:

I liked him best as an experimental dog, but I am not very fond of dogs in any case. I only saw them on experimental occasions. I was not responsible for their kennel management. But I would like to stress the importance of personal character in the extent to which the breakdown can be alleviated or postponed or mitigated by reassurance or leadership.

LIDDELL:

In our early days, one of my colleagues was much more successful in precipitating experimental neurosis than the rest of us. Then we discovered, after he had left, that it was his nervous, anxious management of the animal which was communicated to the animal and hastened the onset of neurosis.

PIAGET:

First I should like to say what great pleasure it has given me to listen to Grey Walter's communication and to express my admiration for his analysis of the conditioned reflex. I shall only discuss the six categories of psychobiological development which Grey Walter dealt with at the beginning of his communication.

The first three of these six categories are concerned with mechanisms which are to a great extent innate, whereas the last three are concerned mainly with acquisition by experience. From the point of view of the psychobiological development of the child this gives a correct picture and I do not want to add a further category to the six proposed. I think, however, that there is another dimension to be considered.

All behaviour presupposes, apart from maturation factors, an acquisition through experience, either in the form of exercise or as direct acquisition. Experience and environment are everywhere presupposed. There are, however, in the development of the child two kinds of experience which are always more or less intermixed, but which can easily be distinguished on analysis. These two sorts of experience give two kinds of knowledge or two kinds of methods of acquiring knowledge. There is first the experience which I will call 'physical experience' or 'experience derived from the physical environment' which is experience in the accepted sense of the term—it is what everybody thinks of, while forgetting on the other hand the second category of which I will speak later.

Experience derived from the physical environment furnishes knowledge taken from objects and gives rise to what one might call an abstraction derived from the object: certain qualities of the object may serve as signals for associations or for conditionings.

I will give just one example: the concept of heaviness and lightness. Evidently, it is by experimenting with objects that the child, before he is able to speak, at the sensorimotor level, notices that there are heavy objects and light objects. Then this knowledge gives rise to associations. He discovers that heavy objects are generally larger and larger objects are generally heavier. You all know the illusion of weight. When you see two boxes of equal weight but of different volume you always expect the larger to be the heavier; this results from an effect of contrast. The illusion does not exist among the mentally deficient nor among very young children. It is produced

58

partly by a weight-volume association. This type of knowledge is acquired by abstractions derived from the object.

There is, however, a second kind of experience which I should like to stress. Experimentation here is also carried out on objects and can be carried out only by manipulating objects. But in this case the knowledge is not drawn from the object and the abstraction does not derive from it. The abstraction is derived from the actions themselves which are performed on the object, which is something quite different.

I shall give only one example, which is a bad one from the experimental point of view, but which is very nice from the symbolic point of view. One of my friends, a mathematician, ascribes his first interest in mathematics to an experiment he made as a child. I should like to emphasize again the fact that everything, even mathematical knowledge, presupposes experience; such knowledge is not innate; it presupposes an experimental construction, an acquisition, learning, but this learning is of a particular kind. It is an abstraction derived not from the object but from the action. To come to my friend's experiment: as a child—I don't know how old he was—he clearly remembers counting pebbles. He had ten in front of him and he put them in a straight line. He began counting: one, two, three . . . up to ten. Then he counted from the other end: one, two . . . etc., and he was very surprised to get to ten. Then he mixed them up, he permuted and he began counting them again and again he got up to ten. This was a miracle to him. He tried every way and always arrived at ten. This is a result which he could not yet deduce in advance although later on he became a great mathematician. It was the experiment that taught him that the cardinal sum is independent of the order. But how did he experiment? With pebbles, yes, certainly. He could have done it with bits of wood, and if he had been an atomic baby with electrons—although they would have been rather more difficult to count. Anyway the object does not matter.

Where did he get his knowledge from? Two ideas come in here: the idea of order and the idea of the cardinal sum. The order is not inherent in the pebbles; you can put them in any kind of order. It is action which introduces a definite order into the arrangement of pebbles. In the same way, the sum is not inherent in the pebbles; the pebbles have no property of being ten. The sum is again a product of an adding operation, of an actual action. These two ideas of order and sum are not properties of the object. The object always conforms to the action, on the macrophysical scale at any rate. But it is not from the object that the knowledge is drawn. Here it is drawn from an abstraction based on the action.

This distinction is very important from the developmental point

59

of view. When it is a question of simple common associations, easily recorded, etc., these two kinds of experience are pretty well on a par, but when it is a question of actual experimentation, that is to say when the child tries to verify something, to ascertain by experiment the validity of a hypothesis, it is obvious that these two types of experience are not on the same level. Experience derived from action is much easier and at about seven years the child can already create logical structures, starting with the conservation of sum, whereas physical experience, that is to say experimentation, comes much later.

The same holds good for social acquisitions. The Greeks achieved the logical, mathematical type of experimentation but not physical experimentation, apart from a few exceptions, as in the case of Archimedes. There is a very great lag between the two. Physical experiment, which seems to be simpler, always comes later, because it presupposes very refined precautions and methods of control, whereas experience where the abstraction is derived from the action is a simple co-ordination of the action leading to operational schemata, which is much easier.

Moreover I should like to emphasize the fact—although I do not wish to anticipate what Mlle Inhelder might want to say later on—that logico-mathematical experience often conditions the physical experiment. In order to interpret a physical property it is often necessary to have an operational schema. I should like to give an example in connection with perception.

We carried out an experiment which consisted in comparing the length of two lines, one vertical and the other inclined at different angles. This comparison is very difficult for the adult. For the small child, on the other hand, it is much easier. The child is able to make much more precise comparisons than the adult. Why is this? It is because after a certain age a perceptive space is organized according to systems of co-ordinates which presuppose patterns based on co-ordination of actions. A small child does not yet have this system. He sees things directly, independently of their orientation in space.

It seems to me that an important distinction has to be made here. Mlle Inhelder will come back later to the question of conditions of interpretation of experiment, in connection with Mr. Whiting's communication, but I just wanted to stress today the two types of experience which presuppose different modes of acquisition, and very probably Grey Walter will propose schemata for the two types.

GREY WALTER:

I think it is a very valuable addition to this classification that one should always bear in mind the difference between a pure sensory impression and one obtained by, as it were, physical experimentation. There is a difference between just looking at objects, saying 'Because that object is larger than another one, it is probably heavier', and the additional information got from actually performing an action on the objects. The experience or learning derived from motor action is different in some respects from experience related only to the receptor system. The process referred to as action, I would suggest, is what engineers call an error-operated servomechanism; in performing an action such as counting pebbles or making some motor adjustment you are matching an internal image of the object with some action which you perform. From the error in the match, you obtain additional information which is easier to evaluate than the purely chance exposure to stimulation.

RÉMOND:

I wonder if, between these types of experience, there isn't a place for something intermediate, where there would have been no actual action, but voluntary and conscious reasoning. Obviously, when we perceive differences between physical phenomena an unconscious association can be created between different facts, and therefore our involuntary experimentation can take place without our having performed any action. But, between this and purposeful experimentation based on action, could there not be a place for voluntary active reasoning? Do you not think that deductive reasoning without action is another way of acquiring knowledge?

PIAGET:

I do not think that this exists: I think rather that reasoning is the product of internalized action. Reasoning is the result of a series of operations which were first actions; it is simply a reflective level of internalization and of symbolization, permitting reasoning, but originating at the sensorimotor level, before the development of language and inner thought. I do not think that your voluntary reasoning constitutes a category to be added to Grey Walter's six stages. It is a repetition on another plane, an internalization of mechanisms.

RÉMOND:

I thought of that because you said that the first phenomenon was much more difficult than the second. When it is possible to repeat, transform and modify experience through action, one is enabled to acquire a certain piece of knowledge much more rapidly and much more thoroughly, whereas in the first case it is a thing that passes, it is something definite which one takes or does not take, which one grasps or does not grasp; it is not so easy to profit by it.

PIAGET:

Precisely, it is because it is a different type of acquisition that internalization in the form of reasoning is simple. In the fields of logic or mathematics we are able to reason and make deductions without reference to experience. It is not the same as regards physical experience. That is the great mystery of mathematical learning: you are very soon able to do without experiment and to carry out voluntary reasoning. But you are able to do that just because it is a different type of experience from the physical experience. You have experimented with your own actions and once they are co-ordinated you no longer need objects; you can continue symbolically, internally. There is a certain logical mathematical type of deduction which a child of seven has mastered, whereas physical deduction seems more difficult.

ZAZZO:

I wonder if there is not in your previous explanation an expression which might give rise to a misunderstanding in the discussion, perhaps because it was too hasty.

In order to define the second type of experience you spoke of 'action performed on an object' which leads to ideas of order and of sum. In both cases—I think you will agree with me—there is action performed on the object.

PIAGET:

In both cases there is action on the object but what differentiates them is the type of action. The knowledge can be derived either from the object or from the actions themselves which were connected with the object; that is the only difference. But there is always action on the object before representative internalization.

BINDRA:

I think there is considerable experimental evidence on the point that Professor Piaget has made. There is, for instance, the experiment of EWERT (1930). He wore lenses on his eyes which inverted the visual image. With these lenses on you might consider him to be in the position of a newly-born infant who has to learn to perceive

62

the visual world. Ewert found that the only way he could get about in his surroundings was by constantly making and correcting movements of different types; he had to make movements with his hands, legs and so forth, in order to 'see' his way. Gradually, as he improved and could see straight, these movements diminished. When after three weeks he took the lenses off, he had to go through the same process of learning to see correctly with the help of awkward movements of arms and legs.

GREY WALTER:

If you imagine a target-seeking projectile that is looking for its target, it has to make a change of course and see if it is more nearly correct. It is not only looking at the target but inspecting its own trajectory, making one correction and then another. It would be the errors in adjustment which would give the information. What you are saying, it seems to me, is exactly what the servo-engineer says when he demands that the error signal should be fed back to the input. In other words, in taking up an object and examining it, one is matching one's idea to the real object and seeing if in all respects there is congruence between the idea and the object. For all I know, just looking at a teacup, it might be a model of a teacup with no space inside. This question of matching is I think included in this general theory, because I am assuming that the animal with reflexive action is capable of doing it. The first model I showed you is constantly orientating itself to a course, and in doing so is acquiring information about the error, or the difference between its own course and the course it should take.

MEAD:

I think it is important not to assume that these are alternatives, but simply matters of proportion. In a great deal of the discussion that we have had on the growth of thought of children there has been a tendency to assume that the sort of thinking in which motor exploration is not possible is in a sense primary, and the sort of thinking where error correction comes in is secondary; in other words, that there is a progressive adjustment to reality in the child as it assumes more mobility and has more opportunities to test its experience. But if you look at cultures that have gone to extremes either of immobilizing or of giving mobility to children, then you can see extreme results of these two systems. An extreme model of the first is swaddling, in which the child has very little opportunity to test its visual experience by the use of its hands for perhaps the first year or year and a half; of the second, the practice of the

Manus, whom I have just been studying, where the adult forms himself or herself into legs for the child and spends the time going where the child wants to go, leaning over so that the child can reach what it wants to touch, etc. In the first case, we find a willingness of the adult individual to accept an untested version of reality very easily, and in the other case we find an absolute refusal to do what we would call 'imagine'. If you present a Manus native with a picture of something, he will say either, 'That is that', or 'I do not know'. All the nuances that are possible with early experience of uncorrected visualizing, for instance, are removed by this very early insistence on continually testing, holding, pushing, pulling of everything the child sees. In most people in our society we have a mixture of these two.

LORENZ:

I quite agree that the two types are very distinct from each other, and I was going to emphasize the point that Dr. Mead has just made about children of different cultures. There are animals (for example, plovers) which, in visual exploration of the external world, do not do anything actively: they just stare. If humans want to form an idea of an object, they will always do some active exploration, even if it is only moving their eyes, focussing one spot after another and turning their heads to and fro.

OTTO KOEHLER (1950), in his very profound experiments on teaching animals and birds to count, found the same type of transpossibility from one sense of modality into the other. He has trained pigeons to the number six. The pigeon will look at several little heaps of grains and then choose the one consisting of six grains, quite irrespective of the order. It need not necessarily be grains, it might as well be pieces of Plasticine stuck on paper in different sizes and forms: the number is the only thing retained. Then the pigeon can easily be trained to take six grains successively falling out of a chute: you can draw out the temporal sequence unrhythmically and the pigeon will stand there and wait for its sixth grain, and walk away unconcernedly if several more drop out.

Koehler has trained parrots to do a still more difficult thing. The parrot is presented with pasteboard cards marked with irregular blotches, varying in number from one to eight. The bird looks at them and then picks the corresponding number of grains and walks away. This is an absolutely outstanding performance.

Koehler made another most exciting chance observation on a jackdaw that had been trained to take six pieces of cheese out of a series of covered boxes. The pieces of cheese were distributed in an

FIG. 14

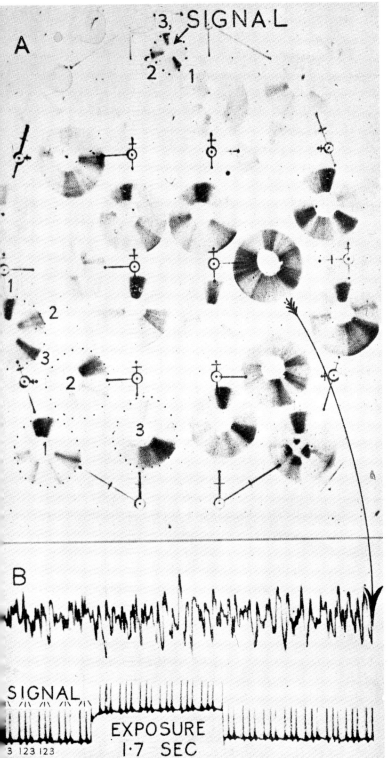

FIG. 15

FIG. 19

ever-varying sequence; often there were several in one box, then again a number of boxes were empty, and so on. In the experiment in question, the bird found one piece of cheese in the first box, two in the second, the third was empty, in the fourth it found two more pieces, making five in all. Then the bird erred, thought it had enough and turned away. After a few steps it stopped, came back to the boxes, made one intention movement of pecking at the first box, two at the second, passed over the third, did two hints of pecking at the fourth box, after which it resolutely went on opening boxes until it got to the one containing the sixth piece of cheese to which it 'had a right'. It was exactly as if the bird said: 'Now let me see, there was one piece here, two here, etc. etc.' until it came to the conclusion 'Why yes, I was quite right, I have another piece of cheese coming!'.

GREY WALTER:

Now I should like to describe some observations concerning the way in which the human brain deals with the information that it receives, and the way in which such information is turned into the raw material of learning behaviour.

I am encouraged to show these records because several of my friends here have said that they feel this sort of approach to brain physiology is in some way a liberation from the strait jacket of Sherringtonian spinal cord physiology. These pictures show, for example, that the differentiation and specification of the brain areas, on which I think probably all of us were educated, though useful for certain purposes, represents only a vague simulacrum of the truth. The brain regions which are so dear to many hearts, though they may exist in a sense, are functionally very much more like the organization we have here today, where it is possible to say so-and-so is a physiologist and such-a-one is a psychologist and yet, although that may be their special role, at times they may be dealing with something quite different.

I should like to skip over the technical features. The input arrangements are very similar to those of the conventional electroencephalograph, but there is a special arrangement to display the electrical activity at the output. Fig. 12 (facing p. 33) shows this display system and indicates the reason for doing it in this manner, which is to show directly the pattern of the placement of the electrodes on the head. In all these pictures you will see a series of white lines and small circles. The small circles represent the electrodes and the white lines are the leads to the amplifying channels, and for each channel there is a cathode-ray oscilloscope.

The little circles are the electrodes, and at the top is the nose diagram, a triangle simply outlining the nose. The subject is lying on his back and you are looking at his head from the top, with the nose appearing at the top of the diagram. Each of these oscilloscopes carries a brilliance change, exactly as a television set does. In other words, the signals in the various channels are transformed into changes of brilliance on the little cathode-ray oscilloscopes like the television voltages which we see as brightness. In each oscilloscope there is a rotating scanning vector which is produced by the operation of the electronic beam inside the oscilloscope, and this line moves round the tube at a controllable rate. The whole arrangement therefore forms for us twenty-two clock faces. Each clock has one hand, and this hand tells us the time. The time it tells us may be our time, Greenwich Mean Time, or it may be brain time. In other words, we can make a part of the brain drive these clocks at its own speed. We may choose, for example, the bottom right-hand side, which is the right occipital channel; we may connect this to a special circuit which generates a speed in the scanning machinery which is synchronized with the brain activity in that region, and then our display will show us brain time. If brain time varies as compared with our absolute scale, then the rotational speed of our clock hand will vary, therefore we have a display which synchronizes what we see, not with our own clock time, but with the way in which time elapses for the brain in that part at that particular period.

The object of all this apparatus is to make possible the recognition of very small regular components for short periods of time, a second or so, against a background of interference or spontaneous activity or activity not related to this particular synchronized process.

Fig. 12 shows calibration records indicating the way in which each pattern is defined. Patterns with a single petal correspond to activity at the frequency of the scanning vector; they may have twice the frequency or three times or four times the frequency with 2, 3 or 4 petals. Therefore, one has a measure of frequency, phase relations, of latency in relation to absolute time, of position and, above all, the chance of extracting pattern from a mush of noise in the same way as a spectroscope can extract from a diluted and contaminated solution the spectral lines corresponding to a particular compound such as haemoglobin.

LORENZ:

If I understood it correctly, in the lower right picture those four flashes mean that these brain cells have a frequency which is just four times that of your hand going round. Is that correct?

GREY WALTER:

Yes, four times to one on the clock in that region. The frequency is read off the meter which says 5 so that frequency is 20. The point is that an irregular, random component, which does not appear on each occasion, is not recorded; unless it occurs on each occasion at the same part of the tube it appears only as a blur, if at all.

RÉMOND:

In that way the instrument is an auto-correlator?

GREY WALTER:

Yes, and a cross-correlator, because you have superimposition of signals in different regions, and the photographic method of recording ensures that the activity is integrated.

One point I want to emphasize is that from records of this type one can infer that alpha activity is a very complex process. There are many alpha rhythms which perform all kinds of functions. I do not think there is ever only one alpha rhythm. With any given individual it is possible to work out what the various alpha rhythms do, and very rarely does a given alpha rhythm component do the same thing for different people. Frequency is not a label of function. That is determined by other factors.

In Fig. 13 (facing p. 33) the subject is being exposed to a known stimulus. We have, on the left-hand side, at the top, the conditions during stimulation with a pattern of flashes with the eyes open. Below on the left we have the eyes shut; in each case on the right-hand side are the records taken after stimulation was terminated. The pattern of stimulation is important. Here it was groups of three flashes together at a group repetition rate of three per second. The pattern rate is represented on the top tube by flashes on our clock face; one appeared on our clock face at about twelve o'clock, one at about five, one at about nine.

During stimulation with the eyes open, one sees this pattern appearing in many parts of the occipital region of the head, as you would rather expect, near the projection or association area for visual function, and also in the anterior region of the temporal lobe, particularly on the right-hand side. The effects of the visual stimulation go far beyond the boundaries of visual projection, and even beyond the zone of visual associations, into the temporal region and into the frontal regions from time to time. We shall see later that the conditions of this spread are dependent on the attitude of the subject to stimulation—that is, not dependent simply upon the existence of his brain, but upon his history and his personality.

On the right-hand side there are records taken after the stimulation, and the thing to note there is that, when the stimulation is over, for several seconds the image of the response hangs on and persists. Notice that of these two, in the one with the eyes shut the persistence is greater, the reproduction of the pattern is clearer, and the spread is more extensive.

FREMONT-SMITH:

The flashing is through the closed lids?

GREY WALTER:

Yes. It is a very bright flash and even with the eyes closed it is still a very brilliant stimulus; but when it was over there was nothing to see—no competition from other signals.

BOWLBY:

How long after these stimuli were they taken?

GREY WALTER:

One second after. One can trace some effect for a period of five or ten seconds even in scalp leads. Of course the potentials are greatly attenuated by the skull and they must last for upwards of ten seconds in the brain itself; in psychotic subjects they may last as long as ten minutes. In other words, the pattern is preserved in the brain, not necessarily in its original form—there are signs of embellishments, abstractions, corruptions, and all kinds of transformations.

RÉMOND:

What is the duration of the integration?

GREY WALTER:

The actual exposures are all of the order of one second, so that if there are three repetitions here we have the superimposition of three rotations of our scanning vector which indicates the degree of constancy of this appearance.

WHITING:

How long does it take for the latency of the light patterns?

GREY WALTER:

There is a long latency. The actual latency for this particular pattern comes out temptingly close to the reaction time of the subject; in other words, not the physiological latency of 30 to 50 milliseconds, but more like 200 milliseconds. That is, it takes a fifth of a second for the pattern to reach the temporal regions of the brain. It takes much longer to develop physiologically, as a pattern; it builds up over perhaps a dozen exposures until this stage is reached and then each individual pattern takes another 200 milliseconds to reach the association areas of the brain. It is rather far from Sherringtonian reflexes—you see the brain acting not as a reflex system, but as an integrative and abstracting organ.

Fig. 14A (facing p. 64) suggests how this may be done. At the top, we have the input pattern. At the bottom again we have the response to the three flashes; in the occipital region we have the same pattern, but if you notice, it is not complete in any one region. We have flash number 1 in one channel, number 2 in another and number 3 in another again. This indicates that the first step in this complicated procedure must be the separating out of the components of the time pattern in different regions by some sort of sweeping or dissecting process by which, so to speak, the beads of information are strung on the string of time. The string and beads are sent through the post as it were to some other region such as the frontal or temporal, and then strung off again. I call this process abscission as compared with the complementary process, abstraction, where the beads are taken off the string. If you want to send someone a pattern of beads in a certain order through the post and you put them in a box they will be jumbled up, so you put them on a string.

LIDDELL:

Do the association fibres transmit the string of beads from the cortex?

GREY WALTER:

Not the long association fibres as far as we can tell; the impulses seem to dive down deep. The latency is too long for it to be a direct cortico-cortical process. After the pattern is dissected out, there seems to be reassembly again in a rather compressed form towards the temporal region. On the right-hand side it is reassembled in a rather expanded, idealized form and, in fact, there are six representations of this threefoldness in different parts of the brain. This is a fairly regular appearance, although it is rather unusual to get so

69

very clear a representation of the abscission effect; one has to take the exposure with the scan at a certain speed related to the alpha rhythms. There is every reason to suppose that this abscission process is one of the alpha rhythm functions; the first stage in recomposition of a time sequence may be dissection by an internal spontaneous rhythm of some sort.

Fig. 14B is a record taken simultaneously with the previous one on a standard machine giving a written record corresponding to the left temporal channel, the one where you see clearly the pattern of threefoldness as the pattern is reassembled. The bottom channel shows the stimuli, in waltz rhythm. The raised part of this trace is the duration of the exposure of Fig. 14A, lasting about 1.7 seconds in this case. Such a record would have to be analysed by some very special means in order to extract the information of threefoldness that it represents. The noise level is high enough to obscure completely, even to the trained and eager human eye, the linkage of this particular abstraction. I think this explains why these effects are hard to observe and why one is bound to use these rather fancy devices to reveal them.

BINDRA:

What dimension of your actual brainwave is represented in your tubes?

GREY WALTER:

Amplitude is turned into brilliance, frequency is indicated by the pattern, and its position in the brain by its position on the display. In these records the amplitudes of the principal components were from 5 to 20 microvolts.

BINDRA:

Is there any way of your getting rid of any artefacts?

GREY WALTER:

Yes, indeed. Artefacts due to stimulation are seen as exactly synchronous with the stimulation and can be recognized easily, physiological artefacts such as those due to muscular activity are not synchronized with the servo device, since they are not related to the brain or selected by the operator. Most artefacts become noise; noise by definition is not synchronized or regular in its pattern, and, therefore, is either not seen at all or else seen simply as a vague blurring of the discs.

LIDDELL:

How does this brain work change from infancy to the adult?

GREY WALTER:

That really is a sixty-four dollar question. It is one of the subjects we are studying now, as carefully as we can.

LIDDELL:

I was thinking of Freud's dream work and the straightforwardness of the child's dream.

GREY WALTER:

The relative simplicity of the child's mind seems to be related to one of the odd things which we did not expect at all; that in young children these peculiar elaborate remote effects of stimulation do not exist at all. Up to the age of even three or four it is very unusual to see any sign of them. You get only a direct elementary response. As far as abstractions and associations go, the picture is extremely simple, and without any refinement. The remote elaborations do not appear until the age of six or seven, and then they start to develop very rapidly.

LIDDELL:

Do you not think there is correlation with the simplicity of the dream?

GREY WALTER:

The child must see things far more simply. The learning machinery has not matured.

Now, to conclude, I should like to describe how some of these results may relate to what we were saying last year about the social implications of some of these observations. In sorting some conventionally analysed records in our laboratory Janet Shipton found by chance that when the records were arranged according to their arbitrary typology, the cards kept coming out in pairs. Mrs. Shipton took the trouble to see in what pairs they came out and why, and oddly enough they were the very pairs of subjects as they had come up for the investigation. The people who chose to come to us in pairs as normal controls had electroencephalograms which had a marked resemblance. We are now trying to see if there is a cerebral affinity, so to speak, between people. In a provincial university town

71

with a mixed population of people of the same age, varied interests, free choice of companions there may be a tendency for people to choose companions who have similar brain activity, not of course because of that similar brain activity, but because they have personality traits which are associated with certain types of brain activity. Oddly enough, this association is best of all between the sexes. Two of these pairs of similar cards were those of engaged couples, and their records resembled one another almost as much as if they had been identical twins. This might throw light on human genetics. Selective mating would account for the continued existence after so many generations of brain types; otherwise one would expect brain characters to be normally distributed like stature.

LIDDELL:

It is well known that long-married couples become more and more similar.

GREY WALTER:

And adopted children become like their adoptive parents.

BINDRA:

I wonder if you had excluded all possibility of any gradual changes in your experimental set-up over the time.

GREY WALTER:

Yes. This observation is based on results from a consistent series of experiments over a period of about nine months. They were designed to study imagery, stereognosis and versatility, as I described to the Group last year.

BINDRA:

Did the subject come in at different times on different days?

GREY WALTER:

Yes. In some cases sociograms have been done on them by other people; wherever A admired B and B admired A, their records were of similar types. Where there was a 'star', somebody everybody admired, but who might have a reserved attitude to other people, there was often a peculiar sort of record. One might be able to plot these so-called sociograms in terms of physiological gradients. In evaluating these results one has to compute the possibility of association of rare features; to reckon whether the E.E.G.s of these people may be associated by chance. We are doing this now, and so far it has been shown that the probability of such aggregation occurring by chance is small.

BINDRA:

It may be that two people come to the laboratory together. They have a conversation on the way and this conversation creates some sort of set in both of them. It is the common set that may be responsible for the resemblance in the two records.

GREY WALTER:

They do not know the nature of the experiment until they come. They are only undergraduate associations; they may be transient— many of them are—but for the time in which they are, they are important. They are people who join the same classes, have the same sort of recreations perhaps. It would be interesting to study just what the factors concerned are; whether they are determined by something more specific than accidental whims.

LORENZ:

What are the records of people with epileptic fits, do you find that their nervous elements tend to fall into step?

GREY WALTER:

Yes, that is the most dramatic of all these appearances, one finds absolute synchronization and regularity.

LORENZ:

That is an example of not saying the most important thing, because it is too obvious to yourself. I think you ought to have struck the table and said, 'When there is a fit, they fall in absolutely!'. This is absolutely conclusive, is it?

GREY WALTER:

Not quite for the general thesis, but it is very encouraging.

LIDDELL:

What about identical twins who have been separated for some time; have you ever run into that situation?

GREY WALTER:

They do tend to remain fairly close. One of the difficulties in applying electrophysiology to the problems we are discussing is that there is a very strong possibility that 80 or 90 per cent. of E.E.G. factors we can measure are genetically determined; and the other 10 to 20 per cent. are in some cases the most interesting. There are some cases for example in which neither the frequency nor the amplitude of the alpha rhythms change; but the response to stimulation does, very dramatically. These are individual cases and some can be modified by treatment.

As far as epilepsy goes, when only one of a pair of identical twins has seizures, the other usually has an 'epileptic' type of record.

FREMONT-SMITH:

If we were all in absolute agreement, would we have a mass convulsion?

GREY WALTER:

It might be very interesting; perhaps we should be convulsed with laughter!

FREMONT-SMITH:

Religious frenzies are perhaps in that category.

MEAD:

As among the people I have just re-studied, the Manus of the Admiralty Islands.

GREY WALTER:

I think the probability of our engaging in a religious frenzy is extremely small!

Presentation: Dr Bindra

BINDRA:

At the McGill Psychological Laboratory there are a number of human and animal studies in progress, dealing with a variety of psychological problems. Originally most of the problems were related in some way to Professor HEBB's (1949) biological or neuro-physiological theory of behaviour; but by now, as often happens, the experimental work has proliferated so much that its relation to the original theory is not always obvious.

The first series of studies that I should like to talk about deals with the effects of variation in early environment on behaviour. Since this might lead us into a discussion on the whole subject of innate as against learned patterns of behaviour, I am going to present a scheme, originated by Professor HEBB (1953), which helps discussions on this topic. As psychologists, we are not concerned with the more or less biological concepts of 'heredity' and 'environment'. Psychologically, what concerns us is the distinction between 'innate' and 'learnt'. The terms 'innate' and 'learnt' are used in various senses and I think Hebb's scheme clarifies some of the confusion.

Factors in the normal development of behaviour: Hebb's formulation

1. *Hereditary:* the *genetic* (and any other) physiological properties of the fertilized ovum.

2. *Hereditary or Environmental: chemical* characteristics of the uterine environment of the embryo.

3. *Environmental: chemical:* nutritive influences of the post-natal environment, including oxygen, water, hormones, enzymes, etc. This refers to the environment of the nervous system, not of the whole animal, so this factor is summed up as the chemical constitution of the fluids bathing the nerve cell.

4. *Environmental: learning: sense-organ stimulation, species-predictable:* pre- and post-natal sensory events that are inevitable in ordinary circumstances for all members of the species.

75

Examples: moving the fingers in a particular way inevitably stimulates the palm of the hand (grasp reflex); first extensive contact with living organism is from parents and litter-mates. Such patterns of stimulation are the basis of the first learning.

5. *Environmental: learning: sense-organ stimulation, variable from one member of species to another.*

The basis of what is usually considered learning: where one can see that learning has occurred, because the animal that has seen or done certain things thereafter responds in a different way from his fellows.

Both factors (4) and (5) are learning factors, though (5) is easy to control for experimental purposes, while (4) is hard to control. Another important point is that both factors (1) and (2) are sometimes called hereditary factors, but actually they are not the same; (1) is genetic, (2) is environmental-chemical.

I am now going to discuss our experiments on dogs. This series of experiments is concerned with the role of early learning or early experience in emotional and in problem-solving behaviour. These experiments were conducted by three investigators—THOMPSON and HERON (1954a, 1954b), and MELZACK (1952, 1954). Since it was a study of the extent of variation in behaviour that could be produced by changes in early environment, the genetic factors were kept constant as far as possible. All the animals used were pure-bred Scottie dogs, and in most of these experiments all the dogs were the descendants of a single pure-bred couple. At the time of weaning— that is, at four weeks—each litter was divided into two groups, a control group and an experimental group. The animals in the control group were raised as pets in fashionable homes in the Westmount district of Montreal. We refer to these as 'Westmount dogs'. The experimental animals were raised in the laboratory, and they were raised in very small boxes. These boxes could be lighted artificially but they were lighted only on alternate days. Each animal was brought up singly, in one little box. These animals had no contact with the laboratory staff; they were fed by a special arrangement. We called these dogs 'restricted dogs'.

After a differential treatment of this kind for about six to ten months, in different experiments, the control Westmount animals were brought back to the laboratory, and then both the experimental and control animals were given a number of tests. All the animals were tested for emotional behaviour, motivated behaviour, intelligence and so forth. The results were as follows:

1. There was no difference in health and vigour between the two groups of animals. The restricted animals were just as healthy, their appetites were normal, and they ate as much as the animals in the

76

control group. Now, this particular finding does not agree with the findings of Réné Spitz, who finds that human infants deprived of maternal care show various defects, and particularly loss of appetite.

MEAD:

These dogs were mechanically fed, were they not? You do not have a human being around who knows that he is neglecting them. With the Spitz babies, they were entirely cared for by people who knew that they did not have a mother, and knew they were being neglected.

BINDRA:

The human infants had been brought up by a mother and were used to this before there was a disruption in this relationship. This is probably quite a different thing from not developing that relationship at all. I think some of the studies that I am going to mention later point in the same direction: what is injurious to the health of the infant is not the lack of mother-love as such, but rather the relationship being formed first, and then broken. This should be an important point in discussions of mental health because, if the rate of break-up in families continues to increase, it might be better to bring up children without strong attachment to one person only.

I think our studies show that it is possible to bring up a dog in a physically healthy condition without any care from the mother after four weeks, and without any close attachment to the mother.

FREMONT-SMITH:

Were there other dogs in cages near your restricted ones?

BINDRA:

I believe they could hear the other dogs.

FREMONT-SMITH:

They were not in separate rooms? They could smell each other and hear each other, but not see each other?

BINDRA:

That is right.

LORENZ:

May I make an objection? If a dog is isolated from other dogs only visually, while still being able to hear and smell them, I do not think he would mind this at all. He would not feel lonesome in the least. So I cannot really regard your dogs as being socially isolated. If you had put them in sound-proof glass cases where they could have seen other dogs they would have been far more socially isolated. When did you separate your dogs?

BINDRA:

At four weeks.

LORENZ:

They are still nursing at eight weeks if you leave them. Until four weeks of age they were in the litter with a mother?

BINDRA:

Yes.

FREMONT-SMITH:

And they saw human beings, too?

BINDRA:

Yes, they probably saw their attendant.

TANNER:

Were they exercised when they were in the boxes?

BINDRA:

No.

LORENZ:

By four weeks a dog might know his mother personally. At four weeks he is able to run, he can gallop awkwardly, he will go urinating outside of the nest box and he will begin to eat.

BOWLBY:

For the first ten to fourteen days I understand it is very difficult to get the dog to learn anything at all (SCOTT *et al.*, 1951); but four weeks is long after that, and I wonder what information you have on their behaviour at that time?

BINDRA:

I have no details on that. I only have details on what happened when they first came out of the boxes.

BOWLBY:

Not when they first went in?

BINDRA:

Not when they first went into this environment. Since there is no mention of this in these papers by Thompson and Heron I believe they did not notice anything particularly worth describing. That is the best answer I can give you.

BOWLBY:

But if Lorenz is right surely they would have howled.

LORENZ:

You can assume that they would have howled for a day or so.

GREY WALTER:

The dogs who were taken away as pets may also have whined.

ZAZZO:

To keep our ideas straight, can you say to what age in a child four weeks in a dog corresponds; that is, in relation to the length of life and of the growing period.

RÉMOND:

It is about a twelfth of the way through the growing period. The dog's locomotion at four weeks corresponds to a child's at one and a half years.

ZAZZO:

In that case the separation was much later than that observed by Spitz, which was at six months.

LORENZ:

I think if we take a point of comparison, we ought to take the development of locomotion and of sense organs. A child of six months is in a stage corresponding to that of a dog just opening its eyes. Very roughly speaking—you can only compare roughly—that would correspond to a dog ten days old which is just beginning to creep and to look about.

BINDRA:

There probably is an important species difference here. Given the same time of nursing, or rather the same proportion of time, the attachment in the human child may be much stronger, because the female dog nurses five or six animals at one time while the human mothers tend to spoil their infants.

LORENZ:

A child at six months will notice if a stranger bends over its crib.

BOWLBY:

Well, that is marginal; not all do till about eight or nine months.

LORENZ:

Anyway, if you transfer them at six months from their mother to a stranger, at first they will be sad and very easily cross, whereas I have once transferred a young dingo, a wild Australian dog, at roughly the corresponding stage to a foster mother. It did not make any difference to the puppy who was just about to open his eyes. He went for the foster mother as directly as for his real mother.

BOWLBY:

That would be in keeping with Scott's findings. After about ten days dogs begin to learn, but not before.

LORENZ:

I agree.

BINDRA:

Another factor that might be relevant here is that, in the case of these dogs, the separation from their normal environment is abrupt and continued for a long time, six to ten months, and this does not usually happen in the case of humans.

2. The next result has to do with *general activity* of the dogs, as measured in two tests. One test involved a simple situation, just a

room with one chair on which the experimenter sat. Each dog was brought in individually, and the experimenter noticed what it did during a period of fifteen minutes. A simple method of scoring the animal's activity was used. The second test of general activity was similar, except that it involved a more complex situation.

In the simple situation there was a great difference in the level of general activity between the restricted dogs and the control, Westmount, dogs. The restricted dogs were highly active, and they remained so for almost the whole duration of the testing period. The Westmount dogs, by contrast, were blasé; they just went in and sat down and did not engage in much activity. In the more complex situation, the difference between the two types of dog disappeared, that is to say, the free-environment or Westmount dogs began to show the same level of general activity as the restricted dogs.

A finding relevant to this is that younger animals in general are more active than older animals. So what seems to be happening is that the adult restricted-environment dogs behave like younger normal dogs, or (which probably amounts to the same thing) like older normal dogs put in a very stimulating (complex) situation.

TANNER:

NISSEN and RIESEN (1949) brought up some chimpanzees in restricted situations; one visually restricted, that is in darkness, and one with locomotor restriction, with limbs encased in heavy cardboard tubes. The net result was that they were retarded in growth, according to ossification standards.

BINDRA:

That sort of thing may be a factor in this experiment.

TANNER:

It might account for your saying that the restricted ones appeared younger.

LORENZ:

This can easily be answered by the weight; I expect the restricted chimpanzees were much lighter.

TANNER:

That is true.

LORENZ:

But these dogs were just as vigorous?

TANNER:

And weighed the same?

BINDRA:

Yes, there were no differences in weight; and actually one of the restricted dogs won a ribbon in a local show.

These differences between restricted and free-environment dogs have been followed for a year and last at least that long. So it seems that restriction early on in life does have some more or less permanent effect on their general activity. I doubt if the restricted animals will ever get as blasé as the free-environment ones.

3. *Problem solving capacity.* The animals were given four tests of ability to solve problems, and here we found marked differences between the two groups. The restricted animals did very badly in all problems, and this marked inferiority in problem solving has also lasted for over a year. I think this handicap will probably continue.

Now, some of our studies on rats (HYMOVITCH, 1952; LANSDELL, 1953) show very clearly that perceptual deprivation early in life has a more severe effect than the same amount of deprivation given later in life. I believe the same sort of thing might be true of our dogs: had they been given these six months of restriction when they were two years old they probably would not have shown so much deterioration in problem-solving capacity.

GREY WALTER:

The Westmount dogs had an extra six months of 'learning to learn', whereas the restricted ones did not have that opportunity. Naturally if you apply the same restriction later in life they would already have acquired the experience of learning to learn. If you have already had some practice at learning you have got that for ever, and no one can deprive you of it.

BINDRA:

Quite true, but, as I said, these animals remain inferior for at least a year after restoration to a normal free environment (in the laboratory), so they had sufficient time to get the same sort of experience. (One of our earliest experiments showed that bringing up dogs in the laboratory as against bringing them up in Westmount did not make any difference.)

GREY WALTER:

This is unlike the rather ill-controlled human experiments, where restriction of the opportunity to learn to read does not seem to affect very much the final level of reading ability; such children may be retarded up to a certain point, but they will come up to the normal curve quite rapidly.

BINDRA:

4. The next result has to do with the genesis of emotional behaviour. All animals were tested three to five weeks after the end of the period of restriction, and again eight to ten months later. The tests consisted in exposure to a number of stimuli designed to provoke emotional behaviour. Their behaviour was classified in three categories: general excitement, avoidance behaviour, and aggressive behaviour. In the first test, exposure to such things as an umbrella or a mask, or a little toy frog hopping about, free-environment animals showed in general avoidance responses. The restricted-environment animals, on the other hand, did not show avoidance responses but mostly general excitement, with no directed responses, either of avoidance or attack.

Eight to ten months later, on the second test, that is, when these restricted animals had had sufficient freedom and experience in the laboratory, they were given the same test again. Now the restricted animals showed avoidance responses and not general excitement, while the free-environment animals gave a high proportion of aggressive responses. I think this tends to show that these integrated patterns of emotional behaviour, withdrawal and attack, are learned, and not simply the result of maturation processes. The two groups of animals were of the same age but their behaviour was quite different.

LORENZ:

May I ask one thing? Your restricted dogs were, roughly speaking, retarded by about one year; they developed later with everything. Now your normal dog did not become aggressive against the frog and the mask and so on until he was about two years old?

BINDRA:

That is right, about two years old.

LORENZ:

A dog at one year is still rather timid. He will not become aggressive until two years. But I would believe that these things are not innate only if your restricted dog did not show them at all. I would expect the restricted dogs to get aggressive just as much later as corresponds to their period of being restricted. Did this happen?

BINDRA:

In the restricted animals, we did not observe any aggressive responses on the second test. But I think the data on avoidance are crucial: the restricted showed avoidance on the second test, just as the free-environment dogs had on the first test, but the restricted animals did not show avoidance on the first test.

TANNER:

Did puberty occur at the same time in both groups? That is the time when any maturational effect is finally established and it occurs normally at about two years in the dog.

BINDRA:

I am sorry to say I do not know.

TANNER:

I should have thought that something like the times of closure of the secondary centres of ossification for the two groups of dogs would give you the answer to the question that Lorenz is raising.

BINDRA:

My feeling is that experience is the important variable in the development of these patterns of behaviour, and the general excitement in the first test is, you might say, the immediate response of the animal to a new situation. There are some studies on rats that show the same thing. For instance, if you give some sort of a painful stimulation to the rat it really does not *avoid* it, it just shows general excitement. If you observe the animal again and again in the same painful situation you find that eventually he develops an integrated pattern of withdrawal. In one experiment, we put rats on a highly heated platform, and all the rats did, on the first one or two trials, was to sit there. They were apt to pick up a paw and lick it and put it down, and pick up another paw, lick it and put it down; but they did not show any directed patterns that would get them away from the situation. Only eventually did directed withdrawal or avoidance responses emerge.

These findings also throw some light on so-called 'spontaneous fears'. Most normal adult animals show avoidance of a number of stimuli. They avoid a snake, the cast of a snake if 'moving', and other such things. The question that arises about this spontaneous fear is 'Is it innate?'. Animals show avoidance of these objects even when they have had no previous experience with them. The chimpanzee will avoid a snake even when he has never had any painful experience connected with a snake, or even seen a snake (as you can know for sure in laboratory-bred animals). Quite obviously no specific learning has taken place; nevertheless I do not think the avoidance of a snake is innate. Even though no animal has specifically learned to be afraid of these objects, yet some sort of general learning, or general perceptual experience, is necessary before the animal will show spontaneous avoidance behaviour.

My argument is that avoidance is not associated with any particular object, but with strange objects in general. These animals have never seen anything like a snake. Most of their experience has been with things like bricks, with bars, with human beings and other things. So the first time you show them something different, they show general excitement, and, if they have already acquired some directed pattern, such as avoidance or attack, manifest that. Had these animals been brought up with snakes right from birth and not seen humans or dogs they would have shown fear, not of snakes, but of these other animals.

HARGREAVES:

If I remember rightly the fear of snakes appears to mature at a comparatively late age and that, before that stage, chimpanzees do not bother about snakes. This is rather like Lorenz's account of the I.R.M. to the hawk.

LORENZ:

I think that Prechtl has excluded the possibility that the reaction to the snake is simply the reaction to anything unknown. If you show them a pipe, which they have never seen, or a tortoise, they do not react at all, but if you show them a snake they make the typical gesture of disgust and wipe their feet on the ground, and that is very specific.

MEAD:

MASSERMAN and PECHTEL (1953) have tried out on monkeys a whole series of model spiders and scorpions and so forth that are much more related to a snake than a pipe or even a tortoise. They got the specific response only to the snake; the monkeys just ignored all the other livestock.

TANNER:

At what age does the reaction occur?

LORENZ:

With a child it is about two-and-a-half or three.

TANNER:

In a chimpanzee is it the same?

LORENZ:

If you raise a child in an environment of snakes, then you will find you can extinguish this reaction as you can that to every I.R.M. by what is called habituation. One of our Zoo directors made similar snake experiments with his own children and they don't mind snakes at all, because they had lived with snakes all their lives; while the hospital children of PRECHTL (1949) react exactly like the chimpanzees; specifically to snakes.

BINDRA:

Let me give you another example to illustrate the point with chimpanzees. The first time they were shown a part of another chimpanzee, the head actually, they showed avoidance responses. Now the interpretation I am suggesting is this: these animals have had experience of chimpanzees all along, but they had never seen the head of a chimpanzee alone. In order for this avoidance of the head of the chimpanzee to occur on the first presentation even though they had no previous specific learning, these animals had to have had previously the experience of a chimpanzee as a whole.

I think that this was also the case with those chimpanzees reared in darkness. They did not start showing fear of strangers or fear of other things immediately after they could see; they started showing this only after they had learned what their normal surroundings looked like. And then, when they were brought an unfamiliar object, they avoided it.

Fear of strangers, I think, also falls into the same category. If a child has been brought up with only one person, or two persons who have always taken care of it, and then exposed to a stranger, the child will show avoidance or general excitement.

MEAD:

You get it even in the middle of a native village where they have been brought up with thirty or forty people around them all the

86

time. There is still a point in maturation where they begin to discriminate and show fear of the people they see least often. The stranger can be someone who lives four houses down. It is very sudden, around eight to nine months as an average. But the people usually recognize it themselves, and so a baby that a week before was accepting any one of twenty people perfectly easily will suddenly develop all sorts of capricious fears and fright of the less familiar. For example, I would become immediately a 'less familiar', even with a child that previously would let me carry it. But if I had been taking a lot of care of a child, then I would be kept in the 'more familiar' class, although the ability to differentiate me when I am working with dark people is very good.

LIDDELL:

I think it is fair to say that there can be individual differences. There will be less of a response to a stranger by a child who has been used to many people than by a child who only knows one person.

MEAD:

There are individual differences among children, but I do not see any difference between societies where children are taken care of very generally and societies where their own mothers are prominent among several caretakers. But in those societies where the child is taken care of only by its own mother, it will show more fear, because in many instances such a child does not like other people.

BINDRA:

This raises the question whether loss of maternal care as such is the significant variable, or whether here again it is the attachment first having been made and then broken. I think our dog studies suggest that it may be possible to rear a child emotionally normally without a close attachment to one person.

MEAD:

But have you any experiment that bears on capacity for attachment? It seems to me that all your tests deal with avoidance and aggression. What do you have about the capacity to make friends and attach yourself?

BINDRA:

We do not have any direct evidence on this.

87

FREMONT-SMITH:

How about the dogs? Do you know whether they made good pets afterwards and became attached to one person in the same way as the ones that had not been separated at all?

BINDRA:

I should suspect not.

LORENZ:

I should expect the opposite. When you buy a dog which has been brought up under hospital conditions you will find that he is still free to attach himself. When a dog which has once attached himself is torn away—especially in the Lupus strains—he is more or less spoiled for ever. But I should be very surprised if your restricted dogs had lost the capacity of attachment.

MEAD:

Would you presume that a dog that had been hospitalized would attach itself in a normal way to one person, or might it have a variety of peculiar forms of attachment? Would it be as loyal, or too loyal?

LORENZ:

I should say it would be unselective and promiscuous in its loves for a time.

FREMONT-SMITH:

This would fit exactly with the concept of the psychopathic child.

LORENZ:

In different types of children, Sylvia Klimpfinger says, quite different reactions may take place. The children may become very introverted and show no tendency to show social attachment at all. On the other hand they may be 'all over you', show a lack of discrimination and be totally promiscuous in their attachments, and both may be the case with dogs, of course.

BINDRA:

That would suggest that the crucial variable is something quite different; it is not absence of attachment as such.

BOWLBY:

I think what is disappointing is that so far this experiment has not studied the functions in which we are interested. What psychoanalysis and mental health are concerned with are social relationships.

BINDRA:

Does this study not bear, at least to some extent, on the capacity to make relationships in humans? From the mental health point of view what is important is the sort of group a person is going to be making relationships in. If he is brought up in close attachment to one person, and later on finds that there is no such thing as an attachment to one person in the society where he is forced to live, then, from a mental health point of view, he would have been better off without that close attachment in his childhood.

BOWLBY:

I think we lack the evidence on which to make such a generalization, so that I rather deprecate the making of it.

BINDRA:

My point is simply this: your studies have brought up some very important variables that obviously affect the behaviour of human infants. I am interested in proposing some sort of a general theory that would account not only for your results but also ours. I visualize such a theory as having something to do with the number and kind of attachments the child makes as an infant. If he is brought up to make a close attachment to one mother you will get one type of result; if he is brought up to make attachments to a large number you will get another type of result, and neither is good or bad for mental health in itself. Whether it is good or bad would depend on the kind of society in which this person is going to live.

BOWLBY:

I think we are still very ignorant of what effect on mental health these different things have. It seems to me we know nothing from these experiments as to what effect on the dog's social relations or mental health the experience has—the evidence is not reported so we cannot draw any conclusions from it. The same is partly true of children where we only know a few things about certain extreme cases. What we know suggests that if a child is subjected to a sufficiently large and changing population of mother figures, so far from being good at getting on with everyone he will be bad at getting on with anyone.

BINDRA:

When they are brought up in a particular society?

TANNER:

Does the cultural evidence support this?

MEAD:

If a child is subjected to a sequence of mother figures which do not recur or which recur at too wide intervals to be significant, then you will have instability. This is not the sort of thing which is described for primitive societies. What we have is a situation where, for instance, the child may be cared for by twenty people, but those twenty people are quite constant. The grandmother and mother and mother's four sisters and father's brothers' four wives and the seven little girls who live next door will all look after the child almost every day. So you have a constancy which is nevertheless subdivided among a number of people.

I would say that the cultural evidence suggests that on the whole there is an easier adult adjustment in these individuals than in the individuals who are cared for by single persons.

HARGREAVES:

It is important to draw a distinction between what you might call 'mothers in parallel' as opposed to 'mothers in series'.

BOWLBY:

Mothers 'in parallel' are probably all right—mothers 'in series' certainly are not.

LORENZ:

I have three or four different explanations for the result of your experiment. Your restricted dogs (a) may have missed some sensitive period with which they cannot catch up, (b) may have a slight detriment done to some I.R.M., (c) may be retarded in their maturation, and (d) may not be changed at all, but, as they have such very restricted individual experiences, they are from their point of view

90

in an entirely new environment. The normal dogs, on the other hand, having lots of experience of very varying surroundings, are always blasé to their environment.

This may also account for the lack of aggressiveness, because in a new environment one is not aggressive. A dog must feel territorial to get aggressive. So the environmental factor is able to account for this. But I would not dare to assert that aggressiveness is not innate. If you ask, 'Is suckling in a goat innate?' my answer is definitely that some of its components are and some are not. The rhythmical upwards-thrusting movement of the kid's head I would strongly suspect of being entirely innate, also, perhaps, a very rough orientation reaction which makes the kid search for the nipple 'on the underside of something'. On the other hand the 'knowledge' of the fact that the mother's udder is between her hind legs is quite evidently learned by trial and error. It is quite evident that there is no inborn orientation towards the udder by smell, as one might have expected. My point is that the mere question 'is aggressiveness innate' is much too simple in view of the possible complication of aggressiveness.

Another technical argument: if you take pure-bred dogs in order to get a more reliable genetic basis of behaviour, that is the worst thing you can do! So-called pure-bred dogs are always bred for form, and the more modern and popular pets they are, the less homozygotic they are as to behaviour. If a dog has the right kind of ears it may have monstrous anomalies of behaviour, yet dog breeders will still go on breeding from it. If you want a dog which is as homozygotic as possible as to behaviour, you must get a dog from a 'professional' police stud, or collies from Scotland, not the modern show-collies. My guess would be that you would get a more level curve of variability of behaviour even with mongrels than you would with high-bred dogs. As you know, the German shepherd dogs are already being bred in two strains, just as carrier pigeons are bred in different strains, and you find that those with a flat spectrum of performance are very poor in looks. If a policeman wants a good dog, he does not mind if his dog's tail curls a bit!

TANNER:

Are we not getting confused between two quite different genetical points? Inbreeding in the sense of brother/sister or father/daughter mating always tends to produce isogenicity and homozygosity for all genes, including those affecting both behaviour and form. We must distinguish this from selective breeding which is breeding for something completely different. If I remember rightly, you were saying that we should not use inbred dogs.

91

LORENZ:

No, I said pure-bred dogs, not inbred; severely inbred dogs would be all right. My tip would be to use dogs of a family which already has a characteristic 'spectrum' of behaviour as for instance dogs with comparatively high escape-reactions and at the same time high aggressive responses. It seems to me this very often happens in the same family. In Dobermans, it is very typical that you get in the same litter very aggressive dogs and very shy dogs, and other dogs which up to the third or fourth year are extremely shy and then get extremely aggressive. My tip is that these rather predictable types of extreme shyness or extreme aggressiveness would be more favourable objects for your purpose because they provide closer analogy.

BINDRA:

I think this is a very good suggestion. Of course, what we do will depend on the problem at hand. If we are interested in dogs of different responsiveness in order to see what is their susceptibility to neurosis, then we would have to follow something like you suggest. But if our problem is to determine the source of differences in responsiveness, then we have to use inbred dogs.

GREY WALTER:

I should like to make a mild and friendly protest. Animal breeding is a great art which has been cultivated over many generations, but not a single genetic proposition about the human being can be sustained at the present time; almost nothing is known about human genetics. I think people may have felt that there was some sort of hope of working out some of the paradoxes and dilemmas in human beings by some genetic trick or observation. I think that is a very faint hope and that even if you found absolutely clear-cut evidence of genetic traits in animals, we should still be quite in the dark as to the psychobiological development of the human child. We cannot envisage yet an experiment which will enable us to separate out the genetic and environmental factors in the behaviour of a human being. The application of animal breeding principles is a very specialized thing which has no relation that we know of to human beings.

LORENZ:

But Dr. Bindra wanted to investigate environmental factors; he was not interested in my genetically different dogs because he wanted to know what to do to prevent the development of anxiety by environmental factors.

GREY WALTER:

He is using animals which have been selected for many generations by breeders with a clear idea of what they wanted; human beings have not been through this process, as far as we know

LORENZ:

It is my opinion that they have.

GREY WALTER:

It is a thing that is impossible to prove and the evidence will still be only a dream as far as the human is concerned.

BINDRA:

That is true enough, but if we are to find some effects of variation in early environment we have to use inbred animals. We cannot generalize from that to humans, as you have said, but indirectly we derive some benefits from these animal studies.

FREMONT-SMITH:

May I ask for clarification? Dr. Grey Walter, you said that you thought there was no evidence that human beings had been through certain processes and dogs had been. Dr. Lorenz said he thought humans had. I would like to get on the record what was the process that you felt the dogs had been through although there was no proof that humans had been through it.

GREY WALTER:

The processes of inbreeding in the first place and selection for certain features, which we identify in cattle as milk yield, in dogs as the shape of the ears, or in cats as the colour of the coat.

FREMONT-SMITH:

You are making a distinction between a deliberate selection and a natural selection?

GREY WALTER:

Human beings have not been through a process where people choose one another as mates because they want people with red hair or they want people with high intelligence. That may have influenced certain cultures for a short time, but whether that has been true over many human generations cannot be proved.

MEAD:

In most small human communities, presumably the sort of communities which were the precursors of our large ones as far as we can tell, there is a very *high* degree of differential selection. In most societies where you have polygamy—and there are a very large number of them—the man who shows the traits that are particularly approved in that society can have five wives or twenty wives in the course of his lifetime, whereas the man who shows disapproved traits may be unable to get any wife, or only a woman who has proved herself infertile. The analogue to purposive planned breeding is very strong in small communities.

HARGREAVES:

I was thinking of a sentence of the report of the last session (Vol. 1) where you said that in some communities a woman with large breasts could not get married at all.

GREY WALTER:

On the basis simply of the mammary glands. A woman is selected for her mammary glands.

TANNER:

This is what you were denying before.

GREY WALTER:

There is some evidence from remote cultures, but can anyone lay down the principles on which mate selection has been based in Western cultures?

HARGREAVES:

From the sales of lipstick, red lips seem to be one thing. The sale of lipstick may have prevented that selection taking place, but it proves that red lips are a selection factor, otherwise you could not sell lipstick.

GREY WALTER:

With regard to the lips and mammary glands, in our culture we have produced a standard of lip redness and mammary gland development which is completely illusory; in this way we avoid selection of the characters we admire, by providing cosmetics and prosthetic appliances.

TANNER:

There is one matter where we have clear evidence of mate selection, and that is for physical size. The correlation of stature of spouses is about 0.2 in England.

HARGREAVES:

And intelligence is a selection factor as well; there is a high correlation in intelligence between married partners in our society. CAROTHERS (1953) maintains that does not exist in tribal Africa; equality of intelligence is apparently sought in marriage in our society and not in some others.

LORENZ:

There is another point of similarity between the breeding conditions of man and domestic animals, and that is the lack of natural selection. A wild animal species is continually subjected to a very severe selection: a wild animal is so cleverly adapted in shape that every tiny detail is carefully 'thought out'.

GREY WALTER:

By whom?

LORENZ:

By natural selection. You can change hardly anything; if you make a beak five millimetres longer or shorter it is evidently bad, and if you make the plumage of the female more roughly spotted it is apparently also bad. The right pattern may be determined in genetically different ways. MAYR (1942) has shown quite conclusively that wild species often are much more constant in their phenotype than they are in their genotype. This is the most convincing proof how sharp selection is! The main point of similarity between domestic animals and man is the complete removal of this effect of natural selection. Natural selection is much more strictly standardizing than that of the most exacting dog breeder. It would seem that this dropping out of the sharpness of natural selection is in itself sufficient to cause what we call domestication. Professor HERRE (1943) who studied the domestication of the reindeer by the Lapps, discovered that practically no factor in the life of the reindeer is changed as compared with the North-American wild caribou. The Lapps are actually unable to influence the life of their reindeer very deeply, because a Lapp family needs for its support more reindeer than it can hold. They have to run after the reindeer all the time;

they cannot keep them from moving. Only in winter a number of families congregate to drive the reindeer to certain islands in lakes where they can better ward off the wolves. So these reindeer graze naturally and have exactly the same ecology as wild reindeer. The only appreciable changes concern natural selection: the Lapps keep off the wolves and castrate the old bulls who get nasty. The domestication of the reindeer is comparatively young historically, and yet the reindeer shows every single trait of what Margaret Mead and I have agreed to call 'vulgarization' (see Vol. 1).

That is one factor which is really common between man and domestic animals. The other thing is what Julian Huxley calls reticulate evolution. The permanent process of branching up into races and into species, which is typical in the phylogeny of most animals, is prevented in man and domestic animals by their recrossing all the time. These are two extremely far-reaching biological factors which you find exclusively in man and domestic animals. And these are, after all, genetical things.

INTERVAL

BINDRA:

The second line of study that I should like to report deals with the effects of sensory or perceptual deprivation in the human adult. A considerable amount of recent neurophysiological evidence has shown that in order for the brain to function normally it has to be constantly bombarded by sensory stimulation. Sensory stimulation appears to have two separate types of function. Firstly, it evokes some sort of specific response (perception). Secondly it has a more general effect of arousal.

We were interested in finding out what the effects of sensory deprivation would be on a human adult. The method was quite simple. College students in need of money were paid twenty dollars a day to lie down in a specially prepared cubicle, with frosted glasses on their eyes. These frosted glasses prevented any pattern vision, though light went through. On their arms the subjects wore long cardboard boxes which prevented them from feeling any part of their body with their hands, though it was possible for them to bend their arms at the elbows. They communicated with the experimenter through a speaker system. They all contracted to lie there for as long as they could, and since the reward was twenty dollars a day, quite a few people stayed as long as four or five days. All the results that I am going to report are on subjects who stayed in at least forty-eight hours.

MEAD:

Do they contract to stay awake?

BINDRA:

No. They spend quite a lot of their time sleeping. The procedure for each subject was as follows: A few days before the subject was put in this chamber, he was given a number of tests. Some of these were sub-tests taken from tests of intelligence, and other tests were made up specially for our purpose. Then, during his stay in the chamber, the subject was given the same or comparable tests. He was given problems to do in his head. Immediately after coming out of the chamber he was tested again. We had a control group which did not go through the chamber but who were given the tests at the same intervals. The effects I am going to report have been corrected on the basis of the performance of the control group.

First of all, there was an impairment in intellectual function. About twenty-four hours after getting into the chamber, subjects began to report that they were unable to concentrate. They could not keep the questions in their head.

FREMONT-SMITH:

This is while they are in the chamber?

BINDRA:

Yes.

BOWLBY:

What are the instructions with regard to the voice? They might keep up a long conversation.

BINDRA:

Sometimes they did. There was an experimenter within reach of the subject all the time, not in the chamber but close by. He was always available because a subject might say, at four o'clock in the morning for example, 'I want some dinner' or, at one o'clock in the afternoon he might want some breakfast.

MEAD:

He is allowed to have food whenever he likes?

BINDRA:

Whenever he likes. Every time he asks for food, the experimenter asks him what food he would like. In that way we avoided giving any indication of the time of day.

MEAD:

No wonder he stays there and his intellect deteriorates!

FREMONT-SMITH:

Do they have any whisky?

BINDRA:

We have not yet been able to get any funds for that!

STRUTHERS:

I think I might bring in something about the conditioning which these men undergo. They frequently go on a binge before they start this performance . . .

BINDRA:

Soon after the subjects reported difficulty in concentration, they also began to show deterioration in objective tests. The error score increased.

TANNER:

Do you pay them to get the correct results? Because after a while you may get the 'couldn't care less' attitude—perhaps about the time they are going to give up.

BINDRA:

They seemed to try hard. They were quite bored inside the chamber because they had nothing to do. I think that that was enough motivation for them to try, and quite often they actually asked for problems.

They also reported some confusion. This confusion and disturbance was reported particularly when they had just left the chamber. Everything appeared different. The colours appeared to be too strong and so forth.

STRUTHERS:

The lighting is kept constant?

98

BINDRA:

Yes. The most dramatic effect they showed was some sort of hallucination—I think that is the only word to describe it, even though the subjects were quite aware that what they saw was not actually there.

BOWLBY:

The hallucinations take place with insight, and the patients know they are hallucinating?

BINDRA:

Yes. These hallucinations started off with relatively simple geometrical figures; the subject saw lines and triangles and things of that kind, and gradually they became more and more complicated. In the fully developed form they looked rather like Disney cartoons, that is to say, they had the quality of being fairly vivid and quite complicated. A subject saw a street corner, for instance, or he saw himself going out in a boat in Nova Scotia. As these hallucinations became more complicated colour appeared. The subjects were not alarmed by them so far as we can tell—in the beginning they were amused. Later they reported that the hallucinations interfered with their problem solving. One subject said, 'I am trying to work out this problem, but I still keep on seeing that damn street corner'.

FREMONT-SMITH:

If a subject has an hallucination, does he keep the same one or does he have a series of images?

BINDRA:

He has changes quite often, but he might report, 'Now that thing's back again'.

FREMONT-SMITH:

Did almost all of them have hallucinations or were hallucinations rather rare?

BINDRA:

Our first ten subjects or so did not report any hallucinations. But when one of the experimenters himself served as a subject and saw the queer things, he reported it, of course, and from that time on all the subjects were instructed to report anything they saw, or heard, or if they had any unusual experience. After that, almost invariably every subject reported hallucinations coming on from twenty-four to forty-eight hours after he began the experiment. Presumably, before this instruction, the subjects thought there was something abnormal about seeing these things and therefore did not mention them.

MEAD:

Or you established a set.

BINDRA:

We took every care not to create a set. We only said in a general sort of way that if they saw anything they should report it.

MEAD:

'If you see anything' is an instruction, after all. How do you discriminate among types of eidetic images?

BINDRA:

These vivid hallucinations were not something they could call and let go at will. They just came.

FREMONT-SMITH:

Do subjects talk with one another in advance on the experiment? In other words, might one subject know what the other subject had experienced before he went in? Are they students?

BINDRA:

Students, yes, but students from different faculties. It is possible that some of them communicated with each other. I think the way these hallucinations appear suggests it is a genuine phenomenon. They appear more or less always in the same way: they start with simple forms and then get complicated. Even if the subjects talked about seeing things, I doubt if they would go into details of the manner in which the hallucinations occurred.

RÉMOND:

What is the importance of memory in your hallucinations, and also, how do you compare them with that sort of dream you may have while you are awake, particularly when you are in a state of mental fatigue?

BINDRA:

I think they are probably very similar.

WHITING:

May I ask if you expected your controls to watch out for certain things?

MEAD:

Who are the controls?

BINDRA:

Their chamber consists of a partitioned section of a room with a bed, and they have to lie down all the time, except when they want to use the toilet, or when they want to eat. They have no glasses or cardboard boxing.

FREMONT-SMITH:

Have they had any hallucinations?

BINDRA:

No, as far as I know nobody has reported any.

MEAD:

If you investigated subjects taking metabolism tests, you might find a large number of hallucinations.

BINDRA:

There are certain other instances of hallucinations. I am told that in many patients who suffer from migraine visual hallucinations are a common symptom.

GREY WALTER:

The teichopsia or fortification figures of migraine have a very characteristic crenellated form, but I do not see any relation between these and the experiences of your subjects. Mescaline hallucinations are the ones which seem to resemble most closely the ones you describe; these are often geometric figures, triangles and more elaborate patterns which develop into fantastic images related to real experiences and are also associated with the paranoid feelings of the subjects. I feel the accounts of your subjects were very similar

101

to those from experiments in which I myself participated. This suggests that if you have an interruption of the sensory inflow, it can have the same hypnotic effect that you get with mescaline, which acts at the same level.

BINDRA:

Is the metabolism of mescaline well known?

GREY WALTER:

It is becoming known. It might be interesting to try the effect of sub-threshold doses of mescaline to see if you could summate the two effects, to accelerate the appearance of hallucinatory experiences in the same experimental conditions.

MONNIER:

Did they have tactile hallucinations?

BINDRA:

Not tactile hallucinations, if I recall correctly, but some movement hallucinations.

MONNIER:

You would have expected this because you repressed sensations by putting a protecting sheet around the arms.

BINDRA:

The subject still had tactile stimulation on other parts of the body.

BUCKLE:

Can you say anything about the different types of people who have different types of hallucinations? For instance, body-image hallucinations I think almost always occur in schizophrenic people; do the hallucinations show any relation to the Rorschach test performance?

BINDRA:

There is no indication of any relation between personality and these hallucinations, but then we have not looked for such a relation very carefully. These are normal subjects, and with the small range of variation in the group we will probably not find any relation.

MEAD:

How are you controlling the sleep situation? Your major assumption is that it is being awake and unstimulated that is significant, and not being asleep. It is the periods of wakefulness within this constricting chamber that induce this perceptual deprivation. These experiments are of people studied with periods of sleep, are they not? For instance, I was once on a 'plane that had been grounded without putting the passengers in an hotel—just pushed to the side of an airfield in Texas. Under these circumstances I slept for sixteen hours. The lights went off, you could not read, there was nothing to do, so one felt one might as well go to sleep. I think it is quite possible that at the end of those sixteen hours my performance would have deteriorated; unless you can control the amount you do not know what is the effect of the sleeping done in this period.

BINDRA:

That is quite true, but most of the sleep occurs on the first night and the first day, and these hallucinations do not usually appear until thirty-six or forty-eight hours.

MEAD:

How about the deterioration in performance?

BINDRA:

They show increase in errors about twelve to twenty-four hours after entry.

MEAD:

I take it you think the hallucinations are the more interesting aspect, and the deterioration of the performance tests less so?

BINDRA:

Hallucinations are the more dramatic and were less expected; they are not necessarily more significant.

FREMONT-SMITH:

How long did it take the subjects to recover altogether?

BINDRA:

After they came out of this situation some of the earlier subjects reported having difficulty in driving. They also had difficulty in

103

judging distance. Later, we told all the subjects that they were not to drive an automobile directly afterwards. But they were quite recovered within a day.

FREMONT-SMITH:

How many students have been studied already together?

BINDRA:

This report is based on about twenty subjects, and there is another group of twenty-five that has just been finished.

The study (BEXTON, HERON, SCOTT and HEBB, 1954) does seem to suggest that the normal working of the brain depends on this sort of sensory stimulation, and that sensory stimulation has two separate types of effects: that of arousal as well as the more specific role of sensory stimulation in perception.

RÉMOND:

Do the subjects tend to become more and more sleepy as the time goes by, or just neurotic?

BINDRA:

Not sleepy. As a matter of fact, the general sign which warns the experimenter that the subject is ready to leave is that he becomes very restless, he starts fidgeting, and things of that kind.

TANNER:

Does he hallucinate more and more?

BINDRA:

I have not had that reported.

MEAD:

Have we any reports on the behaviour of adults who have been subject to eye operations which were sufficiently acute that they had to remain in bed in a small hospital room, and the only sort of communication they had was with a nurse? I would suspect that you might get the same results. You should, unless the purposeless restriction is the thing that induces the hallucination.

RÉMOND:

I have a friend who has had that situation after a retinal detachment, and was obliged to stay for about a fortnight in complete darkness with a bandage over his eyes. He could not chew because of the operation they made on his eye, so he could only receive food by tubing. He was a doctor, a neuropsychiatrist, so he was quite aware of things in that field of experience; anyway, after three or four days, he became neurotic and threatened to break everything in the room. Then he stood up to the situation, but lost about 20 kilos of weight.

GREY WALTER:

But was there not some anxiety about the operation?

RÉMOND:

He knew he was probably going to lose his eye, and his other eye was already very bad.

MEAD:

I was thinking of the condition where the deprivation was purposeful. One of the elements in this experiment is that it is so purposeless, except for the twenty dollars motive, which is obscure.

WHITING:

I know someone who had an operation on her eyes, and she had quite a clear hallucination, she thought she was in another room. She was supposed to lie on her back, but she sat up in bed and said 'I am in the wrong room'. It was a very strong hallucination, and when the doctor came he said: 'This very often happens in cases like this; don't worry about it'.

MONNIER:

I would like to emphasize Dr. Bindra's statement that to understand the effects of perceptual deprivation we must keep in mind that sensory stimulation has two functions: a specific and a general function. I would even say that when you suppress the specific function of sensory stimuli there is a great chance that the unspecific function of this stimulation will be enhanced. We could also say that suppression of a special function in the nervous system enhances the other partial functions. In my experiments on coagulation of the thalamus in humans I observed a similar thing. If I coagulate the thalamic centre of pain in the arm this part of the body becomes anaesthetic, but pain develops now two or three days later in the leg. This means you cannot suppress something specific in the nervous system, without the other surrounding systems becoming automatically enhanced in their function (MONNIER, 1953). It is possible therefore that in Dr. Bindra's investigations suppression of specific sensory impulses, such as optic or tactile ones, enhances the unspecific functions of the visual and tactile cortical centres and that hallucinations arise.

BINDRA:

The next line of research that I am going to talk about concerns individual differences in reaction to stress. Such individual differences have been noted again and again. In much of the work on experimental neurosis investigators have found that some animals break down and others do not. Even in ordinary laboratory tasks such as solving analogy problems one finds that the performance of subjects does not necessarily suffer on exposure to stress. Some individuals keep on working at the same level, some deteriorate, and some actually improve their performance. Obviously there is some variable of individual personality difference which determines which subjects are going to react in each of these ways.

A number of investigators (e.g. FARBER and SPENCE, 1953) recently have tried to suggest that the variable *anxiety* is the crucial one. The general idea is that the performance of people who are anxious will deteriorate under stress; people who are not so anxious will probably remain the same; and people who are not anxious at all might improve.

There have been about sixteen investigations in the last three years on the American continent made with this hypothesis in mind. The investigators have tried to define anxiety in a number of ways, some in terms of Rorschach indices, others of psychometric scales; others have taken ratings and the opinions of a number of clinical psychologists. Then they have exposed the subjects to stress and tried to determine its effects on high and low anxiety subjects. The results in investigations using Rorschach indices and psychometric scales have been negative, that is to say, no differential effect of stress was seen on subjects who had been differentiated on this basis. Nevertheless, some studies (e.g. EICHLER, 1951) do suggest that what clinicians call anxiety does have something to do with performance under stress. Whatever variable determines the responses of subjects to stress is probably related in some way to anxiety, though it is not anxiety as determined by the Rorschach indices.

LORENZ:

I quite agree. I think the Rorschach indices are at fault.

BINDRA:

The approach that we have taken on this problem is this: anxiety is too vague or general a concept, and if there is an individual difference or personality variable that is related to stress, it is probably only one *dimension* of what we vaguely call anxiety. For the present, especially in clinical situations, we have to go on using the concept of anxiety, but we should make an attempt to get some more precisely defined, unitary dimensions which would replace what is now called anxiety. When the physicists took over from the layman the concepts of hot and cold they could not do much with these common-sense ideas, and gradually they evolved more precise dimensions such as temperature, wind velocity, humidity, and so forth. Hot, warm and cold still remain useful concepts in everyday life, but in order to develop any exact studies one has to deal with these more precise dimensions. One of the theoretical aims of this research, therefore, was to analyse anxiety and to replace it by more precise dimensions.

FREMONT-SMITH:

After you have taken the cold day apart in terms of wind velocity and so on, you find you have lost your cold day.

BINDRA:

Of course, you could still use the 'cold day' for certain discussions.

FREMONT-SMITH:

You really have to blend all these units together again, and then it does not quite give you a cold day when you get through.

LORENZ:

That is quite typical of so-called 'injunctive' concepts and definitions. We think of most complex realities as sums of very many constituent characters, some of which may be missing without making the conception inapplicable to a given phenomenon. Therefore it is, on principle, impossible to give a definition of a man, or an animal, or of life itself. The term is, so to say, 'loaded' (injungere means something like that) with a set of qualities, which form a sort of spectrum, grading to both sides into that of another

107

concept. It is a very fundamental error to think that a concept for which you cannot give an implicit definition is not a concept. There are hardly any biological concepts other than these. Some people always say, 'Well, define innate behaviour, and if you cannot, go home'. My answer to this is, 'Define man'.

BINDRA:

I think this greater precision is necessary only at certain times. We can carry on many discussions with *anxiety* and do useful things with it, but sometimes greater precision is necessary.

For various reasons, into which I shall not go just now, we thought that what we have called *responsiveness* is one such variable or dimension. It is probably related to what is clinically called anxiety, and at the same time we thought it might differentiate people with respect to their response to stress.

GREY WALTER:

When you say variable, do you mean an interpersonal or an intra-personal variable?

BINDRA:

An individual difference or personality variable, as opposed to what may be called an experimental variable: a property that, for the most part, does not vary within the individual, but varies from individual to individual.

LORENZ:

Why did you not simply call it readiness to anxiety?

BINDRA:

'Readiness to anxiety' would imply that this is an essential part of what is called anxiety. I do not think it is. I think there are many other things involved in 'anxiety', and responsiveness is only one aspect of it.

The measure of responsiveness is really quite simple. It is based on lack of discrimination between a threatening stimulus and a non-threatening stimulus. Two lights, *left* and *right*, are presented to the subject in a random fashion. One of the lights is always followed by an electric shock, and the other light is never followed by a shock. Galvanic skin response is recorded continuously. Each light is presented twenty times. There is a very characteristic galvanic skin response when the subject is given a shock or when the shock-light appears. The subject gives a reaction when the threatening shock-light is presented, and then he gives a reaction to the shock itself. But many subjects give the same 'double' response to the other light as well, that is to say, to the non-threatening stimulus.

LIDDELL:

Does the shock always follow at a certain interval after the light?

BINDRA:

Yes, after a standard interval of about three seconds. We just count the number of the characteristic double responses given to the negative (non-threatening) stimulus. This number is taken as a measure of lack of discrimination, or responsiveness. We get a tremendous range of scores. There are subjects who do not respond to the non-threatening light at all, and others who respond to the non-threatening stimulus on almost all occasions. On the basis of these scores, we divided eighty subjects into three groups: high responsive, medium responsive, and low responsive.

GREY WALTER:

Are the number of anomalous responses distributed normally?

BINDRA:

For this group of eighty subjects they were, more or less.

These three groups did seem to respond differently to stress as determined by changes in their performance on certain tasks under stress. In general, we found that low responsive subjects actually improved their performance under mild stress. The stress in this particular experiment was the *threat* of an electric shock. The high responsive subjects deteriorated, and the medium responsive subjects did various things. The task they have to do is fairly complicated. To begin with, they learn Chinese symbols for different numerals.

GREY WALTER:

It is a sort of code?

BINDRA:

Yes.

GREY WALTER:

How far up did you start, then? You did not start them on two or three, did you?

BINDRA:

All the digits that were given to them in the performance tests were digits over 20.

FREMONT-SMITH:

When was this performance test done in relation with the right-hand and left-hand lights?

BINDRA:

The non-stress performance was done first, then came performance under stress, and then after an interval of about 10 or 15 minutes responsiveness was determined.

FREMONT-SMITH:

But the stress performance was done while they were being shocked?

BINDRA:

No, there was only the threat of shock. The subject is taken to a table where he is given an electric shock. Then he is told, 'This is the type of electric shock you are going to get. Sit down here, and put your left hand on this shock-grid'. There are all sorts of switches and gadgets to scare him. Then the experimenter tells him that while he is working on the task he will receive an electric shock on his left hand. But actually no shock is given during performance. Stress is simply *threat* of shock.

BOWLBY:

Irrespective of how he performs?

BINDRA:

Yes.

BOWLBY:

The promise of what he is to get bears no relation to how he performs? He is not told that if he performs well he will not get a shock?

110

BINDRA:

No, he thinks he is in for it anyway.

We compared the non-stress performance with the stress performance, and found significant differences between the three sub-groups,
high, medium and low responsive. However, one complicating
finding was that the effects of stress were not the same for different
components of performance. If you take speed as the measure of
performance, you get a different result from that obtained by scoring
errors. The most significant differences between high, medium and
low responsive subjects were differences in speed. The low responsive
subjects, when they performed under conditions of stress, actually
increased in speed. Medium responsive subjects did not increase in
speed. The high responsive subjects did not increase in speed either,
and they showed some disturbance in performance in other ways,
either in errors or in the number of items attempted but not
completed.

GREY WALTER:

In these problems, are they just deciphering a coded series, or are
they doing sums?

BINDRA:

They are given the figure 80, say, in Chinese, which they translate
into English.

GREY WALTER:

Do they have a list of the symbols at hand?

BINDRA:

No, they learn this beforehand. Say they are given the figure 80
in Chinese, they have to translate that into English, halve it, and
then find the Chinese for 40.

GREY WALTER:

I do not know why on earth you chose this particular problem.
It seems to me a most intractable situation. There are so many
variables involved—skill at calligraphy, linguistic ability and so on.

BINDRA:

If the task is too simple the amount of stress to which you have
to submit the subject in order to get any performance decrement is

very high, and people are not willing to be subjected to that amount of stress. If you want to reduce the intensity of stress you have to increase the complexity of the task.

GREY WALTER:

I agree, but I still doubt whether it should be so intricate.

BINDRA:

It should be a problem with which everyone has had the same experience, as far as possible. I should also say that there was an experimental group and a control group, and the control group went through essentially the same problems and the same procedure, except that subjects in the control group were not subjected to stress.

BOWLBY:

What sort of association was there, in fact, between the high responsive people and performance—what sort of correlations were there?

GREY WALTER:

What were the actual statistics?

BINDRA:

They were not treated in terms of correlations. They were treated in terms of significance of difference between the various sub-groups.

GREY WALTER:

't'-tests?

BINDRA:

Yes, 't'-tests. The high responsive group gave a significantly higher number of items uncompleted as compared with the low responsive ones.

GREY WALTER:

At what level?

BINDRA:

At about one per cent.

BUCKLE:

What kind of variability do you get by repeating the tests on the same subjects? Do you find the reactions reliable?

BINDRA:

We have split-half reliabilities on the responsiveness trials. If I remember correctly, there were about forty trials and we got a correlation of about $+ 0.8$.

LIDDELL:

What is the total duration of the test?

BINDRA:

Three minutes.

LIDDELL:

Everything that you do to the subject takes how long?

BINDRA:

About an hour and 15 minutes.

MEAD:

I am worried about something a little different. You did not test responsiveness, in the sense of the confusion between the two lights, until after the subjects had undergone the stress performance?

BINDRA:

That is right.

MEAD:

In other words, everyone had learnt something about electric shocks combined with the demand to do something, and then you gave them this responsiveness test. Did you not control it by taking another group and giving them the responsiveness test first?

BINDRA:

No.

MEAD:

In other words, you taught them the piece of confusion that they were supposed to have.

BINDRA:

If you want to put it that way; but it did not confuse everyone equally.

MEAD:

But, you see, you have got a systematic relationship between the stimuli in the stress and in the responsiveness situations. If, instead of using the electric shock for your stress situation, you had a bull around the corner or a dog that was going to bite or something and then used the electric shock for the responsiveness situation, you would not have had this possibility.

My point is simply that what you test, among other things conceivably, is sensitivity to the idea of electric shock.

BINDRA:

Yes.

MEAD:

The stress performance is a sensitization to the threat of shock. That is a learning experience about shock, so all your subjects have gone through a learning experience to which they have responded differentially, for a reason that you do not know. Then you put them in another experience when they use that learning, and they again give you a measure of their sensitivity to electric shock—or fear of shock—whereas if you made those threats completely different I think you would have a better result.

Also, it would be useful if you could do a set of tests to show how much failure to discriminate stimuli these individuals show. You could have different stimuli with the same affective tone and then very similar stimuli but with a positive affective tone. You might be dealing with 'anxiety'—that is, with a tendency to over-generalize—from the threatening. But you might be dealing with a tendency to over-generalize on the basis of *any* affective tone, either threatening or pleasant, and that would change your theoretical result.

BINDRA:

Yes, this is a very good point.

114

GREY WALTER:

There is another problem in this experiment—the variation in the sensitivity to electric shock. There are many people I know—not necessarily horny-handed mechanics—who can stand a shock from 100 volts or so and not mind about it at all, and others whom six volts will hurt. It varies greatly in different people.

Was this a very supra-maximal shock—tens of thousands of volts or so—from a high resistance source?

BINDRA:

No, it was a mild shock.

GREY WALTER:

Your results may be diluted by this factor: some of the people who look as though they had a high responsiveness might in fact simply have a rather low threshold to electric stimulation.

BINDRA:

Yes; unfortunately we were unable to control this.

LIDDELL:

This factor is important; in a psychological laboratory where we were using simple conditioning with mild electric shock on the fingers we had to abandon it because girls were having hysterical crying fits for no reason.

GREY WALTER:

In my laboratory we have a lady who cannot stand a 12 volt D.C. shock but her husband does not worry much about 100 volts. It seems to be just a question of special skin quality.

BINDRA:

I think all you have said is quite true, and I think what we have called responsiveness is responsiveness measured in a particular type of situation. It is a matter of making this variable more precise gradually, by seeing exactly what it is that makes for the obtained individual differences.

Now we plan to do some experiments on dogs. We are going to see if the same sort of differences in responsiveness exist in dogs, and, if these differences in responsiveness do exist in them, we are going

M

to subject dogs to stress, and then determine whether or not responsiveness is related to susceptibility to neurotic breakdown.

I can now go on to describe another line of research at McGill. This study has to do with the reinforcement theory of learning. Ever since THORNDIKE (1928) put forward his law of effect, saying that connections in learning are strengthened by reward and weakened by punishment, psychologists have been trying to discover whether or not rewards and punishments are necessary for learning to occur. There have been two schools of thought, one saying that reward or punishment or some sort of reinforcement is necessary, and the other saying that reinforcement though very important is not absolutely necessary. Most of the experiments have made use of the learning situation of pressing a lever or running through a maze or some such thing, and then created a motivation in the animal, usually by depriving it of food or water. What exactly happens within an organism when it gets a reward (e.g. food or water) or a punishment? Of course, the food goes into its stomach but in order for this reward to leave any permanent learning effect it must have some effect on the brain. The question is what are the neurophysiological mechanisms involved in this reinforcement.

In the last few weeks two researchers in our laboratory, Olds and Milner, have made a frontal attack on this problem. They have demonstrated reinforcement in the rat by direct intracranial stimulation. They have implanted electrodes, we believe in the anterior group of nuclei of the hypothalamus. Electrical stimulation in this part of the hypothalamus has the same effect for all practical purposes as reinforcement by food in the hungry animal.

LORENZ:

Do you mean they make eating movements?

BINDRA:

No. Perhaps the best example to describe is the Skinner box experiment. A rat is placed in the Skinner box, which is an ordinary box with a lever or a bar sticking out on the inside. The animal is able to obtain a pellet of food by pressing the bar. To begin with it presses the bar accidentally, but gradually it learns that pressing the bar means food and then presses the bar, if hungry, at a very rapid rate.

Now, Olds and Milner do not deprive the rat of food or water; there is no question of any drive or motivation in the usual sense of the word. The animal is placed in the box and accidentally happens to press the bar. When it presses the bar an electrical circuit is made and it delivers through the implanted electrodes a certain amount of current in that part of the brain. What happens then is that very soon the animal begins to press the bar again and again at a rapid rate. One gets almost the same learning curve as you obtain in a standard Skinner box experiment, involving food deprivation and food incentive.

FREMONT-SMITH:

Does the animal salivate?

BINDRA:

No. The interpretation I like is that there is something common to all sorts of reinforcement—when the hungry animal gets food, when the thirsty animal gets water, when the animal which is being shocked finds means to escape from the shock, etc. It is probably this something in common that is involved in the hypothalamic stimulation. This is only one possible interpretation, and it may be quite wrong.

HARGREAVES:

Does the animal become satiated?

BINDRA:

Yes, it does.

HARGREAVES:

I wanted to know whether he became an electroholic. Is it an appetite or an addiction? Is it an appetite that can be satisfied?

BINDRA:

It is closer to an addiction, though it can be satisfied. One other result. If you disconnect the circuit, the bar-pressing response can be extinguished. The animal presses the bar and, not receiving any stimulation, looks round as if to say to the experimenter, 'What did you do?'.

LORENZ:

He is disappointed?

GREY WALTER:

Roughly how often will he do that before extinction; twenty, one hundred times?

BINDRA:

About ten or fifteen times. Of course, with repeated reinforcement and extinction things change. One reinforcement trial will reinstate the response, and the rat will go on pressing like mad, and one or two non-reinforced trials only will be sufficient for extinction and will make him give up.

LORENZ:

It is, I suppose, quite irrelevant whether the rat actually chews and salivates, in other words whether his motor effectors perform the movement. He may be stimulated in such a way that he is 'eating in the higher centres' or 'believes that he is eating'.

GREY WALTER:

This is a very difficult problem because the result depends on where your electrodes are exactly. If they are in certain centres, then the whole brain will get information as if the animal had satisfied himself. But a movement of half a millimetre, probably, or a change of frequency of stimulation might have quite a different effect. Your colleagues have been very fortunate, or clever, in happening to get just the right region.

BINDRA:

They have been playing around with this sort of thing for about five years.

GREY WALTER:

There is a very serious danger that your laboratory will become a physiological laboratory!

LORENZ:

I think this is one of the major findings!

BINDRA:

I should like to get the feeling of this group regarding interpretation of this phenomenon.

118

TANNER:

When he is satisfied does he then eat after that, or does he think that he has eaten? That part of the hypothalamus is, in all probability, the centre which tells you whether you are hungry or not. This is a matter still of some disagreement but it may well be that you are doing exactly the same thing as increasing the glucose concentration in those nuclei. When he is satiated there, is he hungry or is he not?

BINDRA:

I do not know what he does when you put him back in his own cage, but it is my impression that the rat does not show any peculiarities of behaviour.

GREY WALTER:

Does he lose weight?

BINDRA:

No, I don't think so.

LORENZ:

I think this question can be answered by a rather simple experiment. If you deprive this rat of food, you can then show the equivalence of real eating and being stimulated by the electrodes.

BINDRA:

If you satiate an animal normally and put it in the Skinner box, it will not continue to press the bar—because it is satiated. In our experiment, we have a food-satiated animal, but it keeps on pressing the bar so long as it gets the current delivered.

FREMONT-SMITH:

Therefore he must be unsatiated in some respect.

BOWLBY:

Have you put electrodes in other parts of the brain?

BINDRA:

So far in only one rat. The results are not the same.
I think the crucial question here is whether or not we are stimulating

119

the place in the hypothalamus that is involved normally in reinforcement. The crucial experiment might be to give a very strong current in this part of the hypothalamus and destroy it, and then try to make the animal learn by ordinary hunger-food motivation to see if the animal can learn in the same way as normal animals.

LORENZ:

You could destroy it and then see whether you have destroyed enjoyment of eating.

FREMONT-SMITH:

Do you mean you would see if you had destroyed their learning centre?

BINDRA:

No, not the learning centre but the reinforcement centre, or the pleasure centre.

MONNIER:

My impression is that you *increase a readiness to activity* by stimulating this hypothalamic centre; this fact has been observed very often. According to my conception, the rat in your experiment presses the bar again and again, because you increased its readiness to activity by stimulating its hypothalamus, just as hunger, thirst or rage would do. In such states of increased readiness, an activity once started keeps going on.

BINDRA:

No. Activity effects are not cumulative, but we do observe cumulative effects in this experiment. The first time the animal learns it presses the bar and does not press it again for some time, and then gradually it improves until finally it reaches a fairly high steady rate. Now you stop reinforcing the response, and it is gradually extinguished. But the second or third time you start reinforcing the same animal it starts pressing straight away, and the response can be extinguished straight away too. If this phenomenon were due to increased activity brought about by hypothalamic stimulation, you would expect that the same amount of stimulation would continue to have the same effect every time. But we observe a cumulative learning effect.

120

MEAD:

There is something we do not know anything about, one of those common-sense notions which we call 'gusto'. Now gusto is associated with eating, drinking, copulating, and all these various pleasures. People who are good and hungry, or good and thirsty, will eat and drink with gusto. Gusto is a concept or a description which includes both appetitive behaviour and increased activity.

LIDDELL:

Zest.

MEAD:

Yes, zest. That might be an area worth exploring, and very possibly people learn better the things they do with gusto, even though you cannot attach either thirst or food or something of that sort to them. We know that the people who do anything with gusto and enjoy what they're doing, tend to do it well.

BINDRA:

These animals may act with gusto, though we have not noticed, but the question still remains why should the animal choose this particular response or act to perform?

MEAD:

I am suggesting that gusto is self-rewarding and reinforcing, and gusto may also be associated with increased activity as well as with satisfaction of appetite. That would be the bridge with what Dr. Monnier said.

TANNER:

If in a similar experiment one rewarded or gave gusto to the beast every time he *ate*, I wonder what would happen, would he just go on and on and blow up eventually?

HARGREAVES:

What about feeding him with some 'gusto' just when he is approaching to eat in order to see if you could short-circuit the eating?

BINDRA:

Another thing would be to make the animals actually hungry before putting them in the box to see if the learning curve becomes steeper.

GREY WALTER:

I do hope your colleagues will extend their experiments to other animals before they spend too much time and ingenuity, for the rat is a very difficult subject for neuroanatomists. It would be fascinating to see the results in the cat where these anatomical extensions have beenworked out so carefully.

BINDRA:

We do not have any cats in our laboratories, and with dogs we have not had much success in getting electrodes implanted.

MONNIER:

Dogs are not very suitable, because of the extreme variability in the size of the skull.

BINDRA:

The hypothalamus of the dog has not been mapped out, has it?

GREY WALTER:

The cat has been charted with extreme care by Whitlock and many others.

BINDRA:

These comments will be very helpful to us in our further work.

THIRD DISCUSSION

Presentation: Dr. Liddell

LIDDELL:

It seems to me at this time that it would be appropriate to raise certain puzzling questions concerning the psychobiological development of the child. This area of difficulty is well stated in a recent paper by BOWLBY (1953) called: 'Some Pathological Processes set in train by Early Mother-Child Separation.' He says in conclusion:

'Such experimental work as exists suggests that responses learnt under stress are far more resistant to extinction than those learnt when the organism is relaxed, and that exposure to one stress situation has significant effects on later reaction to another by lowering the threshold of susceptibility.

'Thus we find ourselves confronted with the laws governing initial learning by immature organisms in conditions of stress. Unfortunately the overwhelming majority of experiments in the field of learning study exactly the opposite state of affairs—the laws governing later learning in mature organisms not in conditions of stress. It is evident, therefore, that if learning theory is to help us with these central problems of psychopathology, it will need to be extended to cover the special conditions described. Such an extension is greatly to be desired, since it seems likely that it will establish the link between human psychopathology and studies of experimental neurosis.'

Since Darwin and Huxley placed man in nature 75 years ago, there he has remained. And those of us who are making common cause in the study of these fundamental problems of grievous mental injury in early youth must somehow come to a common basis of understanding as to methods and aims. So it seems to me that certain fundamental and puzzling questions that concern us all are the following. What is the nature of the so-called psychic trauma? What mechanisms can the neurophysiologist, the endocrinologist,

123

the experimental biologist, discover to account for the consequence of intolerable stress imposed on the immature organism, remaining as scars upon the personality or brain perhaps for the duration of life?

Secondly, how is it possible for the mother to shield her immature offspring effectively against these otherwise mentally injurious environmental stresses?

These problems concern those of us dealing with infra-human organisms, as well as those who, like Dr. Bowlby, work in the clinical field. It seems to me a fundamental point of methodology— and this to me is the significance of the use of the term psycho-biological—that we have not here a closeted self-limiting laboratory field of operations. So soon as we bring an organism into the laboratory and purport to control the conditions under which we impose stress upon it, we are of logical necessity forced to pursue that organism outside the bounds of the laboratory into its natural living quarters and free-roaming space.

So I thought I would begin by stating that from my point of view there are no commonplaces of behaviour, and any notion that there is routine, or usual, or unnoteworthy behaviour cannot possibly be true. Therefore in introducing problems of methodology I wish to give two or three examples of seemingly commonplace behaviour which would be incomprehensible provided one did not make a psychobiological survey of the animal's life situation.

The first example is this. My naturalist colleague Dr. Nicholas Collias was serving as midwife to a pregnant ewe who was about to lamb. He was out in the barnyard one afternoon when he saw this pregnant ewe staring intently at a pool of fluid. He rightly anticipated that she was about to give birth. Therefore, he stood by, he delivered the lamb, took it at once and prevented the mother from making any contact with it. She could only smell it from a short distance. He used this to induce a magnet reaction in which she faithfully followed him into the laboratory room where he incarcerated her, because another lamb was due. Then he took her firstborn to a distant room and separated it. He came back to assist the mother in her second birth. This twin he allowed her to deal with in the normal manner. She licked it, she induced it to nurse and so on. Four and a half hours later he returned the firstborn. The mother would have none of it; she was already in possession of her properly tended lamb. To permit this firstborn lamb to get nutriment, it was necessary to confine the mother to a stanchion so that the lamb could nurse in spite of her unwillingness to permit it to do so. Then Dr. Collias kept the mother, the wanted twin and the unwanted twin in the same experimental compartment. All of the compartments are fitted

124

with a one-way screen, so the experimenter can withdraw from the room to see what is happening. He watched the mother and timed her rejection butting movements against the unwanted lamb for an hour, and made a note of the number of these. Over the course of three and a half days, her rejection became less and less vehement. She butted the lamb fewer and fewer times, and finally it could occasionally get a drink, but it was permitted to nurse regularly only while the mother was confined to the stanchion. I have a small laboratory class which is conducted as follows. The students have no textbook, they simply see the animals and are taught to write down all that they observe. I brought the class of students into the room with this mother, the favourite twin and the unfavoured twin. I had not seen the mother with these twins before, nor had the class. Dr. Collias had told me privately what had occurred, and I said to the class, 'Now this mother has a favoured twin and an unfavoured twin; let us all guess which twin is which by observing their behaviour'. The mother stood across the room facing us, gazing at us intently. One lamb began wandering round the room, the other made directly for the mother's teat and began suckling. We all chose the wrong lamb! This mother was so vigilant and alert to our watching her that the unwanted lamb was able to slip in 'under the wire' and get a free meal. This is what I mean by saying there is no commonplace of behaviour.

The second example is this. The same class, within a week, was taken into one of our laboratory rooms, 10 feet square with a cement floor. We lined up against one wall. There was a lamb in this room three weeks of age. None of us had seen this lamb before. The lamb stood in the farthest corner, wheeled and faced us, ready, tense, and if one of us approached it would attempt to escape. After some minutes we filed out of this room and went single file into the adjoining room and lined up similarly against the wall. There was another three-weeks' lamb who was a twin to the first one. At once when we lined up against the wall the lamb dashed to us and tried to force itself between our legs and the wall to make as close a contact with us as possible. The difference in behaviour was easily explained. The second twin had been removed from the mother at birth and raised on a bottle by the laboratory staff, though we ourselves were strangers to it and it was a stranger to us. If Dr. Lorenz chooses to extend and expand a little his concept of imprinting, perhaps this is the mammalian homologue of imprinting, which will not last very long in the sheep.

A third example: one of our goats, trained for several months in the laboratory, was observed as it wandered about in the barnyard. A new electric fence had been installed and the goat shortly approached this unfamiliar strand of wire. It hesitantly touched the wire with its muzzle and instantly wheeled and dashed away. But after a few steps it wheeled again, faced the electric wire and precisely flexed its right foreleg. The casual observer would be at a loss to account for this unfamiliar or peculiar instance of goat behaviour. However, the circumstances of the animal's training make its precise but bizarre reaction to the unexpected shock on its muzzle more understandable. It had been trained in the laboratory for several months according to the following regimen. For an hour each day, while confined by a restraining harness and with electrodes attached to the right foreleg, a buzzer was sounded for 10 seconds, followed immediately by a mild electric shock to the foreleg. Forty of these buzzer signals, spaced a minute apart, were given at each session. If the goat kept its foreleg flexed until the buzzer stopped it received no shock. It learned very soon to avoid the shocks and, indeed, had not received a single shock for several weeks. However, its prompt and precise flexion at the sound of the buzzer continued without lapse.

Now, in the barnyard, the novel experience of electric shock on the muzzle promptly released the inappropriate behaviour of running from the fence, wheeling and *then* making the avoidance response—a most unrealistic reaction to a situation meaning danger.

During the past two years further observations indicate that this goat has developed a definite and chronic emotional disorder (which is all that is meant by Pavlov's unhappy term 'experimental neurosis'). Except for the dramatic episode of its unrealistic reaction to danger just mentioned, a visitor unfamiliar with the history of this animal's behaviour would fail to note any striking peculiarities setting it apart from our other goats. However, we accidentally discovered that its pattern of emergency reaction to danger had become highly simplified and stereotyped. We no longer give shocks no matter what the animal does during the test period, and although the buzzer signal has now been repeated more than two thousand times at irregular intervals and for as long as a minute and a half (the original training was 10 seconds buzzer and one minute separation of buzzer and shock) the goat still continues to maintain flexion of its right foreleg as long as the buzzer is sounding. It will not, or cannot, take a chance. When the buzzer sounds for a minute or more the goat shows evidence of pronounced fatigue. Tremor of the flexed leg and gradual sinking of the forefoot towards the floor will be corrected by a sudden forceful flexion just before the foot touches the floor, as if from a hot griddle. Moreover, all sudden stimuli such as turning on lights, starting a movie camera, tapping the goat's side lightly with a wooden rod, instantly evoke a brisk and maintained flexion.

126

Sometimes the animal suddenly and spontaneously assumes the flexed position of the foreleg in the absence of any observable change in its laboratory environment. All alarms are now channelled to the right foreleg.

What keeps this simple and stereotyped avoidance response going when there is no longer anything in the animal's real situation to be avoided? It seems to us that this is fundamentally the same question which the psychiatrist faces in combating his neurotic patient's phobias. There seems to be no reason why the operation of 'traumatic memories' may not be inferred in both cases.

Several years ago we published definite evidences that the neurotic sheep takes its worries home to the barn at night. When a sheep is subjected to the monotony of a rigid time schedule of ten-second conditioned signals spaced six minutes apart, and this schedule is followed day after day, a severe emotional upset is precipitated and becomes chronic. The animal exhibits diffuse agitation in the laboratory, with frequent and vivid startle reactions, laboured breathing, and rapid irregular pulse. Even weeks or months after the tests have been discontinued the animal exhibits its perturbation in the barn at night. With the aid of a long-distance stethoscope the observer, in a shed outside the barn, can listen to the heart sounds of both normal and neurotic sheep. When the flock is resting quietly in the barn, the normal sheep's heart beats slowly and regularly; by contrast, the neurotic sheep's heart may be beating twice as fast with wide fluctuations of rate and with frequent premature beats. When placed on a long recording platform within sight of other sheep, the neurotic sheep, unlike the others, continues its nervous pacing back and forth on the platform during the dark hours, suggesting that its traumatic memories or worries have led to insomnia.

The examples just cited from our own research could be multiplied many times. I have reviewed them here because it is the purpose of this meeting to strive for the convergence and even coalescence of our diverse viewpoints.

Those of us who investigate animal behaviour with medical intent have been frustrated for many years by habitual attitudes of 'interdoctrinal unacceptance'. This is a very happy phrase coined by Dr. Harry Kruse of the New York Academy of Medicine. For example, the statement is repeatedly made that the so-called experimental neurosis in animals can have little or no bearing on human psychoneurosis. This, it is said, is because the animal's emotional disorder is situational. It originates in the laboratory and appears only when the animal is returned to the laboratory situation, actual published evidence, such as reviewed above, notwithstanding. Thus, 'inter-doctrinal unacceptance' irradiates to embrace 'factual un-acceptance', and that, we would agree, is going too far.

LORENZ:

That is what we are meeting for. You always find people who say 'I simply do not believe that'.

LIDDELL:

You publish it, give him the reference, and he still will not believe it.

FREMONT-SMITH:

Instead of saying 'I do not quite understand you' I would like to suggest the term 'contra-doctrinal repudiation'.

LIDDELL:

The two traditions of research originating in the classical studies of CANNON (1936) and FREUD (1935) have, from their beginnings, converged upon the same fundamental problem, namely, the functional significance of emotion. This concerns us in facing the problem of the operational meaning of psychic trauma. This physiological tradition and this psychodynamic tradition will eventually coalesce in spite of the well-known inertia and conservatism of thinking peculiar to the life sciences. The merger will be hastened, I believe, when it is recognized that between the organic and the psychodynamic positions there is another distinct viewpoint—the behavioural or psychobiological position, which, I take it, this Group represents. Those of us who adhere to this position and who have persevered in the study of the animal's chronic emotional disorders brought on by the stresses of conditioning can contribute to an understanding of the functional significance of emotion. We can certainly do so when it is clearly recognized that a division of labour is based upon the well-established zoological principle of homology. This is the great contribution of ethology, that both Lorenz and Tinbergen have employed this principle of homology, and applied it to behaviour as well as to anatomical structure.

The sheep's foreleg and the human hand and arm are homologous structures serving diverse purposes. The sheep's foreleg is one member of a locomotor quartet and that is all. The human upper extremity is capable of incredible feats of manipulative skill. But the sheep's 'locomotor' brain and man's 'manipulative' brain are driven to action by the same kind of primitive, neurohumoral 'emotional' machine.

If symbolizing derives from manipulating we cannot expect the sheep's simple but chronic neurotic disorder to reveal evidences of distorted symbolism or of the operation of a 'primary process' as in human psychoneurosis. But evidences of emotional disability obtained from sheep undergoing the long continued stress of conditioning and from soldiers subjected to the long continued hazards of the combat situation, as revealed in posture, movement, and organ dysfunction show them to be the same in sheep and man.

FREMONT-SMITH:

May I suggest that along with the concept of homology in behaviour, which seems to be absolutely vital to our needs, although we may not be ready to accept anthropomorphism, we should certainly be ready to accept biomorphism.

GREY WALTER:

Would you be willing to accept mechanomorphism rather than homology?

LIDDELL.

I was going to ask what term you would use. I thought when I saw your model I could put wool on it and have it in the pasture!

GREY WALTER:

Indeed you could. In the establishment of a conditioned defensive reflex it is very easy to show that theoretically and in the model reinforcement is not necessary. The defensive reflex particularly is liable to be self-reinforcing, and once established you need only press the neutral stimulus button, because of the feedback loop which I showed you.

LIDDELL:

In other words, your machine could actually, with proper circuits, do what the goat did?

GREY WALTER:

It does do what the goat does. The reinforcement of the conditioned defensive reflex is automatic in this very model, without reapplication of the specific stimulus. Before I brought the model

129

here, I wiped off all the labels I had put on it; I thought they were too provocative. The one which provides for the defensive loop was called 'obsession', because the thing was an obsession; there was no reward, it was a movement like a tic in human beings. This seems to be in essence the caricature of a defensive reflex. One of the questions I should like to ask later on is to what extent in animals and in men is there evidence of the unreinforced conditioned reflex based on repetition.

LORENZ:

That is what I was going to ask: whether you get this kind of independence of reinforcement in anything other than avoidance reactions. It looks very like a neurosis, and looks very disorderly, as if the animal becomes obsessed about some stimulus. Now from the naturalist's point of view, which I am always trying to keep parallel with the causal investigator's point of view, it is of enormous survival value that the animal *does* become obsessed. It would be very inadaptive from the point of view of survival value, if a goose, which has once escaped some predator, did not become obsessed about this method of escape. If after a time he became curious or tried to find out whether that predator really was dangerous this would be inadaptive.

So I think there is some difficulty, as there always is, in drawing the borderline between the still adaptive and the pathological. I wondered whether your goat, which retracted its leg, and reacted with this escape reaction to every stimulus, was not far nearer to the adaptive than the sheep who runs about at night?

LIDDELL:

It is my particular point of view, which I think we can now justify, that all Pavlovian conditioning is stressful conditioning, unlike the Skinner box. I was led to this view by my unfortunate beginning in behaviour research when I attempted to employ the methods of the animal psychologist in attacking the thyroid problem of Dr. Simpson. As I mentioned a few days ago, he wished me to match the common signs of hypothyroidism, slow pulse, retarded growth, muscular slackness, and so on, with a mental dullness which occurs even in the human adult suffering from severe hypothyroidism. Being at a loss how to attack this problem, I found in an old *Journal of Psychobiology* (when the *Journal of Animal Behaviour* was discontinued with the outbreak of World War I, it never resumed publication; for a brief period, under the influence of Professor Knight Dunlap, a journal appeared called the *Journal of*

Psychobiology) an article by K. S. Lashley and Shepherd Ivory Franz which was the original article of a series in which they sought to show the effect of cortical extirpation upon the learning of the rat. They employed a very simple T-maze with the arms bent down, and I modified this as an outdoor maze to test normal and thyroidecto-mized sheep and goats. Here I discovered (to my consternation), that a repetitive behaviour pattern went on of its own momentum without reinforcement.

Briefly the circumstances were these. We built a board fence about an enclosure with three parallel alleys, the middle alley bounded by wire screening. There was a little starting compartment with a door which would fall, allowing the animal to emerge. Then the animal had to find its way down one of either of the outer alleys in order to reach the final compartment, at the end of which there was an iron grill door, leading to the barn, where the flock of sheep were. There also was a small box filled with oats. Either alley could be made 'blind' by the experimenter shutting a door. Now the animal, as I naively supposed, under the motivation of its gregariousness, wanting to join the other sheep, and secondly motivated by its desire to have a bite of oats, must learn to avoid the gate of the alley which was closed (the cul de sac). It would come down this alley, find it blocked, retreat and go round to the open alley leading to flock and food. The animal would learn to do this. Then we could reverse the position of the cul de sac or blind alley, and it would learn to go the other way. Now, to make a long story short, I never demonstrated any definite difference between normal and thyroidectomized animals; even though the thyroidectomized animals were sluggish and only one-third the body weight of their twins, I failed to detect an intellec-tual blunting—if you want to call it so. But in the course of these events I came upon what seemed to me most disconcerting facts about repetitive behaviour. I finally found a problem which no sheep or goat ever solved, namely a temporal alternation in which the animal, on its first trial of the day, must turn right to get into the final compartment and in the very next trial (it returns at once into the starting compartment) it must turn to its left, then to its right then to its left; four times in succession. The animals never learned to do this. All normal sheep and goats could do the first two trials without error, but the third time they would hesitate and sometimes make an error, and more often still make an error on the final trial.

I continued with about eight sheep over a period of three years with three runs a week. They were very willing indeed to do this, but none of them ever mastered it. But the results were dreadful from my pedantic point of view. Neither gregariousness, nor the desire to eat, had any influence on this performance when it was well established. This is what would happen: the sheep, as soon as the trap door fell, would deliberately go down the central alley, dash down the open alley to the final compartment, make a wheeling motion, ritualistically rub its snout through the oats, not taking a single bite, and go and wait to be let into the starting box for the next trial. Then it would turn in the opposite direction, and in spite of making mistakes it was so anxious to get back and try once more and get the matter done that it would not eat. It would go through the motion of eating, but would not eat actually. Then, to check further, we put a wooden storm door between it and the flock to eliminate the operation of gregariousness, but the sheep was by no means concerned at not finding the flock, it wanted only to get back and repeat its maze performance, in spite of its errors.

Still worse was to follow. One of these ewes had a lamb, and out of deference to her condition we fenced her in a little screened enclosure in the barn. I should have told you that not only did the sheep ignore the flock and not bother with oats except for the ritualistic rubbing of its snout along the surface of them, but when I came in at the usual time of day the animals would be clustered around the maze door waiting to be let in. They were anxious to be run. Then when this ewe had her lamb, we put her in the enclosure to suckle the lamb with the flock in the barn, and one day (permit me to anthropormorphize) as I came by she bleated at me with intent, or so I interpreted it. I let her out of her screened enclosure, her lamb trotting along beside, and led her into the maze with the iron grill door separating her from the lamb. She promptly ignored the lamb, which bleated at the top of its lungs and threw itself against the gate. It made a great uproar, but mama ignored it completely and ran her usual four trials through the maze.

GREY WALTER:

I would say this is love not appetite.

FREMONT-SMITH:

Love of you, seeking approval of the experimenter.

LIDDELL:

I do not think so really. I was up in the loft of the barn making observations. It might be so, but I had no evidence that the sheep had so strong an affectional bond.

LORENZ:

Had they run the course very often?

LIDDELL:

Three times a week for a period of about three years.

LORENZ:

There is one thing that bothers me very much. It is one of the things that ought not to be from our point of view, but is. Learned behaviour develops something like an autonomous appetite for it! If this learned behaviour is 'ground in' very deeply, the subject will develop a very strong appetitive behaviour towards it. I can give you quite a number of instances when the same thing occurred in other animals. For instance, sledge-dog mothers often completely ignore and leave their litter in order to join the team, trying to get into their accustomed place and wanting to go on pulling the sledge.

LIDDELL:

The reason I wanted to bring this up was to hear of your own experiments on work drive.

LORENZ:

The most anti-militaristic man, who has hated being trained, will try and see if he can make militaristic movements too if you give him a gun.

GREY WALTER:

Might this not be an example of the natural confusion which exists, particularly in higher animals, between the various forms of adaptation, that some sort of practised learning may here be super-imposed upon associative learning, which you were intending to study? By this very prolonged repetition of an act, which you say was never quite completed, you have simply a ball running in a groove not going anywhere at all except following the gradient.

LIDDELL:

Except for the zest with which they lined up and wanted to be let in.

GREY WALTER:

They actually performed some practised act, however, which may have been associative learned behaviour.

LIDDELL:

I think in favour of what you said is the fact that the dwarf, sluggish, thyroidectomized animals ran with the same persistence as the normal animals, but did not line up at the door; they were passive and inert, and did not have the zestful approach.

FREMONT-SMITH:

Perhaps there is an element of fulfilment of anticipation in this situation. Here you have anticipation of going through the maze, and dissatisfaction until it could be fulfilled.

LIDDELL:

One additional factor I would like to put in the record, showing that you cannot come to any facile chain-reflex or chain-response conception of this repetitive act. I could take the sheep out of the maze and into the barn and allow him ten minutes to cool off anywhere in this series of four trials, and he would take up the next trial in series almost always without error. If he had done his first turn, and turned to the right, then I would haul him out and leave him in the barn for ten minutes, I would return him after this and the very first turn would be to the left, which was correct. So it was nothing so simple as a reverberating time-circuit or kinaesthetic feedback. It was much more complicated.

WHITING:

I am not quite sure of the design of the experiment. When the animal went to a blind alley, exactly what happened? Did you open the gate to put him in?

LIDDELL:

When he found his way into the final compartment, he would automatically wheel and wait at the gate to be let back in the starting compartment.

WHITING:

How was he let in?

LIDDELL:

By me.

WHITING:

Did you touch him?

LIDDELL:

No, I walked around him and opened the gate.

WHITING:

You were there?

LIDDELL:

I was there.

GREY WALTER:

Then you were the reward.

LORENZ:

I want to emphasize that Liddell was not the reward, the running of the maze was the reward. You can see these learned movements develop a strong appetite of their own in circus dogs escaping and running through their loops. When I was a prisoner of war we taught wild mice to run in wheels. We kept these mice in an area between the double windows. They gnawed through the wall and escaped. There was no longer any food in that area, but those mice went back every night to run in that wheel. We could hear the wheel squeaking, and that went on for months and months. They were not fed, there was no recompense at all, but they had learned to run in a wheel and they liked it. I always disliked doing anatomical dissections, but when I see a man dissecting something I say, 'Let me do that for a moment'. That is a phenomenon which is very interesting, because it puts up an analogy between learned behaviour and instinctive behaviour, which is very disturbing to me. It is quite opposite to what we expected. And because it is very disturbing it should not be forgotten for a moment!

WHITING:

I think it is crucial to exclude all the possibilities of the result being accounted for by some reinforcement principle before we say that it is due to some principle of interaction. Would the sheep eat oats after the fourth trial?

LIDDELL:

I cannot remember. I know for the other trials that in his impetuous zeal to get back into the maze for the next trial he would go through the motion of rubbing his snout across the oats. I imagine in most cases he would eat after the last trial.

WHITING:

A possible explanation is that the four trials *altogether* was something that had to go on, after several months, in order to get the final combination of running four times, of eating the oats, of getting back into the flock and getting the evening meal.

MEAD:

Would you still have in your record what that sheep did at the end of the fourth trial, whether it did or did not eat?

LIDDELL:

I could not be sure. I am certain that the sheep always waited for me at the fourth trial.

FREMONT-SMITH:

But did it wait any longer at the fourth trial than at the second or third?

LIDDELL:

He did not go back to the starting place, he would be waiting to get into the barn. I do not remember if he ate or not; but there was a terminative pattern of behaviour—'Done at last!'

GREY WALTER:

It is very hard to design experiments where there is not some reward.

BINDRA:

It seems to me that the mechanism underlying this positive sort of compulsion in the sheep is probably quite different from the mechanism of compulsion in the escape or avoidance situation. Even in the rat you can get compulsive avoidance established very quickly: if the rat is able to avoid a shock by pressing a lever, he will keep on pressing the lever and keep on avoiding the shock almost indefinitely. But another thing that happens is that the rats periodically 'test' the situation. Once in a while, every thousand trials, or maybe every two thousand trials, they do not press the lever and actually get a shock; it seems they are testing to see if the shock is still there.

LORENZ:

The rat, dog or chimpanzee would, after a time, try to investigate whether the danger was removed, and so would the child or any of what I call 'curiosity creatures'. But the wonder is that sheep will not; they are more conservative.

GREY WALTER:

At a certain stage in evolution you get the question asked, 'Is your obsession really necessary?'.

BOWLBY:

At what age were these sheep started on their training?

LIDDELL:

They began their training at about three weeks, not in this complicated problem but in the simple maze with the cul de sac in just one position.

BOWLBY:

The question in my mind is whether this tendency to develop an autonomous drive in learned behaviour develops more frequently if the creature is taught the procedure when it is young, rather than when it is old or middle aged.

LIDDELL:

What, in corresponding terms to the human life span, would be the age of the sheep at three months?

LORENZ:

In that respect they become more complicated than the dog. The sheep is born at what would correspond, in humans, to the age of four years.

LIDDELL:

We get perfectly precise conditional reflexion at seven days.

LORENZ:

The lamb is able to walk and travel as fast as his mother at about five days old. He can follow her easily, which a child would not be able to do before five or six years.

BUCKLE:

It seems to me this kind of behaviour which developed in the sheep is what we would call in humans an example of sublimation. That is, of getting an autonomous drive to do something which is not reinforced by the original instinct pattern. We think it is not reinforcement which produces sublimation but the frustration of some instinct or action. We do see that the sheep has been frustrated at the beginning of this experiment because he has come up to the flock and the gate between him and it has been shut. Could one perhaps investigate variations in regard to the facility with which this autonomous kind of maze-running drive develops?

LIDDELL:

I do not remember the sheep trying to force its way into the barn to join the flock. There was no frustration in that sense.

GREY WALTER:

There is one point about this with regard to humans. Electrophysiology is still very undeveloped, but in the human being at about an equivalent age of the sheep, around four years old, as I think I mentioned at our last conference (Vol. I) the termination of pleasure or an agreeable stimulus (as opposed to the application of pain) has a specific action on the brain. In children aged about three or four years it seems that frustration from the withdrawal of a pleasant stimulus has a more profound and long-lasting action than application of an unpleasant stimulus.

BUCKLE:

I gather this is just one of the points at which human psychologists and animal psychologists do not get together very much. We deal largely with children and deprivation effects, and most animal psychologists think all the time in terms of reinforcement theories. 'Where is the reward?' is usually the question they ask.

MEAD:

We have a concept developed by Professor Boas in the understanding of primitive art which he called 'the play of the virtuoso with his technique'. We find a great many instances where there are repetitive, highly-skilled and perfected pieces of behaviour which are not displayed. For instance, in the fringes of coats made by natives on the Amur River there is a beautiful rhythmic colour arrangement which is put in the fringe at a point where no one can see it. You have to take the coat apart to find it. This is fairly common. Boas' explanation was that there was a self-rewarding pleasure in doing something well, which accompanied doing it habitually. I would think in setting up the experiment we ought to consider that there is no deprivation element in this except the deprivation of the pleasure of doing it. You will find with children who are spinning a top or bouncing a ball that stopping the action is the deprivation, not taking the ball away.

LORENZ:

I think that the task must be very difficult to the animal in question in order to offer this particular kind of satisfaction: a rat would never think it 'good sport' to run a maze, because it would be too easy for him. To the sheep it is very difficult, and that is why it becomes a pleasure.

LIDDELL:

Sometimes I thought of children lining up to go down the slippery slide over and over!

Going back to earlier experiments I did, inadvertently, stumble upon a procedure for establishing real frustration, and it suggested, perhaps, the origins of what in ourselves might be psychological traumata. To save time I shortened the maze so that the animal could perform his repetitive task by just turning round the corner either to left or right. Then, as always happens in animal experiments, the experimenter made more mistakes than the animal. On the third trial of a four-trial sequence I inadvertently left both gates closed. The normal sheep turned correctly but was startled to find a closed gate, so it stopped, turned but came back and looked again and then was very confused and began bleating which it ordinarily never did in the maze. I went down and corrected the error in position of the gates, but the next day, twenty-four hours later, the sheep went through its usual routine until it came to the third trial, where it stopped in its tracks *just before* the place where the gate had been closed by accident the previous day. That suggested a further experiment. Later I fired a revolver at this point on the third trial of one day and the next day the sheep suddenly stopped and then dashed about as if confused and alarmed. This startled behaviour suggested

139

the influence of vivid traces of the formerly blocked sequence of actions.

LORENZ:

May I come back pedantically to a question originally put by Grey Walter? People who believe in the self-rewarding quality of well-known things agree on one point, and that is that the whole mechanism of this obsession is different from the obsession to negative stimuli. Consider what would be the equivalent to an obsession with a negative stimulus if it ever happened with a positive stimulus: supposing an animal has once found in a definite place in a definite situation something particularly good to eat. It would then, never, never be able to learn not look in this place for something more. This would be very unadaptive; we come back again to survival value. Of course, the causal explanation is not solved by that, but we find some reason why a special construction within the central nervous system might have evolved which makes it easy to get obsession to negative stimuli but prevents an obsession to positive stimuli.

But let us examine this. I had a muscovy drake, who had never performed the consummatory act of copulating with a goose. The apparent object-fixations of sexual impulses are really most exactly conforming to the definition of an 'obsession' because they seem to be really irreversible. This is very much like a real object-fixation in humans and, with all caution, I think they possibly might be simply the same thing, though it is for the psychoanalyst to decide that. In this case you had got that muscovy drake exposed to a certain stimulus without even a consummatory act, but nevertheless he kept on to 'look in that place'. Yet I think the mechanism is different from that of the 'obsessions' found by Dr. Liddell.

WHITING:

I think there is something we should take note of in these differences between negative and positive situations. One is that in the negative situation there is a rapid onset of the pain, and equally possibly a rapid cessation. This is contingent on external events. Your positive stimuli depend on slow metabolic processes and a slow onset, and generally have a slow decrease.

LIDDELL:

You would also say, would you not, that the goat touching the fence with its muzzle, stopping again to flex the foreleg and then running is not at all the same as the sheep suddenly stopping in the maze? Here we have detachment from the original situation.

LORENZ:

Definitely.

LIDDELL:

When we first began to study conditioned responses in animals, we attempted faithfully to duplicate PAVLOV'S (1927) procedure. Pavlov's dogs had been caused to stand upon a laboratory table for a very practical reason, namely that he was interested in collecting gastric juice from a gastric fistula, and this table and restraining harness were for the experimenter's convenience in putting a flask under the belly to collect gastric juice and take it away. So, through laboratory tradition and habit we persevered in the unhandy procedure of making the sheep climb a ramp and stand on a table in the conventional Pavlov frame.

We started on the conditioned reflex work with the sheep and goat, because we wanted to cross species lines. We also worked with the 'salivary' dog.

Finally, we drastically simplified the whole conditioning procedure. At present all that is done is to lead the animal into a place against the wall where there is a metal cleat, and put the web strap around its chest and through the cleat. Of course, the animal will struggle at first. Finally, he will decide to stand quietly waiting for the signal and for the brief mild shock upon the foreleg which follows.

Now I want to discuss how our present attitude towards Pavlovian conditioning originated. I first visited Pavlov's laboratory in the summer of 1926 where I met Horsley Gantt, who had gone over with the famine relief after World War I and had stayed there six years working in Pavlov's laboratory. I arrived in Leningrad and was put in touch with Dr. Gantt, and to him I am eternally grateful for rapidly indoctrinating me in Pavlov's laboratory tradition and enabling me to meet the most important people, one of whom was Dr. Grey Walter's friend, Rosenthal.

In the summer of 1929 Dr. Kupalov was sent to A. V. Hill's laboratory as a Rockefeller Fellow, and I was able to borrow him from the Rockefeller Foundation. We spent the summer of 1929 in my laboratory and then went together to the International Physiological Congress in Boston late that August where I met Pavlov for the first time.

Parenthetically, Dr. Grey Walter, I must say that Dr. Kupalov told me why Rosenthal wanted very much to come to Cambridge

141

and why Pavlov wanted him to come was that they wished to establish conditioned reflexes in the British bulldog because of his steadfast and indomitable character, which reminded them of the British! Did he ever work on the British bulldog?

GREY WALTER:

None of our dogs were bulldogs. In the end he had to bring dogs from Leningrad!

LIDDELL:

It is due to Kupalov more than to any one of Pavlov's whole group that I am indebted for getting a new view of Pavlovian conditioning. First of all, Kupalov had convinced himself, and he easily convinced me, that Pavlov's conditioned reflex procedure did not effect what Pavlov purported, namely that the dog lost his independence of action and, as soon as you reduced the environment to a sum of controllable stimuli, all spontaneity of action would disappear and you would have perfectly predictable suites of reflex actions, conditioned and unconditioned. Kupalov at that time told me of an experiment which Pavlov hesitated to publish and, indeed, never did publish (and this has led to Kupalov's undoing at the present time because he has been, as we say, in the dog-house since faithfully reporting this experiment). He told me that the following amazing circumstance occurred in Pavlov's laboratory which disturbed the old gentleman very much indeed and delighted Kupalov. It was as follows: The dog was standing quietly in the harness on the table. The observer was looking at his manometer and suddenly he saw the fluid in the manometer begin to move. This meant that the dog had begun to secrete, *and that was against the rules*—he had no business to be secreting because the experimenter had given no signal. This dog had been trained to expect food when an electric light bulb in front of him was turned on, secondly when a metronome on the beam over his head began to click, and thirdly, when an electric tapper under the edge of the table began to work. The experimenter looked through the periscope when this secretion began and he saw the dog peering over the edge of the table wagging his tail and salivating. Signal number two was given with its usual stereotyped conditioned response. Later in this period the manometer fluid began to move again—secretion! The experimenter looked through the periscope to see the dog leaning towards the electric light bulb wagging his tail and salivating. The third time the dog looked up behind him to where the metronome might have been clicking. Kupalov, as I say, was undone by referring to this as a

142

conditioned reflex *without initiation*. Here then is a conditioned reflex with no stimulus.

It seemed that this conditioned reflex behaviour, which we had all read about in the literature, was dramatized dog behaviour: the stage setting was such that it emphasized stimulus-bound behaviour. But here the dog in the stimulus-bound situation was exhibiting *spontaneous behaviour*. How could this be, if the dog was a passive agent in the clutch of environmental stimuli? Then Kupalov made a second suggestion which has coloured all our future work, and it stemmed from the following experiment in Leningrad.

One tactile stimulator was placed upon the dog's thigh, and another on his chest. When the tactile stimulator pressed lightly upon the shaved spot on the chest once every two seconds for thirty seconds, the dog was fed. Exactly six minutes later the spot on the thigh was stimulated for thirty seconds, no food following. Six minutes later, the positive spot—food. Six minutes later, the negative spot—no food. So there was an oscillatory plus-minus pattern of constant intervals, with respect to time. Kupalov then decided to see if there remained in the nervous system any residuals of this rhythmical temporal pattern by changing to a luminous circle as conditioned stimulus and allowing this to shine for thirty seconds, feeding the dog, and then six minutes later presenting the circle again followed by food. He kept the same time-pattern as before; but now, he found that the dog very soon reacted to the circle with large secretion on the first trial, a small secretion on the second, a large one on the third, a small one on the fourth, and this gradually damped out until the salivary responses became equal for successive presentations.

It occurred to him, therefore, that since the dog's central nervous system could be thrown into a state of readiness in step with repetitive stimuli, this might be a convenient means for bringing about an emotional crisis (experimental neurosis) in the dog. This proved to be so. We adopted Kupalov's procedure and found that in both sheep and goat this was the most convenient means for bringing about chronic emotional disorder. We gave our sheep or goat a ten-second signal and then waited two minutes before the next signal. Thus: buzzer—shock, two minutes; bell—no shock, two minutes; buzzer—shock, two minutes; bell—no shock. We found that this was a very stressful procedure for the sheep and goat.

We then went a step further and found that it was unnecessary to use any negative signal; all that was necessary was to give a ten-second signal followed by shock, wait a constant interval, another ten-second signal, another shock, and so on—positive stimuli separated by equal intervals of time.

143

This led us into a problem which, I think, will be of great interest to Dr. Grey Walter in the next model which he constructs; this is the question of time estimation. We have found the sheep and goats are adept at estimating time intervals up to seven minutes. We do not know what the outside limit in the sheep and goat may be, but we found in Pavlov's book (1927), that if the dog were fed every half hour, and you missed a half-hour feeding, he would start secreting, with an error of two to three minutes either side. But if you focussed his time perception by giving him a readiness signal, that is if you sounded the metronome thirty seconds before the half hour and gave the food, the dog had developed a much sharper time sense and now he would not secrete a drop if the metronome were thirty seconds too soon.

We found the same phenomenon in sheep and goats. If we stood the sheep in the Pavlov frame and gave him a shock every six minutes, he would get restive maybe two or three minutes before the six minutes; and if the shock failed he might maintain his restiveness some seconds afterwards. However, if we preceded the six-minute signal by a ten-second signal, just as in the case of Pavlov's dog, the time-perception became very much focussed and sharpened. This added signal is the straw that breaks the camel's back. You do not get experimental neurosis by marking off the equal time-periods by just a forced reaction to shock. You must give him, one might say, an anxiety signal, a readiness signal, and it is this readiness signal that does the harm.

Without fail, therefore, in any sheep and goat we bring about emotional catastrophe by forcing their reactions into a rigid, Procrustean bed of constant timing, providing the readiness signal precedes the shock.

We can do more: we can still further increase the stress situation by allowing the animal to avoid the shock by flexing his leg at the appropriate time, but then giving or withholding the shock in a random manner.

MEAD:

The signal was monotonous and the shock was jumbled?

LIDDELL:

Yes, we know that monotony is neurosis-producing; the jumbling effect is adding fuel to the flames; you get more rapid neurosis in that way.

HARGREAVES:

Is this really monotony? Is it not repeated apprehension?

BINDRA:

I do not think I have understood this quite rightly. Did you not say that monotony by itself might produce a similar set of reactions?

LIDDELL:

No, the correction is important; it must be monotonous apprehension.

GREY WALTER:

Might it be the incongruity between the regularity of the stimulus and the randomness of the punishment?

LIDDELL:

With inevitable shock the monotonous apprehension *per se* brings on neurosis after some weeks or months. But you hasten it by randomizing the shocks. This is in sheep and goats.

GREY WALTER:

It is a very special case in the sheep and the goats. It certainly is not true in the dog; our dogs gave no sign of minding monotony *per se*; I think they rather enjoyed the drill.

TANNER:

Does the sheep after this procedure get the aberrant patterns of heart action during the night that you told us about, and similar symptoms?

LIDDELL:

We have yet to determine that. I must frankly state that we took too histrionic a view of experimental neurosis. We thought it must be dramatic behaviour, which anyone can see. We now believe that many instances of neurotic, emotionally disordered behaviour, may be as subtle and as easily escape detection as human psychoneurosis.

GREY WALTER:

But the neurotic animal was able to feed and mate in a normal way?

LIDDELL:

That is subject to inquiry. We have reason to believe that one of our so-called normal rams was psychologically impotent. Ordinarily, we have one billy goat brought in for the mating season and one

145

ram. On this occasion we did not bring in another ram but our own ram did not impregnate any of the ewes at breeding season.

BINDRA:

In normal feeding conditioned responses you get general inhibition during the delay period, at least so Pavlov (1927) reported. Do you get any similar thing in avoidance responses?

GREY WALTER:

Yes, you do in dogs.

BINDRA:

The animals will go to sleep?

LIDDELL:

Did you observe sleeping in your experiments?

GREY WALTER:

Yes, in a certain type. This is where I have to make a reservation. There is a typological difference here in dogs. These particular factors—the development of a disturbed behaviour in relation to randomization of stimuli and the extent to which you get sleep or excitement during the delay period of a delayed reflex—are factors which are enormously affected by the individual type of dog. Before typology was thrown overboard that was the main subject of interest in the Pavlovian Institute. These typological differences could be distinguished genetically. The last that was heard, before the work was jettisoned, was that they did breed true. Some animals do go to sleep in a delayed reflex situation, when a quarter of an hour later a violent shock is to be given; but other animals will become agitated and neurotic.

LIDDELL:

This is interesting, because when Kupalov joined us he faithfully observed the sheep and goats day after day. We also had a dog laboratory for salivary-dog conditioning, and we did get the hypnotoid type of behaviour in one dog we were working with. Kupalov diligently observed the sheep and goats for signs of somnolence, and it did not occur. He was quite surprised at this species difference.

Before proceeding further, I must say that we spent a great number of years faithfully reproducing all the principal phenomena of conditioned reflex action which Pavlov had described in the dog, as they appear in the pig, in the sheep and in the goat. Pavlov was an honest and gifted observer; all of these phenomena can be reproduced, even irradiation, and concentration of tactile positive and negative conditioned reflexes on the sheep's thigh. Most of Pavlov's phenomena *are* transferable over a species range.

First of all, we believed that the Pavlovian conditioning situation was essentially a stress situation, and we tested this notion in two ways. In the first place, we conditioned a sheep until we had a well-established conditioned reflex to buzzers based upon shock. We carried on training to between one and two hundred buzzer signals. The animal had quietened down and stood alertly between signals. The signals were randomized with respect to time. In this experiment we were recording respiration, head movement, leg movement, and heart rate. We then carried out the following test. The animal was brought to the laboratory at the usual time every day and placed in the Pavlov frame; the usual apparatus was attached and a graphic record taken of the sheep's standing behaviour. In two months this animal might almost have been used for a basal metabolism test as it stood in its frame. The whole set of physiological functions gradually diminished in intensity until the animal was quite at ease, quite relaxed. Then, after about three months, a single buzzer signal threw him into a most violent and uncoordinated struggle to escape —almost what you observe when the animal has reached the neurotic state. So by habituating the animal to standing without stimulation in this restraining harness the tension-arousing nature of the restraint gradually diminishes and the animal is at ease.

The second experiment was this. We brought the animal—in this case a goat—into the demonstration box (as in Fig. 15, facing p. 65) for his daily demonstration, attached the electrodes and then sat and watched. The animal, with no signals and no shocks, standing at a familiar time of the day, became more and more excited as the hour progressed. The excitement took the form of increased respiration, beginning at about 45 per minute and ending at 135 respirations per minute. The breathing became more and more disturbed; there was teeth grinding and yawning, and fidgeting movements with the leg. If such an animal is let out to pasture for an hour, and two hours later brought back, you find that two hours at pasture by no means alleviates this tension. He now starts the afternoon session almost as disturbed as he was at the end of the morning session where we left off.

BOWLBY:

By using the word 'shock' we are in danger of thinking it is a very disagreeable stimulus. Frustration of the motor response would appear to be what is unpleasant.

N

LIDDELL:

We like to speak of it as an electrical stimulus, and that is all it is. As Dr. Grey Walter mentioned earlier, individuals vary enormously in their experience of the disagreeableness of a minor electric shock. Sheep and goats have almost an innate releasing mechanism to escape from a shock which none of us would feel, or at most feel as a slight tingling.

MEAD:

The animal gives a startle response rather than a persistent, long attempt to avoid, as it would with pain. Can you use this stimulus with this degree of strength and train the animal to avoid it and to avoid situations where it occurs?

LIDDELL:

Yes, this happens in two stages. At first every normal sheep and goat, from a week of age up to maturity, when placed in the restraining harness and given this mild shock, makes violent struggling and plunging movements, and if free in the room will dart away. Then gradually, by habituation, the startle reaction becomes a very perfunctory reflex of the stimulated limb.

BOWLBY:

If the same stimulus is applied in other parts of the body, what is the reaction?

LIDDELL:

Escape. But if you apply it within the apical part of one foreleg it will become a perfunctory reaction and give you the illusion that you have a definite, precise defensive reflex.

GREY WALTER:

In the dog you get snapping. A small stimulus, not a painful one, to the leg or arm of a dog will not produce an escape reaction; most dogs will just snap.

LIDDELL:

It occurred to us to see if we could not study motor-conditioning in a free situation where the animal, if it wished, could have freedom of locomotion. In this case we chose twins, three weeks of age, one with the mother and one without. The twin was connected by a

148

flexible cable from the centre of the ceiling, and this cable brings down the electrodes to the legs so that the shock may be delivered. In all the experiments which I shall be describing from now on the signal was the turning off of the lights in the room; the conditioned signal was darkness. In this way, one experimental unit would not interfere with the work of another; the signal would not leak from one room to another. The lights go out for ten seconds and then the little animal gets a shock on the foreleg. This is repeated every two minutes for twenty darkness signals and then the animal and its mother are led from the room. Meanwhile, the twin in the adjoining room without the mother is similarly connected with a recording system. In a very short time, part way through the first period, all communication by bleating from room to room is given up. The mother gives up first; the lamb bleats persistently but the mother does not reply, and soon the solitary animal has given up vocalizing.

The recording system is simple. The flexible cable from the animal leads to two selsyn motors on the ceiling, and the sympathetic selsyn motors in the corridor record the progress of the little animal about the room by moving a pencil over the page of a notebook. One gets a locomotion chart for the whole period of twenty signals.

The little animal's reaction to the very mild electrical startle stimulus is to rear and dash away, then it comes back to its mother. But after ten or fifteen darkness signals each followed by shock, the animal gives the precise conditioned reflex in the presence of the mother that we have seen in the animal confined by the strap to the cleat on the wall; that is, the simple foreleg movement. In the puppy you will not get this reaction until it is about twenty-eight days old, when a precise foreleg movement is first elicited.

LORENZ:

But the animal does not avoid the shock?

LIDDELL:

No. In the experiments I am speaking of all shocks are inevitable.

LORENZ:

So that leg-lifting develops even if it has no influence on shock avoidance?

LIDDELL:

Yes. We have done the corresponding experiments with the goat with practically identical results.

FIG. 16
RECORD OF ACTIVITY RECORDED BY SELSYN
MOTORS DURING 20 SIGNALS

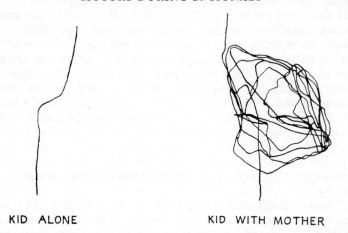

KID ALONE   KID WITH MOTHER

Fig. 16 is the activity chart for the whole period of twenty signals with two-minute intervals for the kid alone and the kid with the mother. Now see what is beginning to occur. The solitary animal is in a temporal strait-jacket, with every two minutes the stimuli occurring. The animal with the mother wanders around the room in between the shocks. It will go and stand by her, typically, and flex the leg precisely at the signal. Then perhaps it will cuddle up next to her during the interval. The observer's chair is in one corner. The solo kid or lamb soon begins to orient towards the experimenter, and it creeps along the side of the room from trial to trial.

FREMONT-SMITH:

You are always in the room then?

LIDDELL:

In the case of this particular chart, yes.

MEAD:

Is the experimenter in the room with the mother and the lamb?

LIDDELL:

Yes, an experimenter also sits in the room with the mother.

150

MEAD:

In the same position?

LIDDELL:

Yes, but apparently the mother reassures the lamb. It may come up to the experimenter and trot away. The solitary lamb or kid comes hesitantly up to the experimenter's chair.

LORENZ:

The diagram on the right seems to show that the room is bigger on the left side.

LIDDELL:

That is the distortion of the recording system. It is not mechanically quite accurate. In our recent experiments we had a one-way screen for each room. The experimenter was not in the room then. In that case, the animal might take a position in any corner. But the same restriction of activity along the wall occurs.

LORENZ:

Along all the wall?

LIDDELL:

Yes. Is it not true in psychopathology that occasionally patients will creep round the walls and fear the centre of the room?

HARGREAVES:

In the film made by the French group who are doing separation studies, you see that very clearly. The children move round the walls with their faces to the wall and their backs to the room.

BOWLBY:

Supposing the same experiment was carried out without any 'shocks' or even without any stresses, would the solo lamb remain more stationary than the lamb which is with its mother?

LIDDELL:

It wanders around, once it is reassured about the experimenter.

LORENZ:

I would say it would wander about more than the lamb with its mother; but I wonder what the mother does all the time. Does she wander about much?

LIDDELL:

She wanders very little. She is bored by the whole proceeding. Typically, she comes in and lies in one place and grooms herself. Her baby comes to her and may jump on her at the shock and cuddle up beside her in the intervals, but she is relatively indifferent to the baby.

ZAZZO:

Have you in some cases made the experiment of separating from the mother the lamb that is normally with her? I should like to know whether in such a case one would observe the same phenomenon of keeping close to the walls as for the twin that is usually separated from the mother. Would the tangled pattern on the right come to resemble the pattern on the left if the twin that is usually with the mother were accidentally or occasionally separated from her?

LIDDELL:

We have not tried that.

BINDRA:

Did both the lambs have the same experience with the mother before the experiment?

LIDDELL:

Yes, they are with the mother the whole time except for this brief period every day.

TANNER:

Does the behaviour of the two young animals differ in relation to the mother in the pasture and in the barn when this has been going on for some time?

LIDDELL:

Yes; there is a difference. The little lamb will be loth to follow its mother and twin into the laboratory. Previously, it has trotted along behind the mother; now it lags behind her. A separation is already occurring, a detachment from its mother, which is observed by visitors.

MEAD:

In the work that Erikson (1951) did in California, when he was studying projective block-play of pre-adolescent girls and boys, the wall was the symbol of the mother in the girls' constructions.

LORENZ:

That is what I also wanted to say.

LIDDELL:

You think that perhaps contact with the wall is like that with the mother?

LORENZ:

I think that the lamb which is without its mother and which is missing its mother has a stronger urge to cuddle, and, lacking something better, it cuddles the wall as a substitute.

LIDDELL:

I think from the behaviour that your supposition is correct. During the whole period the experimenter is a source of ambivalent reactions on the part of the young animal, and in the early stages when it is more mobile it will run towards him and try to wedge itself behind his chair. Then he makes it take its distance and it will approach him when the light goes out, wheel and run away and then come back. Once we wanted to be suprascientific and had wire recording to get the vocalizing of the animal, but we did not see the experiment. One of our lady assistants, a college girl, was sitting in the room as observer. When we ran the tape recording there was silence—then an irate girlish voice saying, 'Dammit, get off my lap!!'; so that was the end of our wire recording.

Now I want to report a further experiment. We selected four pairs of twin goats. One of each pair of twins was taken from the mother at birth and raised on the bottle in an orphanage which was a fenced enclosure where they could see neither sheep nor goats. The other twin with the mother was normally raised in the barn and out at pasture. Each day for fifty days, starting at three weeks old, a dual experiment was performed, the one little goat coming with its mother, the other little goat brought from the orphanage to the experimental room and never seeing its mother at all. All were tested by the schedule of twenty lights-out signals, of ten seconds duration each and separated by two minutes. The experimenter watched through a screen. At the end of fifty of these sessions, in which, therefore, each little animal had been subjected to one thousand darkness signals, separated by exactly two minutes at twenty signals per day, the procedure terminated. The four little goats in the orphanage carried on their orphanage life, and the other four goats were out with the flock as before.

GREY WALTER:

Were the four orphans together in their orphanage?

LIDDELL:

They were together. We wanted to re-test these four animals trained with mother and the four trained without mother at the end of two years; but at the end of the first year, we resolved to allow the four little goats from the orphanage to rejoin the main flock. We carefully arranged this. We brought the large flock of fifty to sixty goats into our rather large barnyard, and then we brought the first little goats from the orphanage and turned them into this paddock. They would have nothing to do with the rest of the goats, but followed their leader, a female, into a little alley. The leader at once menaced one of the other female goats in the large flock and they clashed horns. Then she wheeled and the others followed her back into the alley. We drove the main flock out to pasture, but the little sub-group of four would not follow the main flock. They could hear them bleat as they went in single file over the hill. We finally eased the orphans out into the pasture and they went about grazing as if they had always been used to this pasture—with one important exception: they took no interest in the bleating of the other goats over the hill. They accepted the three of us who were out taking notes as members of the flock, and I remember two of them were grazing around my feet as I took notes. We could not get near any of the members of the main flock—they would scuttle away; but it seemed from their behaviour that we were members of the little flock.

At the end of the second year—the time that the test was to begin —the sub-group of four had never rejoined the main flock. They did not keep away from them, but they did not mingle with them; it was a neutral situation. Now, at the end of two years, did this early experience of being placed in this waxing and waning, monotonously

154

anxious waiting situation in the laboratory have any residual effect on their adult behaviour? They were now two years of age.

Four animals, i.e. two pairs of twins, were brought in and confined by a strap against the side of the room. The movements of the foreleg were recorded on a kymograph in an adjoining room. Each orphanage goat was trained against the co-twin that had been with the mother and flock. Each group of four was trained according to a different re-test situation. The first situation was that for a two-hour period in this mass-conditioning unit the now mature goats were subjected to a ten-second darkness signal followed by shock, every six minutes for two hours—twice as long as they were originally tested. Every day, six days a week for twenty-four days four goats— two trained with the mother, two trained in isolation—were set this arduous task of remaining in the laboratory for two hours, waiting six minutes between signals (all ten-second darkness signals).

FREMONT-SMITH:

Were no mothers present this time at all?

LIDDELL:

There were no mothers present. The goats were all adults and the mother would not be required at this stage. No sheep or goat pays any attention to any other sheep or goat at this age.

Figure 17 is the plot of data from the four goats, the upper two lines from the goats protected during training by the mother and the lower two lines from the ones deprived of a mother's presence. This is a cumulative plot of the number of impatience or 'fretting' flexions of the trained foreleg for each of the four goats when first tested after a two year vacation. The ten-second darkness signal comes on after six minutes have elapsed; then there is another ten-second darkness signal followed by shock, and this sequence continues for two hours.

Two things are to be noticed. In the first place the impatience, or you might say the fretting, flexion movements of the protected animal's foreleg keep occurring. The animals deprived of the parent in training become brow-beaten, or give up. There is another important difference between these pairs. Between the first day and the last day of testing there is a total of about 400 signals. The protected pair missed 25 per cent. of the day's signals on the first day and they continued to miss about 25 per cent. of the signals to the end; that is, they did not get the leg up before the shock. On the other hand, the deprived pair showed steady deterioration in the stability of the conditioned response. They begin as the protected

FIG. 17

ACCUMULATIVE GRAPH OF LEG FLEXION OF FOUR GOATS
DURING INTERVALS BETWEEN SIGNALS 6 MIN. APART

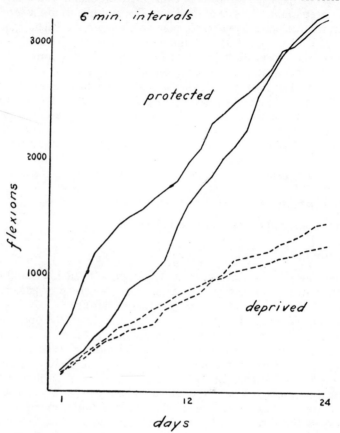

pair does by missing 25 per cent. of the signals at the start, but very soon they are missing more and more signals each day, until by the end of a twenty-four day period, they are failing to react to 45 per cent. of each day's signals. You might say that they are going into a lethargic stage.

FREMONT-SMITH:

It does him no good to make any movement.

LIDDELL:

No, he just gives up.

FREMONT-SMITH:

You call it giving up, but he gains nothing by making that movement.

LIDDELL:

No, but the others who were 'protected' keep on trying.

FREMONT-SMITH:

But still they do not gain anything.

LIDDELL:

No. The whole thing is a fool's game.

GREY WALTER:

As far as the figure goes, it would suggest that the deprived ones are better matched to the situation.

LIDDELL:

In Figure 18 is a graph of the data from four of the other animals —two protected, two unprotected—which were subjected to the two-hourly, daily sessions of ten-second signals every two minutes, rather than every six minutes. Here individual differences between the animals emerge to a more striking extent. This curve seems to indicate that we have two magnitudes of stress to which the two groups of goats were subjected. The two-minute signal interval seems to be the less stressful of the two repetitive time experiments.

MEAD:

The two-minute one is the original?

LIDDELL:

Yes. They all were trained on the two minutes separation of signals.

MEAD:

The lesser magnitude of stress is the one they learned on before.

LIDDELL:

For some ten years we have been puzzled by certain facts concerning the neurotic behaviour of our sheep and goats. You get,

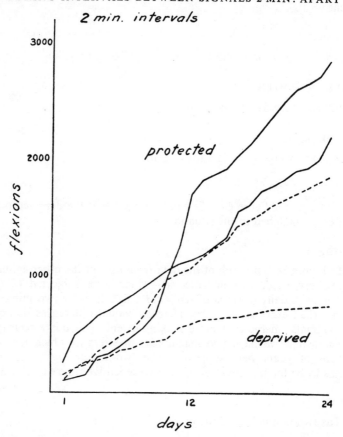

FIG. 18

ACCUMULATIVE GRAPH OF LEG FLEXION OF FOUR GOATS
DURING INTERVALS BETWEEN SIGNALS 2 MIN. APART

2 min. intervals

protected

deprived

flexions

days

qualitatively, two different types of full-blown neurosis if you train
them to repetitive two-minute intervals or repetitive six-minute
intervals.

In the sheep, you get the violent agitation on six-minute separation, but with two minutes separation, the sheep goes into a state of
frozen immobility in which both forelegs will stiffen, and he will
slide back on his haunches.

Sheep and goat again show a species difference in the initial training of the lambs and kids, when they are subjected to this repetitive
signal stimulation with two-minute intervals. The young kid comes
to be rigidly immobile and to raise its trained leg stiffly from the

158

shoulder, and you can get up from your chair and mould him in various positions. He will not resist and he will not escape.

The lamb, however, does quite a different thing. He lies down and puts his chin on the floor, and at the signal, typically, will not make a single ear or head movement. Here he will show absolute indifference to the lights going off. He rolls a little at the shock, and you must roll him over to get the strap off at the end of the experiment. Our animal attendant would come in from the barn and say, 'You have a sick sheep out there', and we would go out and see the half-grown lamb lying on the barn floor, just inert, with the rest of the flock out at pasture. This has happened a number of times; there is a deadening to environment.

BINDRA:

I am wondering about your general interpretation of these findings. What would be the hypothesis, or what sort of conclusions do you hope to draw from this series of investigations?

LIDDELL:

I hope to draw two conclusions. In the first place, when the animal is, let us say, psychically traumatized due to the employment of this monotonous tension pattern, we hope to demonstrate that some residual is left—some 'scar' on the central nervous system which makes itself manifest under stressful training in the adult life. During the stressful training, the one protected by the mother seems to show no residuals of this former stressful training, and we do not know the nature of this protection.

FREMONT-SMITH:

The scar is less if the mother is there?

LIDDELL:

Yes. The psychic scar probably is not there at all.

MEAD:

Did you not also compare the mother-reared twin trained in isolation with the mother-reared twin trained with the flock?

LIDDELL:

I have not got to those pairs yet. We are going to do them, but I will say in anticipation of what we may find that it was very hard to maintain these separated animals in good health for as long as two years. We found that many of our little lambs—more than the kids—gave up the ghost and died before the first year, at around six months. All our flock are worm-infested. We worm them regularly, but the ones trained in isolation even for this brief time are less viable. We almost decimated our population of those trained in isolation. We have the best veterinary counsel and the diet is regulated by our very competent friends in this field.

MEAD:

And they are with their mothers except in the training period?

LIDDELL:

Yes. I do not wish to labour inconclusive data. Let us go on. We are really coming to a tricky point. I want to see whether Lorenz will agree that we have homologues of displacement behaviour, of imprinting and of innate releasing mechanisms in these mammals.

First, displacement behaviour: Figure 19 (facing p. 65) shows our first attempt at having the animal running free in the laboratory room, with the signal a dimming of lights before shock to the foreleg, wherever in the room the animal might be. This animal, as I remember, is three months of age. In the early training, on the third or fourth day, I suspected that this displacement behaviour might occur and had the photographer present, and the picture shows how the animal passes his waiting intervals between the two-minute signals. He goes into phantom-grazing movements. These are real grazing movements. Years ago in the maze, when the animal was first learning it, he would annoy me no end by starting down the central alley, suddenly stopping and beginning to crop at imaginary grass. I would have to get down on my hands and knees and weed the maze every day, and still the sheep would find an 'imaginary' blade of grass and take his time about it. He did this phantom grazing on the bare cement floor.

Another trick the sheep likes to play is to give up and take a rest. Sheep have a sinking-down reaction—if you chase them in the pasture they will sink down and give up. A sheep in the laboratory room would lie down, and very often would get up just before the lights went dim and start walking very rapidly towards the corner where he preferred to be when he got the shock.

BINDRA:

What is the stimulation for this?

LIDDELL:

Nothing: two minutes wait between signals; signals for ten seconds.

BINDRA:

No shock?

LIDDELL:

No. This is behaviour just to pass the time, to relieve the tension.

Now, the goat has a different type of displacement behaviour. He likes to rear up on his hind legs. We used to see them doing that in the maze. They would go along, then suddenly rear up and look over the fence. There was nothing to see. They would sometimes do a little grazing too.

Now the next point. We trained a normal ram three months of age; it learnt to flex the leg at one rate of the metronome, and to leave it down at another rate; it grew and thrived until it was three years of age. It was anatomically a normal ram, but it never impregnated any ewes, it did not show any male aggression, nor did it vocalize after training was well begun. When it died we were without a demonstration animal, and we secured a normal ram, one year of age, fully mature. We put him in the same box that we use for our goat demonstration, and then sounded a buzzer signal for ten seconds, gave him a shock, waited a minute, sounded the buzzer signal again, and so on for forty signals; all he did in response to his first training situation was to show male aggression and, instead of flexing the foreleg at the signal, he began pawing and butting movements. Later a little trait of leg flexion would appear now and again, but mostly masked by pawing and butting.

Then, he gave a menacing bellow, and if you approached him he would bellow at you and try to butt you; he would not wait for his signal, but started butting and bellowing and pawing in the interval *between* the signals. All we got out of him was male aggression. Then we tried this same procedure on another ram, and after a certain point he gave up his male aggressive behaviour and became rigidly immobile, and we never got anything out of him except muscular stiffening, in spite of repeated signals and shocks. So then we have started two little rams on a similar training schedule. Soon butting and pawing feebly emerged; now this male fighting reaction has gone underground in both little rams.

We may here be on the trail of something homologous to the process of repression in psychodynamics; repression is not the same

161

as this homologue at a primitive level, where we have an innate behaviour mechanism being forced underground by habituation.

LORENZ:

I wonder whether you ever had some of your experimental animals on the bare floor of the laboratory as controls without any stimulation. I mean without any stimulation that elicits grazing; of all the activities described, the grazing is the most certain *not* to be autochthonous. You see, the rearing and looking about, though it might be a displacement activity, might also be an autochthonous rearing up and looking for a way out, and so might the aggressive behaviour of the ram simply be autochthonous. But grazing is indubitably a displacement activity. My arguments about the other behaviour patterns are merely those of the *advocatus diaboli*: I really do believe they are displacement activities. But as regards the grazing, I am sure of it. Besides this would be easy to prove: but you need one control experiment to exclude autochthonous grazing; you put a sheep in the same situation on a bare floor without any stress situation.

LIDDELL:

Yes, we did, and got no grazing.

LORENZ:

That seems convincing.

LIDDELL:

We even went this far: we thought perhaps darkness in the sheep and goat might be the releasing stimulus.

LORENZ:

To grazing?

LIDDELL:

For some type of behaviour, because the sheep will congregate together in darkness. But we turned the lights on and off ten seconds every two minutes and observed the animal; it did nothing, it wandered round the room and paid no attention to the lights after the first time or two.

162

BINDRA:

There is an experiment on rats by ULLMAN (1951) that is probably relevant here. These rats were shocked periodically in a situation in which they normally ate. After a few trials, Ullman observed this: just as the time of the shock approached, the rats began to eat at a very fast rate, and kept on eating until the shock was over. Then they sat back, and when the time for the next shock came around, they began eating at a very fast rate again. But in that case the food was there all the time. I should think that *displaced* grazing implies that the animal has probably some sort of an image, he 'eats' what he imagines to be there.

LIDDELL:

In our first conditioning experiments we performed the reverse of this experiment, and confirmed it a number of times, though we have not systematically pursued it. The sheep was confined by the conventional Pavlov frame with a bucket of oats placed in front of him; he reacts to the clicking of the metronome by flexing the leg, he gets the shock and at once plunges his muzzle into the oats bucket and really eats. This is quite stereotyped and we have two or three movie sequences showing it. We did not know what to do with it theoretically, this forced feeding reaction, so we just recorded it and let it go at that.

BINDRA:

The grazing response is a very strong response. When they are out in the pasture, are they not grazing all the time?

LORENZ:

Much of the time.

BINDRA:

Not like rats that eat every two or three hours, and only for about ten minutes at a time.

LORENZ:

This is perhaps important. If an activity is normally performed all day long, then the endogenous production of this activity is of course phylogenetically adapted to this enormous demand; and these activities are the ones that are the first to appear as overflow activities, as we prefer to call them. I can give you a good example of this, the pecking movement in different gallinaceous birds. There is one partridge-like bird—the cacabis, I do not know what it is called in English—which lives in Southern Europe, in stony parts where the bird has to peck all day long to get its fill. And in captivity this species does more overflow pecking than any other gallinaceous bird I know. A similar rule holds true for displacement activities also. The behaviour patterns which we find most frequently as displacements are mostly those which are, so to speak, cheap, produced in great quantities to supply huge demands. That is why the skin-comfort activities are so awfully frequent as displacement activities. And if you ask me what would be the instinctive activity which I would first expect to appear in a sheep as a displacement in a situation of stress, I should have said: grazing—and it would be gnawing in a rat.

LIDDELL:

And in the goat?

LORENZ:

Well, it is difficult to say.

LIDDELL:

I think it would be rearing.

LORENZ:

It might be.

LIDDELL:

I think we must have Dr. Lorenz specify for us where his notion of displacement behaviour may apply to our mammals and where something, perhaps more plasticity, must be added. Displacement activities are innate activities, are they not, not activities built up by training?

WHITING:

I think I am confused out of ignorance. I should like someone to clarify for me what displacement means in the ethological sense.

LORENZ:

It has nothing whatever to do with the psychoanalytical term displacement. This point was brought up in the Cambridge Conference and there psychoanalysts said there was no objection to calling these phenomena '*displacement-activities*', because the psychoanalytical term 'displacement' is always used by itself and there was no danger of confusing it with displacement-activities. As for the displacement-activity, we do not know what happens physiologically when it occurs; but all we know is that when an instinctive activity is released and then re-blocked by the stimulation evoking another, incompatible activity, the animal shows movements belonging to neither of the two conflicting drives but, surprisingly, to those pertaining to an altogether different instinctive activity. We do not know what this type of displacement really is physiologically, but paradoxically we know something about where it happens. It must happen between the central mechanism which releases an instinctive activity and the peripheral motor elements activated by the latter. Besides conflict, there are some other types of situation also evoking displacement-activities, but they all have in common that the already activated instinct is prevented from finding its adequate outlet in the motor patterns normally pertaining to it. In most known cases true displacement-activities are aroused by conflicting drives. The classical and most frequent example is that of aggressive drive blocked by escape reactions. It is very characteristic of displacement-activities that, in this conflict of two given drives, the displacement-activities which appear are always the same. When aggression is blocked by fear in a greater snow goose, there invariably appears a bathing movement. In a pink-footed goose exactly the same situation that will evoke bathing movements in the snow goose elicits a queer sideways distortion of the neck. Only when the conflict gets higher and higher this movement becomes recognizable as the behaviour pattern which, in its autochthonous form, is used for the distribution of fat from the oil gland in the swimming feathers by all Anatidae. So different are displacement activities in species so closely allied to each other that they would give fertile hybrids. This example shows the specificity of the *direction* in which this displacement occurs and also the absolute species-predictability of these phenomena. Dr. Liddell always gets grazing in one typical situation in different types of sheep and he always gets rearing in different types of goat. Displacements go in amazingly different directions in different species. They may be the strangest thing you can imagine: an avocet threatening a rival male suddenly makes the movement of sleeping, putting his head behind the wing and glaring at his antagonist all the time.

TANNER:

In your two species of goose with the different displacement-activities, are these the ones *always* produced, whatever the two conflicting instincts?

LORENZ:

No. Every combination of conflicting instincts may produce its own displacement-activity. A mallard will preen if a slight sexual drive is activated by his seeing a female, while he does not yet want to touch her. If his aggressive drive is blocked by fear he will drink. If both situations are combined he will preen-drink. If he drinks, you will know he wanted to be aggressive and did not dare to. If he preens you will know he wanted to importune the female and did not dare to. So, the displacement-activity is quite specific for one conflict.

TANNER:

And they are all the same within the given species?

LORENZ:

All the same within the given species. Once you have analysed the given situation, you know exactly which drive is conflicting with which by watching the displacement.

GREY WALTER:

Which way round should one use this information as to mammals?

LORENZ:

We know so confoundedly little about mammals.

GREY WALTER:

In your bird species you have information about instinctive behaviour, but in the mammal we seem to know so little, I do not feel quite sure which way round we should start. Should we say: Displacement-activity in the dog or cat or goat or man is so and so and when this happens this is a displacement-activity; or should we start the other way round and say, such and such is a constant thing, therefore it must be an instinctive activity?

LORENZ:

It might be displacement-activity in a given situation. But if you have not analysed what the situation is, and just find a given situation always elicits a given activity it might just as well be autochthonous activity which has been released by adequate stimulation. But the hamster, about the best known of our experimental animals, shows quite a number of very characteristic displacement-activities. When

166

the male hamster pursues the female and loses her suddenly, he always proceeds to preen, to lick himself; and if he wants to be aggressive and does not dare to, he will gnash his teeth. This activity in its autochthonous form is probably used to sharpen the teeth.

FREMONT-SMITH:

Could one see a utility in the displacement in two senses: for instance, preening could conceivably make him more desirable to the female?

LORENZ:

I think that this is far-fetched; no.

FREMONT-SMITH:

Does preening precede sexual activity normally?

LORENZ:

No. But it has a certain survival value, which was emphasized first by TINBERGEN (1940): it may have a cathartic function by working off the blocked drive, by opening a safety valve, so to speak. The major new finding in ethology since our last Congress was by Piet Svenster, a pupil of Jan van Iersel in Leyden, who actually measured the cathartic function of displacement-activity in the three-spined stickleback. He found that frustrated sexual drive in the stickleback produces a parental function in displacement, the movement of fanning the eggs. He could make this animal fan by taking away the female and blocking the sexual drive; then in some animals, he facilitated the fanning by providing adequate stimulation for autochthonous fanning by supplying a source of CO_2. (The CO_2 emanating from the eggs provides the autochthonous stimulus for airing them by fanning.) By this procedure, Svenster got, so to speak, a mixed fanning: displacement fanning slightly facilitated by supplying autochthonous stimuli. Then, by showing dummy females and recording the intensity of the response, Svenster measured the male's readiness for sexual activity. He found that, by facilitating the out-flow of the displacement-activity he had lowered the internal pressure of sexual activity. There are still some objections to his paper, but I do not think they are correct and I think they will be removed by further experiments. Svenster was the first to show that it was really the frustrated autochthonous drive which came out in displacement-activity, and that there was a cathartic function, a safety-valve function in it.

FREMONT-SMITH:

It leads to a real discharge of energy?

LORENZ:

Yes.

BOWLBY:

In psychoanalytic 'displacement' the energy is discharged by an act which is consistent with the original drive. For instance, if you feel aggressive with X and you hit Y, you feel better for it. You relieve your pressure by an act of the same order as the original drive, but to a different object. The existence of psychoanalytic displacement is commonplace. But I believe that displacement-activity, speaking ethologically, also occurs in human beings. I suspect that a great deal of thumb-sucking is displacement-activity; masturbation is likely to be the same.

BINDRA:

It is all right to call these activities displacement-activities, so long as these activities are defined in strictly behavioural terms. What I think Dr. Lorenz has done is to define these activities in terms of certain causal agents: an activity is a displacement-activity when it is brought about by conflict of certain instincts, or an activity is a displacement-activity when the animal is anxious in that situation. I think we have to be very careful and make sure that the activity under discussion is defined strictly without any reference to the causes. It is only when we define behavioural categories strictly in terms of actual happenings, acts, without any reference to causes, that we can legitimately ask the question: 'What are the causes that give rise to that particular activity?' But if we *define* displacement-activity as activity which results from certain types of instincts, it becomes logically meaningless to ask what other conditions produce this same activity. Instead of making 'displacement-activities' a category of behaviour, we should only use grazing, leg flexion, etc., as behavioural categories. Then we can state or argue about the conditions under which that particular type of behaviour, grazing, for instance, is manifested. And then we can state how anxiety, or conflict, can or cannot produce this activity. But using the term 'displacement-activity' is simply begging the question.

LORENZ:

But we do know positively one thing: that in order to get the pink-footed gander to preen, I have first to make him furious by putting a family of greylags before him, withholding the gander of the greylag family, and then he will start threatening and attacking, not thinking of displacement-activity; then I loose the father of the greylags, of which the pink-footed gander is afraid, and then he would do displacement preening. The point is: I must remove the greylag gander first, or else the pink-footed gander would not attack and, if I do not let the greylag gander loose, he will just go on attacking with his neck stretched forward and he will not 'displacement-preen', because the geese without the father will just escape from him without causing him any conflict. In a case like that we know perfectly well which instincts conflict with which.

But you are quite right about our terminology; it ought never to imply that we know the causal explanation; that is exactly why we relinquished the term 'sparking-over activity' which is very descriptive, but which implies a lot.

Displacement means just that the energy which we know to exist, comes out in another way from that in which we expect it to come out.

GREY WALTER:

Energy in what sense?

LORENZ:

Specific readiness to a certain activity.

BINDRA:

Activity appears where it is least expected in that situation.

MEAD:

Irrelevant activity?

GREY WALTER:

Before you can say that a thing is irrelevant, you must know what else could happen, must you not? What are the alternatives?

FREMONT-SMITH:

The goose could do many other things.

GREY WALTER:

How many?

LORENZ:

He could fly away.

169

GREY WALTER:

How many are there, actually?

LORENZ:

Roughly two hundred and fifty.

GREY WALTER:

Two hundred and fifty alternatives, of which the goose's preening is one, and it is always the same reaction? In all these matters we should have some estimate of the alternatives, otherwise we have no information at all.

LORENZ:

In preening alone he would have about ten quite separate instinctive movements, which are not intensity gradations of one pattern. Or he might do any of his expression movements; or he might simply flap his wings.

GREY WALTER:

These things are known to occur as displacement-activities?

LORENZ:

Yes, in other situations.

GREY WALTER:

How many of the two hundred and fifty behaviour modes are known to occur as displacement-activities?

LORENZ:

At least ten or twelve in this species.

GREY WALTER:

If one applies this to the mammal—do we know anything about the number of modes of behaviour of the sheep?

LIDDELL:

They are relatively few.

GREY WALTER:

Much less than two hundred and fifty?

LORENZ:

Much less.

GREY WALTER:

I have never seen a sheep doing anything but grazing!

BINDRA:

You have hit the nail on the head. However, I do not think that the number of modes of behaviour as such is the relevant variable; rather it is the activity or mode with the highest probability of occurrence. That is to say, if you took time-samples of the animal's behaviour, what is the animal doing most of the time? Sheep you see grazing; birds preening; and so on.

HARGREAVES:

Are they always the commonest current activities, or may they be reversions to old common activities? For instance, sucking in cats. I have the impression that early weaned cats as adults develop nostalgic sucking of cushions and things at the time that they have given up sucking. In the adult it may not be habitual, it may only be a temporary reaction. Perhaps the displacement activity, in a mammal at any rate, could be an archaic habitual action.

RÉMOND:

A tic is an activity which arises under some sort of stress and which takes the place of something else. Is this related to displacement-activity?

BOWLBY:

It seems to me a very plausible hypothesis on which to work. I doubt if there is any particular evidence about it, simply because no one has thought about tics in this way before, but it does appear that these kinds of movement occur when other activities are frustrated.

I think that tics can probably be explained in two quite separate ways. One type of tic is probably a form of displacement-activity. The other type is similar in form to an intention movement. (An intention movement is the very restricted brief beginning of a full innate behaviour pattern.) Anna Freud has described (Freud and Burlingham, 1943) children who were going through what appeared to be a completely meaningless repetitive movement and have been able to trace these movements to their origin in a meaningful movement, which is a fully developed pattern of behaviour. In the case

171

that Anna Freud quotes, the brief movement of this kind was the remnant of a full behaviour pattern which had as its content: 'soon, my mother will come and she will bring my coat and my hat and my shoes and she will put them all on'—and he went through the whole rigmarole of putting them on—'and then she will take me away'. After some weeks and months of this it had become an apparently meaningless fragment of a movement. Robertson has also observed something quite analogous (Bowlby, Robertson and Rosenbluth, 1952).

These two hypotheses regarding tics are not in any sense contradictory; it would not surprise me if there were two sorts of tic. Tics are highly compressed, and any one may have more than one root.

MONNIER:

Tics are very often the mere expression of an overflow, something comparable to the tail twitching of the young lambs in Dr. Liddell's experiments or to observations we made in babies with early disintegrated brains. We know from cases of toxoplasmic and rubeolic embryopathy—that is cases in which these diseases occur during pregnancy and injure the brain of the foetus between the third and the seventh month—that these children show later an increased tendency to tics. Those are certainly primitive motor patterns which would be adequately controlled in a normal brain but which appear to be released when the cortical brakes have been destroyed by some pathological process. My impression of tics is that they belong also usually to this category, of released motor patterns in disintegrated brains.

TANNER:

I do not see how the tic could really be a displacement-activity, in that it is not in itself a fully developed movement which does something else normally. It must be a very fragmented displacement-activity, if one at all.

I want to ask Dr. Lorenz whether there are actually any known instances where a particular displacement-activity is characteristic of the young of the species but disappears in the adult; or is displacement-activity always an adult activity associated normally with another instinct?

LORENZ:

Well, I simply do not know, because there are a lot of phenomena which we do not quite like to include in our concept of displacement-activities. There are stereotyped, acquired movements, not so much

172

learnt as ground in, in the way described by Dr. Grey Walter. These may appear in the same way as displacement-activities do. This also occurs in captive animals, mainly because only captive animals have such deeply ground in, stereotyped movements, such as caged parrots doing their typical bowing, which was originally an intention movement of flying away. Even man will show displacement-activities, only his variability is incomparably greater. One man will always tighten his tie and another will flick his ear, but you will find a strong preponderance of skin comfort activities. The tic which originally gave rise to the word is a skin-twitching activity often accompanied by the movement of the hand. I think the genesis of such movement in humans is very complicated. The motor pattern underlying a tic may have originally been an intention movement, but may have turned from an intention movement into a stereotype, and from stereotype it has developed into a displacement-activity.

A more important question is whether infantile movements may reappear. MONICA MEYER-HOLZAPFEL (1938) has shown that bears and monkeys and some other mammals do activities of thumb-sucking in moments of stress. I think I noticed in domestic cats the same thing which Dr. Hargreaves mentioned. I doubt if these are really displacements. They might also be regressions due to disintegration taking place in situations of stress. This might look very much like a displacement, because it appears in similar situations, yet it might be caused in an entirely different way.

GREY WALTER:

Weeping is common in children and relatively rare in adults, and is a characteristic of stress—or does that make it absurd?

TANNER:

I want to ask Dr. Lorenz something again for clarification, since you suggest that weeping might by stretching the terminology be considered possibly as an example of displacement-activity in a certain sense. It strikes me that when somebody weeps you, another human, know what that means. Now, when a goose does displacement preening, what do the other geese know about its feelings, or does it not tell the geese anything at all?

LORENZ:

Well, you have put your finger on it, because we do not know one instance where a true displacement which is not ritualized is understood by the conspecific. In other words, wherever we find a specific I.R.M. responding to a displacement-activity, there already is ritualization. This may be explained by the simple fact that once there is an I.R.M., it selects very rapidly in favour of the sign value of the displacement-activity, and would make it more semantic. The I.R.M. will 'breed' the activity in the direction of semantics. The same process of exaggerating semantic values also occurs with the intention movements. Wherever intention movements are 'understood' by the fellow member of the species they are very apt to be already highly ritualized and distinguishable from the non-semantic homologous intention movements. We know only one example of one expression movement where there is quite clearly an I.R.M. and no ritualization at all, and that is the human yawn whose contagious properties are proverbial. It is exactly the same yawn as in non-social mammals, where it effects no social induction at all. A jaguar or a wild cat, or whatever you want, yawns in exactly the same way as man.

MEAD:

I just want to be sure about what you said. These true displacement movements are not unintelligible to other members of the species. Is the definition of irrelevance applicable?

LORENZ:

Not always. They just happen to be that way because we never caught them in the moment where it was 'already' understood and 'not yet' ritualized, you see. Once the species develops an I.R.M., the thing becomes ritualized so quickly that we have never happened to catch one in the moment where there was already an I.R.M. corresponding to it, and not yet any ritualization.

TANNER:

This is how instinctive movements evolve?

LORENZ:

This is one instance in which we believe we know how they evolve, and that is why we think it is so important: it is one instance where we think we can show causation in the development of instinctive movement.

MEAD:

In this goose that preens when it is interrupted between fear and aggression, the other geese respond to that preening: is that right?

174

LORENZ:

No, not yet. Maybe they do—but it has not yet been proved experimentally.

TANNER:

I think that Dr. Lorenz's point is that later on, after a long time, some goose may discover the significance of displacement preening, and then this will have a selective value, a new I.R.M., and then you have got two hundred and fifty-one movements.

BINDRA:

I should like to state two different interpretations of the so-called displacement phenomenon. I think Professor Lorenz's interpretation is essentially this: whenever there are two instinctual tendencies in conflict there is discharge of the energy or excitation connected with these instincts into a third channel which may be preening or grazing or some other such activity.

My alternative interpretation is this: that, let us say, there are two instinctual tendencies, which when excited together, lead to a general emotional response, a general excitement. This general arousal leads to a release of those activities which happen to be the most prominent in the repertoire of the animal.

LORENZ:

No, they need not invariably be the most prominent. Occasionally you get very rare activity too.

BINDRA:

I think difficulties of this kind can be taken care of by postulating that different thresholds or excitations are required for different types of activities, so that as the animal reaches different levels of arousal certain responses become more likely to occur.

LORENZ:

I want to emphasize that we have no interpretation at all. We just see that in one specific conflict situation one specific displacement-activity occurs. For brevity's sake, I have hitherto only mentioned conflict, but there are other situations where displacement-activities habitually occur, for instance when the specific consummatory situation of some activity is reached too quickly, so that some general excitation is 'left over'. Then there is one special type of displacement-activity which we call 'laziness displacement', and that is a very curious thing. If the specific level of excitation *just fails* to reach the threshold of an activity, you may get a displacement. For instance, if a cat has some incitement to go in a certain direction and then decides not to after all, it invariably preens its neck.

FREMONT-SMITH:

Sort of pretending it never intended to anyway, you mean?

LORENZ:

Yes. Heinroth describes how, when mallard drakes are invited by their females to copulate, they always 'invent an excuse'; that is to say, the drake goes through a few initial movements of copulation and then starts preening. Also, if a mallard is swimming towards a bank and wants to go up that bank because there is some food on it, but it is not hungry, it invariably swims up to the bank and then shakes its tail. This is so specific, and the general level of excitation is so very low, that I would not like to assume that this conflict of wanting to go up to the bank but being too lazy to do it after all causes such a high level of excitation that it must 'come out sideways', so to speak. I think this assumption is not quite compatible with the laws of parsimony of thought. There is nothing indicating a very high general excitation.

Then maybe I ought to emphasize one thing which may even be in favour of Dr. Bindra's interpretation, or it may not, that is the immense drop of potential between the original excitation and the intensity of the displacement-activity. You have to get a stickleback male into a glowing rage and, at the same time, make him desperately afraid, to get just a little bit of displacement digging, which is so low in intensity that Tinbergen at first mistook it for eating. Only by putting a particular strong motivation and inhibition on the stickleback by crowding the tank did Tinbergen succeed in eliciting displacement-activity of full intensity. Then he got all the normal sequence of movements of digging and nest building. In very high states of conflict he even got the glueing activity (the stickleback glues the fibres of the nest together with a special secretion from his kidneys). This activity represents the highest level of excitation of all nest-building activities. This shows that Dr. Bindra's principle of threshold differences may be applied very directly to what I am saying just now. In the case of all these nest-building activities of sticklebacks, activated by displacement, it is quite evident that the digging movements have a lower threshold than the others, while glueing has a higher one. This difference of threshold is quite the same whether the movement be elicited autochthonously or by displacement. In both cases, a lesser degree of excitation is necessary to elicit digging than to elicit glueing. This makes it very probable that the displacement does not influence just one movement, like digging or glueing, but a higher centre which, within the central nervous system, controls both of them. Of course the explanation, that different thresholds determine which activity shall occur, is only applicable within the narrow limits of one specific readiness to certain activities, like nest building. There is no such thing as a 'general excitation', and saying, for instance, that the aggressive drive has a lower threshold than the sexual drive, is in principle nonsensical.

MEAD:

Is it possible that the social irrelevancy of these acts is itself a clue? The non-communicability, the absence of an I.R.M., itself might be significant. When the animal or bird has got into a situation of high social intensity also involving conflict, which interferes with its carrying out the intent to flee or copulate or whatever it is, the assumption of some piece of behaviour with which it can at the same time occupy itself might have survival value.

TANNER:

Going back to the cat, is it not possible that this displacement-activity is one way of saving yourself from remembering everything? If the cat is going off in one direction and then decides that he does not want to go off in that direction after all, it is better from the survival point of view for the cat to wipe the false start right out because he may next time want to go in a different direction. We know some traces persist for some time and if there is no wash-out the animal may start off in the resultant of the new and the old directions, which would be very unfortunate and allow the other cat to get him on the blind side. It would be one way of wiping the slate completely clean, would it not? And it is a method he could use without getting involved with other members of his species.

LORENZ:

That is a finalistic explanation. Yet this aspect of a new survival value is very interesting.

MEAD:

It would have survival value to this individual for future action and also the advantage of *non*-communication of intention to other members of the group.

LORENZ:

Would you say that it is an argument against your explanation that displacement activities *do* so very easily and so very often develop into means of communication?

MEAD:

No, because anything can develop, and as long as you *define* your displacement activity as one which is not ritualized and which does not have semantic content, the explanation could hold.

LORENZ:

Of course, ritualization means the creation of a new instinctive movement, of a new motor co-ordination which copies itself and superimposes itself on the displacement. Once you have that super-imposed independent co-ordination, you have no more displacement-activity in the physiological sense. The trouble is that evidently—we know it by comparative studies—this superimposed, new, in-stinctive motor co-ordination evolves exceedingly quickly once the stimuli emanating from the displacement-activity are taken up by an I.R.M.

FREMONT-SMITH:

I think I have an example, which you all know, which fits in with Margaret Mead's concept; that is what happens when two kittens are at play and attacking each other fiercely with their ears flattened and so forth. All of a sudden one of them, as he sees the other one is about to attack, will turn away and walk off, obviously ignoring the situation and having no intention of doing anything at all, as if he is interested in something else. Then all of a sudden he swings around again and leaps upon the other one. This seems to me to have a survival value, and it is part of what you were talking about.

LORENZ:

I am afraid there is a different explanation. I was just about to mention play as a phenomenon relevant to Dr. Bindra's theory. In play, you find something very parallel to displacement-activities, because in play, as in displacement-activities, there is a consum-matory act, that is, a low-level instinctive motor pattern elicited by something other than its normal specific sort of excitation. This accounts for the fact that in play, as in fits, you may get instinctive activities pertaining to quite different instincts in a quite irregular, chaotic, sequence. In play, and in no other situation, you get the movements of fighting *and* hunting in one sequence. A kitten will stalk another like a prey, then rush at it, stop before it, claw it, do some real fighting movements, rush away, then stand in defensive attitude, with its back up. So in three consecutive seconds this kitten will treat another (*a*) as a mouse, (*b*) as a rival tom cat, (*c*) as a dog, and then switch off and just do nothing.

In Masserman's and Hess's experiments (Hess, 1949) you get something very similar. If you stimulate one place in the hypothalamus, you evidently get the whole instinct away from the highest level which, in Tinbergen's hierarchy, is the highest centre; you get a fighting mood in the cat, and the cat will be less responsive to being fondled; it will refuse to purr and it will then attack some real object. You get all the fighting patterns with the exclusion of other patterns. If you remove your electrode from this spot just a few millimetres caudally, you will get the same movements but dissociated from each other. You will find you can still make that cat purr or eat and it will not be in a fighting mood at all, but you may quite suddenly elicit one lower level activity of fighting, a dissociated blow of the paw or just one spit. That is what was called sham activity originally, sham rage as opposed to real rage. In confirmation of what Dr. Bindra says, in both cases there is some non-specific excitement which is able to circumvent the higher centres and elicit independent, uncorrelated, lower level motor patterns which is something very suggestive and very interesting.

LIDDELL:

Suggestive of what?

LORENZ:

Suggestive of the fact that instinctive activities must be very firmly fixed patterns, as they can be activated in quite another way than the one in which they develop naturally and yet show the same pattern of complicated motor co-ordination.

MONNIER:

I should like to emphasize another aspect of these experiments of Hess (1949). He was able, as you know, to lower the threshold of various instinctive or motor patterns, which showed very interesting plasticity responses according to the actual situation. For instance, when he induced the mechanism of head turning to the right, it occurred frequently that the cat kept this position and started to lick

O

its shoulder. It behaved as if it was trying to adapt the forced posture to the situation, thus giving the impression of some kind of cortical adaptation. I can give you another example of such instinctive patterns secondarily adapted to the situation. For instance, stimulating the hypothalamus you may increase the readiness to activity of the animal. The animal stands on the table with two possibilities: it may fly, or it may attack. If the animal is surrounded by observers and cannot escape easily, it will attack one of the observers. In the other case, if the animal sees a possibility of escaping, it will do it. This confirms the plasticity of the electrically-induced reactions.

LORENZ:

That depends on whether you are stimulating higher up or lower down in the hierarchy.

MONNIER:

I meant a stimulation of the hypothalamus.

LORENZ:

I will give you another instance which Professor Hess himself showed me in a film. He stimulates the centre for head lowering, which is an intention movement downwards. The cat is standing in the middle of a large table and it starts putting down its head. Then it runs to the edge of the table in order to be able to put its head further down than the level of the table. That is, of course, very suggestive of an irradiation to higher centres.

Perhaps I can illustrate what I mean by telling you of a joke. Erich von Holst and I talked about the body/mind problem and asked ourselves what would happen if Hess stimulated my brain centres, my attack centres. I would suddenly remember that Hess had misquoted me in one paper of his and has treated me rather badly in some respects, and maybe I did not like his beard or something. Then I would be quite convinced that I had very sufficient reason for attacking him.

That is only a rather jocular parallel. But before leaving the subject of displacement-activity I would call your attention to a statistical, though not yet certain, correlation between posture and displacement-activities. It seems that blocked, frustrated drive very often finds its way into those activities which are already prepared by the animal's present attitude. For instance, there is a correlation between the intention movements of ducks for flying away and the displacement head-shaking which will take place in this situation. There are some *Anatidae* which show a primitive form of aiming movements, like other birds. Then there are some which only move their heads vertically up and down, like the mallard, and there are some, like diving ducks and geese, who only give a short upward flick of their bill. All these are intention movements, not displacement-activities. In all these species there appears a displacement movement of a sideways head shaking. This never occurs in the species which move their heads in the original way; most of them occur in species which just do this flicking. The movements which are already prepared by the attitude very often appear as displacement-activity, and this licking Professor Monnier mentioned may be a displacement induced in this way.

RÉMOND:

May I take the opportunity to put a question which will take us into a very different subject. I would ask Dr. Liddell how he would define in all these presentations the word or the entity of stress.

LIDDELL:

From my present point of view, stress is to be defined in terms of the organism's preparation to neutralize the stress, and I have tried to define it from Cannon's original description of an emergency reaction in which, in order to maintain homeostasis, physiological patterning must occur to bring about those adjustments necessary to supply the brain, the heart and the skeletal muscles with the materials required for the anticipated exertion, and of course in Cannon's extreme case the cat must fight or flee for its life.

My present conception is that Pavlov's classical conditioning method is a means by which we may greatly refine the quantitative gradations of this emergency reaction in terms of precise stimuli which the experimenter may control, and so it is my present belief that the intensity of stress is to be correlated with the intensity of the bodily processes' anticipation for exertion. When the animal comes into the familiar experimental room where conditioning has occurred, it begins its preparation to meet an emergency, a potentially dangerous situation. We can show, when the animal is standing there awaiting the expected signals for action, for meeting emergency, its breathing is modified, the heart-rate is increased, the psychogalvanic response can be observed. Then the specific conditioning signal, either positive or negative, sharply increases the animal's physiological re-patterning to meet the crisis which is now about to occur. Then when the signal—a neutral stimulus—is given, that itself arouses an alerting response which I find indistinguishable from

181

Cannon's emergency reaction. It is found that the more intensely attention-getting this neutral stimulus is, the easier is the coupling established with the reinforcement. The animal is already in a state of tense expectation, it is in a situation in which it is psychologically trapped—it has given up attempts to escape—and the conditioned signal arouses emergency action which increases in intensity up to the moment of reinforcement. Suppose this perfunctory and mild electric shock forces the animal to make a defensive movement, then the stress is relaxed. So if you are going to speak as Selye does in terms of stressers, there must be relaxers. But when the conditioned stimulus has been given, the reinforcement follows. An episode of intense emergency preparation has now been terminated by the forced relaxation. But this intense preparation decays more and more slowly, and then the next signal ushers in another period of intense emergency reaction, and then (suppose that this is a negative condition signal), the animal is tensed and prepared; the heart beats faster and breathing is more laboured. You can visibly see the goat puff and pant at the bell which means no shock. It is obviously reacting at a higher intensity, but no reinforcement follows; there is no relaxer to follow this new stresser. Therefore, the animal's emergency reaction to the negative condition signal has no drainage, no means of quickly waning.

LORENZ:

Now I understand why you are always changing between a meaningful stimulus and a negative stimulus. It is only now I understant what the positive and negative stimuli are!

LIDDELL:

Then when the animal is ushered out of the experimental room, he is not at once completely relieved of stress, because there is a radiation effect. For example, a neurotic stiff-legged goat is now released from the Pavlov harness, but his leg remains stiff and he limps out of the room. As soon as he goes over the laboratory threshold, the leg loosens up and he can run.

I therefore say that, to me, stress is judged in terms of intensity of reaction. Special conditioned stimuli are stressers and reinforcements are relaxers. From day to day the animal is introduced into a situation which, through habit which is itself stressful, has prepared him to meet emergency. Minor emergencies are ushered in as signals, and the negative conditioned stimulus, in my experience, is more stressful than the positive, because there is no forced relaxation at the end, and very often we have got experimental neurosis from repeating the negative signals over and over because there is nothing to let the animal down or to lower the intensity of its emergency preparation.

LORENZ:

He would like to be rid of the expectation?

LIDDELL:

That is right.

RÉMOND:

You speak about a stress having occurred. You have to have reactions to that stress. If there were no reactions there would have been no stress?

LIDDELL:

To me as a biologist studying behaviour the term stress can only be measured in terms of the animal's reaction thereto, and what is a stress stimulus for one organism may not be for another. I will give you specific examples. One of my experimenters spent the whole year with four goats trying to build up the maximum delayed conditioned reflex, and he began with a telegraph sounder clicking once a second and on the sixth click the animal got the shock. So very soon, the goat began to lift his leg in preparation for the shock say at the fourth or fifth click. Then clicking continued for ten seconds, then he would delay ten to fifteen and twenty. Finally, the best goat had a very well established hundred-second delayed conditioned reflex, which is the maximum we have obtained in any of our goats. Two of them became experimentally neurotic, but this one succeeded in mastering the required delay. We employed a cardiotachometer to correlate the degree of stress with the heart-rate. The metronome clicked, the heart was accelerated, then slowed, then was accelerated again by the next click and so on, so that it continued to accelerate along a saw-tooth type of curve. In the hundredth second, when the animal got the shock, the heart-rate went back within two seconds to the pre-signal level, so sudden was the relaxing effect of this shock. On the other hand, the same goat, standing in the Pavlov frame with intense expectation, received an unsignalled shock. The heart raced instantly and took several seconds to slow down; the same intensity of shock administered to the same animal. The stress under one situation was tremendous before the shock relieved it and the other was minor because it was over as soon as it had appeared.

LORENZ:

If the shock is a relaxer, what is the stresser?

LIDDELL:

The shock in one case was the stresser, in the other case the relaxer. The most amazing experiment which I accidentally did with this animal was the following: in preparing for the day's tests, with my elbow I accidentally closed a switch. The telegraph sounder emitted two clicks and I turned it off thinking the goat had not noticed. Seventy seconds later, he began lifting up the leg. Meanwhile, the heart-rate was climbing. And, at the start of the hundredth second, tense expectancy and tremendous stress was rapidly set up. So I say that we cannot use any rigid mechanistic thinking about the experimenter's control of the stressful stimuli. It is the meaning of the given stimulus applied to the animal which is of significance.

FOURTH DISCUSSION

Presentation: Dr. Whiting

FREMONT-SMITH:

We come now to Dr. Whiting's presentation which, like all the others, will be focussed exclusively on learning theory—and other topics.

WHITING:

And the psychobiological development of the child!

I want to introduce the notion of learning without direct tuition. It is what is suggested by the Freudian notion of identification and superego development; by the notions of imitation and the development of moral values. In every society and in every individual there are some internalized rules of conduct, which govern the individual's actions and made him feel guilty if he deviates from them. The strength of this internalization varies from individual to individual and from society to society. I do not quite know what word to use to describe this because I do not want to get into the quibble of saying that that is not what Freud meant by it, so I will use the word 'X'. I am going to propose that the more 'X' a person has the more he will resist temptation so that the first operational measure of 'X' is 'resistance to temptation'. The second thing this theory says is that if the person succumbs to temptation, either really or in fantasy, he will tend to punish himself. So the more 'X' a person has the more he will resist temptation to break the rules of the society in which he lives and the more he will punish himself if he fails to resist, either really or in fantasy.

Now as to ways which might cause differences in the value of 'X', there are the two intervening variables in Table 2, which I am going to call identification and evaluation. If you have a strong identification with a character who has strong values, then you get a lot of 'X'. Identification and evaluation cannot be measured; but I am

185

going to say that identification is primarily related to the dependency of the child, the need of the child for its mother. So parental behaviour causes differences in identification and differences in 'X' and is called the antecedent variable in Table 2. The first type of parental behaviour which relates positively to identification is nurturance—that is love, caretaking, etc. However, if the nurturance continues without asking the child to do anything in return, you do not get identification. The nurturance must be *contingent*, by which I mean

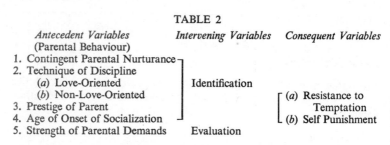

TABLE 2

Antecedent Variables (Parental Behaviour)	Intervening Variables	Consequent Variables
1. Contingent Parental Nurturance		
2. Technique of Discipline		
(*a*) Love-Oriented	Identification	
(*b*) Non-Love-Oriented		(*a*) Resistance to Temptation
3. Prestige of Parent		(*b*) Self Punishment
4. Age of Onset of Socialization		
5. Strength of Parental Demands	Evaluation	

that when the child begins to become a little man or a little woman the mother says, 'Well, now you've got to play your part of the bargain; you've got to be a good boy for me to love you'. If nurturance never becomes contingent you never get 'X' either by identification or evaluation. If, on the other hand, you never get any nurturance to start with you get a lack of conscience and probably a lot of other effects which are suggested by the unloved infant.

When socialization begins the child must be taught to be an adult who has responsibilities and operates under the rules of his society. In the first year of life he is permitted to do very much as he wants; he is nursed when he is hungry; he is permitted to defaecate and urinate freely; he is cared for with respect to cold, heat and so on by the parent. But this cannot always continue and socialization may be accomplished in a number of ways. It may be accomplished entirely by making love contingent on proper behaviour; but other techniques may be used, such as ridicule, physical punishment and so on. Now I want to separate the techniques into love-oriented and non-love-oriented and then I am going to say that love-oriented techniques are those which keep the child interacting with the parent or the mother.

MEAD:

Are you saying 'mother' or 'parent'? Do you mean 'mother' and/or 'father'?

186

WHITING:

I mean 'parent'. I mean anybody who plays the role of caretaking in early life.

MEAD:

Including the child's nurse and grandmother?

WHITING:

Theoretically.

As to non-love-oriented techniques, if you clout the child and it runs away and escapes, the contingency of nurturance has no longer any effect; and, rather than have a conscience, he tends to get away with whatever he can.

There is another thing about the parent that has to do particularly with identification. By identification we mean wanting to be or behave like the parent, so that the greater the power and prestige of the parent, the more the child will be likely to identify himself with him. (Table 2, No. 3.) Let us assume that both husband and wife share the nurturance and disciplining equally; but one is a henpecked person or a person of low prestige within the family set-up, and the other one is the admired person. The theory says that the child will identify with the more admired and more respected of the two, whichever this is.

GREY WALTER:

Is there not a risk of a tautology there? The more likeable person will be more admired.

WHITING:

No; the more a father is esteemed by his wife, the more the child will also esteem him and identify with him.

MEAD:

Are you also including social esteem? The father is the most important person, regardless of personality.

WHITING:

Stated cross-culturally this theory would say that if women in a society had a very low status but did all the nurturing and disciplining, you would have less of 'X' in this society than in a society where

187

the same was true about nurturance but the mother had a relatively high status.

GREY WALTER:

If you have a chief or a big shot of some kind who in his home is henpecked because of the personality of the mother, what does your theory say about that?

WHITING:

It would be a matter of empirical determination.

BINDRA:

Would you be willing to put as sub-headings under 'Prestige'— 'Extrafamilial' and 'Familial'?

WHITING:

All right. To continue (Table 2, No. 4): I am going to say that identification depends not only on the amount of nurturance but also on the age of socialization: the process of identification and evaluation may be accentuated if it occurs at the time of the crucial age period. This is another hypothesis that this theory is going to ask questions about.

Finally (Table 2, No. 5), something which relates to evaluation is the strength of discipline—that is, how strong the values are that the parents hold. You may have a parent who feels, 'Well, you can do anything you want; I do not really hold anything very important about morals', and in that case you might have high identification, but you would not have very high 'X'.

ZAZZO:

I wonder if the diagram you have drawn takes into account the reciprocal aspect of identification? One generally thinks of identification of the child with the parent. Consideration should certainly also be given to identification of the parent with the child, as regards both sexual polarization and all other types of behaviour.

WHITING:

The point is very well taken, I have not got it in and I probably should have. It probably varies with the amount of nurturance that the mother gives to the child. I would have said that the more the mother loves the child the more she would be likely to identify with it.

MEAD:

You are talking about boys, by and large, are you not? The chief point where reciprocal identification comes in is when the parent says 'This child is my sex' or 'This child is the opposite sex'. That is an important element omitted here, but as theories like this are never about girls it does not matter much!

WHITING:

The identification is also close with the parent of the same sex.

Our next job is to translate self-punishment into a particular measure, and the particular measure I am going first to use I shall call patient-responsibility.

FREMONT-SMITH:

As distinguished from impatient responsibility?

WHITING:

No! Patient in the medical sense. In seventy-five different societies we had measurements of the child-training practices including all of those items mentioned in Table 2.

TABLE 3

Projective Systems

Adult
—→ Magical Theories of Disease

Personality
↑   'Patient Responsibility'
|

Child Training   Child
—→
Practices   Personality

Our assumption now was that if these child-training practices had an effect on the child which persisted to adulthood, these personality traits in adulthood would be reflected in the projective or magical belief system of the culture (Table 3). (I have slipped in another assumption here, that the child-training practices in the belief systems change at relatively the same rate, or they do not change at all.)

189

Patient-responsibility is part of this magical belief system. In most primitive societies the cause of sickness is attributed to some agent. This agent may be the patient himself or some other living person, or a ghost, a god or a spirit. A high patient-responsibility culture is one in which the patient himself is responsible for being sick because, as he says, 'I must have broken the festival taboo', or some such.

FREMONT-SMITH:

Self-responsibility for illness.

WHITING:

That is exactly right.

MEAD:

That is one end of a continuum.

WHITING:

The other is that I am sick because of the whimsical action of some sorcerer, ghost or spirit which brought the sickness on through no fault of my own. This is low patient-responsibility, or no patient-responsibility—where one does not accept this self-blame.

TANNER:

High patient-responsibility is the idea of sin then, is it not?

WHITING:

Yes; you are sick because you have sinned. There are societies where all sickness is thought to be due to sin, and there is none where the patient is believed to have no responsibility, but there are many where the responsibility of the patient is negligible. All societies can be put on the scale in the degree to which the patient accepts responsibility, and I am taking this as a measure of the strength of 'X'. High patient-responsibility, high 'X'; low patient-responsibility, low 'X'.

MEAD:

You are not including in the high patient-responsibility the people who feel, 'I am sorcerized because I am successful', are you?

WHITING:

I am.

MEAD:

In addition to sin; success, achievement, beauty, love and wealth? If I am sorcerized, it doesn't matter what for?

WHITING:

If I accept this diagnosis, no.

BOWLBY:

Supposing A thinks that someone else is sorcerizing him because of something he (A) did, that involves the sorcerer as well as A.

WHITING:

Yes. But if A's action completely determines the action of the sorcerer, then the culture gets a fairly high patient-responsibility.

BOWLBY:

It is a matter of degree as to what extent the sorcerer is a free agent and to what extent influenced by A?

WHITING:

Yes. The highest degree would be when it was believed, 'When breaking a particular taboo, automatically the sickness came upon me, completely, inevitably, without any question'. If there was some mediation of a sorcerer who had some free will of his own, then this would get a lower score.

BOWLBY:

And if it is pure whimsy?

WHITING:

If it is pure whimsy it gets a still lower score.

Now I am going to see if there is any relationship between the score for patient-responsibility and the type of child-rearing; our theory says they should be related. I am going to take age as the first variable to test. The theory states that if the dependency relationship of the child to the parents is maximal at a critical period then 'X' and hence patient-responsibility have got to be related to that critical age. The data are presented in Table 4; the mean scores on our scale of patient-responsibility are given for the different cultures who socialize children in the various listed ways at different ages.

191

Let us take the age of weaning first (Table 4, second column), the highest scores for patient-responsibility are in societies with early weaning.

BOWLBY:

What is the range of the scale?

TABLE 4. *Relation between Patient-Responsibility for Illness and Estimated Age at Onset of Various Aspects of Socialization*

The table shows the mean index of patient-responsibility for societies with various estimated ages at onset of each aspect of socialization; in parentheses after each mean is shown the number of societies on which it is based. The age intervals are not of uniform size, having been selected to avoid excessive bunching or spreading of cases in any of the five distributions. In the last line of the table are correlation coefficients expressing the closeness of relation between the index of patient-responsibility and estimated age at onset of each aspect of socialization. Coefficients marked with an asterisk are significant at the 5 per cent. point; those marked with two asterisks are significant at the 1 per cent. point.

ASPECT OF SOCIALIZATION

AGE AT ONSET	Weaning	Toilet training	Modesty training	Training in heterosexual inhibition	Independence training
Below 1.0	11.0(2)	4.0(2)			
1.0 to 1.9	11.6(5)	11.9(8)			
2.0 to 2.4	11.0(10)	11.7(7)			15.8(4)
2.5 to 2.9	9.1(9)	9.0(1)			9.9(8)
3.0 to 3.9	9.5(4)	14.0(1)	13.8(4)		9.0(9)
4.0 to 5.9	4.0(2)	8.0(1)	10.5(3)		9.2(11)
6.0 to 7.9			9.2(5)	12.1(7)	6.0(1)
8.0 to 9.9				9.0(3)	
10.0 and above			9.0(1)	5.5(4)	
Correlation coefficient	−0.42**	+0.21	−0.50*	−0.74**	−0.34*

WHITING:

From 0 to 21; the mean is between 9 and 10. Let us not take this too seriously, but let us just say—since the correlation coefficients are most significant—that there is a suggestion that the age may be a factor of importance, not only in the immediate behaviour of the child, but also in the permanent development of the 'X' factor if we accept patient-responsibility as a way of measuring this.

192

BINDRA:

The joker in all this is the relation that you postulate between patient-responsibility and the strength of the superego. Would you like to say anything about why you think there is this relation?

WHITING:

It is a good question. Obviously I am not particularly interested in magical theories of disease in primitive societies. The theory came before the choice of patient-responsibility. I said, 'Now, what kind of a measure can I get out of this kind of material that might indicate self-punishment?'

BINDRA:

Your postulated relation refers only to the self-punishment aspect of the strength of superego?

WHITING:

That is right. We do not want to rest our case just on this one measure, but it might suggest that it is worth while looking for other, more satisfying and more direct measures.

MEAD:

You have made no attempt here to use a distinction that Erikson (1950) makes between sin as a product of certain situations in the first two years, and guilt in the four-year to six-year period, have you? Have you not got here a possible relation between autonomy around the age of two and patient-responsibility?

WHITING:

It could very well be so.

MEAD:

What you have defined are the cultures in which one says, 'I did it myself'. The emphasis is upon making the child do it itself early.

WHITING:

Maybe I could suggest one other thing. Another measure of self-punishment is the very common therapeutic practice of phlebotomy or bleeding oneself—cutting one's head, or wherever you have a sore spot—to get the bad blood out. This is in contrast to the other

193

therapeutic techniques where a salve or some pleasant thing is used for therapy. One might make the assumption that blood-letting was another measure of 'X' by the self-punishment route.

I am now working on this analysis, and it shows no very consistent relation to the age factor. It does, however, relate very significantly (1 per cent.) to independence-training.

I am working on a third measure and that is sacrifice to the gods as a therapeutic practice. This is also positively related to patient-responsibility, but there is no consistent relationship to the age factor. In superego development there is nothing except Table 4 which shows anything consistent about age. Sacrifice relates to training in control of aggression, however.

FREMONT-SMITH:

What do you mean by sacrifice?

WHITING:

Giving goods to the gods.

GREY WALTER:

Do you include paying fees to the doctor?

WHITING:

It does not include that; it includes giving something to the gods, some specially costly gift.

LIDDELL:

In this self-punishment concept, is there a special case of a suicide or all-or-nothing phenomenon?

WHITING:

Yes. But the data here are so inaccurate that I could not use them as a variable.

FREMONT-SMITH:

Those types of culture where individuals believe that they must lie down and die because they broke a taboo, would they be the ultimate in patient-responsibility?

WHITING:

That is right.

MEAD:

Then you put the Maori at the top?

WHITING:

The Maoris are at the top; they have the highest score of patient-responsibility. The Manus have a score of 14, the Arapesh of 11 and the Samoans of 9.

BINDRA:

Dr. Mead, does that fit in with the general impression you have of these groups?

MEAD:

I think there are two mixtures, as I have said. If you include dying for sin and dying for success, if you then add in autonomy with the emphasis on the period from two to three, this is what happens. But it is questionable whether to regard dying because you are successful, or because you are beautiful in a non-puritanical society, fits into the scheme of superego development. This sort of scheme is perfectly accurate, but may be an artefact of the societies of which we happen to have descriptions. Imagine that instead of a hundred societies we have descriptions, say, of thirty. You can get certain artefacts that have real regularities in them but are only part of the whole. Would you agree with that statement, Dr. Whiting?

WHITING:

Yes, I agree absolutely. This whole thing is an attempt to get out some of the variables in a problem that is exceedingly complex. Let us say that something looms from it, but not come to any conclusion.

TANNER:

May I get this clear in my mind—you are arguing from what we should call between-culture statistical relationships to within-culture statistical relationships, are you not?

WHITING:

That is right. What I am saying essentially is that an individual habit is the equivalent of a custom.

TANNER:

I am saying the same thing in statistical language.

WHITING:

The unit of culture represents the behaviour of a typical individual in a society. If you like, the individual is equivalent to society. So the customs of society are like the habits of an individual.

TANNER:

That is what is worrying me about your approach, the going from the between-society to the within-society.

WHITING:

It seems to me it is legitimate to say there may be something that can be discovered at one level that cannot be discovered at the other, and vice versa.

BINDRA:

You probably have to make different assumptions in order to be able to test the hypothesis at the individual level.

TANNER:

It is rather analogous to arguing from the pathological case back to the range of chemical variation within normal persons. Sometimes you hit it off and it saves a lot of time, other times it is, in fact, a *non sequitur* and breaks down. Every time you suspect something from a pathological case you have got to go back to the normal group and make sure that a similar thing does happen in a normal group; it may not.

WHITING:

That is exactly the design of our research.

The next step is a series of individual studies within not only our culture but several others, to check the hypothesis developed cross-culturally. My ultimate aim would be a theory which could account for relationships between customs in a society, and habits in an individual. No doubt they will not be just the same, but I would like to have the whole theory embracing both.

Almost all of our developmental theory is derived from individuals within a single Western European culture, and so one of the things that we really must do is to try out these principles elsewhere, because they may be cultural artefacts.

Contrariwise, we do not want to stick to this cross-cultural approach and say, 'Well now, this is going to be reapplicable back to our own culture without any corrections'.

Let me go back now to the hypothesis of Table 2. We were able to get a score for each society of the relative importance of love-oriented techniques, and found this was related to patient-responsibility at the 5 per cent. level of confidence. This is one of the few antecedent variables that has been consistent in its relationship to whatever measure we take of 'X'. The strength and severity of discipline in weaning, toilet-training, sex-training, independence-training and training for the control of aggression have the following correlations with patient-responsibility: weaning, $+0.25$; toilet-training, $+0.06$; sex-training, $+0.02$; independence-training, $+0.18$; aggression, $+0.28$. It is interesting that though they are all positive, the only one that is significant at the 5 per cent. level is aggression.

FREMONT-SMITH:

One might anticipate that training for handling aggression would be associated with self-punishment.

BINDRA:

Are these five variables themselves not related?

WHITING:

Very little; if society is severe in weaning, it is not necessarily severe in toilet-training. The full data are given in the book (Whiting and Child, 1953, p. 116). I ought to say that these ratings are judgements made by three judges who had a defined set of scales to use. The reliability of judgement was about 0.75 to 0.80.

BINDRA:

Did your three judges know your theory?

WHITING:

No, they did not, nor did they have any access to the data on magical theories of disease for the most part, because most of this was done on the data from the cross-cultural survey, where the information on child-training is separate from the information on theories of disease.

MEAD:

They were presented with paragraph descriptions, were they not?

WHITING:

That is right.

197

MEAD:

And these were lifted out of the ethnographic descriptions?

WHITING:

Yes.

Let me go on now to the next method of testing this theory. A group of my research assistants went down to the American South West to three societies and made individual-difference studies within three cultures. Two of the cultures were western European—one Mormon, the other Texan—and the third was American Indian, the Zuni. They got scores on approximately thirty mothers and thirty children in each culture and tested the hypotheses on individual differences in three cultural contexts. In addition to this, we are doing the same thing on a large group of four hundred mothers in a suburb of Boston. Except for a preliminary analysis that has been done by Chris Heinicke (1953) on a small part of the sample, these data are still in embryo.

In order to get an individual test of self-punishment we decided on a picture test, of a Thematic Apperception kind, in which we used dogs for actors in order to get rid of cultural artefacts—or attempt to. The dogs were all doing naughty things, like breaking things apart, fighting, stealing a bone from another dog and so on. These were presented to the ten- and eleven-year-old children just like a T.A.T.: what are the dogs doing, what are they thinking of, what will they do next? This was then scored for self-punishing responses, that is, self-punishment with respect to the dog. The respondent says that the dog feels sorry, or he ran and fell down and hurt himself, and so on. We were then able to get quite a surprising number of self-punishing scores. It is what you might call a projective self-punishment test.

In the Mormon and Texan groups, there was a positive relationship between the amount of initial nurturance and the amount of self-punishment. This was not true of the Zuni, partly because we were unable to get a stable amount of initial nurturance.

BOWLBY:

What age were the children?

WHITING:

They were in the sixth, seventh and eighth grades; the test was administered in the school, and it was a pencil-and-paper test.

198

TANNER:

How did you get the rating of the nurturance of the same children?

WHITING:

It was done by interviewing the mothers of these children.

MEAD:

And it was retrospective in regard to the children?

BOWLBY:

It was what the mothers had claimed they had done?

WHITING:

Yes, so we get pretty tentative scores on both sides.

With regard to sex differentiations we got two interesting results. When talking with the parents we asked them which one was responsible for policy with respect to child-training; when there was any decision to make about bringing up the child did the father take it, the mother take it, or did they share it? Thus we got a responsibility-for-policy score, and we found that where the same-sex parent was the one who took responsibility for policy, you had high 'X'.

Secondly, on a cross-cultural basis, with respect to the cultural prestige of men and women, the Mormon males are very high and the Texan males are low, with respect to the household, where the woman is the boss. The highest projective self-punishment score was found in the Mormon boys, and the next highest in the Texan girls.

Heinicke has made a study of five-year-old children using an individually administered test with dolls to give a self-punishment score, and found that the greater the nurturance the more the self-punishment, the more the denial of love as a technique the more the self-punishment and, finally, the more severe the punishment for aggression, the more the self-punishment.

LORENZ:

I should have thought that the positive correlation between the taboo and punishment of sexual activities and self-punishment would be still greater than that between aggression and self-punishment.

WHITING:

That was what I expected, because of the Freudian Oedipus resolution. The severity of punishment for sex in each one of the studies has been tested with each of the measures, but in no instance has it related.

ZAZZO:

We have recently carried out a fairly extensive enquiry in a number of countries regarding the way young children imagine their family. This enquiry was rather rapidly carried out and the main test consisted of the well-known test of drawing the family.

We have not yet finished working out the results but we have made an unexpected discovery. We have tried to assess the valuation of the mother and of the father by boys and girls. In all the social classes and in all the countries where the enquiry was carried out the mother was more highly valued than the father. There is a fairly significant difference: in Italy, for example, the mother was more highly valued in the drawing, if one takes into account certain aspects, especially the height of the mother, which is greater than that of the father, and the execution and finish of the drawing.

That is the first thing, which is perhaps not so surprising in itself. But if we evaluate the drawings according to other factors, especially the frequency of representation of the father or the mother, or the order of drawing the father and the mother, we note that it is not the mother that is preferred by the same children, but the father.

Thus two evaluations are obtained, and this holds good for all countries. We have examined approximately three hundred children in each country.

FREMONT-SMITH:

What age were they?

ZAZZO:

Four, five and six-and-a-half, the pre-school age. We carried out the enquiry in kindergartens and nursery schools.

The question I want to put here is the following: as regards what the child takes as a model, are there not very different levels of evaluation, one being purely affective, which holds good equally for boys and girls, and another of a social order, which favours the father rather than the mother?

The figures we now have show this distinction very clearly with no appreciable differences between the two social groups we have observed.

As regards valuation on the social plane, we have wondered whether verbal expressions might not play some part! While the child is drawing there is a verbal enumeration—for the French it is 'Father, mother and children'—which would result automatically in the father being drawn before the mother. The boys tend rather towards the father and the girls rather towards the mother at that age. The essential point I want to stress is the double aspect of valuation as regards the parental model—from the affective point of view and from the social point of view.

WHITING:

I would like to see the result of that. We made another study on the effect of the father, differentially from the mother, on the projective test of self-punishment. In this study, what the mother did was the only thing that had any influence on self-punishment, with one exception. Some of the fathers did a lot of the nurturing of children and some did not; this made no difference. Some fathers were severe with the children and some were not; this made no difference. The one thing the father did which did make a difference was the degree to which he esteemed the mother. If the father said the mother is doing a fine job in child-rearing, this child had a high 'X' or superego. If the father said he did not think she was doing such a good job, they had a low 'X'.

Another interesting thing here is that this was positively related with the mother's sexual anxiety. The mothers that had high sexual anxiety were not esteemed by their husbands, and their children had a low superego. The role of the father in this particular study seemed to be in support of the mother and not directly influential on the child. This was with five-year-olds. Whether they would change in later life I do not know.

MEAD:

How about the reverse position, the mother's estimation of the father? Did that have no effect?

WHITING:

It was hard to say. Generally speaking, when the husband esteemed the wife the wife esteemed the husband, so that it was hard to determine, but in so far as we could pick the two apart it seemed that the father's estimate of the mother was more important.

MEAD:

These were American children?

201

WHITING:

Yes.

GREY WALTER:

Was it explicit or implicit esteem?

WHITING:

During the course of the interview, we asked the father to describe how the mother was doing with her child-rearing; we probed on this, and from this were able to get a judgment of whether he thought she was doing a good job or not.

GREY WALTER:

Would the child have been aware of the father's attitude to the mother as an explicit statement such as, 'Your mother is a wonderful person' or is it simply that the father is leaving the job to the mother without comment and therefore implicitly approves?

WHITING:

The theory that I am working on suggests that the child must in some way know, either directly or indirectly. It may be just the mother's self-esteem and self-confidence that makes her a better model for the child to identify with.

Another thing is to do with concentration of authority on the two parents. The parents are the nurturers, but in certain societies the disciplining is done by a so-called disciplinarian—a typical case happens in the south-west—called kachina. Here the mother takes care of the child regularly, but somebody dressed up as a ghost, god or spirit comes and visits them. He knocks on the door and says, 'Have you got any bad little boys there?' and the parent says, 'Well, Jimmy hasn't been very good but please don't take him away'. The spirit will then say, 'We have got to take him in our basket' and the mother will say, 'I am sure he will be good'; he will then say, 'Well, are you sure we shouldn't take him?' and finally the mother pushes the kachina out of the house, but the kid is plenty scared and has got plenty of discipline to last him for several weeks. What does this produce, low or high superego? Our theory would say low, because you have got the separation of nurturance and anxiety, the mother standing constantly for nurturance.

The kachina is characteristic of the Zuni and the Zuni have in fact one of the lowest patient-responsibility societies in our sample. An interesting confirmation of this is the sample of individual Zuni children within Zuni culture. There were some parents who used denial of love rather than calling on the kachina to visit them, and in these families we found relatively high guilt. With those who called in the kachina we found a relatively low guilt.

LORENZ:

How often does the kachina come?

MEAD:

Irregularly, mainly in connexion with the big dance feasts. It is very much like the Black Peter, Caspar and Santa Claus—that sort of thing. You build up to the fact all the time that the kachina may come, and then the parents tell the kachina how much punishment they want meted out, and then play the role of being the children's defendants. You have a high degree of insincerity in this picture.

BOWLBY:

Do the children see through that?

WHITING:

I think they do to a certain extent, but there is always a haunting doubt.

There is one other fact of social structure that we can bring in here, and that is polygamy versus monogamy. This comes out as expected. In the monogamous families patient-responsibility is high and in the polygamous it is low. This is over thirty-four societies.

GREY WALTER:

Have you any record of any polyandrous society?

WHITING:

Only one, and it had an about average patient-responsibility.

MEAD:

Have you tried taking ten societies where you had a very large amount of good, comparable data and where you would expect to get significant results? I should think that today the available mathematical methods of studying small groups would make it pay to work with a smaller number of good data.

WHITING:

That is true. But there is always a point of diminishing returns. If the number is too small, you cannot do anything. What we want is more cases better covered. If we have a lot of cases which are good, then we can hope to find something.

MEAD:

In the study of Ford and Beach (1951) which was done on the same sort of material, there was a claim of something like one hundred and nine societies and in forty per cent. the basic incest details were not given correctly. It is dangerous to use material on which you have not good data.

TANNER:

How many societies do you reckon there are good data on, Dr. Mead?

MEAD:

If you want exceedingly complicated points, probably not more than a dozen. I would not attempt to do what Dr. Whiting is doing with more than twenty.

WHITING:

There are about fifteen to twenty of these seventy-five societies in which you have a fairly good number of reliable statements. There are a lot more, however, from which you can get a pretty specific statement about one particular aspect of child-training, such as a very concrete and explicit statement about weaning and nothing else. Whenever I got something like that I included it in the sample, so that I could use it for weaning even if nothing else.

MEAD:

I do not believe that if you do not look at anything else you get the weaning right.

WHITING:

That may be so.

BOWLBY:

I should like to raise the whole question of the relationship between patient-responsibility and what we mean by superego. It seems to me that so far what we have been discussing is the relationship between patient-responsibility and all these different variables. How patient-responsibility relates to the superego does not seem to me to be self-evident. That it is related I do not doubt, but it does not seem to me to be necessarily very closely related. The superego is rather complicated and contains more than one variable.

GREY WALTER:

Can you measure the superego?

BOWLBY:

You cannot.

GREY WALTER:

Then what is the point of discussing it?

BOWLBY:

I think it is useful to try and see how things relate to these psychological functions after which we are dimly trying to grope. The question in my mind was this: how, in a culture, does patient-responsibility relate to law-abidingness: does patient-responsibility relate to successful resistance to temptation?

WHITING:

I have no evidence on this. I would say that even a very law-abiding person, unless he has a very rigid superego, may still be tempted in fantasy.

BOWLBY:

Do we really object to people being tempted in fantasy?

WHITING:

We do not mind about it, but I think you are still going to get evidence of guilt, whether we mind or not. It seems to me that even though we only punish the actual occurrence of deviation, the individual himself who has a strong value for 'X' punishes himself for the fantasy.

MEAD:

There is an aspect that we have not touched on yet—the question of external and internal sanctions. The Manus believed that people were made ill because of their own sins. They had a moral system

205

which was so arranged that you could never be good enough, because the next time you had an attack of malaria somebody would find something you could have done which you had not done yet, so it was impossible to be permanently good. You could always build a bigger house, feed another pig, make another trip, or something like that. Illness was a punishment that showed that you had done something that you ought not to have done, or had not done something that you should have done. So the Manus would get a very high rating in patient-responsibility. Twenty-five years ago, the sanction was externally imposed for acts of commission or omission. A diviner divined why you were sick, you promised to build the house or pay the debt, and you got well. Internal sanctions were relatively low.

Now the Manus have moved in twenty-five years to the position where the most serious thing is *thinking* about doing something wrong, which is far more serious than doing it. *Acts* are now in the province of civil authority and they do not cause illness. If you take your neighbour's wife, the court will deal with you and fine you or put you in jail, but it you are angry with your neighbour for taking your wife, you get sick and you may die. So fantasy and thought are the major sins, though the people would still rank high on law-abidingness and on resistance to temptation. Illness and death are still the results of your own behaviour, but whereas it used to be in action, now it is in fantasy.

WHITING:

There is another study in progress in which a patient-responsibility is being related to taboos, particularly food and sex taboos during pregnancy. There is a very high negative relationship between taboos and patient-responsibility, suggesting that taboos are an externalized form of control as contrasted with patient-responsibility. But in this particular study I do not know whether we would give a different score to the Manus now and then.

MEAD:

You included fantasy behaviour, did you not?

WHITING:

I did in my definition of self-punishment, but not in my definition of patient-responsibility. Law-abidingness can result from fear of external punishment or from superego.

BOWLBY:

Or from both.

206

MEAD:

Or it can be the Balinese position, where you have a preference for balance built into the personality, which is another level entirely (see Bateson, 1949).

WHITING:

By law-abidingness I mean something a little different from resistance to temptation. I mean resistance to temptation with the possibility of external punishment removed.

BOWLBY:

Surely that is a mythical case, is it not?

WHITING:

No, I do not think so. There are instances when one might be tempted, with not the slightest possibility of getting caught, but you do not do it if you have a conscience. 'Thus conscience doth make cowards of us all'. There is no society which depends completely on internalized or externalized control; it is always a mixture of the two.

Let me tell you about an experiment on resistance to temptation in dogs. We got eight puppies and brought them up just about the way Dr. Bindra did. For four months, four of the puppies, starting at six weeks old, lived in isolation and were fed by machines. The other four were not in houses but in the laboratory where they were fed and petted by humans. So we have got a machine-fed group and a human-fed group.

First we tested these in terms of the dependency measure that Scott (1951) used: you put your hand in the cage to see if they will lick it or not. Two of the machine-fed dogs and two of the human-fed dogs licked. This was clearly the result of species temperamental differences and not the result of training.

We were going to try and give the dogs a superego and were going to ask the question: 'Does machine-feeding lead to higher superego or "X" factor or whatever it is in dogs?' I was betting against this. My colleague Dick Solomon said a dog certainly could be given a superego. Anyway, after this differential training, the experimenter sat down with horsemeat on one side and dog chow on the other and a newspaper in his hand. When the dog ate horsemeat, he would whack him over the nose, and when he ate dog biscuit it was O.K. After a relatively short time, all the dogs ate the dog biscuit and did not eat the horsemeat; so let us say we have made the evaluation— the parent has made the evaluation—that you must not eat horse-meat but you can eat dog chow.

Then the dogs were put in the temptation situation, in a room by themselves with the experimenter looking through a peephole. How long would it be before the dogs ate the horsemeat? Was there any difference between the machine-fed and the human-fed, in resistance to temptation by the horsemeat?

BOWLBY:

Who did the whacking?

WHITING:

The person who fed them.

TANNER:

How many whacks did each dog take?

WHITING:

The human-fed dogs took less whacks than the machine-fed dogs, they learned quicker.

TANNER:

Then it might go either way.

LORENZ:

I am quite sure that a really well-trained dog can be left in the situation of temptation for ever and he will not eat the horsemeat; but my prediction is that these puppies who had just been whacked two or three times had not developed a superego. They may have, but I do not believe it.

WHITING:

The machine-fed dogs resisted temptation from thirty seconds to six minutes—that is the range of the four dogs; and the human-fed resisted from six minutes to six hours. One of these human-fed dogs was four days hungry before he ate. He was brought in on four successive days, he ate the dog chow which was there, a rather small amount, and was left there for half an hour and was then taken out until the next day, when he was brought back and again ate the dog chow but did not eat the horsemeat. It took him four days before he finally broke down.

LORENZ:

May I tell two short stories about superegos in dogs? One of my dogs who had been reared with ducks and geese and other fowl, and who quite certainly had never killed one and been beaten for it, accidentally killed an old gander who bit him in the tail so severely that the dog gave a reflexive snap and the gander who was twenty-four years old and had somewhat weak bones got a slight fracture on the back of the skull. The dog got a neurosis from that to the extent of hiding in a garret where none of our dogs had ever been seen; he crept behind some boxes and stayed there, not coming out for more than twenty-four hours; we only found him on the second day.

The other story is this. One of my bitches showed very strong superego when in the situation of temptation with lambs bleating and chickens fluttering about in the farmyard; she would put herself on the lead, coming to heel spontaneously whilst she trembled with temptation. In order to prevent herself being tempted she created the fiction of being on the lead. I think that bitch would have starved to death rather than kill and eat a goose.

FREMONT-SMITH:

In these experiments you did not expect the superego to develop so quickly?

LORENZ:

I should have thought the very short influence of man would have been insufficient to develop any 'superego' at all.

BOWLBY:

It is possible that these puppies that had been hand-fed had been submitted to a good deal of training by the feeder over the preceding months.

GREY WALTER:

Would someone explain to me why the superego has got involved in these experiments?

TANNER:

I was just about to ask Dr. Grey Walter what the relation of superego was to conditioned reflex experiments!

MEAD:

You need to bring in here the relationship between learning in the parent/child situation and affection, so as to differentiate between the human-fed and the machine-fed puppies. Otherwise, you could administer conditioned reflex training and you would have no characterological concept, no intervening variable to explain the difference. The superego idea is probably too complex to use here, but you need some intervening notion.

GREY WALTER:

I do not see the necessity. As Dr. Whiting has described the experiment, the human-fed animals were human-trained animals and they had learned from humans.

WHITING:

Let me ask a sixty-four dollar question. We are going to run a control and have the machine educate the dogs. The machine feeds and punishes both groups. What is your prediction? Which group is going to resist temptation here?

GREY WALTER:

Are they going to be given their instruction in the test situation by a machine or by a human?

WHITING:

By a machine.

LORENZ:

The answer is how much the machine fits into different I.R.M.s waiting for a parent figure.

WHITING:

If it should come out that the human-fed animals would resist temptation even when the machine punished them, I do not know how I would interpret that. If the machine-fed animals came out resisting temptation when the machine punished them, I would say it was punishment by a nurturing stimulus. A stimulus held to be associated with positive valence has more strength than one that is neutral. Five punishments by the hand that fed you counts twenty-five, so you get more inhibitions. I am going to bet a nickel that the dog identifies with a human and not with a machine. That is the essential difference. I think you are going to have to have some kind of hypothesis like identification, some kind of intervening variable.

BINDRA:

Before you do that, you have to use the control that Dr. Bowlby suggested. These human-fed animals are also wandering around in the laboratory, and they probably get some training which the machine-fed animals do not get.

WHITING:

No, they do not. They are all in cages, and they all have the same routine. The only difference is that once a day, for about ten minutes, with the human-fed dogs some person comes in and gives them the food. Otherwise they are treated in a completely standard manner.

BINDRA:

So they are not human-reared, they are just human-fed?

WHITING:

Yes.

FREMONT-SMITH:

You also have to test the limits of the machines. It is quite possible that the dog would not identify with one machine, but if you made an appropriate machine, a warm machine which had certain odours to it and a vocal magnetic tape inside it with a human voice and so on, you could get a machine which was quite within the limits of an I.R.M.

LORENZ:

Try to make a supercanine machine which fits the dog's I.R.M. better than a man does; which, for instance, snarls when punishing and wags a huge tail when pleased!

WHITING:

In other words, if this comes out in this way, the perception of similarity between self and punisher is going to be crucial.

TANNER:

This brings us to what I want to ask Dr. Lorenz. What is the ethological equivalent of identification?

211

P

LORENZ:

It is already complicated, because it means social attachment to a social superior. But to make clear the difference from a simple conditioned reflex: the point in my first story was that this dog had never been beaten, but behaved as if it anticipated a horrible beating.

GREY WALTER:

You mean he imagined something he had never seen?

LORENZ:

No, he had traumatized himself by doing something contrary to any formerly accepted custom of this society. I would mention the case of a dog biting a human by mistake, for instance a dog biting a human who tries to separate fighting dogs. A normal dog who has never bitten a man, who has never been punished for biting a man, gets a neurosis to the extent of trembling, not being able to walk, breathing irregularly and breaking down completely. That is for doing something for which he has never been punished, but which is contrary to some laws of society.

FREMONT-SMITH:

Contrary to his expectations of himself?

LORENZ:

Yes, that is quite true. Then I have another point. This bitch of whom I told you, who put herself on the lead of her own free will in order not to follow temptation, broke down completely when isolated from me. She did it twice, once when I became a Professor in Königsberg, and once when I was recruited into the army. She lost every type of behaviour which was socially learnt. She lost her house-training, and she killed everything she could get hold of. This is also interpretable in terms of neurosis, but you may also say that all these higher social performances of being house-trained and not killing chickens were dependent on the presence of an individual. It is only saying the same thing in different words.

FIFTH DISCUSSION

Presentation of Film by Dr. Bowlby

BOWLBY:

The purpose of this film* is to show how a child responds in a separation situation.

A great deal of work on separation and its effects has been done in terms of long-term separations and the long-term effects; we know them sometimes to be very damaging. More recently, however, we have been concerned with trying to understand what happens at the time of separation and during separation; this is the first cinematograph record we have made of this event. It was made in a hospital because we could foretell that this child would be going into hospital and would only remain there a short time. The child, who is quite healthy before the event, had a small umbilical hernia to be dealt with, a small operation which is known not to cause too much pain.

We selected this child 'at random'. The reason we did it this way was because my colleague, Robertson, and I have so frequently been accused of exaggerating the emotional disturbance of these relatively minor social happenings: eight days in hospital—nothing very much—no real importance! And so we said, 'All right, we'll make a film of the next child to come in who conforms to certain criteria'. One criterion was that he or she must be between the age of 18 months and 2½ years; that is to say, after the child has made a differentiated and focussed relationship to a mother figure, which we know develops only slowly during the first six or nine months. This child, therefore, is well beyond the age when a differentiated relationship has been formed, yet still at an age when the attachment is at a maximum intensity. Her age proved to be two years and five months.

The second criterion was that we wanted a child from a normal happy home. The child selected, in addition to having loving parents, was the eldest child; there was no other child born then, but the

---

* JAMES ROBERTSON: *A Two Year Old Goes to Hospital*. 16 mm. B & W. Sound 45 mins. (Tavistock Clinic).

213

mother was four to five months pregnant at the time the film was made.

It was made in an ordinary children's ward, with a minimum of disturbance. Robertson just had a hand camera. There was no special lighting; it was made in the month of August when the light is good. There was no disturbance in the ward routine at any time and what is seen is just what happens to any child. There are two exceptions to that statement: one is that we asked that at a certain point in the morning of each day a nurse should come and play with the child, because we wanted to have a record of how the child treated the nurse. The second thing is that, because the child was being filmed, she did get rather more attention than she would otherwise have got; for instance her parents were allowed to visit her on four days out of eight, which we understand would not have been permitted otherwise.

The film was shot in two ways. Certain events—coming in, visits, and so on—were filmed as and when they occurred. In addition, each morning there is a period of time-sampling. It was known before the event that between 11 and 12 o'clock the ward was quiet; most of the surgical and medical activities had been completed and lunch was not yet coming round. Therefore, in order to avoid the criticism that we were merely selecting what we wanted to show and that it was a distorted picture of the responses, Robertson filmed by the clock; at 11 o'clock precisely there is an eight-second shot, at 11.5 another eight seconds and so on through to 11.40. It was during this time-sampling period each morning that the nurse was asked to come and play with the child. She came at 11.15 and, during the six minutes when she is playing with the child, Robertson (1953) shot eight-second sequences at one-minute intervals.

Synopsis

Laura is two years and five months old, a first child and so far an only one. She is intelligent, mature, and for her age has unusual control over the expression of feeling. She rarely cries. She is about to go into hospital for eight days to have a minor operation for umbilical hernia.

Although her parents had tried to prepare her for going into hospital, when she meets the admitting nurse she is cheerful and friendly and clearly does not realize that her mother will leave her. Going through the ward she seems less confident, and when she is undressed to be bathed she screams for her Mummy. Within 10 minutes, however, her exceptional control over feeling asserts itself and she is apparently calm.

She is put in a cot and breaks down again when nurse takes her temperature—'Don't like it. I want my Mummy'. A few minutes later Mother comes to say goodbye, and leaves for her consolation a piece of blanket she has had since infancy and which she calls her 'baby'. Throughout her stay this 'blanket baby' and her Teddy make a link with home and are clung to when she is sad or frightened.

When alone she appears calm, but if a kindly person stops to talk with her her feelings appear. Sister comes to greet the new patient and Laura's face crumples—'I want my Mummy'. This occurred throughout her stay; the camera shows that what may easily be taken for calmness is often a facade which contact with a friendly person breaks down.

When the surgeon comes she clutches her Teddy and blanket 'baby' for comfort, and despite his tact she is apprehensive and resistive. Occasionally during the day she asks quietly for her Mummy, but without insistence.

On the *second day* she looks strained and sad, and has difficulty in responding to the nurse who comes to play with her. Then her feelings appear and she cries for a short time for her Mummy. But though she cries little throughout her stay, she takes great interest in other children who cry—as if they cry for her who is too controlled to cry. A rectal anaesthetic is kindly administered, but the strange experience frightens her. Thirty minutes after recovery from the anaesthetic her parents visit. She is very distressed—'I want to go home'—tries to get to her mother but has to be restrained because of the stitches, and rolls about on her pillow crying. As her parents leave she is subdued and seems perplexed. She waves slightly in response to their cheerful going.

On the *third day* she is seen quietly clutching her Teddy and blanket 'baby', not crying or demanding attention and likely to seem 'settled' to busy ward staff. But when a nurse comes to play with her she is at first withdrawn, then in contact with the friendly person her feelings break through again and she cries bitterly for her Mummy. When the nurse leaves her control gradually reasserts itself. This cycle of withdrawal, breakdown, and resumed control is repeated shortly afterwards when the nurse again plays with her. In the afternoon her mother visits, but although Laura has been sitting up all morning and has wanted her mother she makes no attempt to get to her. Mother would like to take her on her lap but is afraid to do so. Ten minutes later a nurse sits her up, but it is 15 minutes before Laura thaws out towards her mother. Then she becomes increasingly animated and friendly, and is transformed by a radiant smile seen for the first time in three days. When Mother says she has to leave Laura is immediately anxious, and as Mother leaves she turns her head away. She does not cry, but shows her feelings clearly by the change in her expression and the restless movement of her hands. Although it is the middle of the afternoon, she asked to be tucked down with all her personal possessions tucked around her and forbids the nurse to remove the chair on which her mother had been sitting.

On the *fourth day* she plays wildly with the hospital doll. She is not visited.

On the *fifth day* her mother visits in the afternoon, and again there is a period of withdrawn behaviour before she warms up to her mother. She asks once to be taken on to her mother's lap, but Mother, restrained by what she believes to be hospital regulations, says 'I'm afraid you can't'. Laura does not ask again. When Mother has to go Laura is pained, cries a little then quickly recovers and sits with pursed lips.

On the *sixth day* a new child is admitted who cries a lot. Laura, very controlled herself, watches him with a tense face. (When she got up she went to him and said 'You're crying because you want your Mummy. Don't cry. She'll come tomorrow'.) She is not visited.

On the *seventh day* both parents visit and Laura is up for the occasion. Although she knows chairs are being set out for her parents she shows no excitement, and when her mother comes she makes no attempt to go to her. She remains subdued. When Daddy comes from the office 10 minutes later he gets a warmer welcome. Daddy leaves first and his going is apparently almost ignored. Just once she says quietly, 'I go with you', but does not insist. When her mother leaves, Laura seems to ignore her going.

On the *eighth* morning she is shaken by sobs. Her mother had told her the previous evening that she would be going home today. Laura had kept it to herself. Now her control has given way. When Mother comes Laura remains cautious, however, and not until her outdoor shoes are produced does she accept that she is going home. She insists on taking all her possessions home with her, even a tattered old book she refuses to leave behind. (When she dropped that book on the way out and a nurse picked it up, she screamed in temper and snatched it away—the fiercest feeling she showed during her whole stay.) On the way out she is seen walking apart from her mother.

Subsequent history

Certain events during the next 12 months are of interest.

(1) For two days after discharge Laura was unusually anxious and irritable. Her voice took on a higher pitch. She slept badly. She soiled herself several times. But after two days her parents felt she was her pre-separation self.

(2) Four months later her mother went to hospital to have a second baby. Laura went to stay with her grandmother and did not see Father or Mother for five weeks. When she was reunited with them she recognized her father immediately and was friendly with him, but she failed to recognize her mother and for two days treated her politely but as a stranger. She remembered the whereabouts of everything in the home, but for her mother alone there was amnesia. She never spoke of hospital, and if anyone else referred to it she made no response.

(3) When six months home she was apparently her normal self and now talked of the hospital. By accident she saw a sequence from the film and immediately became very agitated. She flushed and said angrily to her mother 'Where was you, Mummy? Where was you?'. Then she burst into loud crying and turned to her father for comfort. Her parents were astonished by the strength of feeling which had been revealed.

(4) When 12 months home and again apparently quite serene she was taken by her parents to an exhibition and left in the creche there. She appeared quite ready to stay, but when a photographer appeared she became hysterical and it was an hour before she could be consoled. Apparently the camera was associated with the separation experience in

216

her mind. These two incidents suggest that despite her apparent recovery there remained deep-seated anxiety which could be touched off by trivial happenings.

FREMONT-SMITH:

We are now prepared to launch into the discussion of Dr. Bowlby's film. I wonder, Dr. Bowlby, whether you would like to make some comments at this point to start us off.

BOWLBY:

I should like to relate what we are studying in these children with what Dr. Liddell was saying about stress. He was defining stress as the physiological reactions anticipatory to exertion, and the de-stressor as the fulfilment of an expectation, even though what is expected is disagreeable. It seems to me Dr. Liddell has emphasized the physiological side of stress. I think one can also define stress psychologically by saying that it is any situation which arouses a drive in the organism which is not immediately fulfilled; and, the greater the drive and the more delay in its fulfilment, the greater the stress.

GREY WALTER:

The delayed cancellation of a drive or tropism at the simplest level is an unpleasant situation for us, but it happens so often that to use the word stress seems to me to be rather extravagant. It seems to me, looking at the film, that the time when a child shows most stress is when the statistics of the situation are not acceptable to her. She had been separated from her mother, she had been told this was going to happen; she kept looking out of the window to see if her mother was on the bus; she was wondering whether nurse was friendly; and testing things around her. No one could give her a firm answer. They did not tell her it was going to hurt. It is the fundamental uncertainty of the situation with produces stress rather than the fact that her desire to see her mother was delayed.

BOWLBY:

You mean the uncertainty of when she will see her again?

GREY WALTER:

And whether people around her are as friendly as they seem. There is a nice pretty nurse at the beginning of the film, but then Laura sees her no more. The food comes in, but it is perhaps not the sort she really wants. Someone comes along and hurts her tummy, and so on. They are all minor assaults. It is the uncertainty, the insecurity, based on the statistical insolubility of the situation.

BOWLBY:

I think there is a continuum from the situation where a drive is aroused and is immediately satisfied to a situation where a drive is aroused and completely frustrated. Though it is a continuum, there may be a break in the middle of it. I agree that the word stress should be kept for one end of the continuum.

LORENZ:

I was wondering when somebody would bring up the very difficult question of where the 'normal' ends and the pathological begins. It seems to begin with the question of stress. Stress is what produces neurosis; stress is what the organism cannot cope with.

GREY WALTER:

Stress is a physical term, is it not? It is the force applied, it is not the deformation resulting. The physicist distinguishes in English between stress and strain; stress is the pressure, and strain is the tendency of a thing to bend or break under pressure.

FREMONT-SMITH:

Then you are driven to the position that, since the environment constantly produces a deformation effect upon the organism, life itself must be defined as vigorously stressful throughout; but these particular stresses we have been talking about have been specialized accentuations with a particular element of uncertainty in them.

GREY WALTER:

The time-factor is particularly important, as Bowlby has emphasized. He is speaking really not so much of stress as of strain, as irreversible effects in the organism. The organism is coupled with a certain environment; it looks round for some information on which to base a statistical evaluation. It fails to find it, and permanent deformation is then present and persists, even in other environments, as strain.

The capacity not to be permanently deformed by a situation depends upon the capacity to anticipate the mere passage of time. If you are put in prison for a year, you can say to yourself, 'Oh well, a year will pass'—but a child of two cannot do this.

HARGREAVES:

That implies first the capacity for the appreciation of time, and secondly the capacity to believe in the continued existence of objects when they are not there.

MEAD:

And also a learned expectation that things will turn out all right. At a very early age you can learn in two ways—that the next thing that happens is always going to be bad, or that the next thing that happens is going to be good. This probably is closely connected with the belief that objects will reappear.

GREY WALTER:

There is a phase in development when the child has not got the capacity to say, 'Time will pass'. You can see that in a two-year-old —you can almost imagine that you can see Laura trying to meditate on the nature of the eight days that she has to spend in hospital.

BOWLBY:

Most children of this age are living in the here and now.

BINDRA:

I think what Grey Walter is saying is quite right, but I do not think this is a general definition of stress. There are many other 'stress situations' which do not show the particular features of time and expectation; for example, exposure to cold. One has to distinguish between a stressful condition, a situation which can be defined in physical terms, and the *effects* of stress. I think yesterday Dr. Liddell defined stress not in terms of the situation or experimental conditions, but in terms of the psychological effects of it.

GREY WALTER:

That is strain.

BINDRA:

Yes. But Bowlby also is doing what Liddell did: he is defining stress in terms of the effects the particular 'stress situation' has on the subject.

On the other hand, the position taken by Grey Walter, with which I agree, requires that stress be defined in terms of the features of the situation; they may be statistical features. Adopting such a definition, one can meaningfully state that the same stress has different effects (strain) on different people.

MEAD:

Then you would define stress situation in terms of species, and then differentiate among individuals of that species?

BINDRA:

Yes.

BOWLBY:

I think stress is always relative to the particular individual organism.

BINDRA:

It is the effect of stress, that is strain, that depends on the individual, not stress itself.

BOWLBY:

I think, subjectively, we say we experience stress when we are very uncertain whether we are going to succeed. It has to be a situation which we take seriously and not one we do not care about. Our motivation is strong and we are faced with a problem which is on the verge of insolubility. It may be that we keep our heads and that we solve it ultimately. Alternatively, we may lose our heads and adopt crazy solutions. That may involve something quite different, but subjectively speaking we should describe both as stressful situations. (Schaffer, 1954.)

INTERVAL

LIDDELL:

At what age do you think a mother becomes a bad mother as against a good mother, being the same person?

BOWLBY:

Any time after nine months; any time after the mother is clearly defined as a figure, though I must admit there is at present a lot of debate in psychoanalytic circles regarding this age. Probably the maturation rate differs considerably in different children for this function as it does for others, and detailed research is badly required.

220

LIDDELL:

This child was old enough then to count cases of 'bad Mummy' and 'good Mummy'.

HARGREAVES:

This behaviour on the part of the mother begins to cast doubts on previous assumptions. I think you should emphasize what happened later.

BOWLBY:

Laura showed very little upset on returning home, though during the first 48 hours she did not sleep well and she clung to her mother more than usual.* This is a brief response compared to what is common, partly perhaps because this particular child is much more mature than others of her age; she can cope with time and space a great deal better than an average child of two years five months.

ZAZZO:

The film was most interesting and is directly related to our subject—as was shown by the discussion we have just been having—but when it is a question of proving to sceptics that the child who is separated from the mother shows very serious reactions, I do not think it is very convincing.

I am wondering about two other questions. To what degree are the reactions that we noted yesterday in a child of two and a half—who was very advanced and could have had a mental level of three or four years—comparable to the reactions which you yourself recorded on much younger children, of an age when the child is not yet capable of distinguishing his mother clearly. The reaction of the layman might be to say that Laura gets bored and that's all. There's nothing else necessarily in the film.

The second question is in connection with your previous work on hospitalism in very young children. A very large number of paediatricians would be sceptical about the generalization of the idea of hospitalism itself. You yourself, Spitz and others have always tended to generalize from the cases observed, and it is in fact possible that this is a general phenomenon which could even be found among animals too. This would be another investigation of considerable interest. However, you cannot convince the sceptics if you do not

* During these 48 hours her parents noticed that she was always near to tears, contrasting with her normal self, and that whenever either parent left the room she was upset. She demanded her mother sleep with her and called out in her sleep 'Don't do that to me'.

manage to show the *frequency* of deterioration due to hospitalism. Is it found in all children? It is this, and not the seriousness of certain reactions in certain children, which is open to doubt.

It seems to me that it would be fairly easy to carry out a statistical study on a hundred or two hundred children who had been separated from the mother, in order to discover the percentage of children who do not react in a pathological manner. I do not know if such cases exist, but if they do they would perhaps be exceptions proving the rule.

I have no doubt of the value of your work—moreover you will remember under what circumstances I met you: it was as an expert at a time when I myself was working on these problems of hospitalism; therefore I believe in them. But I wonder what actually is the extent of the phenomenon and I am sorry that as regards this question, which I also put to Spitz, no reply has been able to be given which entirely satisfied sceptics and myself—and I am not a sceptic.

RÉMOND:

I should like to ask what you think about the possible advantages of the stress which the film deals with?

Do you think that such a stress is always dangerous and bad and consequently that it should be systematically avoided or, on the contrary, that it is a factor which can be useful? In point of fact we develop within an environment which is a system of varied stresses, which create equally varied reactions, sometimes very strong. Are not the variations, the modifications, or even the intensity of these stresses very useful to our development sometimes?

Dr. Liddell has already given us his ideas on the question of stress among animals. But I should like to know whether in your personal experience, Dr. Bowlby, and particularly in the film you showed us, you do not think that in the occurrence of this stress there is a factor which may be beneficial?

INHELDER:

The question I am wondering about is whether there exist not merely one but several periods at which the child is particularly sensitive to separation.

Thanks to the work of Anna Freud, John Bowlby and René Spitz, we know the effects of separation towards the end of the first year, which is a critical period during which the concepts both of the affective object and the intellectual object are developed. But do we know the effect of separation at later ages? At about three years,

222

when the representations of self as opposed to non-self are formed, does the child react differently to separation? Finally, is the period of six to seven years, which seems to be a period of profound transformation of intelligence, a particularly vulnerable period from the affective point of view too?

Intellectual development, although continuous, does not keep to any constant rhythm. Periods of sudden transformation are followed by periods of slower adaptation. One might wonder whether the child at the turning point of its intellectual development shows an increased sensitivity to events producing trauma, such as separation from the mother.

BOWLBY:

Well, we had not realized that a child of this age suffers so much! How we evaluate the suffering may be controversial but it is clear that this child suffers in the ordinary human sense of the word. The film was not published to convince sceptics—one case could never do that—but to draw attention to a problem.

I recall one elderly nurse in a responsible position in this country who said to me very candidly, 'This film brings back to me the first child I ever nursed in hospital. This child was a little boy. He grieved for his mother and it simply broke my heart. After that I never saw grief again until I saw this film'. I think there is no doubt that she *could* not see it again. As a method of opening people's eyes to what in a sense they have always known—but to which most people have had to shut their eyes—it has been very fruitful.

We certainly cannot generalize from this film, and we cannot relate what we see in a child of this age to what occurs in a child of, say, under nine months—before the parent has been identified. It may be that they are two quite different conditions.

Dr. Zazzo raised the point that there are many children who escape severe or even any permanent damage, and he asked about the incidence of adverse outcomes. Our evidence is rather scanty. There is no doubt that many children go through what we should regard as severe separation experiences and come through them fairly all right. If anyone asks us what is the percentage of those who come through all right and those who are damaged, we do not know. But I do not think we need be disturbed by not knowing. I am now talking about the practical public-health issue. We know, for instance, that any infectious illness, a disease like poliomyelitis, say, only causes adverse effects in a minority of people. But the whole of public health has been built up on the simple basis that there are certain conditions which cause a sufficiently serious outcome in a

223

sufficient proportion of the population that we think they should be avoided. I think we can say, in regard to hospitalization and separation, that a sufficient proportion of children are sufficiently damaged for these conditions to be regarded as hazards to be avoided—at any rate to be avoided in their more severe forms and to be treated very respectfully in their minor forms.

Dr. Rémond raises the question whether these stresses can perhaps be advantageous to adaptation. We do not know. There must be a threshold below which it might be advantageous, and above which it is disadvantageous; and this threshold, of course, will vary greatly with the age of the child. My own suspicion is that anything which makes an individual lose his head and panic is likely to have a bad effect on his outlook in the long run. We do know that with young children a separation experience can often make them lose their heads. Children cry for three or four days on end; they become quite frantic and desperate. The separation situation can give rise to such overwhelming anxiety that I would be very surprised if it were advantageous. But until we have done a great deal more research, we certainly cannot answer the question.

Mlle. Inhelder asked what are the critical ages. There again, of course, we are very ignorant, but it certainly appears that the most dangerous are under 4 or 5 years. Such evidence as we have suggests that children of 6 or 7 are more able to maintain a time-perspective, and they do not seem to suffer anything like the same degree of damage as the very young children. But just where it is in the first 3 or 4 years that the most damage is done, we have no idea.

LORENZ:

Laura had a very good time-perspective, and she was particularly good at taking a grip on herself. We saw her *not* losing her head all the time. It oecurred to me all the time whilst looking at Laura that she would have been damaged more if she had been slightly less intelligent than she was. This is quite in keeping with what I want to bring forward: you know that dogs are also damaged by being put in a dogs' hospital; you know that the most sensitive and the most trusting dogs refuse to recognize their masters when they come to fetch them. The most dramatic thing is described by Thomas Mann in his book *Herr und Hund*. That is a very beautiful observation on his dog when it was brought to hospital; it describes how the dog would not believe that it was going to be taken out again, and only when he really realized it, did he get back his whole trust and shake off the effect—well, actually he did not quite; he had serious after-effects. The film brought up the question, what really is the trauma in separation? Do you not think that in this child, and the dog, the main trauma may lie in the fact that the mother suddenly and unexpectedly ceases to defend her, that mother allows her to be carried away? That is totally unsuspected from the emotional, instinctive point of view of the child. If mother were a chimp she would start fighting the hospital sister tooth and claw. I think the real trauma is the disappointment in mother all the time. I am quite sure that in the dog who is put into hospital the disappointment in master failing to defend is the real trauma.

I quite realize that this is only one factor, but I wonder whether Bowlby would agree that this is one of the major ones?

BOWLBY:

We certainly do think that the changed attitude towards the mother is a principal part of the damage that can be done, particularly the child seeing the mother as a bad lady instead of a good lady; one of the characteristic things which you get after separation, particularly a more prolonged separation than this one, is intense hatred of the mother. One of the ways in which acute ambivalence towards the mother is created in a child who loves and is attached to her mother is through her having an experience of a semi-long separation and developing intense and violent hatred towards her. Thenceforward she oscillates between hatred and love.

MELIN:

Would she not have been better off if she had not been brought up in that atmosphere of, 'Don't cry'. The whole time you see her starting to cry and suddenly ceasing again. Mother said 'Don't cry' when she came and went. If Laura could have cried a bit more and could have gone to the nurses more with her sorrow it would all have meant less to her.

BOWLBY:

I think the extent to which this child has been taught to control the expression of her feelings certainly puts a special strain on her. We know from other experience that, if a person is unable to cry at the appropriate moment, they are apt to do it symbolically or in other ways over a long period subsequently. It becomes a vicious circle. It is possible that some of the nose-picking which Laura shows is an alternative to crying, is in fact a displacement-activity. The natural thing would be to cry, but as it is she stays put and picks.

LORENZ:

Yes.

GREY WALTER:

Bowlby drew an analogy between the conditions he is dealing with and those of infectious disease, which might be a quite helpful analogy, since the question of prophylaxis arises immediately. As I understand infectious diseases, one of the first important principles which was established as a prelude to public-health control of infectious diseases was the occurrence of natural immunity and the establishment of artificial immunity. That seems an important aspect of this problem too. There is every evidence that some children have a natural immunity to this particular sort of stress; there are some children who appear to survive unscathed whereas other children would be badly hurt. Somebody sometime must engage in long-term statistical surveys to determine why this should be so. This country and other countries cannot afford ever to give to each child who may require it hospital treatment, or to coddle children to whom some social catastrophe may occur. Therefore, we shall have to select, sooner or later, those who require the safeguard of inoculation or some preventive treatment. The identification at an early age by some simple methods of individuals likely to have natural immunity to this condition seems to be the first step towards the administration of a public-health service in relation to psychiatric disorders.

BOWLBY:

This is certainly a very important step, and it involves us in trying to get some understanding of the psychopathology and dynamics of what is happening. Fortunately, however, there is also a very much simpler solution—that is to avoid all sorts of quite easily avoidable separations. I get the impression that between 70 and 80 per cent. of the separations which occur today can quite easily be avoided by ordinary, practical measures without any great expense. That seems to me a simple first step which can be taken, and is being taken, before we go on to the other problem, which I fully agree is very important, but going to take a long time to work out.

GREY WALTER:

It certainly involves a very well-equipped, very patient, team of investigators working over a long period of time. What you were saying about the practical steps that you can advise now is perfectly true of society as it is at the moment, but we must face the possibility that conditions will not always be as good as now. We must contrive a society which will combine the plasticity of a less highly organized society with the facilities of the present society. The chance of the child being separated by accident from its parents is very small, but only a few years ago we saw very dramatically the situation in which a great many children were separated from their parents.

BOWLBY:

Not the under-fives.

GREY WALTER:

True, but the general organisation of society on an emergency basis, which we might have to arrange for again, would be much easier if we knew more about the distribution of this character in the population.

HARGREAVES:

I should like to make a comment on public-health practice. I think, historically, the intrapersonal aspects of the problem of immunology come rather late. If everything that Snow had written about cholera a hundred years ago had been applied, cholera would have been abolished before the vibrio was discovered. He stopped the cholera epidemic by taking the handle off the Broad Street pump; he had become convinced that cholera was something to do with water. I think the first step is very much as Bowlby said, to attempt to reduce the frequency of separation, because a very high proportion of separations in our society are what you might describe as elective separations. For instance, one comment that I think one would immediately make about this film is, 'Why the hell was the child put in hospital?' It is a very simple operation, which can be done in the out-patient department, and the child could perfectly well be managed at home.

Then there are a whole series of social aspects of separation. Take the nature of our income tax legislation, in which the allowance for children is so inadequate that there is a very strong pressure on the mother to go out to work. National policy has been encouraging this, in that you can put your baby in a day nursery provided you work in a factory all day, but you are not allowed to put it in a day nursery to go shopping for an hour. The aim of the day nursery is to get the mother to go and work in a factory. There are a lot of general measures that one could take now; although I entirely agree one does need to know something about those who can undergo the experience without much result and those who show strain.

227

MEAD:

I do not dispute the importance of reducing the role of the hospital as much as possible and creating facilities to permit the mother to care for her child much better than she now can. But there still remains another possibility if instead of always looking at the trauma we also looked at the child who had an immunity. We consistently do not do that, because almost all our skills are focussed on studying the traumatized child. There is as good evidence from comparative studies of society that it is possible to make children able to tolerate separation much more easily, because they trust more people. That is a simple thing to do, though it also requires a large number of social measures. It requires new styles of neighbourhood behaviour, different sorts of community nurseries, and different types of organization. It requires different kinds of housing for grandparents, and a whole series of social measures that fall within the field of public health, which would make it possible for at least a very large number of children to learn that there is more than one person whom they can trust.

We are at present in danger, by emphasizing the importance the mother has for the child when the child has no one else, of increasing the anxiety about separation and making mothers afraid to go out. In some places in the middle classes women are going to have to be psychoanalysed because they have left their children for two days. We are in serious danger of accentuating the situation which lowers the child's immunity to the accidents it may encounter.

BINDRA:

What Dr. Mead has said so eloquently is what I was trying to get at the other day when I was discussing our dog studies. The implication of all the studies was that you can bring up a dog normally without attachment to the mother, and that there may be ways of doing the same in the case of human children.

MEAD:

I want to make it clear, I am not talking about reducing the possible attachment to the mother but getting rid of the fact that she is the *only* person the child can trust.

LORENZ:

I knew that was what Dr. Mead was going to say before she said it, and also Dr. Bindra; that is, of course, trust in other people must be promoted, but at the same time—with dogs—you must be very careful about that, because you will get a perfectly despicable dog very easily if you make him trust *too many* people. I am particularly anxious to make my dog distrust other people as much as I can. It may be a utilitarian point of view that it is good to have a dog that bites other people and loves you, but I confess I like dogs to be like that. This trust in others must cost something; it is not free of charge.

INHELDER:

I agree with Dr. Mead that we must give children the possibility of increasing their social relationships. Particularly in the hospital, contact with their playfellows—certainly without replacing contact with the mother—can help the sick child to adapt to its situation. The study of the bonds established very early between children has been rather neglected. I think their role in development is considerable.

FREMONT-SMITH:

We saw this, in fact, in the film. We saw Laura, did we not, entering into sympathetic relations with other crying children, which not only might have helped them, but did something for her.

There is one other point it seems Dr. Lorenz has touched on here which may involve species differences, and that is the degree to which an animal of one species needs a single or small number of parental figures, and the degree to which it can spread this over ten or fifteen persons—or whether it needs a hierarchy: one, a mother and then five uncles and aunts or grandparents. It seems to me this is again something which needs statistical testing both with respect to the species and with respect to whether or not you would make a characterless child if he has fifteen equal parents as opposed to one.

LORENZ:

I think you have to fix the number of parent-figures. I am quite prepared to believe that the child can be taught to love fifteen people and yet be quite discriminative about what kind of people to love. You have the same thing in dogs; you have family dogs who love quite a number of people and yet they are quite exclusive with strangers.

FREMONT-SMITH:

Do they not have one master?

LORENZ:

Not necessarily.

229

GREY WALTER:

The way in which dogs respond to separation seems to me to depend very much on the type of dog, in the Pavlovian sense. I have no experience with pure-bred dogs, only with mongrels, and there it is quite noticeable that the dogs which arouse the most sympathy and affection in human beings are the melancholic and choleric types, according to Pavlovian terminology, and that includes more than half of all dogs. Those are both extremely sensitive to separation and deprivation, and they tend to work only for one person and to resent any doubt in a situation. They require enormous reassurance and persuasion that the situation is a good one. In a sense they do not really trust their master or their friends enough. If they are taken to hospital they do not say, 'Because my master says it is all right, it is all right whatever happens.' The much rarer type of dog, the type Pavlov called sanguine, is just as nice a dog in the sense that he is capable of forming a close attachment to you, but his relationship to you is not so much of the slave and master as of the colleague. He will not feel he has got to work just for you, he will work with you. He will take a tough situation, such as I described in the conditioning experiment, and work it out and retain almost complete immunity. Although it is a rare type it can be distinguished by the rule-of-thumb methods of the Pavlovians, and it is that sort of process I want to suggest is possible for humans. Obviously the situation is likely to be very much more complicated and there will be more factors to be considered, but there is a possibility that some such typology may exist in human beings.

BOWLBY:

When one talks about separation one is talking about the child being removed from his familiars to a situation where he is cared for by strangers. All sorts of arrangements whereby grandmothers, aunts and uncles are brought in as aids are obviously desirable, but we have got to be careful about the extent to which we do it. For instance, to go back to Laura for a moment, we had a striking episode occur five months after the film was made. The mother had a new baby; she went to hospital and because of complications she was there for five weeks. Laura was looked after by her grandmother whom she knew. The father, for some reason which is not very clear, felt it would be a good thing if he did not visit them.

FREMONT-SMITH:

The grandmother and Laura?

BOWLBY:

Exactly. Now, at the end of the five weeks the mother returned home and this was the course of events. First of all mother 'phoned grandmother and said, 'I'm home now, bring Laura round' and she spoke to Laura on the 'phone. Laura was very excited to hear her mother's voice and very eager to get home. The next step was that they returned home and Laura continued very excited. She opened the door and there was her mother. At this point she went completely blank and after a lapse of time said 'But I want my mummy'. For the next forty-eight hours she failed to accept this woman as her mother.

LORENZ:

She looked at her mother and said, 'I want my mummy'?

FREMONT-SMITH:

In other words: 'You are not my mother'.

GREY WALTER:

Of course, she was a different shape from when she had seen her last.

BOWLBY:

For forty-eight hours she failed to accept the woman as her mother. On the other hand, she accepted her father virtually instantaneously as far as we can make out and was fully oriented to everything else in the house; but the mother was 'washed out'. Now we do not think this was due to pregnancy, because we have got so many other anecdotal stories of exactly this kind from all sorts of other quarters and in other circumstances. This failure to recognize, a failure to accept and respond to, is not uncommon. Of course, there are several things going on here which need disentangling. Some children appear to recognize but cannot respond, and the failure to respond may last a few hours, a few days, even a week. By failure to respond I mean that they do not treat the woman as their mother and do not adopt a 'following response' to her. At a certain point this phase breaks suddenly—it is usually accompanied by tears and protestations—and from that point onward the child glues itself to his mother and remains thus for some weeks or months. The particular thing which Laura showed is just one of many possible reunion responses—about which we still know too little.

231

TANNER:

Do you suppose that this is related to the previous experience you filmed, or do you think that this occurs to some extent anyway—as a result of that second separation—though perhaps not so dramatically as in this case?

BOWLBY:

It is impossible to answer that question; we have not unravelled it sufficiently.

FREMONT-SMITH:

It seems to me not an uncommon experience for parents to be reunited with a child whom they have not seen for some time, and to find the child really is strange. I think, and this may even be true with adults, that part of it is a question of the image that you have developed or carried of the loved one in their absence, and sometimes, I think with a child at least, one has regressed in the sense of going back to the image of the child at an earlier date; one has lost the most recent image of the child.

LORENZ:

May I interrupt with a story; it applies to the word image? It is a story of my little daughter whom I left when she was three and did not see again for about seven months to a year. She loved me very dearly and when we met again she seemed somewhat reserved, but she greeted me very politely and nicely and was very glad to see me. Then when I had left the room, very tactfully so that I could not hear her, she said to my wife, 'But our former Daddy was so much more beautiful'.

TANNER:

I have seen exactly the same thing with adults when the prisoner-of-war returns after being separated.

STRUTHERS:

The points I was going to bring up have already been mentioned, particularly by Dr. Hargreaves and Dr. Mead. One of the things which disturbs me is the very casual use of hospital beds mentioned by Dr. Hargreaves. I am thinking particularly of the most recent edifice erected in America for the study of the diseases of childhood at a cost of $15 million. My own belief is that if they had put $5 million into the hospital and taken the interest on $10 million to keep children out of hospital by providing home services, the community as a social body would have been very much better off.

Dr. Hargreaves' point, why the hell was this child put in hospital for something that could have been done in the Outpatients, is extremely well taken. It probably would have taken a surgeon about twenty minutes to put a subcutaneous purse-string suture in the child with the umbilical hernia; the child would have been home in four hours, and the separation trauma from the mother would have been completely avoided. It applies to a great many operations and conditions for which we admit children to hospital supposedly for purposes of study, which could have been done outside the hospital —probably with somewhat more trouble to the physician or surgeon or whoever is interested—with a lot of the trauma being saved. I think Dr. Bowlby's film should be shown as widely as possible as a propaganda film for the education of young doctors in surgery and medicine; because they need it.

I would like to ask Dr. Mead if I am correct about one point. It would appear to me that the higher the family gets in the grades of civilization or in social status, the fewer the number of people in whom the child comes to trust; and the higher you get in the social scale, the more the child is protected from contact with other individuals whom he should learn to trust. Is that true?

MEAD:

No, I would not think that is so exactly. In the upper classes in many societies you have large groups of servants, gardeners, and so on, and you have a similarity in character structure between the upper-class child and the peasant child, because in both instances they have a fairly wide and varied group of trustworthy persons who care for them. It is particularly in the middle classes,—in a society like Britain from the upper working class through the lower middle class (and this is now being extended into the upper middle class because servants are so expensive),—that you tend to get the small house, the exacting standard of living, the keeping oneself to oneself, the mother sufficiently free from very heavy outdoor labour or factory labour or anything of that sort and also pretty free from a very elaborate social life, and that concentrated relationship between mother and child which is one of the things which produces what we call the lower-middle-class character.

ZAZZO:

In connection with the dangers of exclusive attachment to a single person I call to mind twins with whom I have been concerned for about ten years. Only on two occasions were the twins separated from their mother. It was at about one year and one-and-a-half years. There was no hospitalism or separation reaction. On the other hand, every time—and this occurred frequently—that I studied the separation of twins who were terribly attached to each other I observed disturbances very similar to those you have described. Here it is a case of an exclusive attachment of identical twins brought up together—an exclusive attachment which is obviously very bad.

FREMONT-SMITH:

It seems to me that the attitude and the understanding of the nursery staff and of the doctors in the hospital is something which could be given consideration. There is no reason why the hospital staff should be as un-understanding of what the child is going through, of what the child's expectations are; and I should assume that we could develop some rules-of-thumb which would make it possible for the nursing staff and the medical staff to ameliorate the misery and trauma of the separation where such separation is necessary.

HARGREAVES:

Could I commend the work of Lester Coleman in New York, who is an ear nose and throat surgeon who tackles this problem with great care. He sets out to become one of these associate parent figures and plays the role of carrying the child through. He insists that the child comes to see him two or three times before the operation, in his office. He plays with them, tells them all about the hospital and what is going to happen. They play with the anaesthetic apparatus. In the hospital he says he never gets the elevator, he always fetches the child himself from the ward, because it gives him time to talk while they walk upstairs. You see in his film the child walking up the stairs in her nightgown holding the doctor's hand. 'And,' he says 'in a minute we will come to the critical question.' Always during this stage the child brings up her greatest anxiety, usually anxiety about unconsciousness. 'And shall I wake up?' He sits down on the stairs and talks about this before they go on to the operating theatre; he is prepared to talk about it for five minutes. I think he has shown quite clearly, not only the need for the child of substitute parent-figures, but that the medical staff, if they take the trouble, can get into that role in time to help the child through.

BOWLBY:

Yes, this is true and valuable for older children, but it is very doubtful how much can be done for the very young child, say under three. It is always difficult for people to realize the great limitations in these matters of the very young child.

Presentation of Film by Dr. Lorenz

LORENZ:

What I want to show you is an immature film,* partly meaning that it is about immature humans, and partly that the film itself is immature, because the maturation of what we call ethograms, meaning inventories of behaviour patterns, is incomplete, and this sort of endeavour is doomed never to attain complete accomplishment. We will see a number of behaviour patterns of prematures, newborns and infants up to about one year of age.

(Dr. Lorenz showed his film.)

We concentrated on spontaneous behaviour; we left out the extrapyramidal reactions and others that have been very extensively studied already, and we tried to put a special accent on maturation, and particularly on the maturation of afferent control of spontaneous activity. This growth of afferent control is very essential for our conception of the reflex. We do not believe there is any sharp boundary line between what is generally called reflex and spontaneous nervous activity. As an example let me take the development of what is termed by Peiper (1949) 'der orale Greifreflex', or 'the oral prehensile reflex'. It is released by touching the infant's cheek and it consists in the infant's turning the head and snapping for the finger.

What happens in maturation is this: the new-born kitten, rat or child has what Prechtl (Prechtl and Schleidt, 1950, 1951) calls the breast-seeking movement of turning the head rhythmically from one side to the other. You will see it occurring spontaneously in a premature for about 14 days after birth; a short time afterwards it becomes inhibited by higher centres. At the period when it is not yet releasable by touch it is already inhibited, so that for a time it does not occur. After that it becomes releasable by touch on the cheek, and it is stopped by getting hold of the teat.

In the cat, the interaction of endogenous spontaneous movement

---

* PRECHTL, H. F. R. *Reifen der Frühkindlichen Motorik*. Film aus dem Institut für den Wissenschaftlichen Film, Göttingen.

and afferent control is still more beautiful. Here the movement is not stopped by the finding of the teat, but by finding the hairless area round the teat.

In its final state the 'oral prehensile reflex' is indeed a clear example of a reflex. But its ontogeny shows very clearly that spontaneous automatic movement plays one part, central inhibition another, and afferent control of that inhibition a third. The oral prehensile reflex consists of: (a) one process of afferent control releasing the automatism from its central inhibition, (b) the performance of one quarter of the full phase of the rhythmical and automatic to-and-fro swinging of the head, and (c) the re-instatement of central inhibition by another process of afferent control. In ontogeny, the endogenous movement appears first, then the central inhibition seems to follow, while the processes of afferent control evidently come last.

Something very similar seems to hold true for other reflexes as well. Prechtl (1953) has shown that the gripping reflex tends to show a rhythmical and automatic repetition in prematures. So does the sinew reflex, under certain circumstances, and many others.

A second example concerns the Babinski reflex. To the question 'does a normal adult man have a Babinski?' the accepted answer is no, or at least that this reflex is inhibited by the control of the pyramidal system. Yet, as you will see in the film, Babinski's reflex appears quite normally in adults, only not independently by itself but woven into a context of other movements: those of walking. The typical movement of the Babinski is released every time the foot is put down, at the moment the heel touches ground. When the sole is pressed down, the Babinski is followed by the so-called gripping reflex. You will see that in the film, it is always Babinski-grip, Babinski-grip. As the afferent control matures, the Babinski becomes unreleasable by such simple stimuli as evoked it at first and, from now on, occurs only in the context of walking, with all the superimposed mechanism of learned movements. Adult man still possesses —and uses—the mechanism and the movement of the Babinski and what we call 'a Babinski sign' in the sense of a pathological symptom is just this mechanism minus the complicated nervous apparatus normally controlling it.

GREY WALTER:

Why is the Babinski released by a pyramidal lesion?

LORENZ:

Well, maybe the pyramidal functions take over part of the movement which originally was brought about by the Babinski.

GREY WALTER:

That is rather far-fetched, I think.

LORENZ:

What Grey Walter means is that in pyramidal lesions you get failure of motor function and not of afferent control. I have no answer to that, it may be a serious objection.

MONNIER:

The most important new result of this film is certainly the relationship between Babinski and the grasp.

LORENZ:

I think so too.

MONNIER:

I have a slightly different interpretation of the sign of Babinski. The sign of Babinski is a part of a nociceptive flexion relation. We have many proofs of that.

The observations of Fulton (1943) in higher primates point to a synergy of flexor pattern with the purpose of avoiding the nocive stimulus. These nociceptive patterns are normally under the control of area four. Removal of this area four releases the nociceptive reflexes, described by Babinski, Shaddock, Oppenheim; they are all selectively controlled by area four, and by area four alone. In a more frontal region another centre, area six, controls the grasp.

There is a sign homologous to the sign of Babinski, but in the grasp series, the so-called sign of Rossolimo, which is controlled by another centre. You get it tapping the fourth toe from below; then a grasping reaction occurs. It seems to me that both mechanisms, the nociceptive response called Babinski and the grasping reflex called Rossolimo, are well demonstrated in the film.

LORENZ:

I did not quite dare to mention it, but it was my conviction that the Rossolimo does play a part in this whole series. It is not simply Babinski-grip, but Babinski-Rossolimo-grip with every putting down of the foot. One element of the Rossolimo in every grasp is the spreading of the toes. I think that this element of spreading the toes before grasping can be noticed several times in the film.

237

It was very typical, but spreading the toes belongs still to the nociceptive Babinski series, not to the Rossolimo grasping series.

The other interesting thing is that when analysing the functions of these cortical centres—area four, area six—one gets the impression that altogether these centres control the activity of a normally acting and working human being, called 'homo faber' (Monnier, 1946, 1948). In a pure pyramidal syndrome—they are very rare—after destruction of the pyramidal tract by a shell splinter, we find only spasticity of the fingers and hand in pronation and extension; that is all. In the legs there is no spasticity whatever, but increased nociceptive flexor responses, called 'triple retrait' by the French. There is always very strong flexion in the hip and a tendency to dorsal flexion in the great toe. If we try voluntarily to flex one leg we will automatically flex dorsally the great toe and the foot. This flexor synergy is certainly predetermined, and has a nociceptive function. In physiological terms, this means that the cortical pyramidal centre controls defensive flexor reactions in the legs in order to maintain standing extensor posture, and controls extensor tone in the fingers in order to keep the hand moving freely in the 'homo faber'. The role of this cortical centre (area four) consists in increasing the motility of the hands, of the feet, and to protect at the same time visceral organs such as the intestines (abdominal reflexes) and the testicles (cremaster reflexes).

As an additional function I should mention vasodilatation of the fingers induced by area four. Thus mobilization of the fingers with vasodilatation is a function of area four which controls also the postural tone of the fingers. It would be very bothering if this tone would not be partially inhibited during skilled movements. That is why I call the cortical pyramidal centre in area four a centre for the 'homo faber'.

LORENZ:

It frees the hand from too much postural tone.

MONNIER:

Yes. This postural tone must be controlled electively; it will normally be increased in the shoulder, arm and legs, and diminished at the same time in the fingers. The extensor tone occurs only in the proximal part of the arms and in the legs under normal conditions, while the distal parts (fingers) show on the contrary a decrease in postural tone during voluntary movements. The functional purpose of the pyramidal system is understandable only if the behaviour of the whole individual in activity is considered.

Another interesting feature of the film is the occurrence of a grasping posture in the hands while the baby is sucking the milk bottle. We know in neurology an interesting association between the little muscle called *musculus quadratus* in the chin, which has something to do with the expression of the child during sucking, and the palm of the hand. Scratching the palm of the hand in young children induces a little contracting of the chin; this is called 'réflexe palmo-mentonnier'. It is an example of a synergy between hand and mouth.

GREY WALTER:

The interesting thing is, this is the only reflex of the body which can be excited by a single stimulus, a single electric shock. It is the perfect reflex for the study of the spino-cranial reflex in man for this reason.

TANNER:

At what age does it disappear?

MONNIER:

During the first year.

GREY WALTER:

But does it not persist in about 30 per cent. of the adults?

MONNIER:

Yes, and also in degenerative diseases of the brain—such as the 'scléreuse tubéreuse de Bourneville'.

The last thing I wanted to say concerns the anencephalic newborns. The rhombencephalic type of anencephaly shows only the grasp and flexor patterns; extensor patterns are very rare, such as the stretching of the arms as a late component of the Moro-reaction, with the purpose of expanding the basis of the body. It belongs, I think, to the anti-gravity functions and shows a certain rivalry with the Babinski and the grasping reactions. This is also very interesting in your film. I observed the same rivalry between sucking and the nociceptive withdrawal of the head in the period during which elementary mechanisms are not yet controlled by higher centres.

GREY WALTER:

I have a small contribution on this very fundamental question of the growth of afferent control of the nervous system. An example of this was given by Grossman (1954). He was studying the development of electrical activity, and particularly evoked electrical activity, in small animals. The response to any stimulus in any receptor modality in the very young creature seems to be a generalized response of the brain. One tends to think of the new-born baby as being a very well organized sort of spinal reflex system with a lot of functionless jelly on top, but that is not quite a correct view, it would seem. It looks as if the jelly were working fairly well so as to generalize the responses. A great many of the responses which were shown in the film are the effect of rapid diffusion of activity throughout the upper part of the neuraxis modifying the spinal reflexes even from before birth. You get these violent, extensive and reflexive movements which are quite reasonably called pseudo-convulsive movements. This is the standard, normal, basic element of central response in young creatures.

FREMONT-SMITH:

Do we know in mammals or humans whether there is any motor movement prior to sensory inflow?

GREY WALTER:

It is a difficult experiment to do.

LORENZ:

I think it is possible to do the experiment. The common-sense assumption is that it will be somewhere between the two extremes of total reflex and total spontaneity. I agree that all these spontaneous movements need sensory 'loading up' like Gray's and Lissman's dogfish in which a certain amount of afferent input was necessary for the loading up of the system. But I am quite sure that the co-ordination of the to-and-fro movement is central correlation independent from proprioception and afferent or cortical control.

GREY WALTER:

I wonder if that is true. It is a difficult experiment to confirm; I am not quite as convinced as you are. I feel there is a great deal of stimulation going on in practically all modalities under conditions such as in your film. The immature cerebral regions of such animals as man have a capacity for rapid diffusion of response to stimulation. That being so, it might be more likely that there would be survival value in the capacity for amplifying the effects of small centres of

240

stimulation which would gain more specialized effects later on as the growing animal became more experienced.

RÉMOND:

Even in the adult, the effect of the first stimulus is extremely generalized.

GREY WALTER:

But not the effect of the second.

LORENZ:

I think the only possibility of deciding to what extent this is spontaneous or independent is to watch anencephali. Did any of Monnier's or Gamper's anencephali show the rhythmic movement?

MONNIER:

The bulbo-spinal anencephali show very little spontaneous activity. If there is some rhombencephalon in addition to the medulla and spinal cord, the responsiveness to all kinds of stimuli is greater, but no important spontaneous activity occurs. The new-born rhombencephalic anencephalic reacts at once by a mass reflex to various kinds of stimuli, but chiefly to the shaking of the ground on which it lies. We may induce also a Moro-reflex on shaking of the ground.

I would like to contribute some remarks about the possibilities of measuring the learning process by electrophysiological methods in man. The technique we used was as follows, (Monnier, 1952): a subject had to answer to a stimulus of light (flash) by a movement of the finger. The retinal response to the flash was recorded by electro-retinography (E.R.G.). The cortical response in the neighbourhood of the visual centre was seen on the electroencephalogram (E.E.G.), and the response from the muscle itself by means of electromyography (E.M.G.). This allowed us to measure the motor-reaction time of the subject (Fig. 20). The subject had already had twenty tests before this record. I have chosen this part of the experiment to show what occurs in a subject learning by repetition.

The motor-reaction time shortens progressively: 180, 130, 110 and 90; it becomes shorter and shorter until finally an anticipated response is given. In other words, towards the end of a training or learning experiment the results become better; this is probably due to better attention, and ends with anticipation.

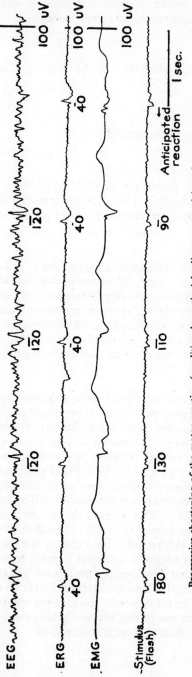

FIG. 20

ELECTRICAL RESPONSES OF THE RETINA (ERG), OCCIPITAL CORTEX (EEG) AND M.FLEXOR DIGITI (EMG) TO REPETITIVE FLASHES

Progressive shortening of the motor reaction (conditional reaction) leading to an anticipated motor response

The latency of the retinal and cortical occipital responses shows little variation

The process of conditioning and learning occurs between the receptory cortical area and the motor centre

Measurement of the opto-motor cortical integration time may be a good parameter for testing conditioning and learning processes

Is the stimulus perfectly rhythmic?

MONNIER:

Not absolutely regular, but about every second.

BINDRA:

From what muscle are you picking up your E.M.G.?

MONNIER:

Flexor digitorum. The picture shows also that in this learning experiment the time-value of the retinal response does not change (E.R.G.). We always get 40, 40, 40 milliseconds. The time-value of the cortical response is also fairly constant in the neighbourhood of the visual field, about 120 milliseconds (E.E.G.). It consists in a huge potential which starts nearly at the same time as the motor reaction. This is a component we studied with Grey Walter some three or four years ago (Monnier, 1948); it is not the initial component of the cortical response, but a component which starts a little later than the specific visual response, nearly at the time of the motor reaction.

Let us discuss now another type of experiment. If we measure the latency of the retinal response (let us call it retinal time), we get usually 30 milliseconds after the flash. The occipital cortex itself responds 35 milliseconds after the flash, and the motor reaction occurs about 120 milliseconds after. These are average values. If we deduct from the motor reaction time the time which was necessary for the optic impulses to reach the cortex (120 less 35), and the time necessary for the motor impulses to go from the motor cortex to the finger (about 10 milliseconds), we get a value of 70 milliseconds which corresponds approximately to the time taken by the associative process between the optic centre and the motor centre. We called this the *optomotor integration time*. Seventy-five milliseconds is the time concerned. In a highly integrative and associative process such as the one required by a subject reacting to an optic stimulus by a flexion of the forefinger, our previous experiment shows that the progressive shortening of the motor reaction has very little to do with the afferent process (cortical time = constant = 40 milliseconds), but has chiefly to do with processes occurring in the associative area, or in the motor centre itself.

FREMONT-SMITH:

How do you know that the shortening was in this 75 milliseconds? Supposing one were to say that the associative process started spontaneously but it still took 75 milliseconds and merely started sooner; it seems to me this could possibly be an interpretation of the fact that actually you end up with an anticipated reaction which precedes the stimulus. You might argue that it had still taken 75 milliseconds in the associative centre, but it had not needed any retinal stimulus to get it there.

MONNIER:

I agree with your interpretation. This would prove that the chief variation occurs between the visual and motor centre, or perhaps in the motor centre alone.

BINDRA:

Yes, but it will not get rid of the objection that has been raised by Dr. Fremont-Smith. There still may not be any change in the crucial interval of 75 milliseconds; the reduction in reaction time may be an artefact of the method.

MONNIER:

I know that in this associative and motor part of the process, the shortening is due chiefly to the attention of the subject. We have experiments which prove that, when the subject begins to be fatigued, the motor reaction shows progressive lengthening.

FREMONT-SMITH:

But in the second one, where the fatigue comes in, it seems to me you ought to be able to show quite clearly that it does take place in the associative centres. It would seem to me that you have not yet answered my objection to claiming that the shortening took place in the associative centres, because supposing a stimulus arising other than in the retina anticipates the signal, you might still come out with a progressively earlier response. Let us take the one at 90. Supposing I were to say that this is merely the result of an anticipated response which did not start soon enough to give you a reaction in advance of the stimulus, what then?

MONNIER:

I agree, but I can give you another interpretation. I mean now that something that has been learned in the sequence of twenty responses to twenty flashes becomes, by means of attention and possibly of some will, more and more trained, and ends in an anticipation which has nothing more to do with the stimulus.

244

BINDRA:

That is probably the correct explanation; but I think, in order for you to make your argument decisive, you still have to exclude the possibility that a person actually starts responding before he receives the stimulus, especially as your stimuli are given at such regular intervals. The way to control this factor would be to trick your subject by interpolating some stimulus that is not the stimulus to which he is supposed to respond. If you put enough of these fake stimuli in I think you could make sure that the subject actually sees the stimuli before he makes the response.

FREMONT-SMITH:

Or you could see that the stimulus came at random intervals instead of regularly.

GREY WALTER:

I should like to say I do not think the mechanism is in any way as you described it.

MONNIER:

I should be very glad to hear another interpretation.

GREY WALTER:

There are all sorts of objections to your interpretation, but I should like to mention two pieces of work which are quite relevant; one is by Pampiglione (1953) at the Maudsley Hospital, on a rather similar experiment during sleepy states, where the completion of a pattern by the sleepy or sleeping subject is the most remarkable feature. In these experiments he evoked the well-known K complex of the E.E.G. by a non-specific stimulus in a rhythmic fashion every ten seconds, then he started to leave out the stimulus and, sure enough, for a while, every ten seconds the K complex appeared even when the stimulus was missing. Even in the sleeping subject an escapement is started which begins to count the time and when the time comes for the stimulus it begins to be anticipatory and gives a response. This response to time is the same thing that Dr. Liddell was talking about, and it involves a much more complex mechanism than you have implied there. There are more involved structures which you have not delineated which do not go up through the cortex but down, into the depths of the brain again.

MONNIER:

I agree that the optomotor associative process may be not only cortical, but cortico-thalamic and thalamo-cortical.

GREY WALTER:

It is the anticipatory reaction which really makes hay of any attempt to measure latencies, because the brain has built up its own idea of when it is going to respond and is not simply responding as a telephone exchange any more; it has built up an anticipatory image of the situation and it is going to respond to that.

Hick (1950) in Cambridge, has published a very interesting paper on the relation between reaction-times and the number of alternatives in choice-reaction situations. The results follow the expected rules of information theory as to the information being related to the number of possible alternatives. I think that is a much more profitable way of approaching this problem, because if you randomize the temporal order, or perhaps introduce some subtle temporal pattern, you begin to see which things you can measure as physiological latencies and which are measures of the cerebral interpretation and storage of pattern.

MONNIER:

I entirely agree. These experiments were done to study the relations between afferent and efferent impulses, and not with the particular purpose of studying learning, but since we met variations of the motor time according to repetitive processes, I considered it worth-while discussing this problem with you, hoping to get new working hypotheses.

GREY WALTER:

One of the difficulties is that the reaction-time experiment looks so simple. 'When you see the light press a key' sounds simple, but actually it is very complicated and involves a number of preconceived conditionings. There is associative learning there in a sense, though very little, because you have preselected his association for him; you have said, 'associate this only with the light'. There is also practice. In your choice-reaction experiment, however, you begin to get something that, although it looks more complicated, is in a sense simpler, or more analysable. Here you have a situation where the subject has to build up an association; he has to decide between all the possible lights which light has gone on and what the correct response is to that light.

BINDRA:

It is a little too complicated if you ask a person to make a choice reaction of this type; you are making the situation more complicated than Dr. Monnier would like it to be.

GREY WALTER:

It is not actually, because the complication is analysable on the basis of information theory the moment you know what the choices are. In this case you do not know what the alternatives are.

In the response to patterns of flicker of 180 to 200 milliseconds, latency was of the same order as that which you give, between 180 and 200 milliseconds. Therefore the latency for the appearance of a cerebral response to pattern stimulation in the non-projection areas of the brain is about the same as the reaction-time.

TANNER:

Does that latency decrease during the process of conditioning?

GREY WALTER:

Yes, it decreases, and then it may increase again when the subject gets bored. You have not provided much reward here except the rather tenuous one of the subject's supposing that you are pleased. If you do that kind of experiment you will find a gradual decrease in the latency. It is not very much; but as the subject begins to get bored or becomes satiated it will increase again and the response may become generalized. In our experiments, as it happens, the boredom is more marked than the conditioning. We find we cannot give the normal human being sufficient reward without its either costing us too much or involving us too deeply with our subjects.

BINDRA:

What happened to your E.E.G. records, Dr. Monnier?

MONNIER:

You see, for instance, this huge component occurring in' the E.E.G. 120 milliseconds after the flash (Fig. 20); it is related to the response of the visual and paravisual cortex. You will see after this huge response a volley of alpha waves. We may say that the optic stimulus induces first a specific response followed by the huge potential, and afterwards, very often, by three or four alpha waves as an expression of relaxation of the visual cortex, after the specific response.

GREY WALTER:

That introduces another effect of which one must beware in these responses. It is known as the 'Bates effect', because John Bates described it first, I think, (Bates, 1950). He starts with a very simple situation in which a normal subject, sitting quietly, is asked to clench his fist or make some movement just when he pleases—several times a minute, but exactly as he likes; he took a series of E.E.G. records during these trials and superimposed them, using the moment at which the subject chose to make the voluntary response as the fiducial mark. He found that just before the movement was made the alpha rhythms fall into step and that the subject makes the movement only at a certain phase of alpha rhythm, or some component of the alpha rhythm—that the moment at which he chooses to do something is determined, to some extent, by a gating mechanism inside the brain which allows him to make it only at a certain moment. Actual 'now' is not within one's free choice, so that will produce a scatter in the reaction-time—and that might have a very important effect.

HARGREAVES:

It is only when a ball bounces that you can catch it, and you cannot catch it between bounces.

BINDRA:

We have a similar finding on rats. Rats are made to cross a barrier under threat of electric shock. They are able to avoid the shock by moving from one end to the other of the grid every 10 seconds. This is a temporal conditioning situation. Then, through an electrode, we pick up the various happenings in the hypothalamus. One sees a very characteristic response just before the rat begins to move in this direction or that. Seeing this characteristic signal enables one to say, 'The rat is going to go now'. We call this characteristic hypothalamic response 'a picture of free will'.

RÉMOND:

Before a rabbit is going to move, he has a very special pattern in his E.E.G. which may not be completely different from the rat's pattern (Rémond et al., 1950, 1951).

TANNER:

While he is making up his mind?

RÉMOND:

Yes, and it is a very recognizable sign; 20 to 30 milliseconds after its occurrence, the motion follows.

About ten years ago we were studying the reaction-times related to E.E.G.s, trying to learn more about the state of consciousness in which a subject might be. We found first that when the stimulus was repeated rather rhythmically the reaction followed very quickly; and sometimes there was no reaction-time—it was instantaneous. When the stimulus was given at random, the reaction-time was much longer. In patients, especially in idiopathic epileptics, the reaction-time was always the longest. But these people were able to shorten their reaction-time when the stimulus was rhythmically repeated, and I have the impression that the ratio between the response to a rhythmic stimulus and to a random stimulus was about the same in normal and in idiopathic epileptics, even if the reaction-time of the latter is ten times that of the normal.

INTERVAL

INHELDER:

Learning theories analyse in detail the experimental conditions of learning, such as the number of stimuli and their rhythm, the subject's motivation and vulnerability. One fundamental aspect of learning seems, however, to have been somewhat neglected by most of the learning theorists, and that is the psychological process by which facts are recorded, or in other terms the 'interpretation' of the experiment.

Dr. Whiting says that a theory of social learning should explain the acquisition of the cognitive structure.

Koehler and Tolman have already underlined the fact that learning implies changes in apperception and in cognition and have shown that the improvement of performance depends upon the precision of the cognitive schema which guides and directs the response process. However, their experiments were carried out on animals and human adults, and not on children. As soon as one studies the developing child one realizes that the cognitive schema which determines the interpretation of experiments is modified by elaboration of mental structures. The child of five interprets the same experimental facts differently from the child of seven or eight years; the latter interprets them differently from an adolescent of fourteen or fifteen.

M. Piaget has called this interpretation of experimental data 'an abstraction' and he distinguished two types: the physical type of abstraction and the logico-arithmetic (or mathematical) type of abstraction (PIAGET, 1951). In these two kinds of abstraction the child is always active: he knows the external world only through his activity, whether it be sensorimotor, symbolic or rational. It is precisely these forms or schemata of activity which are transformed during growth; which explains the relation between age and the structures implied in the interpretation of experimental facts.

I should like to give you very briefly a few examples by way of illustration.

In a first experiment, which was described at our last meeting (see Vol. I), we asked children to draw or indicate by gestures how they imagine the water-level in vessels which are upright, inclined or placed horizontally. The experiment was carried out in three phases.

First phase: the child sees the vessel but not the water-level and has to imagine the position of the liquid. He can either mark a diagram given to him with a blue pencil or he can indicate his reply by gestures.

Second phase: we show the vessel uncovered in different positions and ask the child to draw the water-level as he sees it.

Third phase: we hide the water-level again and ask the child to draw it again without seeing it.

The experiment is, then, very simple and allows us to follow the learning phases which occur for an adequate interpretation of experiments (PIAGET and INHELDER, 1948). Here, briefly, are the results. They were obtained from 250 subjects of three to nine-and-a-half years.

First type of solution: the children of three-and-a-half to four years draw the water inside the vessel without abstracting any special position from the actual water vessel.

Second type of solution: the vessel and the liquid form a kind of rigid whole, which explains the drawings of the water-level in vertical, inclined or even suspended positions, results frequent at an average age of five-and-a-half years.

Third type of solution: the liquid is displaced in relation to the vessel without the horizontal position being abstracted (average age six-and-a-half years).

Success depends, of course, on the amount the vessel is inclined. For the position upside down we have already 56 per cent. correct solutions at six years and 96 per cent. at seven years, whereas for the inclined position we only get 8 per cent. correct solutions at six years, 36 per cent. at seven years, 68 per cent. at nine years and 65 per cent. at nine-and-a-half years.

It should be noted that before the age of six-and-a-half years there is hardly any learning through observation, whereas from that age

FIG. 21
EQUALITY OF ANGLES OF INCIDENCE AND REFLEXION

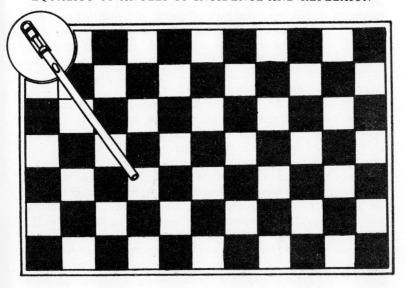

onwards the child gets increasingly receptive towards the experiment. It appears from these facts that in order to interpret this particular experiment in a profitable way a child must possess the specific intellectual instruments permitting him to abstract the horizontal position from the experimental data themselves.

The role of the interpretation of experimental facts, insofar as it is the result of a mental abstraction, is shown by a series of experiments intended to study inductive reasoning in 1700 subjects of five to sixteen years (INHELDER, 1954; INHELDER and PIAGET, 1955).

We wondered how children and adolescents could discover from mechanical devices the equality of the angles of incidence and reflection in a billiard game (Fig. 21). For this purpose we made several pieces of apparatus with the help of Mr. Hans Aebli and Miss Lydia Müller. By means of a cue which can be directed at different angles the child or adolescent can project a billiard ball against a deflecting wall. We asked him to reach with his ball, after deflection, a little figure in different positions and to try to draw up the rule of the game which allows him to succeed every time without preliminary experiments or trials.

Here, very roughly, are the results obtained. During the first phase (five to five-and-a-half years average age) the aim of the experiment for the young child consists essentially in finding in reality the

251

confirmation of his desires and anticipations. Certainly the child is already capable of seeing his successes and failures but he is often incapable of following the path of the billiard ball. When we ask him simply to indicate this by means of a gesture he very often draws a curved line. We have often been astonished to note to what extent young children, through lack of schemata of abstraction, remain impervious to experience. They do not yet feel any real need to compare the different results obtained.

During the second phase (the most characteristic reactions are found at an average age of nine years) the objectivity of interpretation increases. The interpretation of the experiment during this second phase is based upon a set of concrete operational schemata. Such correspondences are found by the child between the directions of incidence and reflection. The child will say, for instance, 'the more bent it is, the more it comes back bent' or 'the more I move this way, the more the billiard ball comes back the other way'. It is, of course, easier to translate the movements by gesture than to conceptualize them. It is during this second phase that the child appears to come closest to the facts; when he is younger he tends to deform them; when older he tends to go beyond them in order to integrate them into a whole system. Experimentation during the second period is, then, very productive. Thanks to operational abstraction the child can work with the apparatus although he is not yet capable of organized research.

During the third phase (the most characteristic reactions are found at fourteen to fifteen years) interpretation consists in translating concrete facts into abstract concepts. The adolescent uses geometrical systems of reference. He says, for example, 'You have to think in straight lines' or 'If you put the cue perpendicular to the cushion the billiard ball comes back on itself'. In this way, by means of a *group* of geometrical constructions, the adolescen tmanages to understand that the angle of incidence of the trajectory is equal to the angle of reflection, whatever the position of the cue.

We wondered to what we should attribute the relatively late appearance of this last form of the interpretation of experiment, since from nine years on children can generally compare angles and know the elementary geometric operations (PIAGET *et al.* 1948). However, during the second period the child is not yet capable of abstracting the equality of angles. This incapacity arises from the fact that the child does not yet try to discover an invariant. But from fourteen to fifteen years on, the adolescent is no longer content to record experimental variations: he attempts actively to isolate an invariant or a function in the mathematical sense of the term. The interpretation of the experiment seems to be always directed

FIG. 22
WATER LEVELS IN COMMUNICATING VESSELS

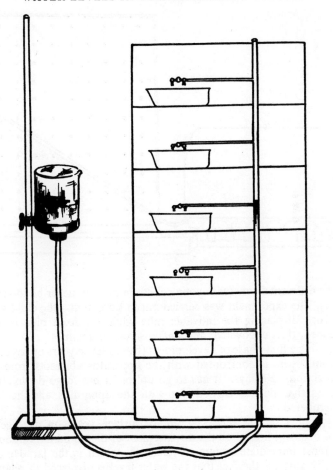

by aims or goals. The abstraction is only an instrument serving the goals.

Here, briefly, is a second mechanical device consisting in communicating vessels (Fig. 22). How will a child or adolescent read the experiment, which consists in observing that in a system of communicating vessels the water-level is always at the same height in the two tubes? In our apparatus one of the branches of the system of communicating vessels is fixed and the other is movable. It is made up to imitate a dolls' house where the child can bring water up

FIG. 23

FALL OF BODIES DOWN VARIABLE INCLINE

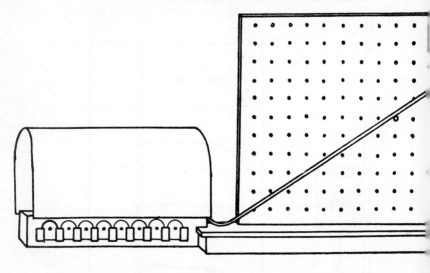

to the different floors (with young children one can never be too concrete). The experiment was carried out in three steps: the child goes
to work displacing the movable tube while the fixed pipe is first
screened, then uncovered, and finally screened again.

During a first phase of development (five to seven years on average)
the child who is confronted with the apparatus abstracts from his
own actions. He says, 'It has to go up' or 'It has to go down'. The
actions that he has carried out with the apparatus are the best
remembered.

During a second phase (seven to thirteen years on average) a
child observes first of all the displacement of the liquid in relation to
the most immediate system of reference, which is the jar. He can
already abstract the fact that the water-level is displaced in relation
to the latter, but he does not yet understand that the two water-levels
are always at the same height. He is still surprised by the experimental variations, whereas during the third phase (from thirteen to
fourteen years onwards) he suddenly observes the equality of the
water-levels. Here we find the confirmation of the same principle:
the search for an experimental constant determines the interpretation
of the experiment.

With the help of a third mechanical device (Fig. 23) the fall of
bodies on an inclined plane is studied in a very concrete way. The
child or adolescent can discover through experimentation that the

length of the trajectory of a ball is related to the height of the point of departure, whatever the mass of the ball. This physical principle is studied by means of an apparatus. The children are free to alter the inclination of a tube which serves as an inclined plane, and the balls, following a parabolic trajectory, jump over a spring-board fixed at the lower end of the tube and fall into one of a series of pigeon-holes. The balls can be retrieved from behind little doors which close the pigeon-holes.

Three ways of interpreting the experiment, each determined by specific attitudes and goals, caught our attention. The young children of five to seven were incapable of recording the experiment and reproducing it under the same conditions. Their activity is guided not by a need for objectivity but by the pleasure of setting something in motion. The child of seven to eleven is already capable of abstracting or establishing the correspondences. He discovers, for example, that 'the more the slope is inclined, or the greater the distance the ball rolls, the farther the ball will jump'. He is interested both in making some experimental variations and in reproducing the experiment, without, however, yet discovering the invariant: the height from which the ball falls.

The adolescent of fourteen to fifteen sets up the experiment quite differently. He is not only struck by the variations in the inclination of the tube and in the length of the trajectory, but also by the unvarying height of the point of departure. Moreover, by means of a systematic consideration of all the factors involved, he observes that the length of the trajectory is independent of the variations of mass.

These few facts, which are only a sample of a wide investigation on the experimental attitudes of the child and the adolescent, seem to indicate that all learning presupposes an interpretation of experimental data. This interpretation of facts or abstractions is, of course, determined by a group of emotional factors which have been made evident by the learning theorists. But it depends also on cognitive factors, such as the intellectual instruments at the child's disposal for the assimilation and interpretation of physical data, and the experimental attitudes (goals for action) which direct the investigation.

During the first phase the child acts through pleasure of setting something in motion rather than to modify the course of an experiment. This attitude conditions a subjective interpretation of the facts. During the second phase the child acts in order to produce a clearly determined, concrete result; this attitude facilitates a more objective interpretation and requires operations of comparison and of measurement. During the third phase the mechanical device becomes more and more an occasion for deduction and verification of hypotheses. The interpretation of facts becomes an integral part of an actual intellectual construction. Thus the forms of learning cannot be isolated from the instruments of knowledge. Both undergo an evolution according to age.

PIAGET:

What is striking about these facts is that physical experiment comes much later than one would imagine. The abstraction of a horizontal line from reality would seem to be something immediate and perceptive. One would think that the baby who can walk has already some idea of the vertical when he is standing up and of the horizontal when he is lying down. Certainly he has the postural notion, but he has no perceptive notion whatever in connection with external space, and certainly no representative notion. In order to 'read' a horizontal line it is not enough to look at it, it is necessary to have the instruments which allow one to 'read' it, and here the instrument is formed by the axes of coordinates, by a system of references. A mathematical or logical apparatus is necessary if the physical experiment is to be reached. Without a mathematical or logical apparatus, there is no direct 'reading' of facts, because this apparatus is a prerequisite. Such an apparatus is derived from experience, the abstraction being taken from the action performed upon the object and not from the object itself. It is definitely based on coordination of action. It is these coordinations of action which give rise to the first abstractions, permitting the construction of logical and mathematical operations, and once these instruments have been constructed the interpretation of experimental data is entirely different from what it was before. This, I think, is the main lesson to be drawn from these facts: that physical experimentation comes much later, even in the cases where it is absolutely elementary, than logical-mathematical experimentation, and I do not think it is simply a question of complexity or facility of generalization. It is that the first experience provides instruments which are themselves necessary for a reading of the second experience: the physical experiment.

GREY WALTER:

Professor Piaget is quite correct in saying that insight into physical conditions is a very late arriving feature in human development. About ten years ago, I undertook some special lectures for schoolchildren who had to leave school and go into industry. I tried to introduce them to the principles of science, and, among other things, I presented them with the Galilean proposition of: you have a 10 lb weight and a 1 lb weight and let them go together: which will reach the earth first? We had a democratic vote on it. Half the class voted for the heavy one; half for the light one.

FREMONT-SMITH:

None for both together?

GREY WALTER:

That did not occur to anybody.

FREMONT-SMITH:

What were their ages?

GREY WALTER:

Fifteen. At least in England, we are living in a pre-Galilean or mediaeval world, as far as the facts of physics are concerned. I think that if you took a vote in the street some people would say, 'I do not know—probably the heavy one', and others would say, 'Oh well, there is probably some catch in it—the light one'.

ZAZZO:

I have also carried out experiments of the same type as Mlle Inhelder and M. Piaget, but on adults, and at a time when our students in Paris did not yet know the details of Professor Piaget's work. I obtained rather strange results; that is to say, educated adults—if one admits that students of psychology are educated adults—failed in the same way as children. In other words, they did not seem to have acquired the concept of conservation, or in any case, seemed disturbed by the experiment. I sometimes thought that the students were laughing at me, that they were pulling my leg, but this was not at all the case.

If a very simple experiment with a glass of water was tried and they were asked: 'what must happen if sugar is put in?' their replies were somewhat baffling. When the water—or the coffee—came half way up, they considered that the sugar melted and that the level did not rise—just like the children you have been speaking about. On the other hand, they were perfectly willing to admit that if the glass, or the cup were full, and one added sugar, the water, or the coffee, would overflow.

In short, it seems obvious to me that the operations achieved by children when they reach adolescence, are very insecure and that it takes very little to make them disappear, even in the case of an adult, and even with an educated adult.

I wonder, as a matter of practical interest, whether a connection should not be established here between the failure which may be observed under disturbing experimental conditions and the well-known difficulty, experienced by schoolchildren in general, of learning and understanding mathematics.

I think that the closer we come to an attitude of abstraction and to operations, the more the affective factors intervene to make solutions less stable. In other words, the study of the pedagogy of mathematics should be directed not solely, as it often is, towards the study of factors involved in an aptitude for mathematics, but also towards the study of a certain affective equilibrium and a certain sensitivity. It is this, I think, that constitutes the obstacle preventing certain children from reaching a given level. I do not think that any special aptitudes are required for understanding mathematics up to the baccalauréat level, or even beyond that; and I think that the failures are not due to an inaptitude or a lack of special mathematical aptitude, but in a general way to affective factors.

You all know of the studies which have been carried out on the differential psychology of boys and girls. It had been thought possible to show that girls' aptitude for mathematics was less developed than boys'. I do not think that there are less developed aptitudes, but that it is the whole personality which causes schoolgirls on average to be less successful at mathematics, all other things being equal, than schoolboys.

GREY WALTER:

You may be quite right, but I should have said that people who are very gifted in mathematical manipulation, not merely in passing examinations, often seem to be almost crazy as personalities. I have never seen a practising mathematician who is not a very odd personality, often with overt symptoms of emotional disturbance. I should attribute the characteristic ability for mathematical abstraction to an inborn imagery factor, which may or may not be associated with certain emotional factors.

RÉMOND:

It could be the mathematics which transforms the individuals.

GREY WALTER:

No, I should say the ability or the liking for mathematics at a very early age is associated with a certain sort of psychological imagery structure, a certain type of E.E.G., too, which tends to encourage such people to become abstract mathematicians. But it may be that a brilliant mathematician is not the same as somebody who passes a mathematical examination.

PIAGET:

If you mean individuals who produce creative mathematics, which is quite a different matter, I am entirely in agreement with you; these are special people, but Zazzo was speaking of that average comprehension which progresses to a certain degree for absolutely elementary and general mathematical operations. Here I entirely agree with him. There is no particular aptitude for mathematics and, in general, those who appear not to possess this aptitude are the victims of a simple affective blocking. In any teaching, when one does not understand anything the first month or two, one can very well get interested later on and make up for the time lost, whereas in mathematics, if a few months are lost in the development of the subject, and especially at the beginning, one very quickly gets a feeling of personal inferiority and has the impression that one can never learn anything. And therefore, on the one hand, one does not make the necessary effort, and on the other hand, as one is sometimes faced by a professor of mathematics who reasons as if the development of the child should lead directly to the stage reached by the Greeks and to productive thought without going through experimental manipulation, etc., there is always a blocking, which derives partly from the child's feeling of inferiority and partly from the atmosphere, which is not created to favour logical-mathematical comprehension.

This, however, does not explain the first part of what Zazzo said, which was most interesting. In the case of a normal adult (supposing that the student of psychology is a normal adult, which is approximately true, although he nevertheless tends to make mountains out of molehills) the fact that the operations which have been acquired by twelve years are no longer understood later on, does not, to tell you the truth, entirely surprise me. Actually I do not think that this fact is peculiar to problems of conservation; in all kinds of fields, one finds some retardation after schooling and curves which reach their maximum at about fourteen to fifteen years and then decline. I think, then, that we were rather more intelligent at adolescence than later.

ZAZZO:

I am not entirely in agreement. Do you not think that this decline, which is certainly noticeable after schooling, is found particularly among individuals who do not continue to work on an intellectual plane? Among the students I was speaking of there had never been any discontinuity; they are students all the time; there has never been a break.

PIAGET:

There are those who do not continue in a general sense, and then there are students; but the latter, as specialists, immediately stop thinking in a large number of fields: a student of philosophy, particularly, no longer thinks about physics or mathematics, etc., whereas during school education he is forced to think about the most varied topics, and he is certainly at a higher level for questions which are outside his professional line.

ZAZZO:

But in the example which I borrowed from your work and which implied no special knowledge at all—bearing on the concept of conservation and the water-level in the glass—I don't think that as regards instruction there is any difference between the schoolchild and the student. I think simply that with the student or with the adult there is a sophisticated attitude. This failure proves, in any case, that this operation is very unstable.

PIAGET:

Yes, I agree.

INHELDER:

Your observations correspond to those made by DENNIS (1953), at Brooklyn Teachers' College. A certain number of students of psychology and of education still seem to reason in an animistic fashion. Certainly reasoning is very unstable. This is why I am studying at the moment each kind of reasoning within its functional complex, without isolating it as I used to do when I studied the operational mechanism of the acquisition of concepts of conservation.

LORENZ:

I would like to ask Professor Piaget a question. Are you an empiricist or an a-priori-ist? I have held a grudge of long standing against a colleague of mine in Königsberg who had the Chair some time before me: Immanuel Kant. Mademoiselle Inhelder has used expressions in defining abstractions which are actually derived from Kant, because she said some abstractions are necessary in order to make experience and have to be there before any experience can ever

260

be made. This is exactly the definition that Kant gives of *a priori*: the 'spectacles' through which we look at things. Space and time, and all the categories which are there before experience is possible, are the conditions under which experience is possible.

In listening to Mlle Inhelder's experiments, I found myself amazed that things which I should have supposed to be *a priori* evidently are not. The same applies to the story which Professor Piaget told us about the number of pebbles. The knowledge that this number will be the same whether we put them in a row or in a heap together, is just one of the things which Kant would have asserted to be quite distinctly *a priori*.

Yet certainly there are some things *a priori*; there must be because we could not begin making experiments without having certain 'working hypotheses' within our central nervous system; for example the working hypotheses that light is projected in a straight line—all our visual reactions are based on that hypothesis. It is a very crude hypothesis, because if light was not straighter in space than it is here on earth where it is deflected by gravity, then one could not see Sirius because its light would go out in curls in space and never arrive at your eyes. A working hypothesis is always a crude basis but is nevertheless there.

Now I think the question of empiricism and a priori-ism is not a problem to be solved at all by philosophy, but by research work such as that of Professor Piaget and his school.

PIAGET:

By learning theory.

LORENZ:

Yes, and therefore I think these observations about the pebbles are so extremely important. I should like to believe it is not *a priori*, but I should like some assurance by having a large series of experiments made about these pebbles.

PIAGET:

I should like to thank Dr. Lorenz for his question. My reply will not refer to the sphere of animal psychology, which he knows better than I, but as regards child psychology, I am absolutely convinced that when there is an alternative between empiricism and a-priorism. It is always the third way which is correct! In other words, development as we have observed it does not show that either a-priorism or empiricism is correct.

Why not a-priorism? Because we have never found a ready-made structure. All structures get constructed, and the example of the order and the cardinal number of pebbles which I quoted the other day is an illustration of this. I even think that in the case of the light in straight lines there is a place for choice and elaboration, because there are several possible geometric schemata: there is the Euclidean straightness, but there could be others too, with curves, and to arrive at Euclidean space, which seems the simplest, and at Euclidean straightness, certainly entails schematization. I think, then, that we shall never find a ready-made piece of knowledge which would be *a priori* or innate. We shall always find it comprises some construction and some experience, or learning as function of experience, but it is here that the distinction comes in between the two types of experience which I tried to introduce the other day.

There are physical experiments, which are experiences in the empiric sense, where we learn little by little, feeling our way, by chance, etc. But there is logico-mathematical experiment, the experiment where the child acts on objects, but where he derives his knowledge not from the object, but from the actions he has applied to objects, and this experimenting leads him to the necessary structures. The necessity which Kant introduced as a criterion of *a priori* is a perfectly exact psychological datum. When he manages to make seriations, and to introduce order into his elements, the child finds the necessary structures; he finds that the sum is necessarily independent of the order; that the order can be reversed; he finds a series of logical relations which appear necessary.

This necessity, however, differs in two ways from Kant's necessity. Firstly, it does not appear as the point of departure but only as the point of arrival for experience. It is a terminal necessity. It is the necessity inherent in a law of equilibrium and not an innate idea which would orient the development from the beginning. It is the necessity corresponding to the most balanced coordination, apart from which there can be no coherent action. The second difference is that it is a necessity which gradually emerges from the distinction between the coordinations of action and the matter on which the subject acts.

I think therefore that the truth lies between the two, although much of what Kant said should be kept in mind: the idea of necessary coordination, but not the *a priori*, because it is a question of a terminal necessity which presupposes an elaboration, a preliminary experience. It is for this reason that I distinguished two types of experience. As soon as one distinguishes them one is no longer an empiricist and one can no longer relate all knowledge to the physical type of experience as the empiricists did. One is faced by a new type of experience which leads simply to necessary coordinations.

Perhaps I have replied in rather an abstract way but you will certainly understand.

LORENZ:

I hope that I understand.

GREY WALTER:

Is it necessary for the human organism to make more than one *a priori* assumption at birth? I should have thought the only *a priori* assumption that a human organism will make at birth is that atmospheric gas inhaled into the lungs supports life.

As to light travelling in straight lines, I should say one's observation of straightness derives from one's observation of light. A straight line is what light travels in.

TANNER:

The question is not what assumption he need make, it is what assumption he does make. This is a matter which can be settled only by experiment, I think.

GREY WALTER:

The new-born infant is not assuming anything, and it rapidly starts to build up a series of hypotheses about what can and what cannot happen. This is opposed to birds and fish which, on the whole, live in rather less variable surroundings and are allowed to make more *a priori* assumptions. We have succeeded uniquely in developing a nervous system which retains a very high degree of plasticity as well as sheer competence.

FREMONT-SMITH:

You think we have freed ourselves from *a priori* assumptions?

GREY WALTER:

Almost. I am not suggesting that *all* the things which are *a priori* or practically innate in other species have to be learnt in ourselves. But we do depend very much on our faculty for investigation and testing.

FREMONT-SMITH:

Do experiments or observations in animals throw light on this? Are there awarenesses in animals which we assume *a priori* which to them are not *a priori*?

263

LORENZ:

Well, I think you have a better opportunity to prove the opposite. Take, for instance, perception of space. Many birds have little or no opportunity of perceiving space when they are sitting in the nest box, because we know that the birds get very little of notion of space by touch. All these very complicated central nervous mechanisms achieving the perception of space are certainly *a priori* in the sense stipulated by the definition. They are something which is existent before experience is made and which must be there in order to make any experience of space possible at all. But they are not *a priori* in the sense of an absolute necessity with which this term is invested in Kant's teaching. I am not quite convinced that any such absolute necessities exist at all. The most stringent necessities, the most universal logical laws, may very possibly be just the consequences of very definite corresponding mechanisms within our central nervous system. These mechanisms make it impossible for us to think in any other ways; hence the 'logical necessity'. And there is no predicting whether such a mechanism is inborn or acquired. In inter-specific comparison we find very often that a function is innate in one species and based on individual learning in another. We certainly must be prepared to find a minimum of inborn and a maximum of learned functions in man. Yet even in man there must be a certain basis of inborn working hypotheses to make the making of experience possible at all. The smaller this basis is, the more interesting it becomes, from the philosophical viewpoint as well as from that of the theory of learning.

REFERENCES

BATES, J. A. V. (1950). *Electroenceph. clin. Neurophysiol.* **2**, 103.

BATESON, G. (1949). *Bali: the value system of a steady state.* In: Fortes, M., ed. (1949) *Social Structure*, Oxford.

BEXTON, W. H., HERON, W., SCOTT, T. H. and HEBB, D. C. (1954). *Canad. J. Psychol.* (in press).

BOAS, F. (1952). *Primitive art*, New York.

BOWLBY, J. (1953). *J. ment. Sci.* **99**, 265.

BOWLBY, J., ROBERTSON, J. and ROSENBLUTH, D. (1952). *A two-year-old goes to hospital*, in: *The psychoanalytic study of the child*, Vol. 7.

BRADY, J. S. (1954). *Electroenceph. clin. Neurophysiol.* **6**, 473.

CANNON, W. B. (1936). *Bodily changes in fear, pain and rage*, New York.

CAROTHERS, I. C. (1953). *The African mind in health and disease: a study in ethnopsychiatry*, Geneva (World Health Organization: Monograph Series, No. 17).

DENNIS, W. (1953). *Sci. Mon.* **76**, 247.

ECCLES, J. C. (1953). *The neurophysiological basis of mind*, Oxford.

EICHLER, R. M. (1951). *J. abn. soc. Psychol.* **46**, 344.

ERIKSON, E. H. (1950). *Childhood and society*, New York.

ERIKSON, E. H. (1951). *Amer. J. Orthopsychiat.* **21**, 667.

EWERT, P. H. (1930). *Genet. Psychol. Monogr.* **7**, 177.

FARBER, I. E. and SPENCE, K. W. (1953). *J. exp. Psychol.* **45**, 120.

FORD, C. S. and BEACH, F. A. (1951). *Patterns of sexual behavior*, New York.

FREUD, A. and BURLINGHAM, D. (1943). *War and children*, New York.

FREUD, S. (1935). *A general introduction to psychoanalysis*, New York.

FULTON, J. F. (1943). *Physiology of the nervous system*, Oxford.

GROSSMAN, C. (1954). *Annual meeting Amer. Branch Int. League against Epilepsy, Boston*, Aug. 22, 1953.

HEBB, D. O. (1949). *Organization of behavior*, New York.

HEBB, D. O. (1953). *Brit. J. anim. Behav.* **1**, 43.

HEINICKE, C. (1953). *Some antecedents and correlates of guilt-fear in young boys*, Unpublished doctoral dissertation, Harvard University.

HEINROTH, O. (1911). *Verh. V. intern. ornith. Kongr.* Berlin 1910.

HERRE, W. (1943). In: Heberer, G. *Evolution der Organismen*, Jena.

HESS, W. R. (1949). *Das Zwischenhirn*, Basel.

HICK, W. E. (1950). *Symposium on information theory*, London.

HYMOVITCH, B. (1952). *J. comp. physiol. Psychol.* **45**, 313.

INHELDER, B. (1954). *Bull. Psychol.* **7**, 272.

KOEHLER, O. (1950). In: Society for Experimental Biology. *Physiological mechanisms in animal behavior*, New York.

LANSDELL, H. C. (1953). *J. comp. physiol. Psychol.* **46,** 461.

MASSERMAN, J. H. and PECHTEL, C. (1953). *J. nerv. ment. Dis.* **118,** 408.

MAYR, E. (1942). *Systematics and the origin of species,* New York.

MEAD, M. (1928). *Coming of age in Samoa,* New York.

MELZACK, R. (1952). *Canad. J. Psychol.* **6,** 141.

MELZACK, R. (1954). *J. comp. physiol. Psychol.* **47,** 166.

MEYER-HOLZÄPFEL, M. (1938). *Z. Tierpsychol.* **1,** 46.

MIRSKY, I. A., MILLER, R. and STEIN, M. (1953). *Psychosom. Med.* **15,** 574.

MONNIER, M. (1946, 1948). *Schweiz. Arch. Neurol. Psychiat.* **56,** 233, 325; **62,** 151.

MONNIER, M. (1948). *Helv. Physiol. Acta,* **6,** 661.

MONNIER, M. (1952). *J. Neurophysiol.* **15,** 469.

MONNIER, M. (1953). *Acta neuroveget.* **7,** 84.

NISSEN, H. W. and RIESEN, A. H. (1949). *Anat. Rec.* **105,** 665

PAMPIGLIONE, G. (1953). *Electroenceph. clin. Neurophysiol.* **5,** 622.

PAVLOV, I. P. (1910). *Work of the digestive glands,* London.

PAVLOV, I. P. (1927). *Conditioned reflexes,* Oxford.

PEIPER, A. (1949). *Die Eigenart der kindlichen Hirntätigkeit,* Leipzig.

PIAGET, J. (1951). *Introduction à l'épistémologie génétique,* Paris.

PIAGET, J. and INHELDER, B. (1948). *La représentation de l'espace chez l'enfant,* Paris.

PIAGET, J., INHELDER, B. and SZEMINSKA, A. (1948). *La géométrie spontanée de l'enfant,* Paris.

PRECHTL, H. F. R. (1949). *Wien Z. Psychol. Pädagog.* **2.**

PRECHTL, H. F. R. (1953). *Naturwissenschaften,* **40,** 347.

PRECHTL, H. F. R. and SCHLEIDT, W. M. (1950, 1951). *Z. vergl. Physiol.* **32,** 257; **33,** 53.

RÉMOND, A. and CONTAMIN, F. (1950). *Rev. neurol.* **82,** 606.

RÉMOND, A., CONTAMIN, F. and ROUVRAY, R. (1951). *Arch. Sci. phys.* **5,** 19.

ROBERTSON, J. (1953). *A guide to the film "A two-year-old goes to hospital": a scientific film record.* London.

SCHAEFER, E. A. (1912). *The endocrine organs,* San Francisco.

SCHAFFER, H. R. (1954). *Psychol. Rev.* **16,** No. 5.

SCOTT, J. P., FREDERICSON, E. and FULLER, J. L. (1951). *Personality,* **1,** 162.

SCOTT, J. P. and FULLER, J. L. (1951). *J. Hered.* **42,** 191.

SNOW, J. (1855). In: *Snow on cholera,* New York, 1936.

THOMPSON, W. R. and HERON, W. (1954a). *J. comp. physiol. Psychol.* **47,** 66.

THOMPSON, W. R. and HERON, W. (1954b). *Canad. J. Psychol.* (in press).

THORNDIKE, E. L. (1928). *Human Learning,* Ithaca.

TINBERGEN, N. (1940). *Z. Tierpsychol.* **4,** 1.

ULLMAN, A. D. (1951). *J. comp. physiol. Psychol.* **44,** 575.

UTTLEY, A. M. (1954). *Electroenceph. clin. Neurophysiol.* 6, 479.
WALTER, W. GREY (1953). *The living brain*, London & New York.
WHITING, J. W. M. (1941). *Becoming a Kwoma*, New Haven.
WHITING, J. W. M. and CHILD, I. L. (1953). *Child training and personality*, New Haven.

Index

270

DISCUSSIONS ON

Child Development

VOLUME THREE

*The Proceedings of the Third Meeting of the
World Health Organization Study Group
on the Psychobiological Development of the Child
Geneva 1955*

MEMBERS OF STUDY GROUP

DR. JOHN BOWLBY

Psychoanalysis

Director, Department of Children and Parents
Tavistock Clinic, London

DR. FRANK FREMONT-SMITH

Research Promotion

Chairman
Josiah Macy, Jr. Foundation
New York

PROFESSOR G. R. HARGREAVES

Psychiatry

Professor of Psychiatry
University of Leeds
Lately Chief, Mental Health Section
World Health Organization

PROFESSOR BÄRBEL INHELDER

Psychology

Professeur de Psychologie de l'Enfant
Institut des Sciences de l'Education
de l'Université de Genève

DR. KONRAD Z. LORENZ

Ethology

Director, Max-Planck Institüt
für Verhaltensphysiologie
Seewiesen, Bavaria

DR. MARGARET MEAD

Cultural Anthropology

Associate Director, Dept. of Anthropology
American Museum of Natural History
New York

DR. KARL-AXEL MELIN

Electrophysiology

Director, Clinic for Convulsive Disorders
Stora Sköndal, Stockholm

PROFESSOR MARCEL MONNIER

Electrophysiology

Professor of Physiology
University of Basel

PROFESSOR J. PIAGET

Psychology

Professeur de Psychologie
à la Sorbonne et à l'Université
de Genève

GUESTS

DR. D. BUCKLE

Psychiatry

Regional Officer for Mental Health
Regional Office for Europe
World Health Organization
Copenhagen

PROFESSOR ERIK ERIKSON

Psychoanalysis

Austen Riggs Center
Stockbridge, Mass.
and
Dept. of Psychiatry
University of Pittsburgh School of Medicine

DR. JULIAN S. HUXLEY

Biology

Formerly Director-General, U.N.E.S.C.O.
London

DR. RAYMOND DE SAUSSURE

Psychoanalysis

Geneva

PREFACE

Those who have read the first two volumes of this series will already know that the Study Group at its first meeting heard and discussed presentations from representatives of various different scientific disciplines which study some aspect of child development or matters relevant to it, and that at its second meeting the presentations, and the discussions, were focused less specifically on the contributions of different disciplines and more upon aspects of child development in which several disciplines are interested, including such matters as the existence of recognizable stages in development and the phenomenon of learning in immature or developing organisms, and particularly learning under stress.

The third meeting focused upon two related topics: the development of sex differences and the development of individuality or ego identity, and the pattern of psychological development which leads up to it.

The discussion of the first of these topics was based upon two presentations: one by Margaret Mead of comparative data from different societies which might throw light upon the extent to which sex differences were determined by nature or by nurture, and the second by Erik Erikson on sex differences in the play constructions of adolescents.

The opening presentations of the second topic were also made by Erik Erikson. In addition to Mr. Erikson two other distinguished guests joined the Group for this meeting: Dr. Julian Huxley and Dr. Raymond de Saussure.

As on previous occasions the meeting, which was held in Geneva in 1955, provided for its participants a week of stimulating and vigorous discussion which, since it was conducted as usual in both English and French, could not have been possible without simultaneous interpretation equipment and the remarkable ability of the W.H.O. interpreters to follow, and communicate simultaneously in a different language, discussion which, as the reader will find, was often of an exceedingly technical nature and couched in the terminologies of a variety of different scientific disciplines.

To the participant observer it also seemed that a change in the Study Group itself contributed to the success of the meeting. At its first meeting in 1953 its members had comparatively little knowledge of the interests, the methods, and the theoretical models of those in other disciplines who studied the problems of child development; by the third meeting their understanding of each other's work was sufficient to enable them to appreciate and to criticize the formulation of those who worked in other fields and to consider its relevance to their own. For this development in mutual understanding the Group owes much to its Chairman—Dr. Frank Fremont-Smith.

The production of the English transcript of the extensive bilingual discussion depended upon the excellent sound recording facilities provided by W.H.O. and above all on Mrs. J. Moser of the Organization's Mental Health Section whose combination of linguistic ability, technical knowledge, and keen interest in the work of the Group has enabled the contributions of its French-speaking members to be rendered in a sensitive and accurate English translation in these volumes.

Dr. Tanner and Professor Inhelder have edited the transcript of this third meeting and have shown again their ability to reduce a week of discussion to the bounds of a single volume while preserving to a surprising degree its content and its savour.

Leeds University   G. R. HARGREAVES

CONTENTS

The Childhood Genesis of Sex Differences in Behaviour

CANDAU (Director-General, World Health Organization):
This is the third meeting of this research study group. It is to be devoted to consideration of socio-cultural influences affecting psychological development.

I am very glad to welcome once more to Geneva the original members of the Group and also our three distinguished guests: Mr. Erik Erikson of the United States, Dr. Raymond de Saussure of Geneva, and Dr. Julian Huxley of the United Kingdom.

Members who have been present at previous meetings of this Group already know its purpose, but it is worth emphasizing, for the benefit of our guests, that the Group is not intended to make decisions or recommendations on any subject to anyone. Its aim is to increase mutual understanding between eminent exponents of the many different disciplines that study child development and its disorders, particularly in the fields of psychology and physiology.

It only remains necessary for me to wish the Group, under its Chairman, Dr. Frank Fremont-Smith, a stimulating and enjoyable meeting.

FREMONT-SMITH:
We might remind our guests and ourselves that we operate on an extremely informal basis. As Dr. Candau said, the purpose of our meeting is to increase mutual understanding. I think that we should feel rather free to interrupt one another, and your Chairman will only step in occasionally when more than three speak at once. In this way we aim to create a group discussion rather than a series of speeches to which the group gives polite attention.

Now to begin with we would like our three guests to tell us a little bit about themselves. (The regular members of the group introduced

13

themselves in a similar fashion at the first meeting, recorded in Vol. I.) How did they happen to arrive at the kind of interest that led them, on the one hand, to be invited to come here and on the other hand, and even more importantly, to accept?

HUXLEY:

I had better begin with the age of about seven when I found myself fascinated by watching birds which were nesting under the eaves of our house just, I think, because they were alive but had a different kind of life from my own. I think it is fair to say that I have always been interested in the fact of difference and the variety of life and of the world as a whole. It was only later that I got interested in the converse problem of what unity there was to be found in it all, and from about 1934 onwards I spent most of my time trying to make a synthesis of the different approaches to biological evolution. How I got into biology was quite accidental. When I was at school I got to a stage where one could take a certain amount of work in a special subject of choice, and I wrote, I remember, to my parents and said 'wouldn't it be a good thing if I took German', because it was then thought I might go into the Civil Service. They wrote back and said 'no, you can go to Germany later and learn German, why don't you take biology?' Well, the biology master at Eton was a genius, and after two months I knew I was going to be a biologist.

Of course, I wouldn't have been invited to join this Group if I had been a biologist interested solely in subhuman phenomena, but I remember that over 40 years ago, when I was teaching in Texas, I had to give a public lecture, and as I had already begun to think of the problem of continuity and discontinuity in evolution I chose as my subject the critical point between subhuman and human evolution. The first book that I published, before the first World War, was about biological individuality, which I am delighted to hear Konrad Lorenz has been re-reading and even finding interesting still. Then I think I am right in saying that the first occasion on which a displacement activity was scientifically recorded was in my long paper on the courtship of the Great Crested Grebe, published 41 years ago. I didn't know what a displacement activity was, but I recorded the facts of this unexplained phenomenon; and I spent a lot of time during the next 25 years, off and on, working on the biological function of epigamic and throat display in birds and their relation to sexual selection. Meanwhile, I was also interested in the various aspects of experimental embryology and growth, especially relative growth of parts; I found myself driven to put forward the

14

idea that the basis for various aspects of growth and development must be sought in some form of field involving gradients. So I was naturally much interested in the then new ideas of the Gestalt psychologists, who were also thinking in field terms, and were interested in psychological development. Then I found myself dealing with a curious feature of some organisms such as Ascidians and Coelenterates—their peculiar faculty of physical regression or de-differentiation: they not only get smaller but they regress to a simpler stage if you maltreat them in various ways—and this led me to read up all I could about psychological regression. Later I am afraid I strayed rather outside the biological field: in 1928, I think it was, I rushed into print with a book on religion as a natural phenomenon instead of a supernatural one—Religion without Revelation, I called it. And later on I had wished on me the task of relating ethics to evolution by the Vice-Chancellor of Oxford, who invited me to deliver the Romanes lecture 50 years after my grandfather had given his celebrated one on evolution and ethics, and to treat of the same subject, so I had to do some thinking about that problem. Recently, I have had to do some thinking about an equally difficult problem for a mere biologist—the Wenner-Gren Foundation have asked me to write something on anthropology from the angle of an evolutionary biologist.

Then, the fact of being in Geneva reminds me that in 1925 I attended what was, I believe, the first international conference on population, here in Geneva. Ever since then I have been deeply interested in this problem, which I think is one of the world's most serious problems, psychologically as well as politically and socially.

You asked me, Mr. Chairman, why I was willing to come here. I should think that the answer is pretty obvious. This type of meeting seems to me absolutely essential in the present state of the world. We have got to a state where we can't progress if we each of us stay in our own little specialisms. I am sure we have got to a stage where we must somehow organize the synthesis of different branches of knowledge. People say that science has got too specialized for that. I don't believe this is true. Only you have got to find out the technique of getting representatives of different branches together, of getting mutual understanding, and of organizing the synthesis. When I heard about this group here, I thought, well, this certainly is extra-ordinarily interesting because here we have ethologists and psychologists, medical men and biologists, physiologists and psychiatrists, all interested in one general problem, and I shall be most interested to see how a group of this sort functions, as well as to hear the results of its deliberations.

Now, if I may I will ask Erik Erikson to tell us a little bit about himself.

ERIKSON:

I should state first what I am doing. I am a psychoanalyst who divides his time up about equally between psychoanalytic psychotherapy, the training of young doctors for psychoanalysis, and research. The psychotherapy fuses, of course, with research, for what in most of your fields is experimentation, in our field is the attempt to delineate previously incurable mental states in such a way that they become more curable. I work at a small sanitarium in the Berkshire Hills in New England which is also a research institute. There some of us specialize in work with young 'borderline cases', which means young people on the brink of schizophrenia or psychopathy. Ours is an open hospital which deliberately takes certain chances with the patients in order to understand them not as victims of fatalistic diagnosis, but as individual cases of what I will describe in a later meeting as identity diffusion, i.e., a particular difficulty attending the age of youth, and this particularly where society and family have let young people down in specific ways. In addition to intensive psychotherapy, we experiment by giving the patients a responsible voice in the management of the 'hospital environment', and by developing individual ways of work productivity. This is my wife's domain. I am also a visiting professor in the Medical School in Pittsburgh where I learn about patients with similar symptoms but different social backgrounds.

I should have said at the beginning that I do not speak English, but a form of American. This may make it difficult for you to understand what I say, yet it is intrinsically related to our general subject. For my friends (my very best friends) will tell you that I am the best case illustration of an identity diffusion, that is of the clinical picture which I will describe to you when my time comes. Identify diffusion results from the inability to integrate one's childhood identifications and adolescent tasks. Well, I was born a Dane. But my father died around the time of my birth, and my mother and I seem to have travelled a lot. When I was three years old I fell ill in a city in Southern Germany. We stayed there, because my mother married my paediatrician. This, I think, has been a most decisive event as regards my later identity development.

FREMONT-SMITH:

Was it a psychosomatic illness?

Well, I certainly needed a father. Later, my stepfather very much wanted me to be a doctor. But I decided to become an artist.

The secret identification with the paediatrician appeared only in the fact that I specialized in baby pictures and portraits of children. To do such portraits, I went to Vienna and joined a friend as a tutor in an American family which was close to Freud. Eventually, I was trained as a child analyst under Anna Freud and August Aichhorn and graduated as a psychoanalyst from the Vienna Institute. In Vienna, I also married an American woman of Canadian origin, and we moved to Cambridge, Massachusetts. One of our neighbours was Frank Fremont-Smith through whose interest I received my first medical school and hospital appointments. From then on I have been living in the medical world as much as anybody could who is not a medical man and my stepfather, the paediatrician, was as right as anybody could be who was wrong! And you may well see that I had to make out of identity diffusion a virtue—and a subject.

Now, as for my preoccupations, the daily work of a psychoanalyst is in many ways cut out for him. But I would mention that the artist in me keeps paying special attention to the 'configurational level', by which I mean something which in psychoanalysis is between the obvious, manifest behaviour and the latent, hidden meaning. I will present examples of children's play, trying to show what a child is saying by the way in which it behaves in space, and how it arranges toys and dolls. In work with very small children, it helps tremendously if one is not restricted to listening but if one can observe, and I think it was here that my paediatric and artistic sides came to some kind of agreement. This was further enhanced when I met Margaret Mead and a few other anthropologists and found that in comparing configurations we spoke, as it were, a similar language and could speak about childhood and culture patterns in a way that eventually made dynamic sense also. Thus I became interested in the relationship of human motivation as discovered by psychoanalysis to people's world images and economic systems: what people are hunting and where and how. Having studied two American Indian tribes, it seemed only right to study American children who were neither Indians nor patients. So I participated for a number of years in a longitudinal study of Californian children to try to understand their particular development in that rapidly growing area which was rather freshly settled compared to the rest of the world.

My special interest is this. In psychoanalysis, which originated in the era of enlightenment and individualism, the original emphasis was on the dichotomy between the individual and his society, almost in the sense that environment as such was essentially hostile to the individual. This, of course, was an ideological distortion of what Freud, at given stages of his studies, had pointed out. Today, the analysis of the ego makes it very clear that no individual could possibly exist, or grow strong, or, indeed, become an individual without society. But how does he do it, and how does society keep the bargain? I think that the psychoanalysis of the ego permits a new approach to the contract between individual and society. If I may make in conclusion what I hope to be a challenging statement, I think I came here with the expectation of learning from this particular group a new approach to the ethological nature of love. But by this I do not mean only the mutuality between mother and child, and not only the pact of personal love, but also such psychosocial contracts as forms of truth, styles of honesty, kinds of justice. All of these seem as indispensable for the human child's development as the life-preserving features of the physical environment.

FREMONT-SMITH:

If I may I will now call upon Dr. Raymond de Saussure to tell us about himself—it is a great joy to see an old friend from New York who was over from Geneva and is now back here in Geneva with us.

DE SAUSSURE:

Unfortunately, although I am a psychiatrist and a psychoanalyst, I am not able to bring you an account of such a miraculous or spectacular cure as that which Mr. Erikson underwent at the age of three years—his own cure and the cure of his mother were certainly determining factors in his career. So I will stay within more modest limits, and as we have been asked to give a biography which begins with the early years I shall keep to the classical pattern of psychoanalysis—although Dr. Hargreaves asked us not to be too classical —and I will tell you here of my oral stage, my anal stage and my genital stage.

In my oral stage I was very greedy and I think I was able to sublimate a part of this greediness in the desire to read and study later on. The anal stage was characterized for me by a liking for collecting and studying butterflies, and throughout my adolescence (which is a rather late anal stage) I developed this liking for making collections. The genital stage was very much retarded too, this time through Calvinism and its very strong influences to which I was subjected, so that I had to go off to Vienna to be analysed by Freud and to get rid of some of these overpowering ancestral influences. I was very grateful to him, but I did not immediately realize the full value of this method and returned later to Berlin to undergo a second analysis with Dr. Alexander and to follow courses at the institute.

Actually, I owe my interest in psychoanalysis to Théodore Flournoy who was Professor of Psychology here in Geneva. Immediately after my secondary schooling I became deeply interested in his lectures in which, as early as 1914, he used to expound his psychoanalytic theories. My interest turned very quickly first towards the similarities or the concordances which could exist between the ideas of Freud and Jean Piaget. Here there were two points of view about psychology, two genetic points of view, which seemed to complement each other but which unfortunately had previously been put in opposition to each other. During meetings of French-speaking psychoanalysts I had the opportunity of establishing the first connexions, which later on were well worked out by my friend Charles Odier. Another of my interests was to find the possible relationships between certain social structures and certain forms of neuroses (de Saussure, 1929, 1946).

In my book on the Greek Miracle (de Saussure, 1939) I tried to show why scientific civilization was born in Greece rather than elsewhere. My great interest for all the problems of psychology intermingled with those of biology and politics dates from this time. When I went to the United States in 1940 I had the very great privilege of following many inter-disciplinary discussions where psychological, biological, social and political points of view were intermixed.

For this reason I was extremely happy to receive your invitation which corresponds to one of my major interests. I am looking forward immensely to hearing you and I shall try to contribute in my modest degree to your discussions.

FREMONT-SMITH:
Now we have had our introductions, and begun to group, if one can use that word in the intransitive sense. May I turn to you, Margaret, to open the discussion and do it in your own way—you have quite a period of time, two-and-a-half days. The principle, as you know, is to ask the opener to have each day about 20 minutes of material to present and then if they are really successful in the two-and-a-half days they can't get it all presented because of the discussion which is stirred up.

MEAD:
My task now is to describe what light anthropology can shed on

19

the occurrence of what can be regarded as universal sex differences, however differently these may be patterned and institutionalized in different societies. Conversely, I want to provide a way of removing from our present formulation the culturally limited ethnocentric and provincial material on sex differences. This means that I will use for the most part extreme anthropological cases. If I talk about something that is reasonably widespread and universal it would be impossible for me to give you any detail—for example of the fact that mothers breast-feed babies in all parts of the world. So I shall select the most interesting cases, with your understanding that these are extreme and that we assume, in between, the existence of a very large number of less peculiar, less extreme behaviour patterns.

I think that we should really start with the child's realization of the fact that it is a human being, which is, I think, more important than its realization of which sex it is. For instance, in Bali, people are unwilling to treat a child under three months as a human being; the new-born baby has no name, is not allowed to enter a temple and is called a rat or a caterpillar. Then there are societies that identify children with vegetables or with animals for a very long time and undoubtedly change the individual's sense of who they are and what it means to be a human being.

Coming to sex differences, I think that we will find it useful to consider first those differences between the sexes which have occurred in every society to date, but which may nevertheless be modifiable. Until recently, for instance, human infants have been breast-fed, the feeding bottle being a comparatively recent invention. As long as human infants had to be breast-fed by human mothers there was a universal condition of the early differentiation of sex roles, as children of both sexes were fed by a creature of one sex everywhere. This ceased to be universal as soon as the feeding-bottle was invented. What looked like a very long and very important element in the differentiation of the two sexes could be wiped out by a single invention. Equally, of course, it could be restored. Thus all of the points that are connected with maternal care of children, or care by another female such as a nurse, a wet-nurse, a foster mother, etc., although they have been almost universal to date, may nevertheless be a biological condition which society is able to abrogate, or change. The whole question of social inventions which may alter present differentiation of the sexes is exceedingly important.

On the other hand, a great proportion of our present psychological theory about differences between the sexes is based upon the presence of clothing. Psychoanalytic theories that are based on the importance of the revelation of the anatomy of adults, or of your little brother,

20

if you are a little girl, of course are based on the experience of the child in a clothed society where the child encounters only the bodies of small children and the bodies of parents in most cases, with the intervening link left out. In any society where the people don't wear clothes, the situation is very different. The little boy may be alarmed by the contrast between the size of his own and his father's genitals but certainly not in the same way as in clothed society because he sees every possible other size in between and is continually assured that, if he continues to grow, he will eventually get larger. In the same way the presence of pregnancy is conspicuous, and in a primitive society where there are no large buildings and no other achievements, pregnancy is one of the most conspicuous events in the life of the child. We have to bear in mind all the time the extent to which our theory of sex differences is limited by conditions in our own society at present.

I want also to stress that, because the early upbringing of girls and boys by one or both sexes is a major device by which the child's sense of its sex identity is carried, every aspect of sex differences in the life of the society (including the after-life) becomes important in the sex differentiation of the growing boy and girl. For instance, you may live in a society where women have no soul, or you may live in a society where women are only permitted into heaven by way of their husband's soul, as with the folk belief in eastern European Jewry that if a man was a good man and the woman had been a good wife she could go to heaven with him and was permitted to sit at his feet for ever and listen to him talk. This image of heaven is bound to affect very small girls in many ways, as their mothers either look forward with pleasure to this picture or possibly chafe against it. Or consider the Aztec belief that a specially honoured place was reserved in the next world for those men who died in battle and women who died in childbirth; the blood of the slain was equated— men or women. The influence such a picture must have on a small girl or a small boy must be quite different from that of a village where childbirth, menstrual huts, latrines and pigs are put over the edge of the village in a rough, rainy, muddy, precipitous spot, and the place is called the 'evil place'. The social structure will affect children from the very start. In some Mohammedan countries, for instance, the only tie the mother has to the child is the milk-tie. If she breast-feeds the child, that gives her a right to it. The fact that she gave it house room in the foetal stage is regarded as irrelevant; the child is the father's child and the mother runs a boarding house. This affects the whole structure—what happens in divorce, the father's rights to the child, and so forth.

21

When we consider how a girl learns that she is a girl, and a boy learns that he is a boy, we must remember that a whole series of attitudes are prefigured for them. In the way they are treated, the way they are named, whether the family are glad a boy is born or whether they say, 'when a girl is born everyone weeps and ruin is brought on the house.' From what we know about the relationship of a mother's attitude during lactation, we may expect that a girl who is born as a ruin in the house probably imbibes feelings about ruin during this stage of lactation. Similarly, we must consider even the prenatal period. If a mother knows, from the moment that she is pregnant, that if her child is a girl its chances of life are very different from its chances of life as a boy, this becomes an important psychological distinction; important to the degree that there are psychosomatic connections between the expectation of the mother and the well-being or degree of activity of the foetus. Even the last moment of birth, just before you know whether the child is a girl or a boy, is an exceedingly tense moment for the whole group of women gathered around who know that when they say 'it's a girl', the father will probably say 'abandon it', or 'kill it'. This creates all through pregnancy an attitude in the mother of two kinds of expectancy, which then may culminate one way or the other at birth.

BOWLBY:

May I interrupt? All the instances that you have given us have been adverse to females; are there similar illustrations adverse to males?

MEAD:

There are the societies that expect the male to die earlier. This was characteristic of the Plains Indians of North America—the Cheyennes, for instance. The boy was indulged because he was going to die. Now, if the indulgence for the boy child is phrased that he was superior or stronger that is one thing, but if it is phrased as 'we give you the special titbits from the table because you are going to die' that is another. It is quite possible we might arrive at the same position in the United States at present, for it has been very widely advertised that male expectation of life is something like five years less than the female, and that all women are going to be widows with large bank accounts while their husbands are dead. I should think that a small boy who is brought up in a household with seven widows with large bank accounts and also read this continually in the press, would begin to get a picture of the male sex as deprived. Or in a period when there is a military draft, affecting males and not

22

females or affecting them very differentially, there may again be a sense of the male being condemned to a more dangerous, a more hazardous or a shorter life.

BOWLBY:
It would be necessary to distinguish, then, between misfortunes connected with the one sex and social devaluation of that sex.

MEAD:
Yes, I think one should. But in using the word 'misfortune' you, yourself, were reflecting our point of view that people don't get killed in war except unluckily. This is the European position—that people come back from war unless they are unfortunate enough to be killed. But there are many cultures in which you don't come back from war unless you are peculiarly lucky and so don't get killed—Japan, for instance; the assumption in Japan is that when you go into the Army you are dead; if you happen to come back that is a piece of peculiar luck.

But to come back to your question; the situation may not be as simple as it seems. We can look, for instance, at Mohammedan countries where the female is articulately devalued and devalued because she endangers the male. From the moment she is born she is a menace to her father, her brother, her husband, and later to her son, because through her they can be dishonoured. But, we do not find in examining the psychology of women in those countries, that they are as insecure as the men; it seems to some extent to be reassuring that you can make that much trouble for that many men. On the other hand, it is exceedingly unreassuring to a man to have these many points of vulnerability in his life, so a rather complicated reversal occurs here. I had a great deal of trouble when I had reasonably feministic young American women anthropologists trying to work on mid-eastern countries, because they assumed that women were treated badly and it was very difficult to focus their attention on the fact that they were looking at a society which was much more psychologically hazardous for men than for women.

FREMONT-SMITH:
Would it not then be asking the wrong question to say 'What does culture do to this particular sex?'

MEAD:
You must always say 'What does it do to both sexes?' Any discussion of one sex without the other is quite useless. You may have a

23

culture which does not verbally discriminate the sexes and has one word for child, say, but even so the social discrimination is there from a very early period. We have no culture that assumes the lack of anatomical sex difference, although we have cultures that ritually relegate human beings to an animal status or that ritually disregard sex for quite a while after birth as far as names are concerned.

Now, if I can leave for a moment this question of the way in which sex differentiation permeates every aspect of social structure, I think it is probably necessary to say here that there is no such thing as the mythical matriarchy that European tradition has constructed. There is no society in which women have the sort of power that men have in most societies. There are societies in which women may nominate for office, there are societies in which they own the houses, there are societies where women are the priestesses or the mediums or the soothsayers, but the nightmare of a female domination that gets conjured up in European folklore is a fantasy. It is paralleled elsewhere —in the Pacific, for instance, by a very widely spread legend of an island of women in which women are able to produce children without the aid of men, and there are large numbers of fantasies in which the men finally break into this society, teach the women how to have children properly and get them under control.

GREY WALTER:

But there is the traditional history of the European matriarchy which is said to have preceded the era of. . . .

MEAD:

We have no suggestion on the basis of anything we have ever been able to examine that there were ever true matriarchies of any sort; as I say, any one of the items that are attributed to a matriarchy may occur separately, but this assumption that there was once a society entirely ruled by women is, as far as we know, a fantasy.

GREY WALTER:

Pure fantasy?

MEAD:

Pure fantasy—so far as we have any reason to judge at present. But the myth of matriarchy has played a very great role in several very important places, in psychoanalytic theory it played a considerable role, and still does; in communism it played a role in Marxian theory by the sheer accident that Engels read an American anthropologist named Morgan (1907), who had been exceedingly impressed by the Iroquois Indians in which the nominating power for chieftainship rested with women.

In constructing a unilateral sequence of evolution on 19th century lines what was done was to start with our civilization and work backwards. Anything we didn't have was earlier and inadequate, so that if you put monogamy and a patriarchally organized society that was patrilocal, patrinomal, patrilineal, patriopotestive and monogamous at the peak, and then you worked back, inevitably you had to have a matriarchal society at one point and group marriage at another. But as far as our present knowledge goes there is no evidence whatsoever for either of these two fantasy institutions.

LORENZ:
The group marriage, I happened to read about that in Russia, was that entirely fantasy?

MEAD:
It is entirely fantasy.

LORENZ:
The group marriage in Samoa, among Polynesians, was entirely fantasy?

MEAD:
Entirely fantasy.

LORENZ:
Oh, I am glad to hear that!

MEAD:
There are various sorts of situations in which, for instance, all the males of a lineage group may have access to their brothers' wives, so that there are various sorts of polygamy and concubinage and special licence, but they do not fall under the head of marriage in the sense that these historical fantasies postulate. It is exceedingly popular at present for commentators, especially European commentators, to describe the United States as a matriarchy. But the United States is a country in which a woman takes her husband's name, moves where he moves, can be legally chastized for not staying where he is, her children take his name, he is responsible for supporting the family and she is not, and so on. I think it is necessary to get rid of this matriarchal daydream at all levels if we are going to be able to consider the question of sex differentiation.

25

ZAZZO:

There are societies where the affiliation can be established only through the mother, the role of the father not yet being known. Perhaps one has no right there to speak of a matriarchy because after all it is a man, the brother of the mother, therefore the uncle, who is responsible for the child. But whether we speak of a matriarchy or not, this fact is very important in the definition of culture: I would like to ask you, therefore, what, in your opinion, is the influence of purely uterine affiliation on the conception of the woman and on her role and importance.

MEAD:

I didn't say all societies were patriarchal, by any means. There are quite a large number of societies which are what we call matrilineal, which means that ties are established through women and that a man inherits from his mother's brother. None of these societies exist at a very simple level—we regard them, on the whole, as an elaboration that is more complicated than the simplest hunting society. In such a society the mother's brother has the power. Power is still in the hands of the male and the fact that it is the mother's brother rather than the father may have important psychological determinants in the constellation of the household, as Malinowski pointed out years ago in the study of the Trobrianders. But it does not change the essential point, that the public power of disposal of property, of chieftainship, and so forth, is in the hands of men. The power goes through women, through your sister instead of through your wife, but it goes from a male to a male.

The only thing I think we can say is that on the whole it is difficult to combine polygamy and matriliny. Why this is so we are not certain, because in patrilineal societies it is quite frequent for women to approve of polygamy and insist upon it; there are many societies in which a woman feels very put upon if she has to conduct a monogamous marriage and will nag and nag her husband into getting her another wife, either to share the onerous duties of sex or bring in the firewood or look after the children or go fishing or whatever. However, when you have a matrilineal society, there is a very strong tendency for what may conceivably be a basic female preference for monogamy to assert itself. Or, you can argue quite differently and say that the tie between the mother and the child is given biologically and that one of the things that human society has had to do is to build up the position of the father, institutionalize it, dramatize it, make it firm and reliable to the extent that the care of the young is dependent upon a stable father. Matrilineal institutions may over-

26

weight the position of the mother and the mother's kin and put the father in a particularly weak role and this may be one reason also why matriliny is less stable. Matriliny tends to yield to patriliny on the whole more easily than patriliny yields to matriliny.

HUXLEY:

This is extremely interesting about matriarchy in the strict sense being pure fantasy; but isn't there a great difference in different societies in the amount of public power and public status accorded to the two sexes? Thus in West Africa you have the queen mothers, though their public role is somewhat overshadowed by the elders. Isn't there a complicated balance, which varies from society to society?

MEAD:

In very simple societies where, for example, there are no buildings of any importance, and there is no political structure for anybody to play a role in, you may have what looks like a very even-handed division. In a very simple food-getting people like the Eskimo, both male and female play absolutely essential economic roles, so that an Eskimo male without a wife is as helpless as an Eskimo woman without a husband. Then you have all the intermediate possibilities from the societies with large harems where women are completely shut off from public life, to the societies, of which West Africa, some Pacific societies, and some American Indian societies are examples, in which women are permitted considerable public roles, sometimes just single individuals as queens or priestesses, and sometimes every woman. Or you may restore even-handedness again as was done in traditional China where although women were confined to the household, they were extraordinarily powerful, so that when modernization started in China these very powerful women moved out and established banks right away. You can sometimes get a measure of the strength that women exercise in various domestic roles by the role that they can play when the barriers are let down and new occupational opportunities are given.

LORENZ:

Was Pearl Buck roughly correct about these things?

MEAD:

Her early book about China is roughly correct about this, I think. The Queen mother, the mother-in-law, had the most enormous power. Every young Chinese girl lived to be a mother-in-law. That

27

was the acme of power. This was reciprocated by the male living for the day when he no longer had any economic or clerical responsibility, so that you had an expectation of maturity roles in which the woman expected to get stronger and stronger while the man expected to retire to a more childlike and protected position. This again is another dimension of the whole picture: women may expect that their position will be enhanced as they grow older, so that their post-menopausal position is one of greater freedom—perhaps even greater than male freedom; on the other hand, they may expect to become less and less desired, desirable or colourful as they get older.

I think, perhaps, I should say here too that there are many students of this subject who feel that the relative safety of women in child-birth today is something that has to be taken into account as a major change in the position and psychological security of the sexes. If you grew up in a society where very many women died in child-birth, so that this was an expected event, and pain was very severe, this permeates the whole position of the girl from the start.

Culture can alter this, however. For instance, in some South African tribes, women are expected to shriek, scream, writhe, and go through the most terrific expressions of agony, and all the little girl children are brought along to watch, so they will know how to have a baby. In other societies women are enjoined to the greatest stoicism, and to utter a single cry would be to proclaim yourself not a woman, and again the little girls are brought along to see that they behave like this. In most of the primitive Pacific island societies where I have worked, and the ones where men are not allowed to witness childbirth, the women are stoical. The men give pantomimes of extreme pain and agony, and have shown me all about childbirth, rolling on the floor and screaming and behaving in a way that no woman under any circumstances in that society has ever behaved. In other words, they either have carried on a memory from some earlier culture that has been perpetuated in the male culture, or this is sheer fantasy behaviour. Now, in this case, you will have young males brought up with a picture of something that happens to females that doesn't happen, and it becomes a component of male psychology and not of female psychology.

One other point about sex roles should be mentioned now, and that is what are the societies which admit transvestism, and of which type. We find societies which do not recognize or admit the possibility of any sexual confusion whatsoever, so that although the spectator interested in constitution might identify a male or female who looked less identifiably male or female than other members of the group, yet the group will have no conception of homosexuality

28

or transvestism, in which case the chances of physical deviation being taken advantage of would be very slight. But there are other societies in which, from the moment the child is born, there are three possibilities: it may be a male, or a female, or a transvestite.

The day on which it is born, whether a bird flies over its cradle, the way it drinks its milk the first time, how its teeth come in—any number of such things may be an indicator of whether this child is going to be, as we call it technically in anthropology, a *berdache*. Among many warlike American Indian tribes, for instance, and among the primitive tribes of Siberia, there is both male and female transvestism. Both male and female transvestites have special religious powers, and therefore have an honorific role in the society. The Plains Indians material is, I think, the most vivid, because you have parents, aunts and uncles, grandparents, watching a small boy literally from birth, to find out whether he will be a man or a *berdache*. The role of the *berdache* is completely conventionalized. A man assumes female clothes and is spoken of as 'she' in most of these tribes. He has special activities, such as a go-between in love affairs, or a story-teller on a war party. Interestingly enough, in some of these tribes any sign of female homosexuality will be punished with death. With this expression of anxiety on the part of the adult as to the future social behaviour of the small males a certain number of small boys decides to be transvestites. The whole role is there and they know exactly how to behave, and in turn perpetuate the institution.

FREMONT-SMITH:

Dr. Tigani of the Sudan told me that there is in southern Sudan a tribe where transvestism is part of the social organization, and there are actual marriage ceremonies between males, one dressed as a woman and the other one as a man. He said this needed to be studied in the next few years because the tribe is still relatively isolated, but would not remain so very much longer.

MEAD:

These 'marriages' occur in various parts of the world. We have them among the American Indian Mohaves, with very elaborate rituals of relationship, with complete denial on the part of the male, who is dressed as a woman, of having any male genitals of any sort, and then fake pregnancies, fake deliveries, and fake burial of the fake child which was fake-conceived.

LORENZ:

How far are these transvestites homosexuals?

MEAD:

Sometimes they are homosexual (that is, have overt sex relations with members of the same sex), sometimes they are not homosexual. You can have a transvestism that is definitely associated with overt homosexuality, but you can have a transvestism that is disassociated from it in every way.

LORENZ:

I ask this question because in psychiatric practice I came up against two male transvestites and one of them was such a beautiful 'girl' that you were surprised to see 'her'. He said for instance, 'Ich bin eine gute Schwimmerin'—he talked of himself as a female but he was not in the least homosexual: he had a double life, as a man and as a woman. The other was a locomotive driver on the railway, who did exactly the same thing. He had a wife and children in a perfectly normal way and, just as some men go boozing for some days, he changed into a woman for a few days.

HUXLEY:

Margaret, did you say that in the American Indian tribes the boys could opt for what they wanted to do; was it a conscious choice?

MEAD:

Well, it amounts to opting, you see, because people keep testing you out—are you going to be brave enough to be a warrior? If you decide not to be so brave, then your role has been decided for you.

TANNER:

At what age would this occur? At what age is the choice made for the child?

MEAD:

Well, the final choice would be made when you go on your first war-party, which would be early adolescence. Everybody has been saying it for years, you see, but the actual choice comes when there is a request or a need to participate either as a warrior or not as a warrior.

TANNER:

Is there any social stigma or devaluation, when a man opts to be a *berdache*, or by his behaviour on this war-party turns himself into a *berdache*?

MEAD:

He doesn't turn himself into a *berdache*. It isn't that he fails, that he becomes a coward and gets called a *berdache*. He just continually opts not to become a warrior.

ERIKSON:

There is a way of opting by letting the supernatural powers opt for you. If a young man can manage to have an appropriate dream, that dream may be interpreted by those who know dreams as a supernatural suggestion to become a *berdache*. It is like an objective curse, only unconsciously opted. There are also ways of being freed of the curse, and being declared cured by the 'experts.'

MELIN:

In what number do *berdaches* occur?

MEAD:

I've never seen an adequate statistical study. In Siberian tribes there are usually several such persons. Among the Omaha, an American Indian tribe, when I was there, there was only one *berdache* out of 1,500 people. But warfare had ceased, and this particular *berdache* was a man that would have been a homosexual in almost any society—in any society, that is, that selected an extreme degree of feminization for homosexuality. He was the only one left, under conditions of peace, where all the pressures had disappeared.

HUXLEY:

Surely the proportion would never have been more than about five or ten per cent?

MEAD:

I think it was probably never more than five per cent. But it's present as a possibility for every male. It becomes a component in his picture of himself, and this tends to force him into a degree of bravery, or masculinity, that is more extreme than occurs in a society that permits a very wide range of possible roles, including a large number of mild ones.

★   ★   ★

MEAD:

In Professor Zazzo's comments earlier, to which I replied only in part, the question was raised of those societies in which physical paternity is not recognized. I think it is important to emphasize that we do have societies of this sort which are patrilineal. In Australia societies which are completely patrilineal, in which women leave their own territory to go and live with their husbands, and children grow up within their father's band, nevertheless, have no explicit recognition of physical paternity. (Children are born as a result of spirit action, women going near centres where spirit children are produced.) So that ignorance of paternity and matrilineal ways of reckoning descent do not necessarily occur together in known human society. This, however, does not necessarily compromise the probability that in a much earlier stage of history when there was no knowledge of physical paternity—and I think we must assume such a period—a man attached himself to a woman and her offspring without any recognition that he had any connexion with these children except through the woman. Thus a likely beginning of the family could have been a male wishing to appropriate to himself the attention of a female and being willing to take the children with her. This would not be a matrilineal society, because you would not yet have a form of social organization which is as elaborate as what we mean by matriliny.

FREMONT-SMITH:

It would be very interesting to get Dr. Lorenz to make a comment on this with respect to lower animals, where presumably paternity is not recognized yet where the family certainly is well developed. Would this explanation that Margaret gave fit in with your observations?

LORENZ:

Perfectly satisfactorily.

HUXLEY:

Surely in many cases something quite different happens. In some species of birds, for instance, the male has no parental instinct whatever and does not play any part in brooding or in looking after the young, in others he does not brood but helps to look after the young, and in still others he has completely similar parental instincts to the female. Clearly, there may be parental instincts without any knowledge of the fact of paternity.

MEAD:

Oh, certainly, yes. We have no evidence at present of what might be called a parental instinct in human males but we have the possibility of a protective response to the young of the species. We find this in some monkeys and in apes, where any male will respond to

32

the cry of a very small helpless member of the same species. The present condition in the United States, in which we have the extraordinary change in the expectation of family size, coupled with the young father taking a great deal of care of the human infant, suggests that at present we may be using a biologically-given potentiality of the human male that has not been used in the history of civilization. In very simple societies, such as the Australian aborigines, many South Sea island societies, and some African societies, the male takes a great deal of care of the young infant. But with every society that we have any record of, with the onset of what you call civilization, division of labour, class structure, hierarchies of authority, etc., one of the first things that has happened has been the separation of the human male from his own baby until any point up to two years, four years, six years, twelve years. In some societies he has virtually nothing to do with his son until he is an adolescent. I think one of the things that we may want to discuss here is whether this is not a *condition* of civilization, and whether one of the origins of creativity in males has not been this preventing them from having anything to do with babies.

ZAZZO:

It seems to me that the discussion would be easier if we distinguished between sociability and culture. I think that this emotive reaction, this very primitive communion, is the first element and the very stuff of human sociability. Culture comes afterwards and can integrate or reduce this mode of reaction. Human society has its root in biology thus defined, given the physical debility and the parasitism of the infant. But culture imposes a certain structure, a certain mode of life, which gives to sociability its particular forms. The biological and social contributions in the human being are basically closely interdependent.

HUXLEY:

If you go to biology, it is quite clear that in some mammals, for example bears, the male has no parental instinct or whatever you like to call it, no interest in the young.

LORENZ:

Though in others the reverse is true. For example in all wild *Bovidae* (for instance, cattle) there is a very strict separation of the babies, because male babies play and are taken care of mainly by the bull, the herd bull.

HUXLEY:

So that there can be a complete presence or absence of a parental something: it may be merely the tendency or desire to look after a helpless creature, but it is in essence, biologically speaking, a parental instinct. I should have thought Zazzo was quite right in saying that a man is biologically endowed with a parental instinct or tendency which can be changed—blocked or accentuated—according to the culture in which he lives.

MEAD:

Don't you think that we probably have to assume a period in human evolution when the infants were entirely taken care of by the mother, when the mother found the food for the infant and the male role was restricted to protecting? Certainly, if we use the other primates as an example. . . .

LORENZ:

The trouble is that we don't know the behaviour of anthropoid apes in this respect. Nobody has even tried to observe in captivity how a chimpanzee father behaves to his own baby. He may have much more parental care reactions than a baboon or a Rhesus, in which we know that he only defends the baby in case of extreme need but does not play with it, does not hug it, does not carry it except when he retrieves it from an enemy. We do not know how many 'female' activities a male chimp has, so there is no source of knowledge for our reconstructing how human fathers would behave if left to their infants alone without any cultural influence.

MEAD:

And we have absolutely no material from primitive societies. The important thing to emphasize here is that every primitive society in existence is as old as our own, that they are all the same species of man, that they all depend on shared, learned behaviour, they all have culture. We find great differences of complexity, differences of technology, differences of the size of units that can be integrated, but the sort of evidence that anthropology can produce is evidence on variations possible to human beings *within* culture.

BOWLBY:

I would like to ask a question. Am I right in supposing that there is some agreement amongst us that human males have a parental response to a helpless baby?

34

MEAD:

A protective response.

BOWLBY:

In what way is it suggested that the protective response of the human male is distinguished from the protective response of the human female? It seems to me that in neither sex is there an inherent tendency to direct the response towards their own baby—that is a learned aspect of the response which occurs after birth.

HUXLEY:

But the general tendency may still be inherent.

MEAD:

If we take what we know, say about the behaviour of mother pigs, or mother sheep and goats, there are a very large number of specific responses of the mother to her own infant that are related to the moment and nature of delivery, the smell of the infant, the point at which the infant attaches itself to its mother in lactating and so forth. I agree that this is very poorly explored, but there seems to be a certain amount of suggestion that there are relationships between the mother and the child that she bears that may be of quite a different order from her relationship to all other infants. You can find societies in which a mother doesn't respond to other infants.

A human mother, when she responds to other infants, may be generalizing an identification with her own mother and then learning a female role in her society. Or she may be externalizing or generalizing a specific response to her own young. Similarly the human male may be specializing a general protective response to the young of the species. I think we need to explore this question much further, and explore in terms of, for instance, the effect on maternal acceptance of the child of the use of anaesthesia at delivery.

HUXLEY:

Then there is your point, Konrad, about the releaser action of certain types of face, the Pekinese and the pug-dog, the little baby face, that seems to stimulate the parental instinct.

LORENZ:

If you are male and observe yourself in your response to a sweet baby, a sweet, helpless baby, I think most of the human race present will agree that our reactions are emotionally, qualitatively, very similar to those of the females. It is exactly the same type of baby that we find sweet, exactly the same type of baby that we want to help and the only difference is that after a short time we want to put it away again while the female will look after it for days on end. So this is a quantitative and not a qualitative difference. Harping again on my teacher, Hochstetter's, pedantically uttered sentence—'there are no primitive animals, there are only primitive characters: what we call a primitive animal is just one which is rich in primitive characters'—I wonder whether Huxley would agree that we Western whites are particularly rich in unspecialized traits, maybe richer than some of the so-called savages. Maybe, from the evolutionary point of view, we are in a similar situation in comparison to the so-called primitives as man as a whole is to his next relation, the anthropoid apes. Maybe, we are particularly plastic, particularly reticulate, particularly, let's say, hopeful from an evolutionist point of view. Anyhow, I am quite prepared to think that in the primitive characters of male parental care, I myself am more similar to Australians than to Red Indians or others of this type of culture.

MEAD:
  I don't think you have any proof of that, Konrad.

LORENZ:
  Let it go. If you ask what culture might do to these emotional reactions, of which Professor Zazzo was talking, which I may translate into unlearned or innate reactions, the answer is that culture might very easily suppress them altogether. Then they may live for ages latently in suppression and pop out again the moment they are not tabooed any more and, if I may jump from species psychology very directly to individual psychology, I know that my father had all the hugging instincts and baby-carrying urges which I have myself, but that he simply was too dignified and could not allow himself to do it. I am quite sure that my father was culturally prevented from giving utterance to these, certainly instinctive, urges.

HUXLEY:
  There is one final point: one of the most exciting things about recent ethological work is the discovery that there may be supernormal stimuli to innate urges; and so culture may provide a supernormal stimulus which quantitatively increases certain responses. Isn't that what you are saying in different terms?

MEAD:
  Yes, quite.

LORENZ:

All baby clothing is an excellent illustration of this.

FREMONT-SMITH:

If I may say one word that is not quite to the point, but because it interests me so much: in trying to think about the problem of international understanding, one asks oneself, where is there a common denominator for all nations and all cultures? One then sees immediately that religion won't do, because the divergencies are already too great; that culture won't do, because the cultural divergencies are already too great, and therefore, one must find something that is more fundamental, from my point of view, than religion, more fundamental than culture, and so I thought that, well, we must go to the biological level. And then, in going to the biological level for the common denominator, what I came to was the parental concern for their very young, which is the common denominator in all human species. I know there are exceptions where they throw them away and where they may destroy them. Nevertheless, no race would survive if there were not very deep parental concern for their very young from the instant of birth on, either through actual parents, or parent surrogates.

MEAD:

But while it is true that no race survives without some concern for the young, yet we have no reason to believe that there have not been many human groups that lost such a concern, or failed to use it in some way, and didn't survive. The Mundugumor, for example, of the Sepik River area of New Guinea, were a non-viable social group, and had probably only existed in the form we knew for five or six generations. They went down at once before contact with the Europeans. It was an extraordinarily weak society and it is an accident of history that they were ever recorded. I think we have to consider that there have been many such small—and large—civilizations, so that we cannot postulate in human behaviour a biological basis which is automatically self-preserving. We have to envisage the possibility of human culture building a superstructure which is non-viable as well as one that is viable.

HUXLEY:

This is very like the old dilemma, which is really meaningless, of which is more important, heredity or environment. The answer is *neither*, because both are necessary. Similarly in man you've got to

37

S

have the innate urges and you have also got to have the cultural environment to bring them out in a viable way.

LORENZ:

And culture may do everything analogous to mutation. Just as you have lethal mutation, you may develop a lethal culture.

ERIKSON:

May I go back for a moment to the cultural evaluation of masculine and feminine? It is my impression, and this is a question to Margaret Mead, that in America it was primarily the generation of young soldiers, coming back from the second World War, which made it seem permissible for a man to take care of a baby. This had something to do with the fact that for them there was no more question that they were men; they had been soldiers, they had fought, and they had taken care of the whole nation. They could do what the women could do without being called feminine or effeminate. On the other hand, it is very difficult to keep young clinicians from calling a man who is less a man than most men 'feminine' in a case history. I try to teach that, for example, a marked homosexual does not have a 'feminine' bearing but an 'effeminate' one, often a mocking caricature of femininity. In the same way, in clinical histories a woman is called more 'masculine' if she is less of a woman, when she really is more 'mannish', often again to the point of obvious mockery. The evaluation of the two sexes seems to be polarized in such a way that if you get a little less of one you automatically assume in your evaluation that there is a little more of the other. Do you think this is the case in other cultures also, Margaret?

MEAD:

Well, I would agree that there is a tendency to evaluate as feminine the male who plays less than the particular masculine role that a given society demands. In very many societies women and children are grouped together, with the male as the final point that children can reach, that sometimes menopausal women can almost reach, and that women in a reproductive stage cannot possibly reach. I should say that there is another tendency in most societies to regard plusses, that is the woman who is *more* intelligent, *more* active, *more* skilled than the average woman, as masculine, and the tendency to regard the man who is *less* strong, *less* skilled, *less* intelligent, as feminine (see, for example Franck & Rosen's, 1949, tests of masculinity and femininity). You do, of course, get odd sorts of things. For instance, in Bali, the ideal for both sexes is a kind of sexlessness.

38

The ideal man looks as much like a woman as a man can look and the ideal woman looks as much like a man as a woman can look, and the disliked and disapproved-of types are the woman with large breasts and the hairy man with large muscles. When the Balinese make a picture of the disliked and disapproved and death-dealing aspects of life they make the witch who has both the extreme male secondary sex characters and the most extreme female ones, with masses of body hair and great pendulous breasts. But there seems to be a general tendency to regard the minus position as female and the plus position as male in a great number of societies.

I think, perhaps, the next point that ought to be dealt with is the question of the devaluation of each sex. You often find in human culture a very high valuation placed on femininity or a very high valuation placed on masculinity in the simplest terms, often in terms of the primary genitalia particularly because of their association with reproduction. In a large part of the Pacific centring around New Guinea there is an assumption that women, in terms of their biological capacities to produce children, have the greater power, and that men, to equal the women, must imitate, fictionalize, ritualize and construct cultural replicas of that power. This is expressed in a large number of ways; for instance the men build great men's houses, which they call wombs, they go through elaborate ceremonies of giving birth to the initiate so that when the boys are a certain age they will be taken over by the men and fed on the men's blood, which then makes them the children of the men. Up to that point they have had the blood of their mothers and the blood of their mothers' brothers (who are the uterine relatives and belong to the same blood-relation-group), but then the men cut their arms, put blood on coconuts, feed it to the initiates and the initiates are now the men's children. In a large number of these ceremonies the entire ritual is a way of asserting that the men are really the creators of the children; that they, not the women, are the makers of men. This takes all sorts of forms, such as imitations of menstruation among the men, with elaborate cutting of the phallus, because they say women are fortunate, they menstruate every month, they are able to get rid of the bad blood within them; but poor unfortunate males have no way to menstruate, so they create a substitute menstruation. This is the more striking, because in so many parts of the world menstruation is fraught with great fear and a great aversion.

In Europe we find virtually the exact opposite of this position, with male achievements being extremely conspicuous. This is so in any high civilization where there is a superstructure of cultural invention in the hands of males; where men build temples, roads, boats, aeroplanes, supreme courts, parliaments. It is evident to the growing boy and girl that what men do is important and what women do is less important, and in this case you have a devaluation of feminine biological capacities in favour of a high valuation of male capacities. The reason it is necessary to emphasize this particularly is that so much psycho-analytic theory is derived from the European position and has assumed that the natural position of the female is to envy the male. This is very often explained in terms of nursery behaviour, but if we take the whole of human achievement into account it is possible to find situations where male achievement is not high and then female achievement may look very large. But we have no society in which female public achievement is such that there is a denigration of the male because the female is able to do so much publicly; that is really the crucial point about the non-existence of real matriarchy.

We then face the whole question of the way in which the actual anatomical differences between a small boy and a small girl and other people's response to them will influence their picture of their sex role. It is customary to emphasize that the male sexuality is conspicuous and the female is inconspicuous and hidden. But this again can be altered culturally. Take, for example, a society in which little girls are told they are probably pregnant, in which every time a two-year-old little girl passes older people, somebody hits her on the abdomen and says, 'Got a baby in there?' So in Bali, little girls between two and three walk with a 'pregnant' posture and this is quite regardless of whether or not their mothers are pregnant at the moment. Everybody teases them about being pregnant, and in such a case, of course, there is a very early emphasis by the culture on the procreative reproductive role of the female. In other societies, little girls may be dressed in a way that will completely denigrate their femininity.

Among the Iatmul of the Sepik River, little girls are dressed in a very feminine way and boys are dressed more like girls than like boys and it is impossible for an outside observer to tell a boy or a girl apart. Even if you look at them sideways, or look at a moving picture, or analyse their behaviour, you think the boys are girls. On the other hand, among the Manus of the Admiralty Islands, the people I was working with last year, it is impossible to tell the little girls and little boys apart because one thinks all the little girls are little boys. This is primarily a question of posture and stance, which in turn is cultivated by the behaviour of the adults. Among the Iatmul, boys are classed with women, boys are allowed to mourn as women mourn. Grown men cannot mourn under any circumstances, and the one thing that little boys love to play at is mourning. After they have announced that they have completely forgotten what it was like to go with their mothers to mourn, they will, if given toys, continually play at mourning games. Thus the society groups boys with women in its response to them and its expectations from them and there is in boys a feminine stance and posture which has to be altered in adult life. In Manus, on the other hand, which is an exceedingly masculine society, in which women are more or less assimilated to male stereotypes in any event, little girls look and act and move like little boys.*

The cultural expectations can thus have a tremendous effect in emphasizing one aspect or the other of the potential behaviour of the child. There are some societies in which the little baby girl is dressed up at six months with ear-rings and great big rings in her nose and a floppy grass skirt, every man that comes along tickles her and flirts with her and plays with her until femininity is very highly emphasized. Bali is a case where there is enormous emphasis in early childhood on the difference between the male and female genitals. From morning to night there are adjectives which mean 'pretty' for a girl, and 'handsome' for a boy. Adults do a great deal of patting their children's genitals saying 'Pretty, pretty, pretty', or 'Handsome, handsome, handsome'. It is a society where there is no doubt whatsoever as to which sex one belongs to. There is enormous ease about other kinds of sex characteristics, but always with this great and very early identification of the self as belonging to one sex rather than the other. There are societies, for example, many near-Eastern countries, in which small males have pictures taken naked, where there is a tremendous emphasis on maleness from very early days so that masculinity is played up well beyond the

*TANNER:
I can most heartily corroborate this statement. Dr. Schwartz and Dr. Mead took somatotype photographs of Manus children last year and I have been examining these. When I first examined the pictures (before this meeting) I was at once struck by the extreme resemblance of girls to boys, an impression which was shared by the other people, both skilled at somatotyping and otherwise, to whom I showed the pictures. So marked was this impression that I found myself searching for signs of a short penis in the girls' photographs, involuntarily thinking it must be hidden in photographic shadow. Certainly without inspection of the genitalia it is impossible to differentiate the little girls from the little boys, though this is easy enough in W. European and American children. Since there is very little actual difference in measurements and proportions before about age nine, the sex difference is presumably conveyed by posture, attitude and facial appearance (one can tell a male without looking at the hair) and in the Manus children both girls and boys resemble European boys in these respects. It may be worth adding that the pictures of adults show a considerably higher degree of mesomorphy, on average, both for men and women, than one sees in American and West European groups.

41

point at which the child would biologically be prepared to exhibit it.

Here again we have an enormous range and I think the only problem for us is to realize how much variation is possible and how much the sense of sex difference can be accentuated or muted by the society. There is some evidence that girl babies a few months old know difference in sex—certainly by the time they can roll over—and that we can recognize a differentiation in the behaviour of girl babies towards men and women. But on the other hand, human behaviour can probably be so patterned that these differences in behaviour can be held in check right up to puberty, We find societies in which the response of males to females as such can be delayed until a very late date. I would mention present day Australia as an outstanding example, with delayed courtship behaviour in adolescence and the tendency to keep schoolboys and schoolgirls in a relatively sexless state till rather late.

I am purposely dealing here only with the social patterning and not yet bringing in what may be innate stages of development. I want, if possible, to have a sort of interplay between Erikson and myself when we come to dealing with what look like universals in children's stages of psychosexual development and so I must clear away first the very obvious social patterning which will speed up or retard sex consciousness.

INTERVAL

MEAD :

I think in the amount of time that we have left we should finish discussing the extent to which we have a universal differentiation between roles of men and women, which in turn become operative in the learning process of boys and girls. It is very important to emphasize that if to be a man is strong, then the child that is weak is not a man, the child that is strong is more of a man, etc. If to be a female is to burst into tears, then if you are a non-crier, you are that less female, and among the Iatmuls, for instance, in New Guinea, not to be able to cry on demand is one of the most terrible things that can happen to a woman. It is far worse than having the wrong figure, because crying is something that is expected of every woman. Every time there is a death, all the women in the group gather together and cry, and the pressure is enormous. I might say that I am reasonably easily suggestible and I usually find it quite possible to cry whenever it is appropriate, and often when it isn't, but in that tribe, I took a large onion, cut it into little bits, put it in my handkerchief, went to a mourning festival and rubbed onion on my eyes,

42

and didn't have one tear. The pressure and the sense of tenseness everywhere is so great that all the people who have the slightest counter-suggestibility to crying are unable to cry.

Any sort of trait that is sex-identified in a given society has this sort of effect. Among the Arapesh, women do the carrying because women's heads are stronger. That means that for a man to carry a load on his head would be to become to that degree a feminine personality. At the limit, however, there is still a set of universals. There is no society that we know of in which men are not stronger than women at the point of strongest work, where men are not expected to drag down the great log for a lost canoe, to hunt the large animal, to go to war, to do the things that involve the greatest display of strength. This does not mean that in many societies women don't do things that men do in others, but the *ratio* is always preserved. So that the picture of strength is systematically presented to boys as compared with girls.

There are, however, some rather striking variations even to this picture. The position of Russian peasants is an example, where the woman is an exceedingly strong person physically, and where there is a certain amount of evidence to suggest that wife-beating in Russia was not a form of sadism but was a necessity. The only way in which the Russian peasant male equalled the Russian peasant female was with a whip in his hand, and society provided the whip. There are also very marked differences in the extent to which the women are smaller than men. All the same this physical difference in strength between the sexes and its social implications survives right through the world until the present stage of automatic machinery. Now, however, we are moving into a period of automatic machinery where we are getting rid of the relationship between physical effort and result, so that you can now press the button on an ack-ack gun, or press the button on a giant lever. The association between sheer physical strength and work productivity is no longer real.

However, in every society that we know anything about at present those things which are regarded as most worth doing are assigned to males. Again there are variations: female goddesses, female priestesses, females taking over almost any function except the exceedingly energetic ones, but when this happens, then these occupations are no longer the most highly valued ones. When we read about an ancient society in which there were female priests, we read of this from the point of view of our own society in which women are not in general allowed to be members of the clergy. Then we tend to say that if the society had female priestesses, these people must have given a very high position to women—which isn't necessarily true

43

at all. The one thing that we can say consistently is that in every society we know anything about, whatever men do is important, and if men dress dolls, dressing dolls is important, if men make baskets, basket-making is an important activity and if women make baskets it is not as important an act. If men cook, it is because cooking is sacred—if women cook, it is because cooking is low-grade.

If you survey the cultures of the world you find curing can be a woman's activity or a man's activity, being a soothsayer can be male or female, making baskets can be male or female, weaving can be male or female, dressing dolls can be male or female, gossiping can be male or female, shopping can be male or female. Almost any sort of activity is interchangeable at this rather superficial occupational kind of level. But if you then look at the evaluation placed on that activity, it is valued when it is male disproportionately to the way it is valued when it is female. It doesn't mean that basket-making by women is disapproved of, but, if a man makes a basket people say, 'Why are you making a basket, that's something that women do! What do you want to do that sort of thing for?' and it is less than, say, making pottery, which is something the male does in that particular society. This seems to be, to date, and in the societies we know anything about, a universal. Now it seems rather difficult to explain it on the simple historical ground that in every society women were bound by childbearing to the home, and by breast-feeding, with no means of locomotion for the baby before you had baby carriages and feeding bottles. It is possible to say that women were inevitably bound to certain tasks such as cooking, and that left men free for all the elaborative tasks, and that historically these would therefore be very conspicuous and important advancements in the life of the society, and that they became more valued. That possible interpretation is one that some people prefer as a hypothesis.

An alternative hypothesis can be derived from the circumstance that boys and girls are both initially cared for by women. Although there are primitive societies where men take a great deal of care of little babies, they can't feed them, so they are always handing them back to the mother to be fed. They can't take them off on long trips. The tie between the breast-feeding mother, or the wet nurse and the baby has been pretty absolute up to the present, so that children of both sexes are brought up and cared for by a parent of one sex. If we take this as a primary condition to date, though not an inevitable one, we can examine the whole process by which the mother treats the children of both sexes differently and the child identifies with the parent. A girl is identifying with someone who

44

smells like herself, moves like herself, feels like herself, and treats her as if she were like herself. On the other hand, the boy is continually given the task of differentiating himself away from the mother and stressing his behaviour as different from what he sees her as being, a reproductive creature. It is possible that an extra urge towards achievement may be given boys in the course of this sort of upbringing, which would not occur otherwise. In other words, there may be no innate urge to achievement in males that is different from an innate urge to achievement in the females, but the conditions of nurture are such that they are differently developed.

Perhaps one of the most fruitful lines of discussion in this group will be the way that a biological potentiality, which is either the same for both sexes and differentiated by upbringing, or different for both sexes and further emphasized or de-emphasized by upbringing, will give us an area of possible intervention in human development. This is also a point of great potential cross-fertilization between ethology, for instance, and cultural study. An exploration of the extent to which children of both sexes have always been reared by their mothers and the meaning of this very close tie might be one of the best approaches that we could have to our subject.

ERIKSON:
As to achievement in males—that even goes for the *berdaches* you mentioned earlier. They became cooks—often famous cooks. A woman could cook, but a *berdache* had the chance to become an artist in cooking. Women could embroider, but a *berdache* became a famous embroiderer. Whether they actually did cook better, I would not know.

LORENZ:
That is the question I wanted to put. Is it not that men—as a universal rule—are slightly more creative in inventions, and slightly more exploratory than girls are, even when they are quite small children? I was always intrigued with the fact that all little boys go for mechanical toys and girls don't, not even when the adored elder brother does so. There is no absolute rule—there are girls who play with mechanical toys—but I think that I see a slight dimorphism in the exploratory behaviour in boys and girls, that boys are more interested in mechanics. In primitive man, at the palæolithic level, experimentation of this kind must play a very large role. I suppose the way in which the first stone implements were invented was by just this kind of play, which you see in monkeys, too, and in apes.

MEAD:

Well, here again it is so difficult to separate the social features because if you take a society which is based on the horse and horsemanship is an important element for men, you will find that little girls do not pay as much attention to the horses. If it were possible to look at such a society, say 500 years ago, it would be quite clear that the association between the male and the horse was a sensible one that had all sorts of psychological concomitants—the man was active, he rode, and the female did not want to go long distances, she was afraid of this great big animal, and so forth. But today in the urban United States, horses have become a female interest as men have taken over the motor car, and furthermore there is now a slight indication that motor cars are becoming female, while aeroplanes become male.

If you look at this closely you begin to wonder whether it is not some *ratio* of degree of activity that must be preserved. Thus it may be that males are not universally more exploratory than females, but that a male-female harmony is achieved in some way by an accentuation to a higher level in the male than the female in any one particular group. We can find societies in which the little boys are extraordinarily non-exploratory, where they are very passive and quiet. In Bali, it is a tremendous effort to get the little boys out of the home and all sorts of rewards are given—for example an enormous great big hatchet-like knife that they can wear in their belts. Each little boy is given a water-buffalo or an ox that is his own, if he will only go and ride it and care for it. The whole society is trying to make the male a little bit more adventurous and a little more exploratory than the female. And after all these pressures have been exerted, he *is* a little more exploratory. However, in most societies the boys between, say, six and twelve are infinitely more curious and brighter than little girls, so that in most societies when I go in to work, I work with little boys. They are three times as interesting, they have got a lot of intellectual curiosity, where girls, relatively speaking, are just little bores. They have already taken on the domestic attitudes—they talk just like their mothers, they have less freedom of the imagination of any sort.

That is true in most societies, but not all. Among the Tchambuli where the women have taken on a great many of the functions that are male in most societies, the little girls were the more enterprising. It was the little girls who would go with me to explore something, who became the informants on language, while the little boys were moping about all by themselves at home. That was a society in which there had been a marked reversal of roles, which conceivably was also psychologically expensive. Our hypotheses either have to be that the male is more exploratory, in all circumstances, than the female, or that for any society to be viable a higher degree of male exploration must be maintained whether both sexes display this character at a very high or a very low level.

GREY WALTER:
It is obviously necessary for an explanation to include the biological difference between men and women, but do you, yourself, think this is a sufficient one, for the observed asymmetry in their social tasks and achievement rating?

MEAD:
I think that is an unanswered question. I am surveying what material we have from existing conditions in existing societies, and trying to present the questions that are raised by it. Most societies want girls to be a little less active than boys, for instance, to sit usually in a slightly more demure fashion, to enclose the body more— there are many varieties of this expectation—to be at home at night, or to wear more clothes, or to behave in a more modest fashion. In spite of great variety these cultural expectancies are remarkably consistent. It is possible to interpret this historically, or to interpret it as a way of adapting girls to their future roles as women. And/or it is possible to say that at the age of two, or three, or four, the human female is less exploratory, less active and less extended than the male. All three of these statements may be true. But these, I think, are the sorts of hypotheses that are suggested by the material. I am not arguing for one as compared with the other at the moment. I am just trying to present them.

ZAZZO:
I would like to make three remarks.
The first, in connexion with what Margaret Mead said about differences between men and women of a physical order (strength, height, etc.) which determine differences of a psychological order. It is quite obvious that for the sexual characteristics there is no question of all or nothing and as regards the characteristics of which you have been speaking, especially height, there is a considerable overlap in the statistical distribution of heights in men and women. It seems to me, however, interesting from the psychological point of view that whatever our physical or individual strength and whatever our height, we keep to the psychological stereotype of our sex. A masculine individual who is smaller and weaker than average will

47

in general keep, nevertheless, to the masculine stereotype, that of the 'stronger' sex.

The second remark concerns the valuation of tasks and the attribution of social tasks to the man or to the woman. Don't you think that in order to make some progress in the understanding of these problems it is necessary to take into account the mode of life, the economic structure and the geographical conditions? A nomadic people does not have the same attitude towards children, nor does it have the same valuation of tasks as a sedentary or agricultural people or as a society based on real estate. I think it is necessary to take these factors into account in order to understand the social valuation of tasks, the distribution of tasks between man and woman, and also in order to understand the importance accorded to the child. In a society where inheritance does not exist the child is differently valued.

Third remark: for some years we have been making a systematic study in my laboratory of differences between sexes, and we have looked for the origin of these differences as far back as possible in childhood. Well, these differences appear very early: at the age of two years they are already considerable. When restandardizing Gesell's 'baby tests' on a French population we discovered that boys from the age of two years, perhaps even before, are more advanced than girls in the tests of motor co-ordination; that boys from the age of two to three years are more advanced than girls in all the tests of spatial organization. On the other hand, as soon as language comes in, girls show for several aspects of spoken or written language a certain superiority over the boys. I won't labour the point. Two categories of factors seem to come into the psychological differentiation between sexes: factors of physiological differentiation, which are often very weak and noticeable very early; they are amplified by social factors, in the first place through examples given by the father and the mother.

MEAD:

I think the only thing that I need to say at this point is that I am not arguing at all against the possibility of universal differences between the sexes. I am trying to present the material from the anthropological field that creates a framework within which we can look at these differences. We only have information on children's language in a very limited number of societies but in every one that I know, the girls are more precocious than the boys in linguistic behaviour to an extent which is measurable.

As to the question of a correlation between stages of technological

48

development and the role of the sexes, and the role of the child within these differently developed societies, when we examine these carefully we do not find a very close correspondence. There are agricultural societies in which the aged are treated very badly, and agricultural societies in which they are treated very well, even though there is the nice farm for them to stay on in each case. There are nomadic societies in which the aged are treated with enormous care even though they are a drain on the economy of the whole community and in which the old men remain the great power in the group, and there are nomadic societies in which the aged have no power whatsoever. So that, although the technology and the stage of economic development will always be a limiting factor in the situation, we have no material to date to show that the technology is consistently important in determining which sex roles or which attitudes towards children will occur.

BUCKLE:

I think perhaps we need to remember that some of the moulding influences are mythological ones, not merely social, geographical and so on. I wonder about this myth of the matriarchal society—just where does it occur, in what kind of cultures, is it a male myth or a female myth, and how does it influence this whole question of the predominance of the male?

MEAD:

There are almost no female myths, as far as we know, which is a very curious thing. Of course it is also something that is very difficult to prove, because one always finds mythology already there when one arrives in a primitive society and women may be the principal transmitters. In many societies women tell the tales, but to date, most of the analysis that has been done on folk tales suggests that there are a very limited number of female myths, and that when they occur they do not spread. Occasionally you may have a myth that could be regarded as a female myth—Bluebeard, I think is one. The Bluebeard story could be regarded as a female fear and it does not diffuse easily. It is a French tale and the French have been one of the most active people in diffusing mythology all over the world; they have human relations with native peoples everywhere, they tell stories to the people, and usually French tales spread. But Bluebeard just didn't spread. On the other hand, the two most widespread myths in the world are The Magic Flight and The Toothed Vagina—both embodying male fears. These spread with remarkable facility.

49

So on the whole we do not think that very many myths are female myths, but whether females are not fantasy builders or simply have not been in a position to build fantasies, we are not quite sure. I think that the matriarchy, the island of women, this whole set of stories are male myths, although in their secondary forms, they may give aid and comfort to some European feminists.

TANNER:

I want to come back, if I may, to Lorenz' question as to whether the little boy was not naturally more exploratory than the little girl. The point I want to make is rather a general one. There is, on average, a difference in physique between males and females that appears considerably before puberty. We have to get it quite clear as to what we mean by maleness and femaleness—there are changes which occur at puberty to make somebody who is prepubescent into male or female, but there are also other non-genital differences between girls and boys existent before puberty, and these may not be anything to do with post-puberty maleness and femaleness, but something which is separate and can best be looked at in a different way. To be concrete, let us think of physique in terms of Sheldon's somato-types. The distribution of somatotypes of little boys and of little girls is in fact different—there is more endomorphy on average in little girls and more mesomorphy (nothing to do with postpubescent sex character) in little boys. Therefore, if the exploratory relation-ship is linked to a basic physique which is present in x per cent. of males, and less than x per cent. of females, this will of itself make little boys on average more exploratory. Whether one can call this a sex difference or not I don't know—this is a matter of the use of words.

FREMONT-SMITH:

As to little girls tending to be more fat than boys, at an early age, that could be for cultural reasons. If the mothers are feeling a bit guilty about having borne a little girl who is going to be in a derogated position all her life, they may have overfed the little girl; we know that obesity in children is likely to be a response of maternal over-com-pensation. So there is a possible psychosocial basis for there being on average more little fat girls than little fat boys.

TANNER:

You would have to extend your explanation to cover the muscu-larity of boys as well, which gets a little difficult. I think this raises genetical questions too. I would presume that there is a balance existing between males and females to maintain this quantitative difference in physique as between the two, and there must be some evolutionary forces acting to maintain it that way. On the one hand it probably is advantageous from an evolutionary point of view to keep a large amount of variability in physique in a population, but it may also be advantageous to have as many muscular active mesomorphic males as possible if you are defending territory. When primate reproduction appears, the female is immobilized for a considerable period, is not able to move from one place to another with the same ease as the male, and is not able to fight for considerable periods. In that case it might be advantageous to push over on to the female the less-useful-for-moving-about characteristics of physique, but nevertheless to preserve these. Though a multi-factorial system, it would act like a balance, I think, because the mechanism couldn't go too far; that is you couldn't get absolutely no mesomorphs among the females, or no endomorphs amongst the males, because then you would lose the variability and that would pull back the system again to where it was before.

ERIKSON:

In general, would it be fair to say, Margaret, that you started with extreme examples and you worked then toward this formulation: there are certain given sex differences which in any culture are elaborated into a certain *ratio*. This ratio rests on many conflicting necessities, one of them being the survival of the young. I would stress that by survival we do not understand merely the first year, as such. In the first year the foundation is created for a baby to become a functioning person, including a parent later on. In other words, survival in a human setting does not mean just to bring up a baby for its own sake and lifetime, as it were, but to bring up somebody who will have the preconditions of becoming a parent later on and a creator of generations to come.

I don't know whether I am the only anxious one in this group, but I felt increasingly anxious when you spoke of the arbitrary changes that are taking place, because I constantly think of what is going to happen to the children. In primitive systems, or at any rate in those which have survived, we are aware of a certain self-correction which establishes a workable ratio, and which does not only depend on what Professor Huxley called the super-normal stimuli bringing out innate virtues. There must be, especially in women, certain correctives, which resist such super-normal stimuli in order to safeguard psychological survival.

51

INHELDER:

As a matter of information I should like to put a question to Margaret Mead, Jim Tanner and Zazzo: what do we know actually about the age of acquisition of walking and, in some cases, of swimming? Are there significant differences between the sexes even for these fundamental co-ordinations, or do these differences not go beyond the normal distribution curves characteristic of individual differences?

MEAD:

Well, I want to go tomorrow into the question of these differences in the young, having sketched out first the adult differences in role that may be important. I would say that here again you find the basic difference that the boy and the girl both learn their motor behaviour from their mother. So, if we find a difference in any given culture between the boys' and the girls' motor behaviour it still does not tell us that it is innate and not learned. To answer such a question we need also the situation where the reverse occurs. In Manus, for example, both boys and girls learn their motor behaviour from their fathers to a very large extent and you have very high motor mobility in both boys and girls, with the girls showing enormously precocious motor behaviour. The possibility exists that there may be a systematic difference in French children, such as Professor Zazzo finds, but not until we do studies of cultures in which children are taught by women, by men, by older children, etc., can we be sure that there are genuine universal sex differences, although I am personally inclined to believe that such exist.

*　*　*

MEAD:

Let me begin today's session by saying that I am still presenting material on adult sex differences as they may be mediated to children, for the present begging the question as to how far they are biologically determined and how much they are culturally arranged, though emphasizing the cultural arrangement. This morning I want to take up two or three points that are a good deal closer to the biological level, and first I want to ask Jim Tanner a question. What happened to the longer arms of boys than girls? I thought you were going to talk about them yesterday, or have they become submerged in the mesomorphic-endomorphic difference we discussed?

TANNER:

I don't think they have. What Margaret is referring to is the fact that the forearm in the male is considerably longer relative to the upper arm or any other part of the body one cares to take than it is in the female. The data, of course, are only on American and West European adults and children so we don't know whether this is a universal finding. I rather suppose so, all the same.

HUXLEY:
There is an overlap in the male and female distribution, I take it?

TANNER:
Certainly. This greater relative forearm length is present from birth onwards. The mechanism of it is that the growth rate of the male forearm is slightly greater throughout the whole growing period than that of the female forearm. This is probably true of the circumference of the forearm also relative to the other parts of the body though this isn't quite so well documented. There are various other similar differences, as, for example, in the length of the index finger. In the female the second metacarpal is longer relative to all the other metacarpals. That again is first visible very early—in fact, in foetal life; so that it is not a secondary sex difference in the sense that we usually speak of them.

There are three ways in which the male/female physical differences may come about. Some are caused by hormone action at puberty; others, such as the longer legs of the male, come about simply because the male goes on growing for about two years longer than the female and since relative to the rest of the body the legs are growing fastest just before puberty, therefore, they end up relatively longer. Thirdly, a very few dimensions just grow faster all the time right from the start, in one sex or the other, which is the case for the forearm.

HUXLEY:
The difference in arm proportion might help to explain why girls on the whole don't seem to be able to throw a baseball or cricket ball so well as boys.

GREY WALTER:
What order of difference is there in the arm lengths?

TANNER:
It would, I think, be around eight to ten per cent.

GREY WALTER:
I should have thought that a shorter lever might match their weight better for cricket balls.

MEAD:

We might come back later to this difference in the arms in connexion with exploratory and other activity of the male in relation
to the outer environment. But I want to discuss first the difference in
type of work, or utilization of energy, in males and females. All
sorts of investigators have commented that on the whole the male
works with spurts of energy and is better at work demanding spurts
than a female, who is in turn better than males at slow repetitious
monotonous tasks. Gesell and Ilg (personal communication) say
that they find this for children as well. However, a culture can reverse it. We have a good deal of material, for instance, on the
behaviour of Czech factory workers, who seem to have a high
tolerance of monotonous work, correlated with apparently a very
high amount of day-dreaming that makes the monotonous work
possible. Among my Arapesh people, in New Guinea, where the
women do the carrying and where they say the women's heads are
so strong, women do virtually no handwork whatsoever. They do
heavy work with the body and come home totally exhausted and sit
exhausted, exactly as the men do. In Bali, we have a different sort
of reversal in that Balinese men hardly go in for spurts at all and
have very poor lifting power. But both men and women have good
carrying power if a load is placed on their heads, and Balinese men
work exactly the way women do with a monotonous, repetitious,
dreamy quality. Normally, the Balinese male does not develop
heavy muscles, but if he goes to work as a coolie and works for
Europeans he develops his muscles just like anyone else, so that
there was a small group of males in Bali who looked like he-men,
whereas the rest of the population, who had not been exposed to
this particular heavy work, had a smooth feminine appearance.
Bali is one of the conspicuous instances, I think, of the extent to
which culture can modify what looks like a significant difference.

HUXLEY:

What about the sculpture and painting in Bali? Isn't that done
almost entirely by men?

MEAD:

Yes, it is done by men, but when a man is carving in Bali, he will use
only the absolutely necessary muscles, with the rest of the body
uninvolved. In contrast, the Iatmul people, who work entirely in
enormous spurts of energy, never do anything except with maximum
exertion. They don't believe in doing any work at all until they are
in an absolute fury; the only way a woman gets her husband to do

any work is to insult him all night long at the top of her voice; or one part of the community insults the other half—'you never caught a crocodile—you never will catch a crocodile, your ancestors didn't catch any crocodiles, you are non-crocodile catchers', and that goes on for about a week. Then the insulted group gets angry enough to go and kill some crocodiles. The whole of male behaviour is based on these enormous spurts. When Iatmul carve the whole body is involved and they get tired very quickly; films demonstrate the enormous over-use of every part of the body. The women work slowly and monotonously and don't share in this big spurt. I think that this sex-differentiated behaviour may be important in conveying to the small child what it is to be male and female, and it is interesting that the Arapesh and the Mundugumor both have failed to differentiate in energy use and both have failed also to differentiate between males and females in personality in general.

LORENZ:
Which of these two people are the river people in New Guinea?

MEAD:
The Mundugumor are the river people who are cannibals and have a system where they change sex-descent each generation. The women are tall and masculine. Their size can be somewhat attributed to the fact that they have all the food; they do all the fishing and they eat what they like before they come into the village. The Arapesh are people where both men and women are mild and parental in behaviour. They also live in New Guinea, about 50 miles away. (See Mead, 1935, 1949 for description of these tribes.)

Now, another dimension of somewhat the same sort that I think is worth considering is the difference in climax structure in the life of the male and the life of the female. The female's life is a series of irreversible events enacted inside her own body which once enacted cannot be denied. First, menstruation, rupture of the hymen, birth, and finally menopause all are irreversible events. Female life moves through a series of indubitable natural climaxes with a rhythm that is internally determined.

From time to time there have been attempts to establish periodicities in males (Hersey, 1931). They have never been controlled adequately in relation to the periodicities in the males' wives and I think there is a reasonably good possibility that they are merely responses in the males to an extreme periodicity in the wives. In some societies this is institutionalized completely, so that when a wife is segregated at menstruation, the husband has to do all the housework and take care of the children, so that you have a periodicity in the life of the male which is at least as irritating as the seclusion of the females concerned.

DE SAUSSURE:

Have you been able to observe correlations between rhythmic work and collective work? When the work is collective is it more rhythmic? When it is rhythmic is it more frequently accompanied by singing than when it is done in spurts? Have individuals who work in a more rhythmic way a tendency to work collectively rather than individually? And on the other hand, when they work individually do they sing while they work?

MEAD:

I don't think we can make any statement about that. It has never really been systematically investigated, although there were some early speculative statements about the relationship between rhythm and work. But I think the problem of whether a male or female rhythm is used all the way through in a society may be more pertinent than the relationship between the individual and the collective.

INHELDER:

To what extent does culture determine the rhythm activity/rest characteristic of the daily individual cycle? Are there cultures where the maximum activity is found in the early hours of the morning, others towards midday or in the evening?

MEAD:

It is possible to find almost every sort of difference in this. There are societies where there are great spurts of work early in the morning, where conceivably the late risers suffer. There are societies where people get up very slowly and organize their approach to any kind of work very gradually. There are people who are very responsive to changes of the wind or changes of the moon and others will plod along at just the same rate, paying little attention to shifts in seasons.

ERIKSON:

How about precision?

MEAD:

I think all the material we have on precision comes from our own society and most of it was work done in the last war. One study was made in which they found women who did fine embroidery were more reliably precise than men watchmakers at a very fine crafts-man's job. I think it is probably important that the watchmaker works with external materials which he is adapting to each other with a very high degree of precision, but the woman who is doing delicate embroidery is still working more with her own body.

FREMONT-SMITH:

It seems to me 'own body' needs to be defined a bit more. This is really a question of whether your own body is using the whole limb or the peripheral fingers, because no matter how external the objects are that the watchmaker is working with, he has got to move his hands and his fingers to do the work.

MEAD:

Both people are working with their fingers, but I think the woman handles the needle much more as a part of her own body than is the case with the man and his tools. The girl does more things with her own body, her body is the theatre on which events are played out, so that if you have a thing like a needle, the way in which the girl uses it will differ from the way in which the boy uses it. Also the needle's relationship to the length of the fingers might be an essential element.

ZAZZO:

We noticed during observations on children between seven and twelve in a cinema that during moments of excitement the boys had movements stretching towards the screen whereas the little girls had movements coming back towards their bodies: they touched their face or their chest. We took systematic photographs in ultra-violet light unknown to the children; on the parts of the film which were fairly exciting or which caused interest we had two very different attitudes for boys and girls apart, of course, from individual differences.

MEAD:

Dr. Zazzo showed me these pictures yesterday. This tendency of the girl to bring her hands back to the body is something we find in many societies. For example, in the balancing behaviour in the boy there seems to be more reaching-out, and if he balances with his own body he is likely to hold on to his penis, whereas the girl folds her arms or places them on to her head and shows more of a with-drawal into the self. This again might be dependent on a whole series of other factors but it does occur with quite remarkable

57

persistency. In a society like Bali where the men behave more like women in terms of extensor activities the men also touch their own bodies a good deal more and bring their hands back to their own body.

GREY WALTER:

Do you remember that delightful passage in *Huckleberry Finn* where Huck puts on a girl's dress to try and disguise himself and goes to visit a woman and is trying to get away with being a girl and she throws him something and instead of opening his legs to catch it as a girl would do, he closes them to catch it as a boy would do; I thought it was a most delightful scene.

MONNIER:

If we distinguish skilfulness in games and skilfulness in technical activities, we get the impression that here also the development in boys is somewhat different from that in girls. Boys may have the greatest skilfulness in games, but when they have to become trained in a technical professional activity, it takes a long time because skilfulness implies self-control. To become skilled, one must inhibit all kinds of impulsive gestures and effective expressions which are a hindrance to technical skilfulness. We have evidence that inhibition of these parasitic affective movements in technical training occurs somewhat later in boys than in girls.

MEAD:

There again we have to be sure whether this is because boys are reared by women and are developing a sort of counter-movement against the movement of their mother. Perhaps if a little boy could start imitating his father and working as his father works from the time he was very small, this sort of difference might disappear.

Now, to turn from this question of rhythms of work and types of work and types of climax structure to the question of creativity, which is a basic problem between men and women; there again, it is possible to make the simple historical point that in any society that has permitted women to do something as women they have become highly skilled. Most of the discussion that goes on today about the relative achievement of men and women is a discussion of the achievements of women in a man's field. We say, well, we have let women work with music now for hundreds of years and they do nothing; but actually we have only let them do something that has been perfected and elaborated by men, that is designated as male and which, therefore, may be expected to introduce a great

58

many blocks and difficulties in the performance. We must consider the possibility that whenever a creative activity can be defined as female it may elicit the capacity in females; it will never be elicited as long as it is defined as male. I think that should always be systematically taken into account.

However, let us go on to a rather different point and that is the extent to which the male explores and works with the external world, and imposes form and structure on it, whereas the female tends to confine her activities more to her own body. This could be regarded as the basis of differences of creativity. Small girls, especially in as primitive society, are all well assured that if they wait they will have children; an individual woman may, of course, be unfortunate and not have a child, but the expected thing is that one will have a child and that one doesn't have to do anything whatsoever except *be*. If girls will continue simply to be girls until they are big enough, someone will marry them (in these primitive societies of which I speak every woman is married, at least once) and they will have children. Any urge towards any other form of creativity would be muted as compared with the possibility of making children, especially in a society where the production of children is so conspicuous because so few other things are produced that are of any importance. The climax structure and work rhythm come in again here also, I think, because the woman has a child, she doesn't have half a child, three-quarters of a child, or nine-tenths of a child, she has a child or she doesn't have a child. Now, in contrast to child-bearing, male tasks, in most parts of the world, can be quantitatively sub-divided— you build a house, and then you build a bigger house. Achievement can be graded, and compared, and you can go on from one achievement to another. Irreversibles in male achievement usually have to be phrased in biological terms similar to women's achievements— for example, that a man who has not begotten a son is not a man. But for most things, the difference between the single complete achievement, in a woman having one child or two children, and the graduated achievement of man who is continually going on to build new bridges, or to conquer new worlds in one form or another, seems to be a pretty systematic one.

At least in those societies that have been looked at we find this tendency for women to rest for a long period as small girls and at puberty and simply wait, not acquiring more than the minimum of skills that are necessary for marriage and then, having had children, to rest on their laurels and to feel this is an adequate enough achievement. This contrasts with the males' continually going on to more and more and more activity, and corresponds to the difference in climax structure wherein male reproductive life may go on for a very long period with different degrees of continuity and discontinuity, whereas the female reproductive period is cut off sharply and clearly. These points, I think, must not be underestimated in their effect not only at the moment that they occur, but as expectations held out continuously to children.

LORENZ:

I am very much struck by the fact that when we speak of female creativity we are always thinking of a female's creativity in the man's field of work. Now how about the field of typical feminine activity in one culture—let us say weaving. I understand that in the early stages of our culture weaving was particularly feminine and the word 'wife' derived from 'weaving'. Is there any record whether the *technique* of weaving, the loom, was invented by a woman? I know of one instance of something which was definitely invented by women and by women exclusively, and that is the very intricate details and varieties of knitting, that is still being invented by women and I have seen my mother—all my anthropology is derived from observations of my own family—invent very intricate new patterns, but I don't see my mother inventing a loom.

MEAD:

I think that you could say that the women have invented the stitches. In ancient Peru, where we find every single stitch that has ever been thought of in weaving, weaving was done by women. But what you suggest is rather what I would expect also—that the women would invent stitches and the men would invent the loom.

HUXLEY:

On the other hand I understand that the Bayeux tapestry was not done by Queen Matilda's women at all, but by a guild of men embroiderers—the creativity there was in the hands of the men.

MEAD:

Yes, weaving in Peru was feminine and in Europe a great deal of it was masculine, but you get the same sort of invention in the stitch in both instances.

LORENZ:

I would like to know of cultures where the women do the fishing. Do you think or can you show there that the method of fishing is also invented by women, because that is what I expect, you see.

MEAD:

It is almost impossible to show how any of these methods were invented. Women have different methods from men, but that doesn't at all preclude the men having invented them for the women to use.

HUXLEY:

One very interesting changeover was that from boys to women in representing female parts on the stage. Once women were allowed to, they became great actresses. Does it mean that women are naturally better in interpretative roles than in creative ones?

MEAD:

It is possible the interpretative roles come easier. It is possible that all of those forms of creativity where a pattern is imposed on the material are more congenial to men and all of those forms where one responds to the form of material are more congenial to women. I would like to stress another point. Take for example mathematical ability: it may be that the most gifted mathematicians will always be men, that the real mathematical gift might occur in one-tenth of one per cent. of the male sex, but always in males. Then the maleness of mathematics gets defined from the genius. Or it may on the contrary simply be that a larger percentage of men than of women deal well with mathematics and the stereotype is set up and communicated to children that way. Or it may be that historically men have dealt with mathematics to such a degree that mathematics is thought of as male. I don't feel that any of our cultural material is of an order to do more than raise these questions.

FREMONT-SMITH:

Margaret, would you say that once a sex-differential role has been established, such as in reference to mathematics, that then it would be extremely easy for the society to perpetuate it, and rather difficult to break through and change it even though there wasn't any biological reason for it?

MEAD:

Yes, I would; furthermore if you take some of these very simple primitive people, they may count to 20 or 24. The brightest person in that group—a mathematical genius—might count up to 50 and might not be able to perpetuate it, whereas in the societies like ours people with relatively low IQ will learn algebra, because the whole society is permeated with mathematics.

61

HUXLEY:

Would you agree with the point which Konrad Lorenz raised yesterday, about a sex difference in readiness to be interested in and in ability to control mechanical devices? That is rather important in a mechanical society, and I should have thought as you change from the sort of crude mechanical technology of the 19th century to today's advanced technology of electronics and so on—from Lewis Mumford's paleotechnics to neotechnics—that would make a very considerable difference.

MEAD:

Except that, you see, electronic machinery is the sort of thing which is more congenial to a woman.

HUXLEY:

That is what I meant. The difference in mechanical ability would only be effective in the paleotechnic period.

ZAZZO:

Two remarks concerning this aptitude for mathematics which is supposed to be greater among boys than among girls. I think there are two factors—a factor of spatial organization which seems to be more developed, more precocious, among small boys than among small girls, and an affective factor. We might have some doubt as regards a real difference in aptitude for mathematics between the sexes; it is less a question of aptitude than of the relations which may exist between affectivity and logical thought. We can show that even if boys succeed on an average better than girls, nevertheless 90 per cent. of our schoolboys fail to understand mathematics, and this failure is not due, I think, to a lack of aptitude for mathematics. A person of average intelligence can go quite far in the realm of mathematics if he is not hindered by all kinds of affective difficulties. There must be a reduction in affective reactions if logical thought is to proceed harmoniously and clearly. This reduction perhaps works less well for girls on an average than for boys.

HUXLEY:

I think Dr. Zazzo has made a very important point—that you are dealing with something which is not a specific aptitude to perform some action, but what in biology we call a pre-adaptation or a prerequisite for such performance. These prerequisites may differ considerably and may have a very big effect on final results.

62

INHELDER:

If we compare two groups of boys and of girls of the same age we do not in fact observe any significant difference in the development of logical functions. On the other hand we note slight differences in the formation of spatial representation, for example when it is a question of transformations and developments of geometric solids. Moreover, we note that these differences, which are very little pronounced among young children, take on greater importance with age. But sexual differences are not the only factors involved, there are also factors of exercise and, because of this, of school and cultural environment. Those children who at all ages have much richer possibilities of manipulation and visual-tactile exploration have as a general rule better spatial representation. The mental image in its spatial form seems originally to be the interiorization of movements of exploration (Piaget & Inhelder, 1948). This is why we think that the differences observed between the performances of boys and girls are not only linked to sex but are due rather to the intervention of a number of causes, among others, sensori-motor exercise and the school and cultural 'climate.'

DE SAUSSURE:

I would like to make a remark along the same lines as that made by Professor Zazzo. In the clinic we see from time to time women who protest against their femininity, accepting masculine activities and showing even great aptitude for mathematics and for mechanical questions, simply because their affectivity is directed to this side. The question I should like to ask is this: in certain primitive societies, does one see enough women with such a desire, so that all of a sudden an activity which had been masculine up to then is thereafter taken up by women?

MEAD:

I have never seen a primitive society where one had a very highly developed masculine protest in women. I have seen societies where women have played a great many roles that in other societies were masculine—where they fought, climbed coconut trees, took long voyages and things of that sort and did them as well as, or in some cases to the exclusion of men, but the particular kind of release of energy that we see in our society in a woman who wants to be masculine and wants to show what she can do, and that she can compete, I think is a more sophisticated development. We don't have really any true analogues at the primitive level. For instance, the Eskimo woman knows how to build a house as well as an Eskimo man does, and very often she is stuck and has to build a house. She may be travelling on one sled with two children, and her husband on another sled with the other and doesn't get there. As she builds the house she comments: 'This is not of course a real house, this is just a put-together shack of no importance, that a mere woman is cutting out of snow. This amounts to nothing at all. This is not a house, it is just a shelter against the elements'. I think that position is a little more common in primitive societies than the other one.

GREY WALTER:
Could you tell us something about the aspect of personality which is reflected in our Western culture in hobbies, which often reflect rather more faithfully the personality of an individual than his occupation does? It is rather rare in English society for a woman to have a hobby, but I gather in America there are women's clubs and so on that fill the place of hobbies in men's lives.

MEAD:
Well, my first general statement would be that hobbies are male. You may have derivative hobbies in the female. If all the little boys that a little girl knows collect stamps, she may collect a few.

HUXLEY:
Is this so in primitive cultures too?

MEAD:
It is so in any society that I know anything about. Sheer hobbies in the sense that one has them in England don't exist in primitive societies, they are a special rather late development. But the elaboration of leisure in theatricals, in offerings, and so forth, tends to be a male activity in all the societies that we know anything about. One of the things that happens is that the minute you get an elaboration of leisure you get this preoccupation of men with activities that superficially look feminine—dressing dolls, cutting out pretty little cut-out things, cutting leaves and flowers up. In Bali the men spend hours and hours cutting pig fat into roses, and then some more hours fashioning little pigs out of rose leaves. An enormous amount of time goes into these activities, almost as if when a society gets to a point when it has leeway for leisure then it is possible for males as bi-sexual creatures to play games at what it would be like to be a woman. I think this generalization could be supported, for example, in relation to the arts, and the tendency at many periods for the arts to be regarded as feminine. That is, you

64

have first a period of extreme rigour, like the American frontier, and no art at all. Then as the arts develop more and more, they are first taken up by women and then they are taken over by men. Most of these symbolic activities, hobbies—stamp collecting, gardening, fishing—may be in this class. Consider the efforts that a culture has to go to make a woman fish for pleasure. However, I know two or three women executives now who fish.

LORENZ:
Oh, but in Florida nowadays sport fishing is nearly an exclusively feminine occupation.

MEAD:
But they are not fishing for pleasure!

GREY WALTER:
The modern Atlantic woman has two lives, in a way. I mean that her longevity is great, so she has a pre-menopausal and post-menopausal life, and she isn't usually greatly encumbered with children in the second life. In your experience of developing American culture are women of post-menopausal age becoming hobby-ridden?

MEAD:
No. They are becoming social-organization-ridden. Clubs, community services, good deeds—a proliferation of inter-personal relations. But painting, for example, is work again. You see, painting is done in response to the belief that one *ought* to find out how to express one's personality, and I don't think should be properly defined as leisure.

If you look the world over, the participation of women in games is extraordinarily small. There is one small case-history (Wolfenstein, 1946, Mead, 1955) in this particular field. About ten years ago, a group of us conceived the idea of short-circuiting the relationship between contemporary child psychology and the child reader. The idea was to get psychoanalysts and anthropologists and child developers to plan what four-year-olds ought to read and then get a book written and give it to them. We went about this in a very elaborate way, we convened a group of specialists and the specialists enumerated what a little girl should know about having a little sibling, that mother would get tired, there was no room on mother's lap, and things of that sort, and that she should be allowed to help with the baby clothes. But the male writer who wrote the story invented a creature called a *rampatan*, and, while mother and father

65

had a baby, little Sally had a *rampatan*. And a *rampatan* could be anything you liked. It could fly, it could swim, it could go on the land. It could have the head of a rabbit and the tail of a snake, or the head of a lion and the body of a pussycat. It was a delightful story and after it was written, we tried it out on mothers, on children and on fathers. The children knew what the *rampatan* was about. The fathers knew what the *rampatan* was about, but the women said that they couldn't see what in the world this *rampatan* had to do with a woman having a baby.

GREY WALTER:

I want to get my picture clear of how you are looking at our present culture. Do you yourself notice, or has there been described, a significant sex difference in the attitude of children to the non-reflexive diversions such as television?

MEAD:

No, I should say not. In the United States at present, so far as I know, there is no difference in the spectatorship of girls and boys in spite of the fact that the content is on the whole masculine. Now whether that means anything except that parents use the television set as a baby sitter, and whether we are talking about children or whether we are talking about adults, I wouldn't be sure. But of course spectator sports in adults depend on men far more than women.

FREMONT-SMITH

There is one point that I would like to bring up here. In human societies there is the greatest possible difficulty in separating out biological sex differences from the influence of the social organization. I want to come back to Konrad's remark yesterday about the bull playing with the little male bulls and ask whether we haven't made a false dichotomy between the human race and the lower biological species, in the assumption that in animals we can see quite easily the pure impact of genetically determined sex, whereas in humans we have to disentangle it from the culture. I wonder whether it may not be true in a good many animals that the culture plays a role right from the beginning also?

HUXLEY:

But there isn't any culture in animals!

LORENZ:

Practically none is known. There is a certain cultural element in social, sexual and nest-building behaviour in chimps, as Hayes (1951) and Nissen very clearly showed. Tradition is important to such an extent that it is difficult to breed chimps if you haven't got a sexually experienced one, and you have got to start with one wild-caught chimp in a colony in order to teach them how to copulate. And then hand-reared chimps don't nest-build, though the motor patterns involved are very probably instinctive activities. But wild-caught ones do build a nest, and there was hitherto only one captivity-reared chimp on record who knew how to do it, and he was reared by a wild-caught mother. And that is practically all I know about animal culture!

FREMONT-SMITH:

What about bulls?

LORENZ:

All that is purely innate.

HUXLEY:

Culture, surely, is only definable as the result of the cumulative transmission of experience.

LORENZ:

Julian Huxley once said that the traditional knowledge ˙of dangerous predators which I have demonstrated in the jackdaw was hitherto the only example of this kind, but since then Nissen and Hayes have found two or three other instances.

But I want to ask something which is pertinent to this question. Vertebrates in general are protogynous hermaphrodites, which in simple words means that they are hermaphroditic in the general layout of their anatomy and that, as a rule, female characters develop before male characters. For example, many young birds are hen-coloured and develop cock plumage later on. There are very few exceptions to this rule. There was one paper by a man named Winterbottom (1929) which Julian lent me and made me read about 20 years ago, and this man made the difference between aretic and aphroditic characters in species. Aretic characters are characters developed in phylogeny by the male sex first and aphroditic characters are characters developed by the female sex first. For instance nipples, the utriculus prostaticus and other primarily female characters which men carry are aphroditic characters. All of you know that

67

the distribution of pubic hair when it first grows is female, that mammary glands grow for a certain time in the pubescent male and so on, and therefore, I always took as a matter of course that little boys wore skirts, when I was young, and generally are treated as girls and look like girls. And in Holland there are regions where the little boys up to five years are dressed absolutely as girls. In the islands of Vollendam and Markendam as the only sex-distinguishing mark they have a round disk sewn to their bonnets to tell whether they are male or female. I was very much surprised when I heard about this society where all children were dressed and treated as boys, and my question is now how is the little boy in our society discouraged from behaving like Ma? What are the reinforcements for imitating Pa and not Ma? And, vice versa, how are the reverse reinforcements effected in that New Guinea society, and do the little boys in this society retain some feminine characters afterwards?

MEAD:

I should say that in our society a baby boy is discouraged from behaving like a female from the moment he is born. The first time his mother picks him up in her hands, her hands are saying to him 'You are a little male'. A great proportion of his learning is communicated kinaesthetically very, very young. In all the societies we have been talking about it is the mother who is the operative person. But in Manus the father is exceedingly important, and has become steadily more important in handling little girls, and I think this case more or less supports the position I have been taking all along, that it is the mother who makes the child into otherness, if it is a boy. American mothers call their children Caxton and Jones and Smith now at the age of two—'Go wash your face, Jones', they say with a heavy voice that is going to turn these little boys into proper males. The goading of males into being males that goes on in the hands of women, and the treating them as 'other', as 'different', as 'not myself', is very great. But just let men raise the little girls—they try to make girls just like themselves. The tendency of fathers who rear daughters to turn them into males and want them to behave like males, and to move like males, and show the attitudes of males, is probably stronger than the tendency in the mother towards the little Lord Fauntleroy, wishing her son had been a girl. But the mother who makes her little boy feminine differs from the father, who says, 'This is the way to behave—stand like *this*, hold your punt like *this*, paddle like *this*, don't paddle like that, paddle like this'. He is not saying 'I wish you were a boy', he is saying 'behave like a human being, there is only one way to behave'.

68

Dr. Sears (1953) has done a study of male and female choices in nursery school-children, and the extent to which the girl will want to do the thing the father does, and be encouraged to do it, while the boy is discouraged by the mother from wanting to do the things that she does.

LORENZ:

But I am still astonished that the boy treated by his mother in that way does not become a female-imitation man, but becomes a real man. He is taught not to be like a female, but why does he imitate his father—which he does.

MEAD:

There are many societies in which the small male has almost no contact with the father at all, and where the mother has to do the teaching, so we have societies in which the mother teaches the boy to be a male-like creature, and we have societies in which the mother teaches the boy to be a female-like creature.

LORENZ:

Well, I had better come out and be honest about what I am aiming at. I do believe that there is a certain unlearned element—something like an IRM—which makes the little boy actually seek for somebody to take over the father role. Sylvia Klimpfinger has evidence for that in a hospital—a hostel—where all the children are reared by the female staff alone, and all these children—the boys more significantly than the girls—go for the gardener who is the only male accessible to them. This led me to suspect that there might be an unlearned preference for what to imitate—boys to imitate Pa and for girls to imitate Ma.

MEAD:

Well, I suspect that there is a very early capacity for sex-differentiation, and that there may well be an IRM by which female babies discriminate between male and female nurses. You would not necessarily have to say the child was seeking for a model, but with the capacity to discriminate and then with the developing of the sense of the self, the search for the particular type of model may begin.

BUCKLE:

As to why the boy tends to imitate the male, surely we must consider why the boy rejects the female. I doubt whether it is a

T

sufficient condition that the mother expects the child to be not like her. Surely there is a rejection of the mother by the child.

MEAD:

Ultimately, in adult life we have the rejection. But is there a mechanism in the young child that, for instance, rejects the female? Dr. Arthur Mirsky (unpublished research) did a study of the sense of smell in boys and girls, taking into account Freud's statement that we paid for our upright posture with giving up our sense of smell. He found that up to puberty boys' and girls' sense of smell was identical, and from puberty until middle age men's sense of smell goes way down, and in late middle age it is restored and is again quite comparable to the female. That would look to me like a clear case of a mechanism of non-identification with the mother, that the girl has to keep her identification with the smell of a female, has to accept milk and the smell of milk, and the whole female body odour. One of the things that the male does is to reject the smell connected with maternity and infancy. This happens at puberty and not in early childhood.

BUCKLE:

There is a good deal of fantasy evidence, isn't there, that might be produced here—the male fantasy of the fear of the women, the dentate vagina, the Island of Amazons, and so on. As you said yesterday, these are all characteristically male fantasies which form part of a whole complicated defence against a fear of women. This may go back and be connected in some way to the original situation of care.

MEAD:

And vice versa. You also first get rejection fantasies in the female. The only question would be whether with the parent of the same sex the fantasies are comparable because the girl, in rejecting or being fascinated by the stranger—the father who only comes home at night —is in a different position from the boy who has to cope with something that is there all day long, every day, every minute.

ERIKSON:

Maybe for later discussion it would be important to differentiate between various forms of rejection. One can speak of fear of women on the part of the boys in the sense that they have fantasies as to what might happen to themselves if they *do* something *to* women —that is one thing. The other rejection would be based on an identification with women—how would it feel to *be* a woman in spite of otherness in body structure. There is also the fear of pregnancy aggravated by such questions as to where and how will the baby come out, and what it would do to a boy's body.

A second point I wanted to make for future discussion is that the example given by Dr. Lorenz can probably be broken down into any number of part mechanisms. You said there may be an intrinsic search for a father in boys. In your example the gardener was the only available man. But where there is some choice, it may well be that the gardener would still be preferred. He is a man who works outside, who does something to the ground, has tools, has a technique. I would think a clerk sitting in an office in the same building would not have attracted quite the same attention. In other words locomotion could be important, the outdoorness, the handling of tools, the circumscribed technique—all of these things.

MEAD:

We have been able to watch the identification formed by several small boys whose fathers are intellectuals in households that share a Peruvian cleaning man who works with a vacuum cleaner—the little boys adore the Peruvian cleaning man with the vacuum cleaner.

RÉMOND:

I should like to ask Margaret Mead what, according to her, are the attributes of masculinity. Don't you think that 'authority' might be one of the attributes of the masculine sex, which is found in many present societies and perhaps even in primitive societies? Authority would go with initiative, while on the feminine side one would find rather submission and passiveness. All this could be attached to the one of the two persons who went in search of the other sex. It is the man who makes the approach to the woman, rather than the contrary, which gives him a certain initiative and finally a certain authority which imposes his presence on the other. From this there would follow a whole series of other qualities which would be masculine qualities. What do you think then of the importance of this division of authority between the two sexes?

MEAD:

I would like to break that into two, I think: the related authority of father or mother—that is, which parent, the father or the mother, is the more appropriate disciplining person—which is one part of the picture which builds up into a husband-wife relationship, and the other point about the male seeking the female. Now among my

71

head-hunters in New Guinea, the Iatmul and Mundugumor, the female seeks the male, and the males say it would be much too dangerous to make a proposal to a woman unless you knew whether she wanted you or not. So that all the provocative initiative comes from the women and the women send insults to the men, which arouses the men's sense of initiative and, shall we say, authority, to a sufficient point so that the men are then able to court the women. I think it is both a fairly complicated problem and also a very simple one on an anatomical basis. It looks reasonably clear that the physical initiative belongs to the male, and passivity, and receptivity and intraception belongs to the female, and any extreme reversal of this position is likely to be awkward and inconvenient. Nevertheless, there are so many stages and phases and repeats and elaborations in this whole picture that it is possible to turn the female into a provocative, seeking, teasing person.

ERIKSON:
I think we should add these two words 'awkward' and 'inconvenient' to the one 'expensive' which I suggested earlier for inclusion in our special vocabulary.

INTERVAL

MEAD:
I think perhaps the next thing we ought to tackle is the implica-ations for sex differences of the very protracted human infancy and the question of what we are able to say at present about the stages that the psychoanalyst usually calls pre-genital. This is the point where Erik Erikson and I overlap greatly, for I have relied a great deal through the last 20 years on his clinical work and his charts of pre-genital development. As he built them up, I have tried to apply that to different cultures and having done so to emerge with new hyotheses that we could test. The first point I want to raise is the question of *latency*, because it seems to me that this is a problem where we again overlap with the animal world. To what extent the young child of each sex, after a period of fairly vivid affective re-lationship to parents and to its own body has a sort of—I don't know whether I should use the word 'moratorium', because you are using it for your adolescent period, Erik, but in a sense it is a kind of moratorium.

72

ERIKSON:

A psychosexual moratorium: the later one I would call psychosocial.

MEAD:

A psychosexual moratorium then—a period when what looks like a straight line of sexual development is held in abeyance and the child turns away from the affective libidinized relationships to other people and concentrates on its own learning. One of the very interesting points has been whether there was such a thing as latency in girls. We have pretty good evidence for most societies that there is a short period for boys. It may sometimes be rather artificially defined; for instance, if children are sent to school at six, latency begins at six if it hasn't begun before. The child is taken away and subjected to an education outside the home, which in practically all instances is mediated by a stranger in some shape or other. There is indeed, an almost universal use in human societies of the stranger as the educative influence to break with the home, whether through an initiation ceremony or in school (Hart, 1955). In girls it is a very open question as to whether there is this withdrawal from psychosexual activity to anything like the same extent as in boys. In any society where girls continue to be treated as desirable little feminine objects you get a consistent and uninterrupted line of giggling self-conscious behaviour, with the girls giving a clear picture of being more or less available for sexual advances at any point as far as they themselves are concerned (with, of course, a large number of social restrictions built up around them). Fright or fear may be built over this receptivity, extreme shyness may be laid over it. But there is a contrasting picture between boys and girls as if this period of latency functions some way for the boy in a way it doesn't for the girls.

We have had relatively little information about the psychosexual development of the girl as compared with the boy. Psychoanalysis was built up on assumptions about boys and assumptions about the way little girls felt about little boys, and most women who have done any psychoanalytic work on childhood have suffered from a masculine protest which is a little more extreme than the typical one, so a lot of psychoanalytic literature on girls has been concerned with revolt of one kind or another against Freudian theory that in many cases is utterly unrelated to girls. But by one of those extraordinary, happy accidents, two weeks ago I was sent a paper by an American child-analyst named Dr. Judith Kestenberg (in press) and was very much struck with it.

Dr. Kestenberg is working with a slightly different approach to the

73

whole problem of the hymen from any approach that I know of. I have tended, on the whole, to see the function of the hymen as protecting the juvenile male; it does not, after all, protect the juvenile female against any full-grown male; it may be a protection if you build up an elaborate ritual and send men to jail if they have sex relations with too young a child, but the hymen itself does not present any particular barrier to a full-grown male. It does, however, present a certain degree of discouragement in adolescent play, so that one of the possible ways in which the hymen may have functioned is to decrease the amount of adolescent and pre-adolescent sex play and to prolong the period of play without penetration, which occurs in so many peasant societies where you have the type of sex relations called 'bundling', in which the pair of future lovers will spend nights with each other but without puncturing the hymen. A good proportion of this looked as if it were a way of deferring sex activities for males. Now Dr. Kestenberg is advancing a quite different theory, based on very extensive work with little girls: that the hymen's function is to make the female genital inaccessible to complete exploration (see Birch, 1954).

We have a great deal of clinical material to suggest a failure on the part of the young female completely to integrate any picture of the inside of her body. Dr. Kestenberg suggests that what the hymen does is to interfere with the female child's self-exploration and that this defective exploration combined with a vaginal sensation which she cannot localize are important elements in the development of early female sexuality. The unrealized, or only partially realized, interior of the vagina becomes projected on dolls, on puppies, on parts of the mother's body, on all the small round, soft, pleasant objects that the little girl carries around and cherishes. There is no doubt that we do have a greater acceptance of such objects on the part of girls than of boys. You can get boys to play with dolls and, by a considerable amount of effort, you can equalize the playing time between them and girls for a short period. But there seems to be a rather constant acceptance, on the part of girls, of dolls and doll-substitutes. Dolls are not universal in primitive societies, but they are universal in high civilization, which suggests possibly that one of the necessary prerequisites to psychosexual maturity in the female of the sort that will fit into a high civilization may be this period of delay and the long practice at mothering. Dr. Kestenberg's is a very new hypothesis and is based almost entirely on clinical material. We haven't had time to check it across the cultures that I know something about. There are some other bits of it that are very interesting. She discusses the tendency of the girl to nag and identifies very carefully several periods in the girl's development when she nags. The nagging of women is notorious in many cultures; the mother nagging the child is an exceedingly widespread phenomenon. Dr. Kestenberg suggests that this nagging which can be identified in the behaviour of little girls, is the response to unlocalized vaginal sensations that may begin very early and are unplaced but irritating.

TANNER:
 I just want to put a question to Lorenz. Do other primates have hymens or not?

LORENZ:
 I don't know.

MEAD:
 Guinea-pigs?

TANNER:
 That is different. In guinea-pigs and in other rodents there is a vaginal plug which disappears as a result of oestrogen secretion. The disappearance is one of the signs of puberty in these animals. But oestrogen doesn't do anything to the human hymen—I mean directly!

MEAD:
 As far as I have been able to find out, no one who is an authority on primate anatomy knows of any primate that has a hymen. This is distinctively a human characteristic. Whether this particular theoretical formulation of Kestenberg's is anything more than suggestive I am not prepared to say at this stage, but I do think that one of our problems in the differentiation of male and female is the type of early sexuality (Henry, 1941) and the type of early maternity that are experienced by the girl. One finds that girl children as compared with boys are more prone to put things inside things and those things in turn inside something else. Erik Erikson is going to show us presently slides of contrasting play constructions of girls and boys.
 Certainly something that needs very careful exploration is the precursor of later sexual behaviour in little boys and girls. Here again, we have a terrific degree of contrast. There are societies that forbid all childish manipulation of the genitals; there are societies in which adults put children to sleep playing with their genitals, and there are societies in which groups of people are more or less

joined together by genital association. Among very simple Indians, like the Kaingang in South America, where there is a sort of marriage linkage group—a man will sleep with this or that woman for a fairly short period and children will be added to groups by a very conscious and elaborate sexual manipulation quite young. So one has all varieties of behaviour, from adults who participate in the capacity of young infants to be aroused to societies in which there is a very sharp taboo on any such arousal. I think this is necessary to say because there have been theories that the taboo on masturbation was a necessary concomitant of humanity and that is simply not so, if we follow the range across different sorts of societies. I think I mentioned last year the Siriono and Lepchas where the boys of twelve have access to their older brothers' wives, and where all sexual competition is removed very young. They have as sex partners, the wives of those who would normally be prohibitive, frightening, competitive, towards themselves. Both Siriono and Lepchas are people who, in spite of several hundred years' exposure to higher civilization, have been remarkably resistant to its influence.

There is also a considerable amount of material from complex societies which shows that, for the élite classes, there is a tendency to postpone sexuality for a longer period than in, say, a peasant group or a working-class group in a large city. The point to which the society permits, indulges and enjoys the potential sexuality of young children, and the way in which that is made part of the social organization is another factor which we have to think about in this sex differentiation question. I would think, Konrad, that we ought to have some cross-referencing from animals and birds to human beings about the way the sense of the one body and the sense of the other are developed. Case histories of individuals show that never having seen another human body can be important in determining the psychosexual development and can be considered with the sorts of experience that a child has with its own body and with the bodies of its parents.

LORENZ:

I think self-exploration of that type, curiosity of one's own body, is something very specifically human—the difference between the highest anthropoids and humans may be only quantitative, but if so it is huge.

ERIKSON:

By human, do you mean the species or the culture?

LORENZ:

The species. I am sure that this interest in one's own body, self-exploration, and so on, is the same practically for all human beings.

GREY WALTER:

The mirror test would be pretty specific for that, wouldn't it? There are very few animals below man that take any interest in their own reflection.

LORENZ:

Yes, certainly. The mirror deceives the animal into thinking there is another animal. He is deceived, but still he is interested, he grabs behind the mirror.

GREY WALTER:

But there is no identification.

LORENZ:

No, there is no identification, they do not realize that it is them.

GREY WALTER:

Chimpanzees do, I think.

LORENZ:

Well, I don't know—I think they would.

GREY WALTER:

I seem to remember Lashley told me they act as if they do.

HUXLEY:

It would be very difficult for birds, for instance, to build up a body image because so many of their reactions are to specific releasers. For instance, parent song-birds react equally well to an artificial gape—provided that it is coloured right and has an artificial tongue in it—as they do to their own young. They don't react to their young, they react to a coloured pattern which wobbles. In the same way the male robin reacts aggressively, not to a rival bird, but to a patch of red feathers. It is not a question of a body image, but of an automatic releaser.

LORENZ:

Yes, and actually the treatment of their own body shows you very prettily how little self-exploration takes place in birds. Dela-

77

cour's observation (personal communication) of the Mandarin drake shows that, too: you will remember the bird which failed to grow the ornamental fan feather and yet persisted for years preening the empty air above its back where its feather ought to have been.

HUXLEY:

He just reacted automatically, like the song-bird parent who puts food into the artificial mouth.

ERIKSON:

Concerning the question of latency, if one takes the whole life-span of any animal and compares it with the human life-span, is the possibility of genital intercourse as delayed in any animal species as it is in the human being?

FREMONT-SMITH:

In a condensed life-span you might miss the latency because it would take place in a few days, or weeks, instead of several years.

HUXLEY:

An elephant lives absolutely a long time but he becomes mature relatively early compared to a man. Man is undoubtedly partially neotenous or paedomorphic, in that his juvenile stage has been relatively prolonged. Indeed, sometimes it is prolonged into the sexually adult phase. You don't get any brow ridges in adult human males, because their absence in all primate young has in him been prolonged into adult life.

LORENZ:

And my argument would be that this retardation of becoming a real adult also implies a long residence in the phase of exploratory curiosity which in animals is extremely limited and in all of us, in humans, persists.

TANNER:

Nevertheless, the primate growth curve is very much closer to that of man than it is to that of any of the other mammals. The dichotomy that one sees in comparing mammalian growth curves is between rhesus and chimpanzee and man on the one hand and the others on the other (see Tanner, 1955). If the psychological inference you draw from this is correct it would be very interesting to know what goes on in the rhesus' and the chimp's minds during this time.

HUXLEY:

If I recollect right, a chimp becomes sexually mature at about seven or eight years and may live to forty or fifty. I should have thought, in reference to what Konrad has said about exploratory curiosity being prolonged in primates and especially in man, that this is a biological necessity. If you are going to become a successful biological type through the possession of greater intelligence, you want a longer time for learning.

LORENZ:

It is one of the many conditions that made man Man.

HUXLEY:

And as J. B. S. Haldane pointed out years ago, a pre-condition of that was arboreal life with only one young at a time: otherwise you would have competition *in utero* between the foetuses, with the death of the slower growing ones. So there would have been automatic selection favouring rapid development *in utero*, and the effect of this would have been carried over into post-natal life. It is one of the most beautiful insights that Haldane ever had.

MEAD:

There is a good deal of evidence (Mead, 1935, passim) that this period of latency and exploratory curiosity in boys is stronger than in girls, although I have seen one society where it was reversed, but reversed expensively. This was among the Tchambuli, which was the one group that I worked with where there was a very striking reversal of the expected personality characteristics of each sex: it was not a matrilineal society with structural reversal, but just personality reversal. The men were gossipy, giggly, catty, they went shopping, they spent all their time on their clothes, they had given up warfare and although they were head-hunting people they bought their victims, and then one person held the head-hunting victim while a little boy went and stuck a spear into him and then he was a big man. The women, on the other hand, were bold, brusque, adequate. They were co-operative, they worked in groups, they had moveable stoves so that whenever a group of women wanted to do anything each one carried her own stove and set it down next to the other one, so that there were twenty women cooking and slapping each other on the back. The women did all the marketing and were responsible for the productivity of the society. The men were the consumers. The women had shaved heads and the men wore ringlets, and if they didn't have ringlets, they made ringlets. So that it was a quite striking reversal on the general personality level. Now usually in societies that have initiation, the common male initiation is in a group, and the common female initiation is for a single little girl when she reaches menarche. It is very difficult to get enough little girls at menarche at the same moment, so if you are going to pay attention to the biological reality you have to take one girl at a time. But the Tchambuli had reversed this and they initiated one little boy at a time and fussed over him and dressed him. He acted like a shy little debutante. In this group the little girls were very much like little boys, active, enterprising, curious. It was the little girl who went everywhere I went, carried my camera and wanted to know how the camera worked, and showed the characteristics that we associate with small boys. So the greater curiosity of boys is certainly reversible, but reversible under rather extreme conditions.

It is interesting to speculate whether the post-menopausal stage in women in which women are freed from child-bearing is a stage of the same sort as the prolonged childhood that gives males a period of freedom from psychosexual preoccupation. If women have survived through the menopause they then usually have a higher expectation of life than the men. In many societies post-menopausal women play an exceedingly important role as the custodians of the past, the responsible element of conservation in the society. This may again represent a biological change, because the menopause is also something that does not occur among primates—or at least it is not a regular aspect of primate physiology as we know it at present.

LORENZ:

The oldest chimp of known age, who is 34, Alpha, has had a baby this year. Only a few years ago chimps were still supposed to be perfectly sterile and perfectly senile at this age.

But do you know what Fraser-Darling the stagman wrote on the subject: he said the more tradition, culture, intelligence, personal learning play a role in the ecology of animals, the more important, and valuable, were the old individuals, even if they did not reproduce any more. This, of course, is the case with deer; where the old, old females which are years past reproduction are the leaders and the most powerful social agents; everybody obeys these old, very old ladies. Fraser-Darling's principle might apply to man more than to other living creatures, particularly as compared with anthropoids.

MEAD:

I think in primate societies the old males are treated very badly and have very low social duties.

LORENZ:

Well, I think that's again dependent on something different. The old male is simply chased out by the usurper of his dominant position —that happens with baboons in zoos.

MEAD:

Yes, but this type of dominance is not based on the same sort of knowledge that the old deer has.

ZAZZO:

I should like to come back to this definition of the period of latency. I don't want to minimize the psychosexual reactions in defining this period, but I wonder whether there isn't a certain danger in using these psychosexual reactions as a starting point, as an essential explanatory basis for the definition of this period from six to ten-eleven years. It seems to me that there is a much more general phenomenon of which the sexual reactions are only a factor. It is the general reactions of sociability and of affectivity which are obviously different at that age from what they were previously.

This period of latency is not a radical break with what went before. One notes that even in children between three and six years there are important differences in the social reactions of boys and girls, the boys' reactions being much less affective than the girls'. In the kindergarten, girls are often together, they have activities involving two or three; the boys are much more isolated in their games and other activities. It seems to me that this is accentuated during the period of latency. The contrast that I would like to point out also is that between the affective reactions of the period of three-six years and the social behaviour, the collective life, which starts from six-seven years onwards. Now this form of sociableness is very different from what can be observed previously, and even if there are sexual components there are also others of an intellectual nature. From six-seven years it seems that boys and girls have many more objective interests and activities of a logical, intellectual kind leading to a social life with children of their own age, and to the formation of groups of the same age, which was not the case before six-seven years. This activity continues up to eleven-twelve years; at twelve years it splits up again and one sees again the formation of pairs of friends. Before that there is a reaction of the social group, of the school group, against pairs of friends. One of my colleagues at the Sorbonne, Mr. Cousinet, noted that during the school period between seven and twelve years the whole group reacts aggressively against the formation of pairs. I think, then, that there is a danger in relating the whole description of the period of latency to purely sexual behaviour, the word 'latency' being itself dangerous. We observe a much wider affective phenomenon of which sexuality is only one aspect.

MEAD:

Well, in using the term 'latency' I am perfectly prepared simply to define this phase as a phase when the child gives up overt competition with adults and goes in for a long period of sociability with peers while it is learning. The thing that it seems one finds almost everywhere is the boys giving up the close relationship to the family and going off by themselves. There are societies where the children are kept very warmly and closely in the family and the group does not live in large villages and you may not find children's groups, but whenever there is a large village where there are enough children to play together, then the tendency to play together in a group seems to develop. Here again we have the problem as to whether one thinks of man as having originally lived in towns of two or three hundreds—because if you take a group of semi-nomadic mountain people, such as one finds in parts of New Guinea, there isn't any group of children to play with. There will be the rare family that has three little boys, and they may have a much better time than other people, but children's gangs simply don't exist. I think we have to consider the gang, or the peer group, as a potentiality, but we can't include it as a necessary condition of maturation because living conditions often wouldn't make it possible. A children's play group where children meet for two days once a year is a very different sort of experience from playing together for half of every day.

In using the term psychosexual, I was not referring it only to sexuality but to the difference between the period when the little boy will still treat his father as a rival and the period when he more or less gives that up and consents to wait and roam, and acquire a fair number of skills before he comes back into the rivalry position with adult males. We do have very striking contrasts here between the rivalry of tiny children and that of ten-year-olds. Again culture can accentuate this difference. Among the Mundugumor, little boys of seven will stand up and defy their father over the sister because the sister is supposed to be the proper exchange for a brother's wife. But the males among the Mundugumor are always taking their daughters and exchanging them for extra wives for themselves. And so these small boys of six and seven years old stand up and defy their fathers in a row over a woman, when the sister is considerably older

82

than they are. Such an extreme precocity, in terms of size and ability, is certainly a distortion of what one might normally expect.

MONNIER:
Sending the child to school at the age of six is more than an artificial social intervention in its development. From an electro-physiological standpoint, I think we would all agree that between five and seven there are definite signs in the EEG which point to the fact that the brain of the child has acquired adaptive functions. Because of this maturation of the brain and new adaptive functions, the child is now able to proceed from the exploration of his body to the exploration of the social surroundings, including the school collectivity. Young Arabs I had the opportunity to observe in Beirut, where there is no school obligation, develop spontaneously at this age of six to seven a definite social activity, in spite of the lack of school training. They start to sell things on the street and develop a kind of productive activity.

MEAD:
You can get this change much earlier. For instance, among the Aymara of Peru, four-year-olds are sent out as herders of whole herds of little pigs. Groups of them go out together and they will work together in a way that you don't normally expect to see until children are six or seven. Among the Manus play groups are formed between two and three: and play groups of the same general type that Professor Zazzo was describing as so very characteristic of a later stage.

GREY WALTER:
In regard to the electrophysiological correlates of development and latency I think one should add that, at any rate in our culture, the scatter of this second climacteric in children's brainwaves is very much wider than six to seven years; in fact, the thing that astonishes nearly everyone who studies this subject is the enormously wide scatter of the date at which children are through their second EEG climacteric, which is centred roughly around the school-entry age, about five or six. At that age there is a very wide distribution of degrees of cerebral maturity.

MEAD:
How about sex differences?

GREY WALTER:

As far as we can see—we have made quite careful analyses statistically—none of this scatter relates to sex differences at all; the distribution curves for little boys and girls superimpose quite exactly.

DE SAUSSURE:

I just wanted to recall that among the characteristics of the period of latency Freud stressed the appearance of defence mechanisms. I think that these defence mechanisms play an important part also in the differentiation between the sexes because, particularly for boys, they are partly a defence against affectivity and partly an intellectualization. With this intellectualization there is an isolation between feeling and the intellect which is probably much better developed in the boy than in the girl. The latter can maintain feelings much longer, or if she protests she does it rather by means of an hysterical repression whereas the boy's way would be rather through obsessional defence mechanisms.

HUXLEY:

There are two or three points to consider. One is the point that has already been brought up with regard to the slowing of development and the prolongation of infancy. Konrad Lorenz was telling me yesterday how very intelligent dolphins and porpoises appear to be; I don't know whether we know anything about their rate of development, but that of whales is incredibly fast. A whale which will weigh 100 tons when adult weighs several tons at birth after only about eleven months' gestation; it becomes sexually mature at two or three, and dies of old age, as far as we know, before twenty. It would be very interesting to know whether the development of dolphins is similar.

Another quite different but very interesting point: my wife reminded me that in the Museum at Tréguier in Brittany there is a remarkable exhibit—the plaits of hair of Renan, the great writer and theologian, which were cut off at the age of nine. In those days little Breton boys, I don't know whether of all classes, were brought up with long hair and dressed as girls in order that the fairies shouldn't steal them. It is perhaps of some further interest that Renan was very much dominated by his sister Henriette. I also remember seeing recently a photograph of Oscar Wilde in boyhood: his mother dressed him as a little girl—a fact which again may be significant for his future development.

Finally, in one tribe, I think it is the Bons they are called, in Orissa in India, the women are very handsome but are said to be sexually very frigid. When the women are eighteen or twenty, they choose boys in the pre-pubertal stage and bring them up to be their husbands.

MEAD:

You get that in parts of China where the child-nurse, the little girl who has been the nurse and therefore the surrogate mother of the baby boy, later becomes his wife.

HUXLEY:

I don't think this was an outgrowth of a nursemaid relation, I think it was the way they chose their men; in any case it must have a profound relation to this whole problem of differentiation of sexual identity.

LORENZ:

I have one question that came in my mind when you described the Tchambuli men with the ringlets, who giggled and so on. Quite a number of activities which we ascribe to femininity are in that case transferred en bloc to the other sex. On the other hand we find that certain single characteristics, which we in our culture call male or female, can be transferred separately to the other sex. Now I would be interested to go through all of your material to see which activities go to the other sex together and which activities occasionally singly; and here is the reason why I am interested in this: you know the old story which came up in our last meeting but one, about the relative sexuality in birds, where every sex can perform everything which is characteristic of the other sex, but en bloc. A raven or a jackdaw may behave as a male to a socially inferior partner or completely as a female to one ranking higher than itself in social order, and the sex of the partner does not matter in the least. But the two sets of male and female activities are never dissociated and never mixed. To one given partner the bird behaves either as a male or as a female. Interesting exceptions to this do take place when the social rank-relationship between two sexual partners becomes reversed, for instance if one of them is weakened by illness. J. Nicolai observed this in European bullfinches (*Pyrrhula europæa*): a male was slightly weakened by an illness and instantly the female switched to male activities and vice versa.

Now it seems to me I have to put my question by *reductio ad absurdum;* do you have any society where, let us say, the male is giggly and catty, as we put it, and at the same time strong and a fighter? The question is what is inseparably associated, and what can be transferred to the other sex.

MEAD:

We might find that there were key turning points—for example, the continuation of the falsetto voice might carry these other characteristics with it; or the handling of hair again might be sufficiently crucial so that it might carry other points with it. But I don't think I know of any society where you have women of the reproductive age with shaved heads in which you don't simultaneously have a diminution of femininity in general.

FREMONT-SMITH:

I wonder whether there is any indication in ethological studies that there is one leading character which the others follow.

LORENZ:

Well, with all these potentially ambivalent birds, dominance is the character which determines all others. The dominance relation of one bird to another will determine whether this bird feels 'male' towards his partner and 'female' to another.

FREMONT-SMITH:

And everything else goes with that?

LORENZ:

Everything goes with that; it is called a 'determopath'.

This refers again to a question that I had put to myself; you call certain characters masculine or male and then, when they appear in the other sex, too, you say that they are 'transferred' to that other sex. I wonder how much you are justified, from the ethological point of view, in calling these characters 'male', for short, and talking of 'transference of male characters'.

An interesting thing is that most of what we call 'male' in our culture would be male in the chimp and would be male in the greylag goose and would be male in the horse, and those female characters, cattiness, giggliness, coyness, are all typically female characters in chimps, horses and geese. What your American mother expects of male and female babies, respectively, are just the same, stereotype characters.

86

Yes, and if you look at this from a broad evolutionary point of view, you find that there *is* a greater frequency among males of dominance, large size, exploratory activity—all those things that we are accustomed to think of as masculine. But in a few cases, you get a total reversal, as with Phalaropes and Painted Snipe, and in a great number of cases you get sex equalization, either by both sexes looking and largely behaving like females, or by both sexes developing equivalent mutual display characters, and in that way behaving like males. This occurs in correlation with the mode of life of the species.

A rather important point is that these characters don't always go together in evolution. In species like the Grebes they go together—all the characters are equal in the two sexes, with minor quantitative differences; but in most song birds for instance, the male feeds the young but doesn't brood them: he's half feminine.

MEAD:

There are just one or two other aspects of this problem which I think might be relevant to our discussion. If we look at the way in which an infant is prepared to be an adult in any society, you will find societies in which both male and female infants are treated passively—so that the mother gives the food to the child, who is never expected to demand it; the child lies in a limp, relaxed way, is supported under her breast, is carried around in a net bag, and this passivity of course is a part of the relation between the mother and the child.

If the mother-child relationship has this great emphasis on passivity, then the first years of life, or the period when the child is carried and is breast fed, will have to be reversed later, and may have to be reversed very harshly.

On the other hand, both boys and girls may be treated as exceptionally active, as the Manus do for instance, where the child is encouraged to the highest degree of activity and the mother's breast is treated as a piece of plumbing entirely under the control of the child. Instead of the mother who takes her breast and gives it to the child in what is a complementary inter-personal relationship, you have a mother who happens to have a piece of rubber tubing attached to the front of her person, which happens to be connected with the milk, and the child grabs it, pulls it, pushes it, yanks it around, and you have a more or less continuous battle over it between the mother and the child; the mother isn't very comfortable and the breasts become elongated and unattractive very quickly, with the

87

terrific batterings they take. Now when the children begin to eat, the parents start to stuff the child's mouth with food, and whereas in Bali this is the standard form of feeding which is passively accepted by the child, in Manus the child grabs the food away from the adult and gets a lump in each hand and feeds itself.

FREMONT-SMITH:
No sex differentiation at all?

MEAD:
No sex differentiation—this is true of both boys and girls.

Now traditional Manus culture involved putting very heavy social coercive taboos on girls later. This exceedingly active little girl was expected to go everywhere and do everything her brother did. She swam as well, she managed a canoe as well, she went where her father was, she expected to grab everything that she wanted and then when she was betrothed she had an enormous mat put over her head, and she was told that from then on she couldn't go anywhere where there were men, and had to stay with women—of whom she had a rather low opinion: they also had mats over their heads. It took very heavy sanctions to enforce this new behaviour.

There are all sorts of varieties of this kind of thing. Among the Bathonga in South Africa, for instance, at weaning the child is sent to the mother's village and indulged and played with, and allowed a great deal of licence—up to the time the little boy is about twelve, and then he is sent back home and the men put him through a perfectly terrible initiation ceremony to get him back into shape. One of the things we have to keep carefully focussed is events in the pre-figurative phases of adult sexual life, all the way through from the way one sleeps, the way one is fed, and the way one is taught to walk, and the extent to which one is disciplined, and the degree to which these disciplines are appropriate for males or for females and the degree to which they are or are not differentiated between the two.

In the United States at present we have a period in which little girls are allowed to dress like little boys, which is the reversal of the European period where little boys were dressed so much more like girls. We have an early differentiation in clothes followed by—at about the eight-year- period—little girls all being allowed to put on blue jeans. It is a period when little girls flatly refuse to wear skirts, and there is just beginning now the ritual initiation ceremonies where children graduate from the eighth grade at about thirteen. In one of the famous experimental schools they started the evening in blue jeans, boys and girls dressed exactly alike, and then separated, and the girls went out and dressed in very pretty party dresses, the boys dressed in 'party' boys' clothes, and all came back and finished the evening with a dance. So that we see the development of a new ritual appropriate to handling this particular emphasis.

In any educational trend or in the examination of any social system in terms of sex roles, we have to remember that we don't know whether we get the greatest facilitation of growth by interference or non-interference. That is, you may agree with Gesell and Ilg's contention (Mead, 1947) that five is a much better age to start school than six, and conclude that in the United States we start children to school at the age when they are least prepared to go there. But we don't know whether starting children to school at the age they are best prepared to go there will produce the maximum effort or not. We don't know for instance whether the greatest degree of feminization of baby girls and masculinization of baby boys from birth would be the way to develop the bisexual capacities of each. There is considerable material that suggests that this doesn't develop whole human beings, that you don't develop the person as much if you over-develop the bipolarity between the two sexes.

There is one rather obvious comment that gets made on sex differences, and that is women deal with people, and men deal with things. Professor Zazzo said, for example, that little boys organize space better and have a greater interest in mechanical things, in things that are constructed. But it raises the question as to what, in different societies, is considered as things and what as people. In some societies, for instance, teaching is male; but when it is assigned to males then you may be dealing with public roles and there may be little discussion, little emphasis on certain types of human relations. Erik, do you want to make your point about the old Professor here? The point you were making last night about the fact that we permit the elderly professor to take a maternal role to some extent towards his student again?

ERIKSON:
Well, referring back to the puberty rites where the men behave in a certain ritualistic way as women, we said that this obviously had the meaning of telling the novitiates: from now on the group will be mother to you. We also said that this takes place in specific relation to the initiation into a new life stage, a clan, or certain occupations. I added privately my impression that in our specialized life, certain occupations take over that role. I thought of some such occupation as a professor who is permitted at least in some

cultures a lesser degree of display of masculinity. He can wear longer hair and have a certain leaning toward, let us say, 'unmanly' interests.

FREMONT-SMITH:
It is respectable to be gentler. . . .

ERIKSON:
Gentler, more aesthetic, more impractical.

MEAD:
And this of course is true of the physician, as well as the professor, In other words, you have in the parent-child, in the mother-child, in the father-child, in the contrast between the sexes, a great set of models which may be used at any point in the institutional structure. The mother-child relationship may be repeated later between a man and an adolescent, or between a man and his wife. The whole institutional structure, when one looks at a society, can be analysed in terms of the recurrence of themes, with changes of sex roles very often, from one point to another. And we can't really understand the problem of personality or identity in any specific culture, without understanding the way in which at different periods in life, and in different occupational situations, one or another of these possible patterns of relationship can be used.

Sex Differences in Play Construction
of Twelve-year-old Children

ERIKSON:
Saturday morning lends itself well to an interlude between this week's and next week's discussions. I will present material from an investigation of sex differences in play construction of twelve-year-old children, which will continue our discussion of sex differences. At the same time, it will prepare the matter of clinical observation. These children were the subjects of a long-range developmental study. Almost twenty-five years ago, the parents of every third child born in Berkeley, California during a given period were asked to participate in a study made possible by a grant from the Rockefeller Foundation to the Institute of Child Welfare in the University of California. Dr. Jean Walker Macfarlane is the director of the study. I worked with her when the children were eleven, twelve and thirteen years old (they are now about twenty-five) and one of the procedures employed was that to be reported here.

Here, then, a new medium comes up for discussion. Such play observations as I will report today originate primarily in clinical work though I will reserve the discussion of clinical observation as such for next week. But I would like to tell you one brief clinical example in order to demonstrate the survival-value of play observation at any rate for the *therapist*. When I first came to America, I was asked to see a little boy of eight. His main symptom was soiling. This boy had been seen by a number of outstanding child psychiatrists, and they had not been able to find out what was wrong. There always came a moment in therapy when the boy would soil and stop responding to psychiatric questioning. Why? Not being able to understand his particular dialect too well, I started to play with him. Suddenly there was a gleam in his pale face, and he said, 'Let's play grocery store; I am the truck driver and you are the grocery man. I will deliver nuts to you.' 'Nuts' means crazy people—that much I had already learned in contact with American psychiatrists—so I became eager to see what he was going to 'deliver'.

He took plasticine, made balls of different sizes and different colours, and loaded a dump truck with them. Then he dumped the 'nuts' in the corner of the 'grocery store' which I had built for him. He took one big red ball and said 'This is Mummy nut'. Then he took a number of small red balls and said, 'These are the baby nuts' (I noticed that he took as many as there were children in his family). Then he took a big green ball and said, 'This is Uncle nut'. So I said to him 'Why does this family have an Uncle nut but not a Father nut?' At this point he soiled and left the room. The conclusion was obvious, that in his family there was an uncle, a somebody called an uncle, who was in the centre of what this boy had kept from his psychiatrists. This proved correct. His mother had told him, 'You can tell the psychiatrists everything, but if you tell them about the uncle, father will kill me'. But in play hieroglyphs, he could not help delivering the real 'nuts', in his family situation. This is not unconscious material, yet he did not realize that he had expressed it until my question made him aware of it. Such experiences, then, establish the clinical working hypothesis that, if you give an acutely troubled child play material to work with, the child will in play language in some way express his trouble, and this especially if you do not just listen to his words, but also watch the configurations of colour, size, arrangement, and so on. This is a statement on the *clinical* use of play, not on the nature of play. In other words, I want to disavow a 'traumatic' theory of play as such.

FREMONT-SMITH:

It seems to me highly important that when the child was asked the crucial question he didn't answer it, but instead had a vegetative response which he couldn't control, and defecated. This is an essentially psychosomatic situation in which the cortex cannot function and the lower centres are released, and you get a body-response which may be in behaviour or may be in a vegetative reaction.

ERIKSON:

Now in this case, and in others, play observation helps the therapy to survive even where full verbal communication fails. When I came to the Guidance Study in Berkeley the problem was different. I was not supposed to interview the children, because here the survival question was, how does one keep a long-range study together? There were parents who had trustingly given their children for two interviews every year, who had themselves come twice every year, who had let the children be photographed, tested, measured, and they had done this for the great Rockefeller Foundation and for the director of the study. The idea that their children would be exposed to a psychoanalyst, so it was felt, might be just one good thing too many. Here the study had to survive *me*. My work then consisted primarily in an attempt to take the data gathered on these twelve-year-old children, and to write a dynamic biography with a measure of prediction. My only systematic personal contact with the children consisted of a play method which was meant to give me one fresh impression in material to which my clinical eyes were accustomed. Each child, on three occasions half a year apart, would come into my room and find the following situation there.

There is a square table with a square blackboard of the same size. Any configuration built on this table will thus appear in an imaginary cube and have clear co-ordinates. Beside and behind this table there are two shelves with toys: blocks, people, cars and animals. There was no systematic selection of toys. I went to a toy store and bought what was available. In that sense (as in others) this cannot be called an experiment.

Now when the child came in I would say, 'I am interested in moving pictures. I would like to know what kind of moving pictures children would make if they had a chance to make pictures. Of course, I cannot provide you with a real studio and real actors and actresses; you will have to use these toys instead. Choose any of the things you see here and construct on this table an *exciting* scene out of an imaginary moving picture. Take as much time as you want and tell me afterwards what the scene is about.'

The children built their scenes and I sat at my desk. I sketched the intermediate stages, scenes that they built and then changed or replaced, and noted how they seemed to go about their task, and their whole attitude towards the play. At the end I asked one question: 'What is the most exciting thing in this scene?' This was necessary because often when I looked at the final scene, there was nothing obviously exciting. In the case of a girl, there may be a living room, a little girl playing the piano and the family listening to her; or in boys, there is traffic on the street, there is a policeman, everything is quiet. There seems often to be almost an amnesia for my suggestion that something exciting should be presented. At the end of the procedure I would tell them that the scene was very nice, and they would leave. Then I would photograph the scene.

While this was not the purpose of the study, gradually I received a definite impression of sex differences. I blotted out the 'M's' and

93

'F's' on the little identification tags which can be seen in the pictures, and give the scenes of seventy-five boys and seventy-five girls to two advanced graduate students, one man and one woman, with a list of block configurations. The problem was: could they identify my criteria for particular block configurations, such as a simple enclosure, a building, a bridge, a street crossing, and so on, and then could they rate each picture for the presence and absence of such configuration. This statistical procedural basis was published in two papers. (Erikson 1951, Honzik 1951.)

Now as I show you some pictures, I wish you would pay attention to whether there are blocks at all, or whether there aren't; if there are blocks, whether they make for high buildings or low buildings, whether the buildings are open or closed, whether the whole construction is in the foreground or in the background; and whether the buildings contain people and animals or are surrounded by people and animals. The sex differences lie in these simplest spatial relationships.

FIG. 1

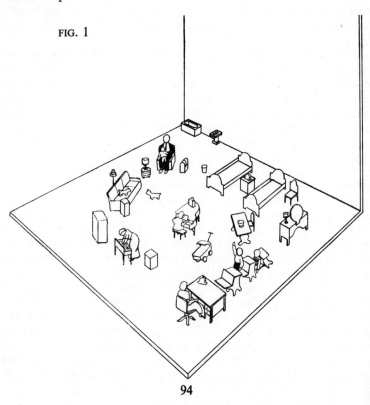

Fig. 1, I would classify as an open interior. There are no walls around the house, nor walls separating the different rooms of the house. This is a kind of construction which occurs significantly more often in girls' scenes.

HUXLEY:
This kind of construction represents a number of rooms for different functions, study and sleep and so forth though, doesn't it?

ERIKSON:
Yes, but without walls. There is a study, a kitchen, a bedroom. Within the 'typical' configuration there was usually a 'unique' element, which would lead me further into the history of the child. Such unique elements I will point out later.

FREMONT-SMITH:
Did you know the history of the child before she came in?

ERIKSON:
I knew some of it, but I would take a fresh look after the play construction because of that clinical working hypothesis—that if you give a child space to play with, she will not only be playful in a variety of ways, i.e. express mastery, but also indicate what she has not mastered entirely. I may add in this case that the distribution of the toys over the whole table I have come to consider a sign of good balance in a child. Later on I will show you some examples of constructions which are entirely built against the wall, or entirely out in one corner, in which case a particular strain can be assumed.

INHELDER:
Was the child talking while playing?

ERIKSON:
No. Most children would not, until they said, 'I am finished'.

FREMONT-SMITH:
The majority of these children became sufficiently preoccupied so that they worked silently?

ERIKSON:
Yes. In fact, the degree of concentration was really surprising. 'Conflict' may be too strong a word, but to see a twelve-year-old put a chair there, or a block, and then pause, and then take it away

and put something else there—you could feel that the spatial task had a peculiar fascination.

INHELDER:

Very young children are absolutely unable to work and play without talking; verbal and manual activities in the beginning are intimately related.

ERIKSON:

Yes. This is one reason among many why a transition would have to be made in any developmental study between the age when the child would prefer to play on the floor, or would play with the toys without the aim of a final construction, and the age when the children would be able to 'construct' silently. This was *constructing* and not play in the sense of toying, handling, or manipulating with running commentary.

FREMONT-SMITH:

Would you say that these twelve-year-olds a good part of the time were sufficiently preoccupied that they lost their awareness of you as an observer?

ERIKSON:

In an overt sense, yes: in the vast majority of cases they paid no attention to me. However, I have the impression that a thorough analysis would find references to the observer both in the content and in the spatial arrangement.

BOWLBY:

Of course there is always a communication because you have asked them to communicate.

ERIKSON:

Yes; a communication condensed into a completed construction with a theme. If one compared the verbal output that appeared at the end of these play constructions with that in Rorschach tests, or TAT tests, it was remarkable how, in this case, the energy of confabulating was apparently absorbed by the activity of constructing and how very brief were the stories told at the end. In fact, I often had the feeling that the children often told me 'just anything' and that the important thing was in the arranging.

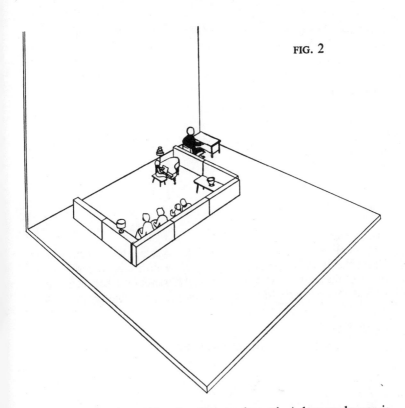

FIG. 2

Fig. 2 is what I would call a 'low enclosure'. A low enclosure is one that is only one block high, has no ornaments, no roof, no tower, but on occasion an 'elaborate front door'. This again is on the whole a feminine construction. Boys build such enclosures primarily in connexion with more complicated structures. In this case, the low enclosure is attached to the background, in fact, it opens up toward the wall.

TANNER:
These are all twelve-year-olds, aren't they? Some had reached menarche and some had not, I take it. Was there any difference between pre- and postmenarcheal?

ERIKSON:
I undertook one preliminary study with our paediatrician on the appearance of a particular play configuration which seemed to have

a relationship to the appearance of the sesamoid bone in the hand (which in turn is related to the menarche). There was a definite relationship.

GREY WALTER:
What is the number of children?

ERIKSON:
In this play study there were 150—75 boys and 75 girls.

TANNER:
All twelve years old?

ERIKSON:
Eleven, twelve or thirteen—the children came twice a year so it was either the end of the eleventh year, the twelfth year or the beginning of the thirteenth. Today I am not differentiating between chronological ages but refer to the overall maturational stage of pre-puberty.

INHELDER:
Then you have two or three samples from each child?

ERIKSON:
Yes.

BOWLBY:
Was there any essential difference between the first, the second and the third presentation?

ERIKSON:
Overt differences, very much so. But often with a theme that goes through all of one child's constructions.

LORENZ:
I was going to ask the opposite question. Was there a significant similarity or identity for the same child in the three constructions?

ERIKSON:
Overt similarity, in some. Identity of themes in most. I will illustrate this later.

LORENZ:

Sufficiently so that you could say of any one of them: I recognize this as. . . .

ERIKSON:

No. Only when I analysed them would I see what theme ran through. Maybe after having analysed a few hundred more I would learn to recognize individual styles.

FIG. 3

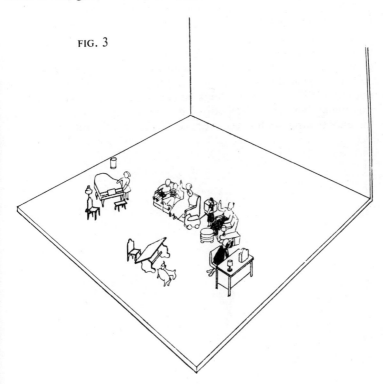

Fig. 3 is a very feminine configuration. Not only are there no walls, but a round arrangement of furniture, with either an animal or a male breaking into the circle. Sometimes both appear—such as father coming home on a lion and right behind him, upholding a semblance of law and order, a policeman. The Fig. 3 configuration was done by an Italian-American girl. You see how visibly excited that family is. The child spent quite some time turning their arms up in the air. The exciting thing is that a little pig has run into the

99

family house, and in this case it is not the policeman, but the dogs who are trying to protect the house.

HUXLEY:

Coming in also?

ERIKSON:

So it seems. I might mention that after a while I became so used to sex differences that it disturbed me when a boy did something which I thought only girls did. There was one boy who built such a scene of a round configuration of furniture, he had a whole row of wild animals march into the house. This boy said 'Goodbye', went to the door, stopped, and said, 'There is something wrong', turned around, and rearranged the animals on a tangent to the circle, walking by, not into the house. Do you think he had noticed that I thought there was something wrong, telepathy, I mean? At any rate he was one of the only two boys who ever produced such a configuration.

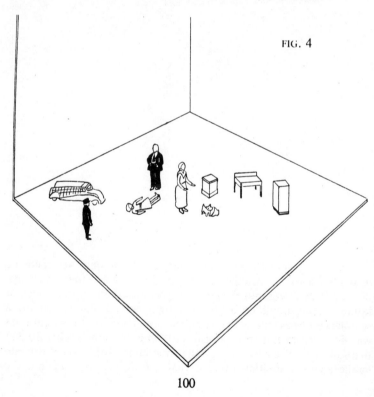

FIG. 4

Fig. 4 is also a feminine configuration: there is a lack of differentiation between indoors and outdoors. A home scene (a little dog overturns a bowl) and a traffic accident fused into one another without any differentiation of indoors and outdoors.

ZAZZO:
Is the surface on which you build always the same size?

ERIKSON:
Yes, certainly.

HUXLEY:
The diagonal arrangement in Fig. 4 is curious—does it represent anything? Some tension between something or other?

ERIKSON:
Yes, indeed, a conflict between staying close to the wall and wishing to get away from it. It has to do with tension over emancipation from the mother. It is as if the accident would indicate 'You had better stay close'—while the little dog represents mischievousness.

LORENZ:
I was a very strictly brought up child, and I distinctly remember a time when I was just allowed to take walks by myself, to go hunting, and to go fishing alone. And then I never went on trodden pathways, but always in diagonals across the fields. I can definitely remember that this was to prove my own independence.

ERIKSON:
Fig. 5 is a girl's high enclosure, with only one ornamental block—and that is on the gate. Again, the opening is toward the back wall. Inside there is a bullfight which the family watches.
Now we come to the boys. The policeman is of all people the figure used most in the boys' constructions, twice as often as the cowboy, for example, who certainly in Western America is an outstanding image of identification. But there is an exclusively masculine scene at this age—just traffic and a policeman to guard it. This does not need illustration.

101

U

FIG. 5

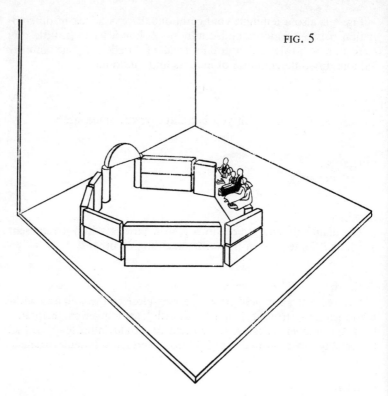

GREY WALTER:
You had cowboys available?

ERIKSON:
Yes, and Indians.

Fig. 6 is a boy's construction: a locomotive constructed out of blocks. I would definitely call this an 'elaborate building', and as a building it is a very masculine construction. Yet, when I asked the boy 'What is so exciting about it?' he said that is a very, very narrow bridge, which that train has to squeeze through. This boy had an acute and painful phimosis. Thus what dominates at the moment as a discomfort or a conflict enters by way of a unique detail in what otherwise is a normal and in fact outstanding performance.

Fig. 7 is a typical boy's construction. There is an Indian who wants to attack a fort, which, as you see, has many guns. Boys, more often than girls, erect buildings, cover them with roofs, provide them with ornaments and other items which stick out: towers, guns, etc.

FIG. 6

FIG. 7

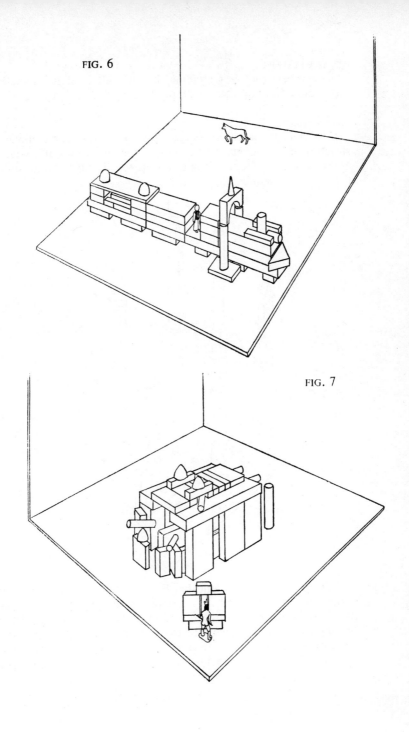

Why is it typically masculine, because after all it's something rather closed in and there isn't any traffic?

ERIKSON:
It is typically masculine because it is the erection of a complicated structure. This configuration can occur together with traffic or it can alternate with traffic. I will later on list together the various criteria for masculine and feminine.

FIG. 8

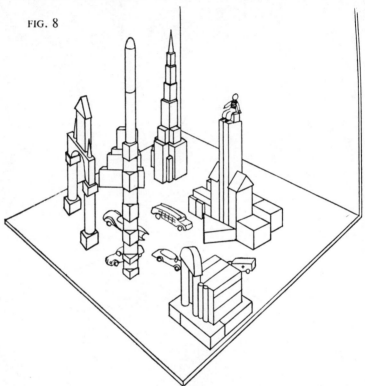

I do not need to point out that Fig. 8 is a boy's construction. It is almost too masculine. It isn't just height that is masculine. In connexion with the highest towers and buildings there is in the exciting or unique element a downward trend, as if such height went too far. He 'stuck his neck out'. In this case, the exciting element is that the proud boy sitting on top of the world is really insane, and in fact, on top of a sanatorium.

FREMONT-SMITH:
He said that?

ERIKSON:
Yes. Some of the highest buildings are counteracted by some downfall, some danger. I asked another boy who built the very highest tower, 'What is the exciting thing about this?' he said, 'You must not touch it. It is built in such a way that it would collapse, if you touch it.' I might add that ruins, that is buildings that have broken down, are exclusively male, with one exception which I will show you later.

HUXLEY:
In Fig. 8 the gateway is very like the feminine gateway you showed before. Do boys frequently add that to their constructions?

ERIKSON:
Yes, there are, of course, low enclosures, gateways, and other 'female' configurations in boys, but they are mostly in conjunction with a high building. In this construction, the gate is actually that of a bank and the 'insane' boy had tried to break into it. Thus the gate is part of an intrusive theme, which leads to the downfall.

RÉMOND:
Do you allow the child a fixed time to build what he wants to show you, or do you give him as long as he likes?

ERIKSON:
It is not fixed.

HUXLEY:
How long was it usually?

ERIKSON:
Anywhere from two minutes to half an hour. Some children would get it over with very quickly, and get out, though not without leaving some message which would indicate their motivation for this. The only child who entirely refused to build a construction, and said that it was all too childish a task was the smallest child in the study. I think she, too, got her message across.

We now have enough elements available to decipher just a few more complicated statements.

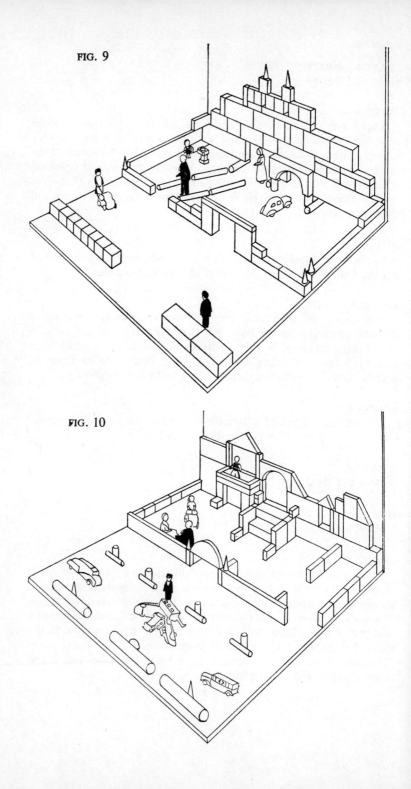

FIG. 9

FIG. 10

Fig. 9 is by a boy who at the time was highly dependent on his mother, and with a certain 'façade' of aloofness. This is expressed by a high façade, leaning against the background. But not only that. When I asked him 'What is the exciting element?' he said that this man (the 'father') has placed some bombs underneath that façade. You can see the cylinders. So here again, his high façade, if you pushed slightly, would collapse. But now let's see how such a theme may develop as time passes.

Fig. 10 shows his later construction, again a façade, this time well founded, but still against the background. The boy standing there, high and mighty. The same cylinders which before had represented bombs are now out here, each one kept by a peg from rolling towards the building. So he has regained safety. I cannot go now into that critical year in the family history.

FREMONT-SMITH:
He has regained safety, but he has not forgotten the danger?

ERIKSON:
He has 'displaced' it. Yes.

LORENZ:
My only objection is that it is too beautiful!

ERIKSON:
I know—it was my objection too for a long time.

Fig. 11 you may also find too good to be true. Here is the only child whose mother came in with her. I had to ask the mother to wait outside.

This child builds a boardwalk against the back wall, and another one coming out into space. Not a diagonal then, but two separate tendencies, to hang on to the background and to come out. Let me show how the repetition of a theme underlines this configuration. Here is a cowboy guarding a bull. Here is a policeman guarding a bear, a tiger and a lion. Here is an Indian guarding the baby. So that you see that in content and form the emphasis is on the 'Mother watches over me, I hang on to her'. In this particular case, attempt at a symbiosis with the mother was clinically evident.

Incidentally, only two children ignored the table altogether. One was this girl, the other a very meek little coloured boy. He built under the table. He nearly made me cry. He didn't dare to build where the others did.

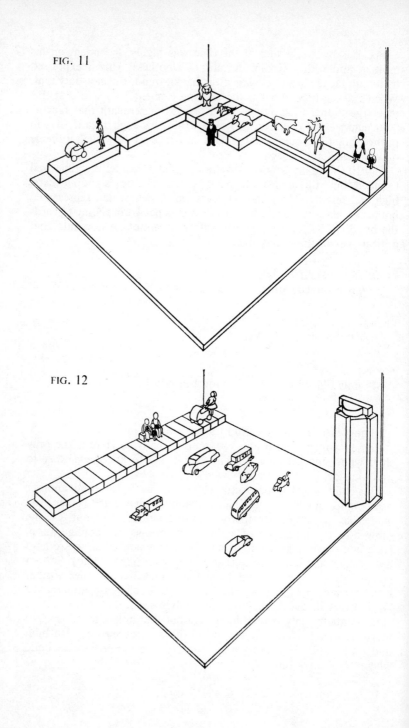

FIG. 11

FIG. 12

Fig. 12 is the construction made by the same girl half a year later. The conflict over emancipation from the mother is now more clearly counterpointed. There is a 'tower', hugging the background, and there is a board-walk reaching out, and the children sit and watch the world go by. Such changes in configuration often correspond to clear-cut changes in the interview material secured by other workers. Incidentally, the only high towers built by girls are in the back third of the table, and the highest tower built by any girl was built on the shelf back behind the table.

Fig. 13 is an example of the development of one theme during one session. This boy was an enuretic. He started with this phallic tower out in the foreground. Then he took the tower down. His configuration then went downwards and backwards to Fig. 14. He moved it into the background, and made it a low enclosure such as is typical for girls. At the same time, his final story 'regressed', as it were, for it concerned a sleeping baby.

HUXLEY:
Was this in the same interview?

ERIKSON:
Yes. In later constructions he overcame these trends. Here in Fig. 15 is his brother, at the time more 'outgoing' and more masculine. The similarity of initial configuration is uncanny. I do not believe that he could have possibly known what his brother had built. He starts with a phallic tower of more moderate height. But then (Fig. 16) he builds outward, retaining the tower, and adds what I call a 'barrier'—an exclusively male configuration. By the same token his story is concrete and up-to-date: this represents the entrance to the San Francisco World's Fair.

Let me now try and summarize the masculine variables and the feminine ones. The channelization of traffic through tunnels and street crossings is masculine and so is the erection of elaborate and high structures. To this corresponds the theme of the policeman who arrests dangerous motion, and the theme of a downward trend which counteracts excessive height. Then, on the other hand, simple walls which merely enclose interiors are feminine, with an emphasis by ornamentation on the vestibular access to the interior. Interiors without walls are feminine. So is the intrusion into such an interior of a dangerous or mischievous animal or male creature. On the other hand, the peaceful scene, say of a girl playing the piano for the family, is also a typically female 'exciting scene'. Enclosing a space

109

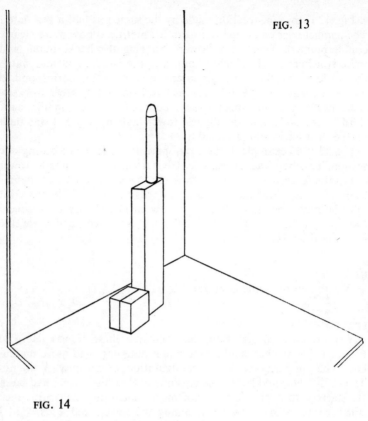

FIG. 13

FIG. 14

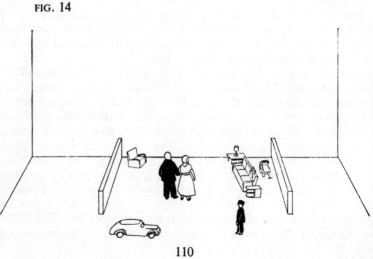

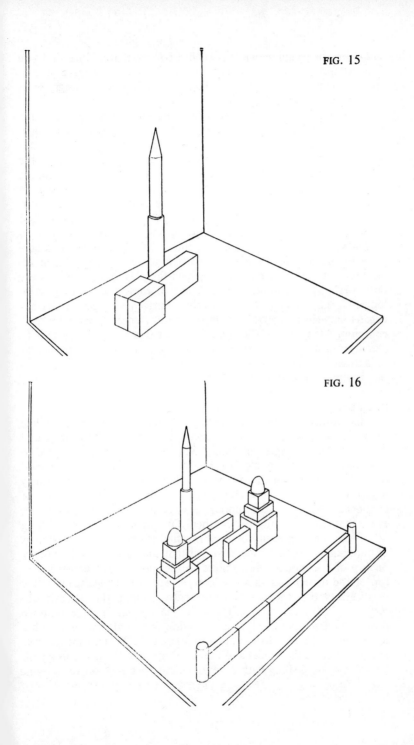

FIG. 15

FIG. 16

with three or four low walls is such a common procedure that you have to specify whether or not such an enclosure appears in conjunction with high buildings, whether it is enclosing things, or is surrounded by things.

Without prejudging the discussion, one basic fact can be stated now, namely the analogy between the sex differences in play-configurations and the primary physiological sex-differences, that is in the male the emphasis on the external, the erectable, the intrusive, and the mobile—in the female, on the internal, on the vestibular, on the static, on what is contained and endangered in an interior. You will recognize immediately that these are all configurations which in Margaret Mead's material appeared in manifold cultural elaborations. Contrary to what some of you may think in an analyst looking at his material, these differences came as a surprise to me, having leaned toward a kind of anthropological relationism at the time. The age at which the play constructions were done perhaps determines the closeness of these themes to physiological facts. At ages eleven, twelve, thirteen changes in the sex organs as well as overall sex impulses must enter at least the preconscious awareness of the child. Whether this has to do more with actual information, by direct observation, or with a particular kinaesthetic tension, or with instinctual drives or something else—this I will leave for the discussion.

ZAZZO:

What always bothers me with psychoanalytic explanations like those you gave us just now is that the symbolism is too direct and too close. For example, the wall which would symbolize the need to lean on the mother—couldn't it really express a much more general fact, of which the seeking for the mother's support is an extremely important aspect for the child, but only one aspect: the lack of confidence, the desire for support is something much more general, even, than the need for the mother. The phenomenon of 'sticking to' or 'closing' has been observed in small children. In the drawings of children up to three years we see that the copy is made directly on top of the model, they adhere to the model, they construct on top of the model and they are not yet capable of measuring space or disassociating themselves from space. Among the patients observed by Mayer Gross and among the hypoxic people that we observed ourselves there was a regression to this attitude of sticking to the model. You notice it for example in the Porteus mazes: our patients stick to the model and they can't get out of the mazes again. I think we are dealing with a very general phenomenon showing at various levels the subject's difficulty of autonomous expression. In the small child this phenomenon is so obviously linked to the need for the mother that I think it would be dangerous to consider automatically that the keeping close to walls is a hanging on to the mother. I see the mother as a particular case, extremely important, but which cannot furnish the principle explaining this general attitude.

ERIKSON:

I think that your observations support my point. I used the word 'mother' to connote one image of dependency among many, and yet the original model of what one was 'attached' to. The fact that sick people would show a tendency to 'adhere', and, as you said, to 'regress' would give one the right to say that these people wish to lean on somebody in a way which is modelled on the original need for maternal protection. In my material, I would add that I had at my disposal ten years of observations made by others and ratings by other workers. It is true, of course, that these ratings did not always concern a lasting manifest and conscious mother-dependence. Often such a dependence is sporadic, latent, and unconscious, and must be inferred from behaviour and from projective tests. So, if I say that there was a coincidence between spatial tendency in play and some kind of mother-dependence in life, this is not a symbolic judgement. All the same, I would conclude that to accept a wall as a symbol of a mother in imaginative material opens up much to our understanding which would otherwise remain hidden.

My reference to 'mother' was not intended as a full causal explanation. I think this has been imputed to me rather on the basis of what an analyst is expected to do. I described something and I pointed to a configurational relationship.

ZAZZO:

You spoke of mothers and it seems to me you spoke explicitly of mothers when one gets close to a wall. Now since yesterday I have had a bad foot because I twisted it and I go along holding on to the wall. Is it the need for my mother that makes me hang on to the wall because I twisted my foot and why did I twist my foot?

ERIKSON:

Well, of course, in reality walls are not mothers, mothers not walls, and a *mal au pied* is only deplorable. But in imaginative material, a wall can symbolize maternal protection. I would claim a right to use such a symbol in an individual dream or play-act, if

113

the associative material supports it. Here, the probability is supported by a comparison of these children by independent observers.

PIAGET:

As regards space I should like to say a word on the difference between boys and girls. We find differences as regards space in all kinds of connexions and not only in games. For example, in the results of factorial analysis, the spatial factor is better represented among boys than among girls. On the other hand, in experiments on perception we generally get better results—that is less pronounced systematic errors—among boys than among girls. As regards space representation I think that Mlle Inhelder would agree with me —it is true that we have not carried out systematic studies on the differences in the sexes—that there too the boys are slightly advanced in relation to girls. I note then a difference as regards cognitive functions (perception and intelligence). You show this, moreover, from the affective point of view in the symbolism of play. There are complex relations between the two kinds of fields. It is very possible that we are dealing with transformations that are simultaneously affective and intellectual. I myself would certainly think so. But it is also possible that one of the factors involves the other and I know psychoanalysts who consider that it is the affective factor which constitutes the primordial one and that this leads to intellectual transformations. I think personally that there are here a series of correlated factors without one factor dominating the other, because the affective (or energetic) aspect and the cognitive (or structural) aspect of behaviour are always interdependent and inseparable.

HUXLEY:

I was going to make a rather similar observation. That boys are more interested in mobility, in traffic and in the outer world, and that, as we heard yesterday, they are more mechanically inclined, are obviously correlated, as you say, with their own anatomy, but is it necessary to think that there is only one cause of this? Is there not also perhaps a higher tonicity and a greater interest in manipulation, and these then get focused on their anatomy, and the two reinforce each other and build up a complex structure?

ERIKSON:

I think that these sex differences are less symbolic than they are the experimental stuff out of which symbolism emerges. Now, in spite of my instruction to present an 'exciting scene from an imaginary

114

moving picture', little of the kind was produced. These children go to moving pictures once or twice a week. In 450 constructions there were very few motion-picture scenes, and there were hardly any dolls who were named after famous motion-picture stars of the kind that are on the billboards, in the press, and actually on the walls of the children's rooms.

Next, take the actual aspirations of the children. The cowboy was used much less than the policeman. There was an aviator figure available, and at that time, there was an enormous stepping-up of armament in the air. Some elder brothers of our boys and many of the boys themselves, at that time, wanted to become aviators. But the aviator figure was chosen only a little more than the figure of the monk. There were toy automobiles. For the young girls as well as the young boys in California, the wish to drive and some day own an automobile is very important. In fact, Margaret said something yesterday about the automobile already becoming more or less an accessory of the American female, while the airplane becomes the symbol of the executive male. This has an interesting sociological counterpart in the fact that in California it is now the girls who ride horses, and that many boys consider it effeminate to be a passionate horse-lover. Nevertheless, the girls in these constructions use much fewer automobiles and horses. All of this would make it difficult to come to any simple sociological explanation for the preferences shown here. The use of space and of things moving in it seems to serve more basic 'play-tendencies'.

INHELDER:

Have you also found appreciable differences in terms of age in the way children represent these scenes? Do the youngest ones take more elements from immediate reality, whereas the older ones elaborate the events symbolically? We have observed during imaginary games between several children facts which, at first sight, seemed contradictory. Emotionally well-balanced children of five to eight years, playing in groups of three, improvised imaginary games whose elements reproduced fairly faithfully their daily life, whereas those of eight to ten years seemed to take a very special pleasure in making up symbolic scenes (every symbolic game of course pre-supposes a certain amount of fiction). This late symbolic development is no doubt due to the difficulty experienced by children in improvising symbolic scenes involving several children. Have you noted similar differences in your individual symbolic games or have you, on the contrary, noted a development in the opposite direction, going from pure fiction to a more faithful copy of reality?

ERIKSON:

I know the play of smaller children only in clinical situations. It was obvious that in these constructions girls, more often than boys, would immediately put people together, a trend which may correspond to what Margaret said yesterday about the woman's closer relationship to people in preference to things and ideas.

GREY WALTER:

Could I ask a rather general question? I wonder whether you could help those of us who lack background training in the field of psychoanalysis to assimilate these very rich titbits of information, by suggesting how we could regard them from the standpoint of the theory of communication? The first thing I personally should like to have defined would be the noise-level and the band-width of the channel through which you and the children are communicating. This play of theirs is essentially a language. But in my case the channel is of unknown band-width—I don't know how many bits of information can be conveyed per second, I don't know how rich a language it is. I haven't yet gathered how many things the child could do. And I don't know the noise-level—I don't know how much randomness there is in the choice of the items the child used.

ERIKSON:

I have described how the child comes in, and how the child finds on these few shelves a great number of blocks of all sizes and shapes. . . .

GREY WALTER:

Always in the same position, equally accessible for each child?

ERIKSON:

Oh, yes. Rearranged after each child leaves, in the same way, except that of course the blocks are lying in a heap, the small blocks by themselves, and the big blocks by themselves, and the ornamental items by themselves. Then the toys are arranged in boxes, but, as I said, they were toys of all sizes, materials and colour. Since I had no principle on which I could standardize I just took what I found.

FREMONT-SMITH:

About how many toys were there?

ERIKSON:

I would say about ten cars; and there was an airplane, which was almost never used. There was a little family, father, mother, a boy

116

of let us say fifteen, a girl of twelve, a little girl of six, and a little boy of five, and a baby. These were German dolls, and came in a box, and were beautifully done and could be bent. Some of the other toys could not be bent. The policeman was a lead figure and so was the aviator.

Speaking of communication, I would like briefly to add something which may not refer to Grey Walter's question. But I cannot deny a feeling that not everybody would get such constructions from children. If one is used to eliciting information from people I think one behaves differently than if one wonders if they are going to give or not. In the way I invited the child to perform, I may have expressed that I expected something pretty good here. Afterwards, I was myself very much impressed with the fact that much of this was too good to be true. Maybe my clinical experience made me select the right combination of stimuli. The procedure has been repeated once by some other workers on a large scale with college students, and the results were disappointing. But when I asked, 'Did you give instructions?' the psychologists said, 'Our instructions were like yours. We asked them "Build on this paper the most *traumatic* scene of your childhood"!' That explained, of course, the fact that the students immediately shrank and did the most conventional things, carefully hiding anything that might have been traumatic. In my work with college students I used the instruction to produce a *dramatic* scene out of an imaginary play.

FREMONT-SMITH:
Nobody else tried your instructions with these children? So that you are the only sort of receptor for the material? It has been brought out again and again in such simple things as taking an IQ on a child, that the relationship established may make an enormous difference in the IQ result. One would expect that the children would feel at once that someone has a natural understanding of them and that they would be freer and bring out material which they might not bring out to someone who did not have an equally receptive understanding.

MEAD:
I think it is also important in connexion with Grey's question to point out that these objects are all highly culturally patterned. Blocks of this sort have been made for children in western European and American culture for a long time, and they represent a crystallization of age-long symbolism. The fact that you can't bend a policeman might also be regarded as symbolic. All the objects are very

highly standardized. We can compare this with Margaret Lowenfeld's world game, where she has made a systematic attempt to get all possible relevant material. That is, if the towns have lamp-posts in them, then there is a lamp-post in the test, and so forth. She is attempting to present the child with a vocabulary range that is very wide, whereas what Erik was doing was giving them just enough material with which to react. Now when I use play materials I restrict them a great deal more still. A doll, a snake and a teddy bear, for instance, is a very good combination. You can do almost everything with it, and you don't want much more, if what you want is to get a general pattern rather than individual differences.

GREY WALTER:

I like to think of these observations as linguistic ones, because they are using at least a culturally determined vehicle in the same class as a language, which one can define in terms of letters, syllables, phonemes and so forth. Do you consider the elements with which you provide the children (approximately twenty elements apart from the blocks which are the punctuation marks and spaces in the language, so to speak) as letters or as words? For example, can these elements make nonsense? If a child says a word, that obviously has a meaning, it has a semantic content, but a letter has no semantic content, except some single letters like 'a' and 'I' in English and so on.*

*Reading through this discussion I feel that these clinical methods could be enormously improved if they were planned and analysed as problems in Communication Theory. Unfortunately, this is beyond my competence but I would refer to the first Gospel in the New Testament of Communication, the *Mathematical Theory of Communication* by Claude Shannon & Warren Weaver (1949). As an example of this approach to linguistic problems, one can synthesize sentences mechanically in English by working out the transition probabilities of words and phrases as they are actually used. This means that given, say, the word 'there' to start with, the most likely next word statistically is 'is'. Proceeding cumulatively in this way the following sentence was in fact generated purely mechanically —I believe it was the first coherent spontaneous utterance by a machine: 'There is no reverse gear on a motor cycle'. This statement is not only syntactically admissible, it also happens to be true, and, what is more, could be considered analytically of great significance as coming from a machine, for it implies perhaps —'in a system which maintains equilibrium by continuous motion, stability is obtained by sacrificing reversibility; creatures that require inherent stability must accept the condition that time has an arrow pointing to the grave'. This nonsense is in the Lewis Carroll category because it should make one think more carefully, in this case about the probable significance of statements and behaviour such as Erik was describing; to what extent is their content dependent on transitional or structural probabilities; which of these probabilities are culturally and which individually determined? Can one devise a system in which these questions would be answered explicitly? Would such a system clarify basic problems such as the respective importance of nature, nurture and culture?

ERIKSON:

I cannot answer this except as a recipient at the other end of the communication of highly fragmentary and heterogenous elements of some kind of a language. The child might be 'speaking to me' while he builds his scene, in another case the photograph of his scene will 'speak to me' half a year later, after I have studied the case history, and in another case it speaks to me only now, twelve years later, when I hear what has happened to the child since. Until I know the language, it is hard to discern nonsense.

GREY WALTER:

A last word on this—you were giving the children, as far as I can see, apart from the blocks, about as many elements as we have letters in our alphabet. Now if these are in the nature of letters, it would give them an enormous vocabulary. If, on the other hand, they are in the nature of words, the scope is much more limited. If you have only given them about twenty words, so to speak, then there is a relatively small number of things they can say. Your observations would have a different significance for us according to whether the features you observe are selected from an enormous possible range of presentation or whether the range is more limited.

FREMONT-SMITH:

Couldn't one say that the same objects are representing at one time a letter, and at another time another letter, and at another time a word, and at several times a whole sentence, and that this increases the complexity and potentiality from what, if looked at objectively and not symbolically, are a rather limited number of objects?

GREY WALTER:

Yes, I suppose you might be able to distinguish between your sexes or your children, by saying that in one case or one group of cases these objects seem to be handled as if they were letters or phonemes; but in another case, or at another age, they were handled as words, or phrases, or sentences or whole narratives. That in itself would be a very interesting way of analysing because that is the way children themselves start a language. They make syllabic sounds, mere phonemes without semantic content, or with little semantic content and they build up, as we all know, an accepted language.

HUXLEY:

I think Grey Walter is begging the wrong question. This is not a language in the technical sense, but a set of sounds which are not accepted as a language. I would also think that it is not play in the strict sense. The children are constructing works of art and, of course, a work of art has to have its own vehicle of communication. If you like to call it a language in the broad sense that is all right, but in art the vehicles of communication are always multivalent learnt symbols, as Margaret Mead has said. In learning to speak, the child has to make the 'ga, ga' sound spontaneously to start with, but eventually it is learning something which is imposed upon it, a pattern that has been formalized by the culture. Here in Erikson's studies, the child is inventing something—free creation for himself, with objects that are certainly limited in their cultural implication, but with an amazing range of possibility comparable to that of an artist or a producer who is putting a play on the stage. I really do think that to try to force this business into a strict linguistic framework is begging the wrong question.

GREY WALTER:

I still maintain that this is a language in so far as they are using pre-formed symbols. There is a difference between an artist who is given a pencil and who can obviously draw as many pictures as he likes with a pencil, and one who is forced to make a *collage* from pre-formed structures.

HUXLEY:

Yes. On the other hand, these children can use this limited range of pre-formed symbols just as a poet can use words—he has only got a limited range of words but he can create poems of an amazing range of difference.

LORENZ:

The question about the noise factor in psychoanalysis in general is one that interests me deeply. Might we bring the discussion back to

120

that? You see the question is how much randomness is superimposed on and hiding lawfulnesses? That is one very important question. When Erikson began I thought, well, how does he know that half of the children didn't just do random things without any lawfulness, without any communication function at all? And now it seems that practically none of them did.

GREY WALTER:

Well, you can tell that easily, it seems to me, and that is why I suggest a theoretical analysis. I quite agree with Huxley that one might not want to describe this behaviour as language necessarily, since this implies some use of the tongue, but this situation of Erik's is some code of communication, if you like. Now, in any code you could estimate the probable noise level very roughly, from the redundancy; how many times must a signal be repeated before its significance is certain? If the children use a highly redundant means of expression you can guess they are working on a noisy channel because it means they have got to overcome the uncertainty of communication, say by repetition. It seems to me that you have got the material there already. It would help me, personally, very much to know what the degree of redundancy is; for example, how repetitious was the expression of any particular relationship.

FREMONT-SMITH:

Redundancy might not be only due to noise.

GREY WALTER:

No, but it is one of the chief ways of guessing, when you cannot measure the noise directly.

FREMONT-SMITH:

But it is quite possible that redundancy might have an entirely different derivation from means of overcoming noise. I think this is peculiarly true of the kind of material that Erik is dealing with, where you have the repetition in child behaviour, and in child

121

play, which is far beyond any possibility of just trying to break through noise.

LORENZ:

May we come back once again to Grey Walter's question—'How do you diagnose noise in your observations?' Now, the parable of noise may be not immediately intelligible to some of us. So, let me explain it: if you record a curve of the sound waves reproduced on a gramophone record you'll find that there are a lot of irregularities superimposed upon the regular curves rendering all the single notes that go to make the music. When we hear the record played our ear is very well able to differentiate between the sound produced by the regular curves of the record and the sounds produced by its irregularity and by the shortcomings of the instrument. All the latter accidental and random waves we perceive as 'noise'. If you listen to the record longer, the noise gradually fades into the background and is not consciously perceived any more. Now, how do we make the analogous differentiation between the relevant lawfulness and the accidental noise-background in scientific observation? In the sensory data we receive both are mixed in a complete tangle. This is the question which rankled with me, because I do not know how we do it, and, of course, we do do it.

We put a fish into a tank to see its fighting movements. And now this fish—I always like to give concrete examples—rushes into one corner and slowly starts to weave to and fro with its head and none of the observers records it because everyone knows that this fish just happens, by pure chance, to be lying obliquely with one of its pectorals touching the ground and causes the weaving movements by pushing against it while continuing its permanent, rhythmical fanning movements. So an observer worth his (or her) salt knows instantly that this particular weaving of the fish's head is just 'noise'. In the next moment the fish swims free and now he suddenly starts jerking his head to and fro in another manner and instantly my student starts writing furiously to report his jerking. Now, how does one know? One knows because one has seen it before, and this is exactly where the relation between redundancy and noise, mentioned by Grey Walter, comes in. The more often the observer, or any recording machine, has recorded sets of data in which a lawfulness is mixed with random noise, the better it is able to differentiate between the two. Conversely, the more noise is contained in the sets of data, the more repetitions are necessary to be tolerably sure of the

122

lawfulness contained in them. One knows, because one has seen it before, and recognizes it in exactly the same way as a physician recognizes some symptoms because the symptom is not a jerk in itself but is part of a syndrome. The recognition of a syndrome is slightly akin to the perception of a melody. It has a meaning, because one has seen it before. This jerk is not just a jerk, but is a very slight intentional movement, the beginning of a definite behaviour pattern. My student records it because she recognizes it. This recognition is purely perceptional, and we must confess that we do not do it by a rational act. You know how, when listening to an old gramophone for the first time, you think you hear only noise and you find it very difficult to hear the melody at all, and after a very short time you find that your perception has effected a 'retouchement' of the sensory data so that you hear only the melody at the time of playing; this suppression of noise is an achievement of Gestalt perception.

I know that when Grey Walter talks about the noise and the difficulty of eliminating it he means scientifically and mathematically abstracting from noise. In observing fish fighting, it would be very difficult to find means as rational as his, and, I must add, we have given much thought as to how we do it. I think we simply do not do it rationally, we let our perception do it, and therefore I am very interested to hear what Erikson has to say about it.

GREY WALTER:
I agree with Konrad that recognizing what is significant in a patient's condition against a background of random behaviour is a question of Gestalt perception in the sense that this means the perceiving of a whole pattern, but I suggest that the determination of what the Gestalt is, is statistical. It is a fact that a skilled person can make a significant observation of fish behaviour or of one of our electrical records, but this is achieved by a process of statistical appraisal, which need not be conscious. I suggested last time we met, in connexion with the theory of learning, that the perception of pattern *is* learning, and learning *is* perception of pattern—the two are tautologous, and the question is how particularly the psychoanalyst tunes his learning filter to admit the statistically relevant material and to exclude, or allow for, the existence of a random component in communication. The channel between the two people, the analyst and the analysand, or between Erik and his children, cannot be a perfect channel; the ideal channel has no noise level and there need be no redundancy because the communication is perfect.

But the ideal channel does not exist. In the technique developed by Freud and his pupils, a filter system was set up so that it is possible for the symbolic material contained in the case history or the subject's conversation or work or play to be selected against a background of conventional noise, which might in conversation be remarks as 'fine day, pity it's snowing' and so forth; a lot of polite nonsense that means nothing. Without going into details at all, the important point is that these filters are in the analyst and in the patient and the analyst's task is to match his filters to those of the subject.

The question that still remains, of course, is how he does this and then decides in his appraisal of the material, *a posteriori*, which of the signals has significance, exactly as in the observations quoted by Konrad. Konrad considers that a certain mode of behaviour is irrelevant because of certain physical facts which by a process of association he has learned reduce the significance of that behaviour. He may, for example, have discovered that in a certain situation the patient or the animal has no alternative mode of behaviour. But, in another situation, where there is less constraint, a similar mode of behaviour he *decides* is relevant. I suggest that invariably this decision is based on an acquired habit of statistical appraisal. It seems to me that, in all trained observers' experience, there is in fact a high degree of selection by scientific filtering and that Erikson has constructed an elegant filter-situation and has been making experiments with as great a significance as the experiments electrophysiologists make, where the filters are more obviously mechanical. In all such experiments the detection of a pattern depends upon the operation of statistically determined filters which are set to emphasize relevance—we EEG folk call them 'analysers' rather than analysts.

FREMONT-SMITH:

I might add one other point which bothers me a little bit—that is the complexity in the system where you have two human beings as the two objects of the communication. It becomes very hard then to define where is the end-point to which the communication is directed; the filters are actually built into the ear of the person who receives, and the person himself, who changes all the time, is very intrinsically part of the channel. We can almost say there are three or four persons at the end of the channel who are receiving his message and who are receiving it differently, and sometimes one of them receives it and sometimes another, and they also merge with one another.

GREY WALTER:

You mean that one analyst, for example, may be able to interpret or make sense of material which another analyst could not? That Erik might pass on some material which he had collected to one of his colleagues who might be able to make sense of it when Erik could not?

FREMONT-SMITH:

Yes, but also my point is that one analyst is several analysts.

GREY WALTER:

Yes, of course—or certainly a complex one—again like our electronic analysers that contain banks of filters. Just to make clear what one means by the statistical approach to such problems: in any system of observation, if you define and predict a certain pattern of behaviour, then in that system there is a finite possibility that the pattern will occur by chance—and one's duty is, either unconsciously by reason of being a clever chap, or, consciously by reason of previous training, to determine what are the possibilities of finding this pattern by chance. There is still a fundamental difficulty in all such work in deciding how likely we are to observe a certain pattern by purely chance concatenation.

The noise component in a signal is by definition unpredictable from moment to moment, but in animal behaviour, unpredictability may be quite healthy. In fact, I would add the suggestion that what a psychiatrist calls neurotic behaviour may, in some cases at least, be abnormal in so far as it *is* predictable. Of course in this problem 'predictable' has no philosophic meaning: it refers only to the limitations of the observer.

LORENZ:

Of course, the unconsciously working computer which we call Gestalt perception works on exactly the same principle as statistical deduction. It has to have the same basis of data. The likelihood of correct results is just as much dependent on the broadness of inductive basis. I always maintain that in simple observations of nature, of very complicated phenomena, it is always Gestalt perception which sees things first. This might be a personal difference, for my Gestalt perception is considerably cleverer than my inductive research. And I have a very strong impression that it is the same with Erik. We are both clinical observers. Grey Walter is very highly trained in evaluating his Gestalt perception, and doing the same as us, but statistically. Most clinicians have a wonderfully trained Gestalt perception for this kind of symptoms and they are absolutely unable to tell how they do it and what is the real basis of their intuitions, as they call them. And I am, of course, convinced that the process of conscious and rational induction and that of Gestalt perception are functionally analogous.

GREY WALTER:

I'd say most of us in human neurophysiology rely very much on the Gestalt hunch—which later on we justify or discredit by making elaborate planned experiments. I think most of my colleagues would agree that most of our physiological observations or discoveries have been made by hunches—Gestalt appraisal later justified and rationalized by experiment.*

*Going over this discussion with my colleagues, the idea occurred to me that, for those of us who work in the biological domain at least, the essence of our scientific training and scientific method is: (1) to learn how to keep our hunches on the associated level, without assuming causality, either *a priori* or *a posteriori*, in this way preventing our guesses from becoming myths or superstitions: (2) learning how to design experiments to determine the direction of association, that is the causal relationships between the events which we guessed—and later proved —to be associated. Statistics have a bad name in some quarters because these two stages or planes of investigation have not always been kept distinct. In this connexion, the terms association, statistics and causality apply equally to the design of scientific experiments and to what I have suggested as the mechanism of thinking in general. For example, the development of a child, according to Erikson's schema and my translation of it (see p. 192) may be considered as the record of a person's success or failure in learning to distinguish between guessed associations and experimentally verified causal relations. Again, Erikson's observations of play are, as he says, in this sense not fully fledged experiments for, though he has established an association between history, sex, personality and play, he was not able to prove that the play behaviour was causally related to history and personality; the children may have had inborn personality traits that contributed both to their family situations and to their play, just as their inborn sex characters certainly did. It is interesting that this formal classification of method immediately reminds us of the perennial practical difficulty of assessing the respective contributions of nurture and nature to human development.

Claude Bernard, the father of physiology, specified for a 'true scientist' what we should now call an 'error-feedback system' between 'experimental theory and experimental practice'. In studying the brain specifically, of course, we have the additional difficulty that, for that organ, every experiment we make is also an experience—a distinction that our French colleagues cannot logically accept!— so that we have an additional feedback loop between subject and experimenter. None the less, what encourages me is that, as well as emphasizing the difficulties and errors and limitations of human biology, I think that discussion on these lines may help us to work out methods of study to unite our disciplines and appreciate one another's contributions.

LORENZ:

The German word 'Nachweis'—to prove something is a 'Nach-weis', which means the 'after-showing'—implies that you have seen it before in some other way. And I was impressed by the fact that some modern American learning-psychologists try to do without the hunch, and put the question of 'either, or'.

FREMONT-SMITH:

And become progressively more sterile!

ERIKSON:

Let me come back to these questions (in as far as I understand them) in connexion with the clinical part of our discussions. Today, I

FIG. 17

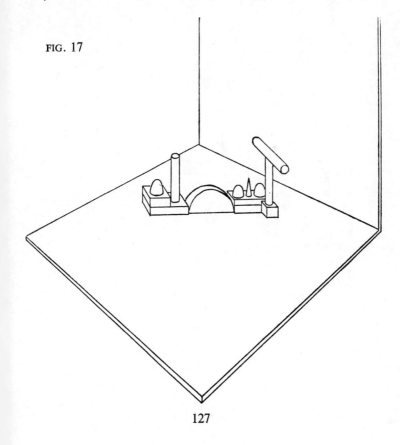

will conclude with a few examples which show how unique biographic themes will break through. Consider the construction of a boy whose mother died when he was five years old. The family had wondered at the time whether the mother could have been saved if the ambulance had come in time. His father had not discussed these circumstances with the boy and had, in fact, assumed that they had not been taken in by the child. However, our workers perceived a certain change in the boy at that time and had wondered what he knew. He remained non-committal. At age twelve, he is asked for play construction. He builds a street crossing, and explains: 'Here (in the foreground) is an ambulance driving towards that house (in the left background) where a woman is dying. As it approaches this crossroads here another car is coming out of this garage (in the right background). Ambulance and car collide. The question is

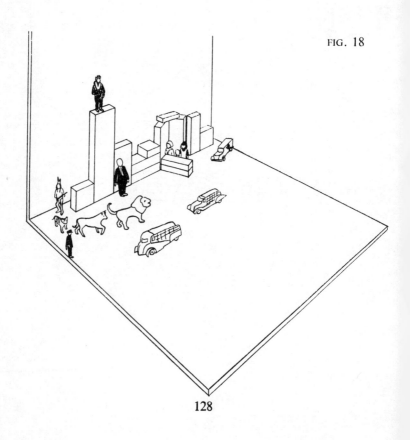

FIG. 18

whether the ambulance will be on time to save the woman.' I asked him 'Do you think the woman will be saved?' and he said, 'Yes, I think so'. Thus, his construction rectified circumstances which he had been supposed to be ignorant of.

Fig. 17 is one of the very few girls' constructions which consists of blocks only. It is the only one where the top is bigger than the bottom. This is a child who was born with a head deformity. This cylinder was by no means easy to balance, and she spent some time doing just that. Thus, on the one hand she wanted to show that she could balance it, while at the same time she made the top more prominent than the bottom. At the same time, the great primitivity of this construction points to an intelligence problem. I think the scene could be very well assigned to a much earlier age; there was no content to it at all.

Fig. 18 is by a child who had a congenital heart defect. She had a very much enlarged heart. It had been decided that this should not be discussed with her. She had never mentioned it, and had never been asked about it. So here again we have an example where the question is, is this biographic item which seems all-important to us, also important to this child, so important that it would appear in her play construction? Now let us see what she communicates.

She builds a tower-like structure very close to the background, as part of a kind of irregular wall. I will read the rest, from a publication.

'On the highest block stands the aviator, while below two women and two children are crowded into the small compartment of a front yard, apparently watching a procession of cars and animals. Lisa's story follows. We see in it a metaphoric representation of a moment of heart weakness—an experience which she had never mentioned 'in so many words'. The analogy between the play scene and its suggested meaning will be indicated by noting elements of a moment of heart failure in brackets following the corresponding play items.

'There is a quarrel between the mother and the nurse over money (irritability). This aviator stands high up on a tower (feeling of dangerous height). He really is not an aviator, but he thinks he is (feeling of unreality). First he feels as if his head was rotating, then that his whole body turns around and around (dizziness). He sees these animals walking by which are not really there (seeing things move about in front of eyes). Then this girl notices the dangerous situation of the aviator and calls an ambulance (awareness of attack and urge to call for help). Just as the ambulance comes around a corner, the aviator falls down from the tower (feeling of sinking and falling). The ambulance crew quickly unfolds a net; the aviator falls into it, but is bounced back up to the top of the tower (recovery). He holds onto the edge of the tower and lies down (exhaustion).'

HUXLEY:
What is the child in the foreground?

ERIKSON:
The 'older boy' doll. It was not clear whether he was left there by mistake or belonged to the construction. The girl did have an older brother.

This is a statement in the language of play regarding a most relevant experience which had not found access yet to words. However, right after the construction the girl went for a routine physical examination, where she confided to the doctor that she had strange feelings now and again. In other words, the play medium had loosened up whatever kept the communication from words.

HUXLEY:
I am coming back to the very basic point raised by Grey Walter. In anything like this—in language, in play, in art—don't you have two things involved, communication and expression. The individual expression may be forced into a more or less formal pattern, either by the limited choice of symbols which you have here, or because the pattern has been forced on you by the cultural use of a language. The children here, as far as I understand it, were essentially wanting to *express* themselves. In the background of their minds, doubtless, was the idea that this would communicate something to you, but their primary need was expression. Whereas in language, in the strict linguistic sense, the primary need is communication, which you have to learn in order to carry out. I should have thought these children are more like the artist who paints to please himself, and doesn't bother about communication.

ERIKSON:
Let me say here that I never asked any of the children whether their construction meant to them what it meant to me. I am convinced the vast majority of them would have said to me, 'Don't be silly; I just made up a scene—as you asked me to do'. Some kids might say, 'Well, aren't you pretty clever', and half acknowledge the meaning. Others might say, 'Don't be absurd'. Some might laugh,

130

some be deeply disturbed, and some be so annoyed that they wouldn't come to the next session, because why should they build movie scenes for me and then be told that 'I know something about you that you didn't know you were telling me'. But since I could not and would not confront a child with the possible meaning of his play, unless it was therapeutically indicated, it remains an open question whether self-expression contains an unconscious communication.

FREMONT-SMITH:

That that is so is emphasized by the children's preoccupation— that they were doing something for themselves, and that they had to be reminded afterwards to tell you what was exciting in it, or what it was all about.

ERIKSON:

Let me come back to the example of the boy with the plasticine balls. He knew for sure that I wanted to find out something that he had not told anybody. When he noticed I was on the right track his symptoms appeared—in other words, these hidden contents are defended against, in the individual, in varying degrees. Only patients can and must gradually accept interpretations—because they need to.

RÉMOND:

Dr. Huxley wanted to distinguish between communication and expression in order to define the content of the constructions which Mr. Erikson showed us, but I wonder whether one can in fact find any 'expression' here, at least as far as this term comprises anything intentional. Is it not just a matter of 'noise', that is to say a non-significant piece of behaviour. The child does what he does not necessarily in order to express something. He may do it just by chance. It is only after the event when he is asked what he has done that he interprets it and gives value to it. At that moment certainly expression comes in and communication as well, but did they exist before?

HUXLEY:

In these constructions that we have been seeing, although a great deal of the motivation and symbolization may have been unconscious, it seems obvious after what we have heard this morning that

131

they were expressing certain tensions, certain background or immediate discomforts and conflicts. I have been quite convinced by the demonstration. But of course the subject may afterwards give a rationalized and essentially untrue interpretation or explanation of his constructions.

The Syndrome of Identity Diffusion in Adolescents and Young Adults

ERIKSON:

I want to start with a statement made by Dr. Zazzo at one of your previous meetings. This, incidentally, is not an attempt at an advance appeasement in regard to any methodological difference we may have, but the acknowledgement of at least one common platform! He said that psychologists are perhaps wrong in looking only for the limit of intelligence, meaning at a certain age, say, the age of fourteen to eighteen. 'The age of twelve to thirteen years marks perhaps a new departure. Intelligence is nothing if it is not creative and intelligence can only be effective if it goes back to certain affective sources. Now it is perhaps during this period from fourteen to eighteen years that the human being, coming into contact with new social, human and affective realities, manages to give a deep, concrete sense to all the perceptive-intellectual mechanisms which he has acquired during the scholastic period' (Vol. I, pp. 169-70). What is said here about intelligence also applies to that accentuation of psychosexual differences which Margaret Mead spoke about. Namely, whatever has been accentuated in childhood will have to be given a deep concrete sense at this age—a sense which I call a sense of *identity*.

Now I would think that every participant in a small group like this should first characterize the kind of research experience that he is concerned with most of the time, and most intensively. I, therefore, would like to discuss clinical observations and then work toward social studies, hoping that then we can have a discussion which will combine Margaret Mead's anthropological and my clinical material in a fruitful way.

I now want to discuss one more play construction in some detail.

X

FIG. **19**

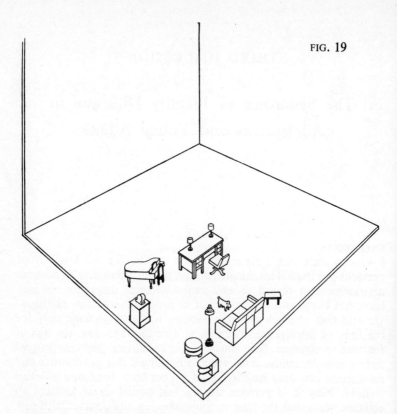

The construction shown in Fig. 19 is taken from a study parallel to the one which I undertook in Berkeley. The arrangement of table and toys, and the instructions are the same. A girl of twelve enters. Let me briefly account for the configurational message which I received from her behaviour. She *walked* like a girl who 'makes like' a boy. Yet this had an almost perfect hermaphroditic balance, such as some girls in early puberty have. She *built* a round scene of furniture, that is, an exquisitely feminine scene, but she built it way out in the left forward corner, which, as I said, indicated to me a great need for independence. Building that far out in space is often combined with a daring of a kind which may cause the individual to 'stick his neck out' too far. So now, we have (1) a 'boyish' style of walking in a girlishly pretty person (2) an 'independent' location of a 'feminine' configuration. Now, within that configuration of furniture a little *drama* took place. There was a piano and a piano chair. With a vigorous motion the girl pushed that piano chair in, a 'unique element' which I have noticed in only two children. It obviously connotes: 'Nobody is going to play, if I can help it'. Then the girl put a fluffy little dog in the centre of the round configuration, thus adding another typically 'feminine' element, and said 'This is it'. I asked her—'What is the most exciting thing in that scene?' and she said, 'This little dog wants to jump up on the couch and sleep'. As she said 'and sleep' she made a maternal gesture of holding and rocking a baby in her arms—a gesture such as among men only Konrad Lorenz could demonstrate. I then asked, 'What is going to happen?' and she said, 'He probably won't be able to sleep, there is too much noise'.

In addition, then, to the dualism within the configuration, you have a dramatic opposition in content, namely, the wish to rest in a soft place, and disturbing noise, and two opposed postural styles, mannish and maternal.

This girl's mother is a well-known singer. Her scene seemed to me to be a significant pointer to the fact that this girl must have been impressed, as a small child, by the fact that her mother made so much noise, and this while sitting at the piano or in conjunction with an accompanist, of whom the child may have been jealous. For their joint noise may well have drowned out the girl's own signals telling of her needs for the mother to come to her. This little scene, after so many years, says: 'If only my mother had sent the pianist away, stopped all the musical noise, and had me rest in her arms instead'. This scene, then, points to a very specific form of 'separation from the mother', one which can happen when the mother is very much there, and you can see how in a carefully arranged stimulus-situation such a basic theme simply and quickly expresses itself. A sketch of this girl's life would show that certain biographic data amount, in fact, to long-range variations, extending over many years, of the brief statement of play themes as developed in a few minutes. One of the girl's college advisers exclaimed: 'How can anybody be as dependent and as independent at the same time!'

But now let me come back to the 'message' of those few minutes. Maybe we clinicians selectively notice conflicts because it is our business to do so. On the other hand, the girl can be shown to repeat one message in a number of languages: spatial, gestural, thematic. This can be explained on the basis of Freud's repetition-compulsion, meaning that whatever experience was traumatic, i.e., rendered the individual unable to manage the quantity of excitation which stormed in on him, is repeated over and over, either through talking it out, or through redreaming it, in different variations on a theme. There is, in fact, a certain stereotyped repetition in all neurotic symptoms. It came to me yesterday when we talked about communication value that such repetitiveness in a sense is like an SOS, which you repeat over and over, not only in order to get rid of inner excitation and to master the memory by repeating it actively, but also, as it were, to ask: 'Won't somebody please perceive my message and help me?'

GREY WALTER:

In such a situation, where the doctor and the patient have chosen a conventional channel to speak, and when the patient is incapable of making a really dramatic statement of conflicts or stresses—he doesn't actually come to you and say: 'For Christ's sake, help me'—then he is using for this purpose a noisy channel, and repetition may be the only means by which he can convey the information about his state and thus overcome the noise-level. Repetition may be the major feature of psychoanalytic communication because the analyst deliberately restricts his channel to the conventional means of communication—I mean in those cases where he is not using one of the more elaborate means of abreaction, such as narcoanalysis, as a means of producing material of more emphatic significance. Perhaps that is why conventional analysis is notorious for its duration and why the ultimate message seems so childishly simple in comparison with the effort.

FREMONT-SMITH:

It seems to me 'conventional' is the wrong word: the conventional means of communication is the one that the ordinary doctor or the parent uses; actually the analyst is using a variety of non-conventional means of communication which the child can send the message along.

GREY WALTER:

I mean the conventional psychiatric interview where the patient is just talking, or lying on the couch and talking, rather than hypno- or narco-analysis and so on. In those latter systems the psychiatrist is resorting to the expedient of raising the amplification, so to say. This may help but will only be confusing if the signal noise ratio is low. In a conversational or non-participatory technique repetition to the point of redundancy may be the only effective stratagem to get through the noise of a conventional channel—even when the message is really quite simple.

LORENZ:

Thomas Mann, who is a very good psychoanalyst, has realized the principle of the necessity of redundancy because of the noisiness of the channel. In his novel on Joseph (Mann, 1948) he says this explicitly where Joseph interprets the three identical dreams of the Pharaoh.

DE SAUSSURE:

You indicated as one of the characteristics of this girl that she had a conflict of dependence and independence at the same time. From the clinical point of view what characterizes her is just that these two tendencies of independence and dependence, although they are contradictory, are not conflicting in her case. She has managed to isolate these two tendencies. One of the reasons why she might have special difficulty in the formation of her identity is that through a defence mechanism she has isolated the two poles of the conflict which she has consequently never resolved.

As regards repetition-compulsion, I think that it is only in a very secondary way that repetition-compulsion acquires value as a communication. Initially, it is merely a kind of impossibility of stopping the discharge mechanism, just as in physics there is a force of inertia. The moment an unconscious charge becomes too strong it has to become apparent the whole time; so clinically what the individual is trying to do is to stop, by means of suppression or through other defence mechanisms, something which actually is striving to appear the whole time; it is only secondarily that this process is used for communication.

ERIKSON:

Yes, I merely thought that it may be valuable to take a fresh look at the repetition-compulsion from this angle. If somebody was in a train accident and then talks about it again and again, his friends find it at first interesting and then gradually boring, but they say to themselves, 'Well, he needs to do that', i.e., for the purpose of unloading traumatic excitation. But this is an accident that came from outside, and for which there are words. But I am referring here to a different situation. Let us say a little boy loses his mother when he is five. Nobody discusses it with him. He may express in any number of ways that he needs to have it discussed; these ways are not recognized and his character seems to change. Years later, the question which he wanted to ask them clearly breaks through in a play construction, and this in the same manner of a repetition of a theme on a number of levels. There may be an almost biological tendency in

137

children to try to communicate by symptomatic repetition something which they can neither say nor manage by themselves.

GREY WALTER:

It might be helpful to transfer this situation to a biological level and ask what survival-value, if any, this process has—supposing there is an inborn tendency for animals and particularly primates to repeat themselves. The IRMs that Konrad Lorenz describes are used repeatedly, are they not? Behaviour patterns appear again and again but their repetition can have very little survival-value unless it improves communication. It seems to me that there is a tendency, as Dr. de Saussure said, for the communication to be repeated by sheer momentum but that ultimately the survival-value of such a mechanism is that by repetition the signal is transmitted more accurately. The two are not incompatible by any means; the mechanism may be an inborn individual character, but the advantage may depend on social gain in clarity when there are many other things going on. It might be interesting to know from the biological standpoint to what extent the tendency to repeated behaviour patterns has, in fact, a high survival-value.

LORENZ:

I think that it is permissible to identify the compulsive repetition of which Erikson is talking with the repetition of instinctive activity in normal animals. Yet the question whether this repetition is adaptive, has a survival value or not, is something which has very strongly occupied me already, because I am subject personally to very strong compulsion to repetition of traumatizing experiences in which I misbehave, in which I fail to behave in the manner I like to remember myself having behaved—in other words, in situations where I have made a fool of myself. In such cases I have to go through and through this experience again, re-enacting the scene and saying the things I ought to have said to the chap.

HUXLEY:

So that there are really two grades, aren't there? The first is the basic impulse to perform a certain type of action as a result of the conflict; and the second the later stereotyping of it either individually or in evolution, as a means of communication. Displacement activities, for example, may be *expressions* in origin, serving to get rid of excess tension, while later on they become a means of communication.

138

I find Konrad's point an interesting one because what has always puzzled me is this: people find it much easier to get over a traumatic situation if they can communicate about it to others. Erik has already given the example of the way in which, after an accident, we bore all our friends by describing it again and again. In some way the mere expression of it, particularly the repetition of it to people we like, with whom we have a particular bond, enables us to get over it, to adapt to it and forget it. Now, the striking thing about neurotic patients is that they cannot do this in respect of some important event or sequence of events. It looks as though what happens is not that this mechanism, which has a healing and survival-value as Konrad described, persists too long and becomes pathological, but that it fails to start at all. It then requires a new person to enable the healing process to start and achieve its proper end.

If we consider the child whose mother died and who was never able to discuss that event, from clinical experience we agree that, had he been able to discuss and adapt to the event in the period immediately following, this healing process would have been completed efficiently. As it was, since there was no one with whom he could communicate, this didn't occur at the time and the healing process ceased. It wasn't until a new situation arose—a situation of communication—that the healing process began again. I would emphasize strongly the communicative significance of the play session which Erik had with these children. The fact that Erik is there as a human being determines the situation—and I would expect that the precise communications which these children made were very dependent on their perception of Erik as a human being.

If one gives to a hypnotized person a post-hypnotic order which he cannot completely carry out, he repeats it or repeats something which is intermediate. For example in one of the cases quoted by Moll (1889) in his work on hypnosis, he gave the order to a very timid girl to stretch out her hand to him as soon as she woke up. The moment she stretched out her hand she began to tremble and from that moment every time she wanted to stretch out her hand she began to tremble without being able to shake hands. Here we see behaviour which is repeated because it has not been able to be completely expressed. We also note that there has been no correction; this girl has not improved her behaviour after x times; she does not shake hands any better. On the other hand, as soon as Moll had hypnotized her again and had made a stronger suggestion she became capable of giving her hand without trembling.

We see that this repetition is much more an expression than a communication; if there were communication there would be improvement.

In neurotic situations the phenomena are much more complex. There are at the same time elements of repetition-compulsion (as in post-hypnotic cases) and elements of communication. It is owing to the latter that behaviour improves and the general situation changes.

The example quoted by Erikson of this child who was never able to speak of the death of his mother is precisely an example of unfinished discharge because the discharge should have come from outside, which creates a much more complicated situation.

The example quoted by Lorenz about his own behaviour, which forced him to repeat a certain reaction a certain number of times, was different because the behaviour came from him whereas in the case of the child the incitement to discharge came from outside. It is possible, therefore, that favourable circumstances would permit him suddenly to discharge his emotion and an improvement would follow. It is for this reason, too, that the communication element is much stronger in a neurotic situation than in an experimental situation, for example.

ERIKSON:

We come here to a generalization which is important to our further discussion, namely, the containment of the mere discharge in a workable communication. The girl of twelve could push in the piano chair in the play scene; in other words, she had the medium and the capacity to do symbolically what she would have done in reality when she was a child—if she had not been a child. Because of the long-drawn-out childhood in human beings, the traumatization by events in which we are unable to communicate simply because we are children, i.e., are not listened to, or have no means of communicating, is of a specific quality. I would say that the mere humiliation of having been a child is one of the most basic facts of human existence.

It so happens that my quotation from Shaw's autobiographic notes (Erikson, in press) contain an item which I call 'the noise-maker', which will provide a fitting transition to my next point. When Shaw was 70, he was asked to write a preface to five novels which he had written in his early twenties in five years, writing five pages each day. He did this compulsive feat during a period which I will later call a psychosocial moratorium. He was a clerk in an Irish merchandizing house and he was not unsuccessful by any means, but he felt not like himself in this situation. He left Ireland, went to England, and he said he did not intimately associate with members of his own age group for something like seven years. You find such self-imposed psychological moratoria in the life of quite a number of outstanding people. So when he was a famous man then it was decided to publish those five novels, and he wrote a preface to them. Of course, he ended up by saying—for heaven's sake don't bother to read those five novels but listen to my description of what kind of a human being I was when I wrote them. He wrote one of the sharpest autobiographical statements which I have ever read. It is not known as a major psychological work simply because Shaw had the additional compulsion to make everything seem funny. At the end of this autobiography he says in regard to his identity as an actor on the stage of life, 'in this, I succeeded only too well', a statement of integrity which admits that some are forced by their very identity formation into successes which feel just a little too good.

Among the many elements that Shaw described in his own development is the identity of the music critic—his first identity as a writer, the novels having failed him as he failed them. He describes how, when he was a child, he was exposed to an oceanic assault of music making; his sisters and uncles and cousins played trombones, violincellos and harps and tambourines—and, most of all, his mother sang! During his psychosocial moratorium (which, as I said, I will define later) he taught himself the piano and he did this with the utmost of noise that he could manage. He says 'When I look back on all the banging, whistling, roaring and growling inflicted on nervous neighbours during this process of education, I am consumed with useless remorse. . . . I used to drive (my mother) nearly crazy by my favourite selections from Wagner . . . which seemed horribly discordant at that. She never complained at the time, but confessed it after we separated, and said that she had sometimes gone off to cry. If I had committed a murder I do not think it would trouble my conscience very much; but this I cannot bear to think of.' If you will permit an interpretation which Shaw does not propose himself, he did not, as it were, cancel out the trauma of having been invaded and assaulted with musical noise as a child, he turned it around and did it to other people, calling it his education. Only later, at a time when he had made enough noise to abreact, as we would say, did he become aware of the aggressive nature of his musical self-education. But now he compromised by becoming somebody who

141

writes about the musical noise other people make, and this led him closer to his identity as a writer, and sublimated his aggression in criticism. The name he chose as a music critic, incidentally, was Corno di Bassetto. The few people who know it, know that it was the meekest musical instrument in existence. He said 'not even the devil could have made it sparkle'. You see the strange way in which people can manage their lives if their culture gives them leeway to do so, and if they are gifted in utilizing this leeway. As Corno di Bassetto, he became a music critic who was in no way meek, in fact, he said, 'I cannot deny Bassetto was occasionally vulgar; but that does not matter if he makes you laugh. Vulgarity is a necessary part of a complete author's equipment.'

In Shaw was a man of genius, which includes the gift of finding his identity as he imposes it on the world. One might say that his autobiography was part of his professional work, he lived a professional autobiography. This is, of course, one extreme of identity formation, if one of the most instructive ones. Shaw says about his youth, 'everyone is ill at ease until he has found his natural place, whether it be above or below his birthplace', but then being Shaw, he has to add 'This finding of one's place may be made very puzzling by the fact that there is no place in ordinary society for extraordinary individuals'. How many people feel they are extraordinary even if they neither have the gift of Shaw to impose his identity on his neighbours, nor live in a period in which enough space is given for such special realization of themselves? We seem to be living at a time when, in many areas of the world, the choices are very much reduced and the need for conformity very much increased.

But this is what I would like to end up with tomorrow and not what I would like to start with. So now I would like to finish this morning with a very general statement as to what I consider identity to be, and with a brief example of what a transitory failure in identity formation would look like. To find one's identity in late adolescence means to find an orientation toward one's self and others in which one feels most oneself where one has come to mean most to others, i.e., to those others who are closest. This is by necessity a statement of relativity, because as we grow we move within a changing and expanding group of people. We select as we are selected and this interchange must lead at the end of adolescence to a feeling that what one means to others, and what one feels one is, largely coincide. You might also say that the sense of identity is a sense of inner continuity and sameness in development, in that what one was made to expect as a child, and what one can anticipate that one will be, coincides with what one is. We will go into all of this in detail later—

here I would just like to emphasize the sometimes fatal, sometimes happy relativity of it all.

A happy aspect is what I would refer to as mutual recognition. I have a small collection of interviews which I had in one great university with the most gifted batch of doctoral students. With great regularity during their formative years, one teacher or aunt or friend of the family became very important, partially because the student became very important to that individual, and a mutual recognition took place which I think is very important for finding one's self as a young individual. Obviously, this can be with a master to whom one is an apprentice, with an older friend who wishes to be selected as a guide, or some neighbour, relative or friend who says the right thing at the right time. For this recognition to occur the individual needs three things: he needs to be free enough from his past problems to be able to choose the right person or the group of people, who have a recognition in store. Then there must be people in existence who are looking for just the kind of young person he is. Finally, it needs certain cultural circumstances which favour the two meeting.

Identity diffusion is something that which occurs when this is not possible, at the right time and in a certain proper dosage. Identity diffusion is a syndrome that many young people have in common, although its forms are seen as sicknesses or bad habits with a variety of causes. If people with identity diffusion are found in a certain acute bewilderment, they may be suspected of being schizophrenic. If they happen to appropriate a car—because to drive around in a car gives them the feeling they are somebody—they become delinquents, and if they happen to cross a State line, maybe Federal offenders. If they use drugs to feel like whole people, they are on the way to addiction. In all of this it is important to know that whatever the inner dynamics, there is a relatively autonomous factor common to youth, namely, that whatever the representatives of society will tell a young person he is, he is more apt to become. I mean here something which I believe is in a way analogous to imprinting in the sense that the young individual is ready to respond selectively, even as his environment is (or should be) ready to recognize him as such and such, and to offer him a series of mutual responses through which he would find out what, within the roles of his culture, he can make of himself as he is. I say this, because eventually we should come out with a unified theory which includes all of childhood or pre-adulthood, from the mutuality with the mother in babyhood, to that with a segment of society in late adolescence.

Let me now turn to therapeutic material, and with it to my home

143

ground as observer. The role of the therapeutic observer is one that is only now being studied systematically, in the sense that he should learn to understand better what kind of an instrument he is, what kind of instrument he becomes as he works with patients, day after day. When I read the reports of your previous meetings, I was flooded with envy as I conceived of you as people who have time to arrange experiments, to observe, to think, to converse, during all those many, many hours which we spend with individual patients. And yet one should hope that even in such individual observation one would become an instrument that recognizes and conceptualizes some kind of regularity. Let me discuss briefly a number of pitfalls in therapeutic observation, because the recognition of its 'equations' circumscribes the use of an instrument in at least one relevant way. Anybody who is forced by human misery to play, and tempted to overplay, his role as a helper and as a systematizer, will by necessity come to short circuits in his own attitude toward people and the world in general. We therapeutic observers have a contract with the material under observation. The contract says that through observation we hope to help the patient back into life in an improved condition. We cannot ask him any question, even if it is based on an ever so good hunch, out of mere theoretical interest, if the question is a violation of the contract, although at times the very contract will oblige us to make him feel worse, before we can make him feel better. However, we can never plan experiments for the purpose of finding out what does not work; we must always unequivocally support the therapeutic process: thus each insight derived from the understanding of failure is bought at the expense of a much more personal failure than is true in dealings with other material. Now this particular contract certainly, as Grey Walter would say, defines the 'band' of our receptivity.

[Mr. Erikson then presented an example of an episode of severe identity diffusion in a young man of about twenty-two who was preparing to do missionary work. He discussed the patient's history, emphasizing those images in the family history which provided the growing child and youth with an inventory of identity fragments too irreconcilable to be integrated during his identity crisis.

(1) the family's migration from rural Minnesota to industrial-urban Pittsburgh; the parents' nostalgic attachment to Minnesota and the family's visits there (the pure 'North country', agrarian, ethnically and religiously homogeneous, 'old country' tradition;

144

the smoky city, ethnic 'melting pot', emphasis on success and progress).

(2) the mother's attitude toward babies and children of varying ages, her loving trust in smaller children and her concern and despair in the face of certain tensions connected with the growing-up of an impetuous boy (association of 'back home' in history and geography and early childhood in life-history).

(3) the boy's vigorous and impatient, yet sensitive temperament, and its contrast with the mother's image of a small child.

(4) early conflicts between voracious dependence (wish to get everything any time, and without end) and need to get away from mother (association of having hurt mother by being vigorously independent and having forfeited the happiness of early childhood —of the North country—of the homogeneous past).

(5) his early conflict between fear of and identification with the city-bred, ruder, 'lower', and ethnically more mixed children of the neighbourhood, of whom his family seemed to disapprove; the phallic-aggressive orientation of the 'education' bestowed by certain boy leaders on the neighbourhood children; their bragging about sexual freedom, and the occasional free discussion of incest; delinquencies related to automobiles; abortive 'gangs'.

(6) the boy's discovery of the saxophone as an instrument permitting both loud and tender expression, and as a 'social tool', permitting both distance from and belongingness to a certain high-school 'crowd'. His family's mistrust of that crowd and their limited approval of that magic instrument, the saxophone.]

Mr. Erikson continued: Those who like to play jazz not only make concerted aphonic noise, but also develop a particular language, particular nicknames, a proudly deviant subculture which gives many an individual—especially if one does not fit in anywhere else—a home, as it were, at any rate a transitory one. These people 'recognized' in our patient a 'hepcat' and he became, and still is today, a very good saxophone player. Those of you who know the American novel *From Here to Eternity* will remember the touching and tragic case of a young soldier, to whom his trumpet had become an essential extension of himself, an 'oral outlet', a tool to express perfection, and a bond with other people, and the vehicle of a private religion which helped him to overcome murderous identifications—until society deprived him of it.

[Mr. Erikson then discussed the patient's relationship to his
145

father, who, as a soil conservationist and plant pathologist, had found a quiet and constructive place in a bustling and competitive community. He continued to demonstrate inter-relationships between:

(1) the boy's association of his father's love for plants (that which grows without passion or malice) and his mother's for babies (who need you more than they want to leave you) both of which left him with the feeling of being too loud, too locomotor, too 'criminal'. The boy's intense jealousy of father's and mother's objects of care.

(2) the patient's attempt, in late adolescence, to follow his father into his profession, a sudden break-through of bewildering, aggressive impulses, and the attempt to over-compensate these by a sudden turn to missionary work—work which would combine rebellious flight from home and locomotor search for another land with the ascetic task of becoming paternal-maternal himself in the role of saving 'savage' souls. It thus would also express what real trust he *had* experienced and an almost excessive acknowledgement of his parents' love.

(3) the conflicting roles in the schooling of missionaries: all proving equally 'available' to him—the 'practical missionary' because of his vigorous devotion; the 'studious teacher' because of his outstanding gift for Asiatic languages; the 'religious advertising man', because of a certain histrionic toughness, originally associated with jazz.

(4) certain irreconcilable elements in the patient's psychosexual and psychosocial development.

(5) available diagnoses for such a disturbance.]

Mr. Erikson continued: I hope that it is quite clear that I do not for a moment doubt that the diagnosis is important; that an identity diffusion of a severely neurotic type will have to be treated differently from a paranoid or psychopathic one. Nevertheless, what I pointed out in very rough outline gives the *psychosocial* dimension of the crisis which left this individual in an inescapable dilemma.

FREMONT-SMITH:
Was it a sudden break?

ERIKSON:
It was a break that took weeks to develop. At the time he wrote to a friend 'The air here is bad, this is only half air, the rest is heavy

146

exhaust and virulent gases that hang like a shroud over the city and sicken your lungs, until you feel like the half air had made you half alive'. Well, such a statement can be a paranoid reference to a poisoning environment; it can be an exaggerated form of the well-known complaint concerning 'smog', and yet I would say it is also the language of sensitive young people who thus express their being suffocated by conflicting identifications. At any rate the young missionary tried to pray by staying in church all night and finally became aware of the fact that his suffering was somehow outside of his prayers. He says 'It is a curse which has personal meaning and has come from nowhere' and finally, he wrote to a friend 'It seems to me that only a complete collapse can force me to re-examine my life'. This is not an empty phrase. A certain kind of collapse at this age can be semi-intentional. Some young people think themselves deeper into the collapse because they feel that only on the rock bottom, as it were, can they find a true moratorium and a new beginning.

LORENZ:
They do their utmost to dissolve, like the chrysalis of the butterfly which dissolves almost absolutely before re-formation.

HUXLEY:
Isn't it like shock treatment in that shock destroys some neurophysiological structuring and gives the patient the opportunity to rebuild a new structure, a new pattern?

ERIKSON:
It so happened that the friend, who had been the recipient of the letters I mentioned, engaged with him in an impressive theological correspondence as to where the point is when it would be almost a sin to try and solve a conflict as a religious one, challenging God to do a miracle for the individual, while the love of God somewhere presupposes the capacity to believe in some other human being, who may have the means of help. It was in this mood that he sought psychiatric treatment.

If one is called upon to help a man who has found his identity but suffers from inhibitions or anxieties, the situation is different. Let me make it clear that there are neurotic inhibitions or symptoms which go together with a reasonably good identity formation. In this case, one only wants to resolve inhibitions and phobias which are leftovers from the past kept alive by the present. Here a psychosocial moratorium, an additional identity formation is not called for. Now, in America 'classical' neuroses become rare, except in certain areas. In Pittsburgh I hear much about American families who still have ten or eleven children, with grandparents who still speak only Polish or Czech—miners' families and steelworkers' families. There, old forms of neurosis are relatively more prevalent. Otherwise the so-called classical cases are disappearing in America for the simple reason that in America getting something like a solid identity formation is becoming even harder than in some other parts of the world. However, if I may misquote Konrad Lorenz— in this case the exception of today may well be the rule of tomorrow, which means that what is now identity disturbance in particular individuals, and on a large scale in America, may well enter other areas as industrialization progresses.

In the kind of patients that I am speaking of, there are experiences during the day, and dreams at night, which clearly show the need of the patients to see themselves reflected in a friendly, and, as it were, consistent, unharmed, and unhurried face. The patient mentioned had a dream in which he saw a person whose face was surrounded by white hair (like the therapist's) travel in a horse and buggy (such as his grandfather had used) through the Minnesota country-side. The face of that person turned into a horrible Medusa-like mask, and he was not sure it was not his mother. In this dream we can see the present (therapy) condensed with the most trustworthy past (the 'old-fashioned' grandfather, now dead) and the mother's face. That face, of course, had left an 'imprint' of the earliest conflict between basic trust (hope, love) and mistrust (Medusa) in early childhood. The dream illustrates how in the identity crisis (at the end of childhood) the earliest conflicts may have to be resolved once more. I may add that the image of the homogeneous grandparent is waning in America, yet in many families the last integrated personality roles for a number of generations were those of early settlers of pre-industrial times, or maybe early industrial captains, managers or workers. The children, when they took their hand or made them read stories of a homogeneous life, felt in them something which is very hard at this moment for many children to gain from their parents. That is especially true where mothers do not trust themselves, in either representing tradition or their own tastes or even the public's changing tastes, and orient themselves by what the experts say in magazines. The trouble is, of course, that tradition cannot change as fast as the experts' opinions, so that all of this is bewildering for children.

In the treatment of such a patient, then, I would combine an attempt to define the patient's present social experiences as clearly

148

as possible, with the discussion of 'transference' phenomena, and that of corresponding infantile conflicts. This, of course, means that the therapist has to concern himself with social facts. It also means that rather disturbed young persons in many cases can regain or maintain a much greater ability to work and to judge social situations than they would under a prolonged vacation from work life when, especially at this age, they are in danger of making the role of being a patient the basis of their identity. This is a general danger in America right now—to be a patient under psychoanalysis in some circles is a perfectly good full-time occupation, and provides status in itself. We experts now have to re-define our relationship to the culture in which we live. But this, too, means we have to acquire knowledge of psychosocial processes.

In missionary school, the patient we have been discussing had been an outstanding student of Chinese. During treatment he made use of the particular American moratorium which permits, and in fact encourages, young people of any class to be workmen for a while. Here he learned that any occupation has its own code and its own restrictions and limitations. Young people often think that it is in occupations far away from their parents, that the happy people live, the consistent and the honest people. It is often a part of the symptom of identity diffusion that everybody else, such as the people in Paris, the people in the country, or wherever one isn't, seem to be the happy and the decent people. They are the ones with a free and healthy sexuality, who love their work and are free of anxiety. It is, therefore, good for such patients to learn to know work situations, but, of course, they can at first tolerate work situations only if they do not mean continuation of their own careers, and thus long-range commitments. When my patient, for the first time, really enjoyed his work in a steel mill, he said aloud to himself—'My God, this is as good as studying Chinese!' This is a strange statement, but maybe you will understand that to me, it was a good sign, for he had realized that any number of work methods carry their own satisfaction within them, and while at this moment he would not have wanted to go back to Chinese, at any rate he had accepted work as such as an important part of himself.

GREY WALTER:
Do these Medusa dreams have any primary sexual significance?

ERIKSON:
I am sure they do, as a gaping 'void', a vacuum, the 'inner space' of the female. The Medusa's face with open mouth and surrounded by hair in the form of snakes was thus interpreted by Freud.

149

GREY WALTER:

I was surprised that your interpretation was mainly cultural. I should have thought there were so many personal symbols there as well, which could be equally important for the communication aspect of this therapeutic experience.

ERIKSON:

I speak of the cultural aspects here because we are discussing identity formation, not therapy or communication as such. My point is that such dreams contain the negative mother image of early childhood, i.e., they contain in condensed form all the moments when the mother felt strange, dangerous, or unhappy. In other words, while as a late product they are symbolic of the sexual horror of femininity, the facelessness also represents a concentrate of that typical early experience, when the mother becomes a frightening stranger. What I hope to indicate here is the way in which such early mistrust can continue through childhood and become embedded in those identity problems which reach a crisis in late adolescence.

BOWLBY:

My own approach to dreams of this kind, especially if they occur early in the treatment, would be to see to what extent I could determine the patient's feelings towards me from the material in the dream. The kind of way I would approach it would be: to what extent is he seeing me as a damaged and damaging mother? Or alternatively, to what extent is he seeing me as an amiable and protective grandfather? It would appear to me that these are at least possibilities alternating in his mind. The other aspect of it, to which I would give attention, would be the possibility, or perhaps likelihood, that the mother is not merely a mother who might be dangerous to him. He is dangerous to the mother also, because when he did things she didn't like, she cried. Therefore, he was always damaging her and, no doubt, she conveyed that to him in rather effective and implicit ways. My own preoccupation in such a situation with a patient would be to ask myself to what extent is he afraid of hurting me in the present treatment situation, and how much guilt and anxiety he is experiencing in the treatment vis-à-vis myself in the here and now.

ERIKSON:

I am completely in agreement. I reported the cultural aspect here as an introduction to our theme of 'the psychosocial development of the child'. Therapeutically, I would deal with it by a combination of what you have just said and what I said earlier. I would call the culture difference into the therapeutic interpretation, explaining, for example, the grandfather's actual historical position and his more homogeneous background. I also would try to objectify the mother's suffering for him, to clarify her position in her own life, and his position in her life, and so on. I would think that it is this combination which is called for, for the mere question (which I would, indeed, bring up with such patients) 'Did you feel that you could, or would, or did damage me?' can at times increase the magic danger for him, and, as it were, verify the infantile-paranoid position that if anything happens to a significant emotional partner, he must have caused it.

Now, I would like to list quickly the particular components of the syndrome called *identity diffusion*, whether it has a paranoid or other kind of flavour. May I say that Professor Huxley suggests we should call it dispersion and not diffusion, which you may want to discuss.

So if we now may turn from extreme (if transient) pathology back towards the universal elements in this 'normative crisis': I would say that every young person has these feelings at one time or another, and they are implicit in many things young people do. I in no way assume they must be pathological. I have already mentioned a *sense of time diffusion*, namely, a morbidly changed attitude toward the flow of time, toward past and present. To some extent this is an aspect of adolescence, elaborated by the specific conditions of adolescence in given cultures. In Germany when the preoccupation with ruins was a romantic hobby, young people would be preoccupied in their poems with ruins and with the beauty of the dead past. Each item that I will mention now I consider a possible aspect of extreme pathology; more often one of transitory pathology, and most generally one of adolescent imagery, which in various countries is variously connotated.

A second item is *identity consciousness*—that means an extreme form of self-consciousness. You are constantly conscious of your own appearance and with your impression on others. This is something which in the normal adolescent is a transitory matter, and in some people persists, and this not only in pathological cases but also in many creative people, which may account for a certain vanity of some creative people, a preoccupation with their own biography.

Another very important aspect is *negative identity*. The negative identity would comprise everything which a young person has learned he should *not* become. Some young people, when they feel that what they have been equipped with for life is not sufficient to create a positive identity, quite suddenly 'decide' on a negative one.

151

For example, a young person can become a borderline psychotic or an addict or a delinquent, or he may suddenly, in rather a spectacular way, become something which his parents had no idea they were indirectly fostering throughout his early life.

Young people sometimes 'choose' to become patients, because that is the only thing that they can become under the circumstances considering what they have brought along with them and what the world offers them. This, of course, can become a kind of pathological youth movement. You have groups of addicts in the large cities, you have groups of homosexuals often with little real and lasting homosexuality being developed in individuals. It is more a way of life with these young people, who feel that they are 'somebody', because at least the homosexuals will say that they belong. It gives them, at least for a period, more of an identity than they would have at home or at work, or in college, where they may feel that everything that is said to them excludes their kind from the potentialities of their culture. There is at the moment, apparently, a world-wide problem of young people looking for identity in strangely clad gangs. You may remember that in Los Angeles and in Southern California we have the 'zoot-suiters'; those are young boys with a particularly large, flat hat and with outfits that are very dandy-like. This is a tendency which has gone round the whole world, with similar names even. In Israel I met a psychiatrist from South Africa, who told me about a development among the Negroes in South Africa, and said, 'We call them the zootsies'. I think the anthropologists would call it 'culture diffusion!' Then you may have heard that in Russia there are complaints about gangs of young men in strange dress.

HUXLEY:

In London their counterparts are the teddy-boys, who dress in Edwardian style.

ERIKSON:

I emphasize this merely because this negative identity can be supported by a uniform which makes one something that does not fit the culture—it fits in the Edwardian era, or it fits into Mexico rather than into America, or into America rather than Russia, and so on. Here we would find a connexion with the enormous appeal of 'positive' youth movements in uniform who are idealistic but revolutionary.

Then I have discussed already *work paralysis*, the inability to work or unwillingness to work and the loss of that particular pleasure of

152

work completion which this boy expressed by saying, 'The steel mill is almost as good as Chinese'.

Then there is the sense of *bisexual diffusion*. Such young people have states in which they do not feel quite clearly as members of one sex or the other, which of course very much makes them possible victims of the way of life of homosexuals or of an ascetic turning away from sexuality, with dramatic breakthroughs of impulses.

There is also *authority diffusion*, which means that they can neither simply obey nor give orders. Any situation of rivalry and competition, any situation of hierarchy of authority makes them feel panicky. And, finally, there is *ideological diffusion*, which has already been mentioned.

Now, to turn to the positive side. Each one of these items is a potential danger, I would think, at one time or another for an adolescent. However, there is in any working social structure a complete set of complementary institutions which help the individual to alleviate all of these aspects of identity diffusion. Ideological movements of great variety give an answer to all of these problems such as giving *time perspective* to the individual by interpreting what he is doing and what his society is doing in a particular way so that, at least for a while, he will know where he is and where he is going; by giving him a *self-certainty*, in regard to what he is, permitting him a certain amount of role experimentation, say, as a student or an apprentice, or a member of a fraternity or a youth group, by permitting him occupational choices that he can experiment with until he can choose a final one.

TANNER:

I wonder if you examined, with this sort of thing in mind, people who have been expatriated either forcibly or from their own choice? At the end of the war, I had to do with the psychiatric rehabilitation of returning prisoners of war, and they had a very recognizable syndrome. It was partly depression; but what you are saying about dispersion of identity seems now very relevant to the symptoms that they were having. The one thing which impressed itself on us very much during this rehabilitation, was that these 'neurotic' POW's were not constitutionally predisposed or 'proper' neurotics, but simply people who had been isolated from their culture, and had developed queer ideas of their culture during this period of isolation. When they came back, one of the things which had a great effect on rehabilitating them was a system we started of sending them out to work on the work bench with other people in the local community;

they tried four or five different sorts of work each. This was probably the most effective single measure.

HARGREAVES:

It is interesting that in the British programme for the rehabilitation of repatriated prisoners of war the term 'job rehearsal' was developed to cover this phenomenon.

HUXLEY:

Isn't it really role-rehearsal, not merely job-rehearsal?

TANNER:

If you put it as role-rehearsal, perhaps I should say that the other chief therapeutic thing was learning how to dance with the nurses!

ERIKSON:

This remark is a very fitting one. During the war I worked in a rehabilitation clinic and I would not be surprised (it's so hard to know these things about oneself) if it was not the one decisive experience which made me take the identity problem seriously. I saw some very disturbed men there, who had broken down because of long isolation and most of all because of the long preoccupation with work patterns that were not their own and could not be related to anything they had learned. To play the role of the soldier 24 hours a day is pretty hard for the majority of Americans. This has to do with the particular identity which is prepared in American youth, namely, the belief that you live for your chance; there is what amounts to a deification of The Chance in American life (your time will come —the right thing will come along—don't let anybody make a sucker out of you—don't let anybody fence you in, etc.). Under conditions of war and of industrial organization such beliefs pose a very difficult identity problem.

* * *

PIAGET:

I have been most interested by the remarks made by Mr. Erikson before he described the case at the end of the morning. He made a general observation about the way that family experiences and, particularly, the satisfactions or the difficulties of the child in relation to his mother and father later condition his successive experiences, and in particular his adaptation to society. This problem seems to me to raise questions as regards the process itself, that is as regards the explanation of this continuity, and I should like to put one or two questions to Mr. Erikson especially from these two points of view. The first of these problems is the analogy with intelligence and cognitive processes in general in which we find also continuities of this kind. Then the second problem is the explanation of this continuity itself.

First, I would like to say a few words about the analogies with intelligence. When we study the development of cognitive functions, sensori-motor development, the development of perceptions and of patterns of intelligence, we continually find that early experiences or experiences from far back can equally have an importance throughout life and can orient research and orient solutions in many cases. I am not, of course, speaking of the conscious applications of previous methods or previous solutions to new problems; on the contrary, I am speaking of unconscious transfers and unconscious generalizations, and on this plane it seems to me that there is a possible comparison with the continuity of affective life. For example, on the sensori-motor level the infant makes all kinds of experiments with his hands which will play a considerable part in the organization of space, in causality, etc. and these initial experiments can explain therefore, by unconscious analogies certain choices between intellectual solutions which will occur later. But it is not only a question of general phenomena; even in the biography of individuals and in the differences between individuals we find these kinds of continuity between old situations and present situations, and this can occur at any age. If I might take an example from my own biography to help you understand what I want to say: before I became involved in psychology, I dealt with zoology, I dealt with terrestrial molluscs, that is to say with problems which do not seem to have any connexion with psychology. However, there are connexions; there is the fundamental problem of the relations between the hereditary structure and the environment, the problem of genotypes and phenotypes that we were speaking of last year and which we find now come to the fore in psychology. But when I began considering how I approached a psychological problem, and especially during discussions with colleagues, seeing that our points of view and starting points were different, I often found that there was an unconscious continuity and that without wishing to do so I thought as I had thought formerly, that the same way of posing problems keeps coming back. This dates from an education very far back and of which frequently one is not conscious. It is because of these least conscious things that very frequently we put questions in a way which is incomprehensible to our partners or contradictors. So it seems, and this is my first point, that there are fundamental analo-

155

gies between this continuity of old experiences and of present situations from the affective and cognitive points of view. One finds parallel processes in both fields.

Now I come to my second problem, which is that of interpretation. There are two fundamental interpretations of continuity which is both affective and intellectual: that which I will call static interpretation and that which I will call dynamic interpretation. Static interpretation consists in saying that the individual clings to old conflicts. These old conflicts are recorded somewhere in the form of latent conflicts to which are attached memories and unconscious representations. Then throughout life, and especially at the moment of his moulding as an adolescent and at the beginning of adult work, the individual without knowing it assimilates to the present a past which has been preserved entire. It is the solution calling for this preservation of the past just as it stands which I will call the static solution.

Secondly, there can be a dynamic solution, that is to say that the past can be preserved, not in the form of conflicts buried in the unconscious, or of memories or representations buried in the unconscious, but in the form of what I will call action patterns and reaction patterns which are more like habit than memory. That is to say, one gets into the habit of reacting in a certain way, one reacts first in a certain way towards one's family, and reacts again in the same way in analogous situations, so that here is something which is more comparable to continuity in the cognitive field, where obviously it is not the unconscious memory of former situations which acts on the present, but attitudes of mind, modes of reactions, which are preserved and applied to new situations. In the second interpretation there would not be preservation of the former conflict, but the individual would continue to re-create the same conflicts. He would live through situations which are reproduced, which are re-created, without there being necessarily conservation, which seems to me personally to be somewhat difficult to explain in the unconscious. In the same way from the cognitive point of view he would continually adapt former solutions to present problems simply through the continuity of reaction patterns and not by conservation of anything.

HUXLEY:

Isn't there a third possibility which is like the second, but in which you regard the internal situation, the conflict, the method of reacting, as itself a psychological organ capable of development and change? The change in this case is analogous to maturation but not entirely automatic and intrinsic; it is related to external changes, so that you could have intrinsic organs for dealing with conflict themselves changing in the course of time. That is how conflicts can get resolved, isn't it?

DE SAUSSURE:

It seems to me that Piaget distinguished between, on the one hand, a static situation and, on the other hand, a dynamic situation. He said that for him the solution seemed to be the dynamic solution, but in fact what we observe clinically is that there are people who adhere to the static situation and cannot get rid of it. For example, I think that the girl who pushed the chair in against the piano was not conscious of what this meant and probably she would have to become conscious of what it meant if she were to change her whole behaviour towards her mother. As long as she is not conscious of its significance she will repeat these actions or similar actions because she does not know why she does them.

PIAGET:

Of course, there can be a clinging to the past in some situations, but what I wonder is whether the past situation is always a fact and not sometimes the result of an interpretation. In the case of the girl and her piano stool, we have a piece of symbolic behaviour which of course recalls precise previous situations. It remains to be seen whether this symbolic behaviour is the result of a reaction to something which has been preserved in the unconscious, which is always there, and which is interpreted in this way, or whether it is the present representation of a present conflict which itself prolongs previous conflicts without their being exactly the same. In the case of the girl, I should not like to pass judgement; it is Mr. Erikson who should enlighten us here; but in the case of the young man he described, the clinical case which he developed at some length, without being able to deny absolutely that there is conservation of a previous conflict I think that a large part of the second interpretation is possible.

I do not think that there are bare facts in the affective field any more than elsewhere. A fact can always lend itself to an interpretation and I think that precisely in this field the interpretation plays a fairly big role.

DE SAUSSURE:

But there are patients that we observe during long periods who always repeat the same thing, and once we manage to put a finger on the tender spot we see that they stop repeating it.

157

ZAZZO:

In the examples given by Dr. de Saussure, isn't there a stress on the pathological? Is there not some danger in starting from a pathological method in order to make up a theory of affective evolution? Perhaps we should leave out of consideration the pathological cases as explanations of affective evolution.

DE SAUSSURE:

It is exceedingly rare that anyone completes his affective development without there being more or less deep fixations and without there being more or less strong attachments at certain stages of the affective development. But actually, I am not pretending that there are necessarily fixations or stoppages. I am simply noting that in a very large number of cases stoppages do occur and particularly at certain difficult stages.

ERIKSON:

In discussing identity diffusion or any other developmental crisis we really discuss a period of life when past and future meet, when patterns of the past have to be translated into possibilities for the future. Different people under different conditions find better or worse solutions for these tasks. Obviously, then, what Professor Piaget calls 'static', remains a hindrance to change, while what he calls 'dynamic', are patterns which (as Dr. Huxley said) can adapt to new situations. I would say that patients are by definition people who ask for help in overcoming 'static' fixations, and in making 'dynamic' patterns more adaptive.

As for people who can solve this kind of matter for themselves, what you said, Professor Piaget, reminded me of a volume of letters Freud wrote at a critical period in his life to a friend in Berlin. As a young man Freud had passed through a stage in which he was intensely interested in the German philosophic movement of Nature Philosophy. He had loved Goethe's Ode to Nature and had become a physician because he wanted to 'unveil nature's secrets'. Then something happened to him, as it happens to many young people: and he concentrated all his passion on the strictest methods of the physicalistic physiology of his day, doing brain sections, and publishing papers on neurophysiology and on paralyses in children. Then relatively late he settled down as a practising neurologist. At that time he went through a severe crisis which is reflected in the letters. Attached to these letters is a very strange document, namely, something he called a 'Psychology for Neurologists', which I must say is very hard for me to understand, but which I think Grey Walter would be interested in because it describes the brain as a kind of central agency for incoming and outgoing excitation.

The letters make clear how Freud gradually applied the viewpoint and the method of brain physiology to psychology. In analogy to his work in brain physiology, where he had dissected brains at various stages of development and reconstructed the development of certain brain centres through infantile life, he made, as it were, sections at various stages of psychological development until they formed an epigenetic continuum.

I wonder if you had in mind such a transfer of a work pattern from one field to another? This sometimes throws entirely new light on the second field. But it certainly can also lead to a belated identity crisis, until the patterns prove to be transferable. For the choices which lead an individual to his identity formation include of course choices of an occupational identity and an intellectual identity, both based on the affective sources of his interests. At the same time you also have to ask what choices are possible for him in the light of his desires and inhibitions, and his special aptitudes and limitations. In addition to all this he must find recognition and through it—I don't know whether feedback is the right word here— a constant replenishment. Shaw called it a continuous 'resource'.

So I think that the identity development of a young individual is certainly not only based on the choices which he has to make because his affective sources push from behind, but also on conditions which pull him toward opportunities for accomplishment, recognition, and replenishment. But I would say that the first choices he makes, in which a full reciprocity and mutuality with the environment is established, will remain important for all his life. Anything further will be variations and applications of his original thinking.

BOWLBY:

I should like to return to Professor Piaget's alternative hypotheses which he described as the static interpretation and the dynamic interpretation of the clinical material, because I think those two alternative hypotheses underlie some, at least, of the divisions amongst psychoanalysts at the present day.

There are, I believe, many analysts who think in terms of Piaget's static interpretation and who feel that their main task is to reach back into the patient's history where the problem originated and that, once that has been reached, the problem will come unravelled and the patient 'unfixated'. The other way of looking at it—Piaget's dynamic interpretation—is that a person comes to adopt certain methods of resolving conflicts and these he persists in using throughout his life. As Piaget himself put it, the person recreates the conflict and the solution in each moment of his experience in his life. Although these processes may undergo some evolution and change, some solutions seem to be such that the person is fixated in them and can't use other solutions.

These alternative ways of looking at the same phenomena lead, I think, to two different psychoanalytic techniques. There is the technique which, to give it a rather slang description, comprises 'digging up the past', burrowing for forgotten memories of past events. The alternative technique is based on observing the way in which the patient, in his relationship to the analyst, proceeds to deal with the situation in which he finds himself by using the same old maladaptive procedures. In other words one recognizes that in one's consulting room in the here and now one is presented with a first-hand demonstration of the way in which the patient has always solved his problem and which he is likely to continue in. That, of course, leads to a technique which is based on the analysis of the transference in the analytic situation.

Now, although these two techniques are not mutually exclusive—most analysts utilize both techniques in some measure—it remains true that some analysts greatly favour one end of this spectrum and other analysts greatly favour the other end. Which end they favour depends, I think, on their theoretical position. I personally favour the dynamic one, the interpretation of the here and now in the transference relationship. (See Strachey, 1934, and Rickman, 1951).

HARGREAVES:

It seems to me that there are two possible childhood reasons why you may limp. One is that in some moment of time, through some episode, you broke your calcaneus: the other is that you were born in China, and your feet were gently bound, then bound a little bit tighter, a little bit tighter still and so on. I would have thought that, in fact, both alternatives may occur, in psychological terms, in individual patients.

Some fields of therapy particularly tend to attract for treatment the kind of case for which I have used the broken calcaneus as a metaphor. That is the case in which in the middle of trying to solve one of the expected psychosocial crises of infancy and childhood the child meets some exceedingly traumatic episode, like the death of the mother that is never mentioned frankly to her. The other kind of case corresponds to the gentle binding of the feet. Lady Asquith tells in her autobiography of how every time her father passed her sitting at table, he used to straighten her shoulders and say 'Sit up,

Margot'. That is obviously as influential over ten years as a single episode, although the kind of effect is probably different. It leads not to the tendency to re-create a single traumatic episode, but to the tendency to re-create a pattern of relationships.

I think the fractures are much less common than the binding, but are inclined to be written up more because they tend to be more dramatic. I think they do, in fact, often respond to a therapy based on a static conception. The situations that arise from the binding don't get written up so frequently, or at least they didn't in the early history of psychotherapy, and often, I think, they don't respond to this type of treatment.

INHELDER:

If I understood your point of view properly, Mr. Erikson, the adult should reach a certain equilibrium or, as you call it, a feeling of 'integrity' to the extent that he is conscious of the continuity of his development. According to you, this continuity would be due to a process of 'identification'. Well, in order to get continuity and development, identification is not enough. In order that the individual at the end of his development should become something other than what he was at the beginning, a process of differentiation must also intervene. How do you envisage this process of differentiation and how would the transformation be possible if there were only identification without differentiation?

HUXLEY:

This, if I may say so, is what I was suggesting after Piaget spoke; that you have to regard attitudes, approaches and methods of solving problems as something alive, as part of the developing human organism—indeed, as organs of the organism; accordingly like everything alive they are capable in certain circumstances of developing into something different. In purely organic embryonic development, you may get an arrest of change in certain conditions. If you deprive a tadpole of its thyroid it won't metamorphose into a frog; but if you then give it the proper dose of thyroxin it resumes its interrupted development. The frog also illustrates a frequent paradox of development—the co-ordination of continuity with discontinuity. The development of the tadpole into a frog is a single continuous process; but it passes through the crisis of metamorphosis, which makes a true discontinuity between aquatic and sub-aerial existence. This idea that mental structures and complexes and so forth are alive, parts of a living organism, and therefore, can change and develop, is vital in what Bowlby and Piaget were saying.

161

LORENZ:

There is no real discontinuity and nothing is really static. Everything is a process, only sometimes the process is fast and sometimes it is slower. I always get muddled up by this conception of opposites: the opposite of static is dynamic, the opposite of structural is functional, and the opposite of continuity is discontinuity. There are no such contraries! There are all gradations between continuity and discontinuity, and even if I jump, the worst that will happen is the continuity of the jump—you can slow down a jump, you can make a slow motion picture of it, and the jump doesn't differ from the slowest motion in quality.

HUXLEY:

Perhaps instead of using the word 'discontinuous' we should say 'distinct'? Nothing in biology is ever completely discontinuous, but many things may be highly distinct or distinctive. May I amplify my previous example: the pattern of organization of a tadpole is highly distinct from that of the adult frog and the organism passes from one to the other by the process of metamorphosis, which introduces a high degree of discontinuity. At metamorphosis there is a rapid change from one relatively stable pattern to another; but I agree with Lorenz that the stability is only a relative stability, because there is always some degree of change going on. At any rate there are long relatively stable periods separated by short periods of rapid transformation of pattern; the latter are essentially processes of change and the former essentially processes of maintenance.

LORENZ:

And if we take a highly accelerated process, a crisis, in which you have to move from one attitude to another very quickly, you have to unbuild much before you build the other thing. If you do it slowly you will make the change in such a way that there are no crises. I think the main aspect that ought to concern us biologists is that whenever you have a period of very highly accelerated change you have a period of increased vulnerability and danger. That happens in the metamorphosis of the frog, and when a bird hatches out of an egg, and when a human person goes through puberty. These are the critical periods of quick changes. I think that the acceleration between two critical stages is what we ought to emphasize more than the absolute speed of the process.

HUXLEY:

Yes: the function of one type of process is transformation, and of the other is maintenance.

162

GREY WALTER:

At the first meeting of the group we discussed this very problem: the question of whether abrupt changes do or do not occur in children. It seems to me that we have defined it, in fact, as being the capital problem in the whole of this discussion. We decided that there probably were abrupt changes and, of course, this is very important in working out a theory of development of the nervous system, whether descriptive or analytical in the Freudian sense, or biological or cybernetic. The existence of what cyberneticians call step-functions, or relatively abrupt changes which, though not absolutely discontinuous, have a relatively very high rate of change, has a very powerful action on the whole theory, because the derivative of such a process, of course, is correspondingly large. We know that, in general, biological receptors are responsive to rates of change rather than steady states. So, an abrupt rate of change will be perceived in an exaggerated way. Thus the sort of effect that Ronald Hargreaves was talking about, where Lady Asquith had a repeated series of small gentle shocks, would not necessarily have had the same derivative value as a single sudden large one. In a simple system the two *might* be equivalent. But in a system that undergoes abrupt transition and responds mainly to rates of change, then a sudden event occurring during one of the transition periods would have an exaggerated, apparently anomalous effect. The whole subject I think is treated very well in Ashby's book (Ashby, 1952).

ERIKSON:

I think that 'continuity' and 'discontinuity', 'static', and 'dynamic' are terms with implications of particular controversies in each field. They short-circuit, as it were, what I want to discuss, namely, that a child grows in relativity to other beings that grow around him, who are themselves passing through various stages. Therefore, any stage he reaches will have a psychosocial connotation and it is that psychosocial connotation that may create a discontinuity. Now this fits with what Konrad Lorenz said in this sense—that such psychosocial discontinuities are specially dangerous during periods of great velocity of change, either in the organism or in the milieu.

By psychosocial connotation I mean something like this: there are mothers (and I presume there are cultures) who, relatively speaking, favour babies. There are others who favour older children. A boy who has got used to the fact that he is the eldest and for a while the only child has to realize that it isn't just he who is the most wonderful thing in the world, but whoever at that moment is the baby of the family. From this moment on, he can gain new status in the family only by relinquishing the rewards of being a baby and trying as quickly as possible to gain the rewards of being a big boy; one who doesn't cry, and who doesn't demand. This he may learn sooner or later, with fewer or more regressive episodes in which he tries to be a baby again. If, during such a crisis, somebody dies, or gets sick, a war breaks out, or the family moves, such changes in the various departments of life have a cumulative effect: they get too much. I, therefore, referred to the development of identity as one in which one can establish continuity out of discontinuity, or, in Huxley's words, maintenance in change. Somebody who really grows up has to maintain a ratio of components: the baby is still in him when he becomes a big boy.

LORENZ:

The difficulty is the crisis. If you are a crab you must moult in order to grow, but you must take good care to preserve the continuity of your life in the meantime, because you are very easily eaten in the process. The point that I want to bring out with this is the vulnerable state.

ERIKSON:

As for young Lady Asquith, what her father may have done all her life became humiliating for her at a particular period in her life, when it became significant in a crisis.

ZAZZO:

Certainly we should take into consideration that it is society which accentuates the stage of development and imposes on the child breaks in continuity: the beginning of the primary school is a very clear example of social discontinuity which corresponds to a new stage of psychobiological evolution. It would, therefore, be worth while comparing different situations in order to understand the formation of identity and psychological differentiation—different situations, different groups where the child is found. A little while ago you spoke about twins: this is an excellent example of the group where the individual experiences considerable difficulty in differentiating himself and where he manages with the utmost difficulty to affirm his identity. There is actually an affective and intellectual pathology of twins which shows to what extent this integration into a biological group makes identity, the affirmation of the person, difficult.

A second situation which is very general is the situation of the child within the family. Again this is a biologically determined group where the child occupies an absolute place or, more exactly, where he lives as an absolute: when another child is born, a brother or a sister, and when the structure is thus modified, the child may be profoundly disturbed: he no longer knows exactly what is his place in the group. Then to consider the school, where the child is admitted between six and seven years. Professor Wallon, establishing a connexion between his own research and that of Professor Piaget, made the following remarks about this period: on the intellectual plane the child begins to be able to understand the idea of unity on the arithmetic plane. He begins to acquire invariants, to use Piaget's expression. Simultaneously, on the social and affective plane he begins to understand himself as a unity among other unities, interchangeable unities, and it is a very important new development in the feeling of identity: he has a stronger identity because he feels himself living as one among others. It is no longer a biological group, it is a group which has a much more mobile structure and where the individuals, all of more or less the same age, can change their role, change their place and change their situation. Identity of self and differentiation are created interdependently. Here we see a discontinuity which is explainable by the psychophysiological maturation itself, where quantitative changes, which are very rapid at this age, lead to a whole restructuring of the mentality. There are also, and I would stress this, social structures which society imposes on the child—particularly the school, which involves a new reorganization.

INHELDER:

In the present discussion we seem to be imagining that everything happens as if, throughout all the mutations due to the outside environment, the child maintains his identity. Could we not envisage another hypothesis: that the child does not only go through transformations under the effect of outside factors but he also contributes actively to his own metamorphosis?

ERIKSON:

I can only say yes. The present is the elaboration (through interaction with the environment) of the child's past.

INHELDER:

He contributes to his own differentiation, to become another being different from the one he was before.

Y

Let me say it this way: Identity is not the same as identification. In fact, it is exactly that which overcomes identification as a dominant mechanism. I believe that in my own field this is an important point to emphasize, namely, that the final identity of the individual is not the sum of his previous identifications but is a more highly differentiated complex in which earlier identifications become part of a more unified whole. William James once spoke of 'the self he murdered', by which he meant, I think, that particular potential person that would be the sum of all the previous identifications with which the individual cannot do anything under given conditions. William James also says how sometimes a young person wonders whether the self he killed was not the better one.

I would emphasize in this connexion that identifications in childhood are, by definition, identifications with part aspects of people and not with whole people. A child who identifies with his father cannot possibly identify with the whole father: he identifies with his size, his occupation, his potency, or with any number of these, but it is always a part aspect. Out of mere identifications a whole identity could never grow.

Now there is another aspect to this. In a functioning social system I would think a child, as he grows through the various stages of his childhood toward adolescence, is faced with a comprehensible hierarchy within his own family, a hierarchy of roles beginning with the younger siblings and ending with the grandfather, or great-grandfather, or whoever belongs to the wider family. All through childhood, this gives him some kind of a set of expectations as to what he is going to be when he grows older, and I have a feeling that already very small children can identify with a number of people in a number of respects, and establish inside a kind of hierarchy of expectation, which then must be 'verified' later on. That is why cultural change can be one of the changes that can be so traumatic for identity formation, because they break up the inner consistency of that hierarchy. This, for example, one can see clearly in Pittsburgh, where whole European villages were transferred to an industrial neighbourhood, and tried to maintain their collective—that is national and religious—identity.

What has been described in psychoanalysis as identification is, in later childhood, already pathological identification—it is what I would rather call over-identification. It implies the necessity of settling accounts with a particular person, let us say the mother or the father. I am sure every child has to do this when he is young, and every child has to do it over again at critical periods, but on the whole,

166

in a functioning family life, the child has much greater freedom in identification than our case histories would make us believe.

As to what Dr. Bowlby said, I do not want to evade the point about different psychotherapeutic philosophies in psychoanalysis, although we are apt to confuse the scientific interpretation of life data with the therapeutic interpretations given to the patient. One could answer this by referring to different periods in the development of the psychoanalytic method itself; one could answer it by referring to the various approaches to patients of different ages; and then again one could refer to patients of different syndromes, the changing epidemiology in the neuroses of our time. I would say it is best to be guided by the patient in any given situation. The kind of patient I mentioned this morning is a young person in an acute identity crisis. One will find out soon enough that he would not stand for any exclusive discussion of his past. The simple result of doing that would be that he would break down further. For one of the aspects of this whole syndrome which I will discuss later is time diffusion. In young people with identity problems the attitude towards time as such is very pathological. They feel that there is no future, and that the past is malignant. They may feel in a tremendous hurry to catch the bit of future there is or they may suffer from a slowing up of time experience, and move as if in molasses. It takes hours to wake up, it also takes hours to go to sleep, and it is very hard to adhere to any schedule at all.

Now, to take such patients and to say 'Lie on a couch and I will sit behind you, a mere screen for your free associations' is, of course, completely out of the question. Such patients come to you to find the remnant of an identity, with a last hope of a 'recognition'. You are a teacher, a master, or whatever—and not just a transferee of the old father. In fact, as I may have an opportunity to illustrate, these patients 'transfer' the very earliest experiences of selfness and otherness. But they experience these with traumatic immediacy. They want to see that you are there, and will not disintegrate or evade.

If one is called upon to help a man who has found his identity but suffers from inhibitions or anxieties that are left over from the past, the situation is different. As I said yesterday, there are, of course, neurotic inhibitions or symptoms which go together with a perfectly good identity formation. In this case, one only wants to establish that these inhibitions and phobias are the result of left-overs from the past; here an additional education, or an additional identity formation is not called for.

	1	2	3	4	5	6	7	8
I. INFANCY	Trust v. Mistrust				Unipolarity v. Premature Self-Differentiation			
II. EARLY CHILDHOOD		Autonomy v. Shame, Doubt			Bipolarity v. Autism			
III. PLAY AGE			Initiative v. Guilt		Play-Identification v. (Oedipal) Phantasy Identities			
IV. SCHOOL AGE				Industry v. Inferiority	Work-Identification v. Identity Foreclosure			
V. ADOLESCENCE	Time Perspective v. Time Diffusion	Self-Certainty v. Identity Consciousness	Role-Experimentation v. Negative Identity	Anticipation of Achievement v. Work-Paralysis	Identity v. Identity Diffusion	Sexual Identity v. Bi-sexual Diffusion	Leadership Polarization v. Authority Diffusion	Ideological Polarization v. Diffusion of Ideals
VI. YOUNG ADULT-HOOD					Solidarity v. Social Isolation	Intimacy v. Isolation		
VII. ADULT-HOOD							Generativity v. Self-Absorption	
VIII. MATURE AGE								Integrity v. Disgust, Despair

The Psychosocial Development of Children

ERIKSON:
I indicated yesterday just what kind of material we clinicians deal with and today I would like to indicate into what kind of orders our observations may fall. On the chart (Chart I, on opposite page) the Roman numbers mean progression in age and the Arabic ones progressive potentialities for differentiation. For the moment please pay attention to the diagonal only. The steps of the diagonal contain *the gradual unfolding of the human personality through psychosocial crises.* These crises are, of course, determined both by what, at a given time, is ready in a child to develop and what, at the same time, is prepared for him in his social system in the form of provocation, prohibition, elaboration, connotation, and so on. In the sequence given in the diagonal, you have in each box two psychosocial criteria, one a more positive, one a more negative one. The crisis consists of the conflict between these two tendencies and if the crisis is lived through positively, productively, creatively, then the 'good' criterion will outweigh the 'bad' one. This does not mean that ever in human life the 'bad' one is entirely 'overcome', nor that the accentuation of the negative one could not appear again in certain crises. There are other considerations, too, of a philosophic kind, which must keep us from treating the 'bad' criteria as preventable or something that can (or should) be prevented or cured away.

Now, if I may briefly state what is in each box. The chart makes each box equally big; this is an artefact of systematization. In any individual, or in any given culture, the ratio between the contents of the boxes can vary tremendously, but of course, only within certain systematic limits, as we pointed out when we spoke of sexual differences. As to the sequence, however, I would be rather adamant that it must not vary. The terms *basic trust* and *basic mistrust* sum-

169

marize much that has been emphasized recently in psychiatry and in public health, especially by Doctor Bowlby. He and Dr. Spitz have emphasized the circumstances which hit the specific vulnerabilities of this stage and cause lasting 'basic mistrust'. As to the *psychosocial modalities* which I wish to introduce here, the social modality of the first stage would be (in basic English which is what I started with and hope to end up with) to learn 'to get what is given' and to experience particular givers and forms of giving. Then, also in basic English, you could say that at this time the child learns 'to get somebody to give' and then, by way of a most primitive psychosocial mechanism, the child learns 'to get to be the giver'. I am sure that all languages have certain very simple designations of the basic modalities in human relationships. The first problem would be to relate the infant's means of receiving with the mother's ways of giving, and also, of course, her ways of withholding. These herald in the first crisis which comes to a head (unless otherwise accelerated) through such physiological changes as teething, which is a disturbance in the main organ of receiving, or through the second great 'cause' of this crisis—conflicts in and with the person who is the principal giver.

Of particular importance here are those states of impotent rage which are provoked in the infant when communication is jammed and he feels the victim of inner tensions that he cannot manage because the environment does not know how to alleviate them. This would be the ontogenetic source of the sense of evil, a 'basic mistrust' which combines a sense of mistrustfulness and of untrustworthiness. Here is the ontogenetic experience of the sin through which paradise was forfeited for ever. It is obviously difficult to know what mechanisms are at work at a time which is one of relative lack of differentiation between outer and inner experience, between body and mother. But this seems to be the stage to which our sickest candidates for identity diffusion regress—as Bowlby pointed out yesterday, when he rightly interpreted their dreams of the faceless parent as also connoting the fear that the patient may destroy the therapist, his new protector, as well. There seems to be an affinity between this earliest crisis of trust in the maternal environment and the adolescent crisis which concludes childhood and tests one's capacity to trust society at large: a complete and relatively unpredictable breakthrough often occurs in late adolescence.

Now at each stage I should very briefly mention its relationship to one of the major social institutions. For I wish to claim in all earnestness that certain universal and basic social institutions correspond to the stages of the life cycles and more, that they exist for and because of these life crises. For example, the crisis of trust and mistrust persists in and endangers every individual throughout life. But every individual can find it collectively annotated and, as it were, stylized in one universal institution: religion. In every prayer, in every turning toward the supernatural or superhuman there is an attempt at re-establishing the sense of trustworthiness in relation to a god, to fate, or to history. In the first stage, the infant receives, through the maternal persons, whatever 'faith in the species' is present in them. He learns to expect that people and institutions will know how to give and restore faith. More modestly, the psycho-social gain of this period can be said to be an enduring pattern for the solution of the recurring crisis between trust and mistrust. This, in homogeneous cultures, prepares the child for the collective ways of reinforcing the solution through periodical rituals.

The transition from one stage to the next accentuates one of those normative discontinuities we talked about yesterday: in order to learn to be independent the child must have learned that he can depend. I speak now of II.2 in the diagram. But let me briefly refer to I. 2, the precursor of autonomy during the trust stage. It is one of the main aspects of systematizing in an epigenetic way, that everything which appears in the diagonal is in some form already present in the first horizontal. Progress is a differentiation at various stages of something that has been prepared in all previous stages. Anybody who has watched babies can already see autonomy in them, a wish at times to be left alone or to be free of things which at other times they want very much. This wish occurs at that age only off and on. If it becomes too predominant too early, a factor is created which influences the ratio between trust and autonomy, and between mistrust and doubt, and remains in some way systematically influential for the development of the further stages.

In connexion with the establishment of the sense of autonomy, let me make a few points which are really significant for all stages. Different cultures emphasize autonomy in entirely different ways, but always in ways systematically related to the rest of the culture. There is always a minimum sense of autonomy which the life style of a particular culture must insist on, and a maximum which it can tolerate. Amongst the Sioux Indians the babies all have their feet swaddled as tightly as possible; on the other hand, amongst the Yurok in California the feet are deliberately kept free so that the grandmother can massage them every day: there you have one of those differences in accentuation which (as I have tried to show in *Childhood and Society*) imply a systematic relationship not only to

171

other items of child training, but also to world-image, economy, sexual differences, etc. Then, of course, different children are entirely different in their temperamental characteristics: only in the interplay of cultural and individual style can you get what in a given individual would be a true sense of autonomy.

There is one other systematic point which I should have mentioned earlier. When I speak of stages, I refer primarily to what *results* out of a stage at the *end* of the stage. In child development a stage is often determined by what the child is *beginning* to master. I am talking about a stage as the time at the end of which the ego will master a particular conflict in such a way that the individual, as it were, can forget about it. The relative but enduring solution has become a part of him. It is like the difference between making the first steps, i.e., learning to walk—and being able to walk in such a way that one can forget the fact that one can walk and only think of where one wants to walk.

Finally, I must emphasize again, that all these stages are intrinsically related to the psychoanalytic theory of the basic drives and of the ego: unfortunately, the mere presentation of the stages will preclude a detailed discussion of this inter-relationship. The first stage was related to what, in psychoanalytic psychosexual terms, is called orality and sensory-tactile erotism. The stage of autonomy versus the stage of shame and doubt is related to anality and to muscular development. For 'libido-development' as well as 'child development' and social accentuation have in common certain modalities, such as holding on and letting go, retaining and releasing. The sphincters, as part of the muscle system, can become the dramatic place where holding on and letting go is particularly emphasized to a degree dependent on how much the culture wants to emphasize it, and how much emphasis the individual can tolerate. From intense experiences of being held on to, of holding in, of holding on, of being freed, of letting go in relation to persons, objects, and feelings, can come a sense of autonomy; that is a sense that the child can master himself and his environment *more* than he needs to be mastered and to have things done for him. This basic ratio can later influence many modalities, characterizing, in turn, basic social attitudes such as a hostile ejecting, letting loose, or repudiating, or a tolerant letting pass, letting live, letting go. The whole stage is, of course, what the Germans call 'Trotzalter'.

LORENZ:
How would you translate 'Trotz'? Spite, cussedness? Stubbornness?

172

ERIKSON:

Trutz, an earlier form of Trotz, is something more positive than mere cussedness. It rhymes with Schutz.

INHELDER:

Opposition?

LORENZ:

Entêtement? The French verb 'bouder' is a mild sort of translation. . . . in der Ecke ist . . . Trotz.

ERIKSON:

Aber wie kommt das Kind in die Ecke?

HUXLEY:

'Stubborn' is better than 'obstinate'. 'Obstinate' is more passive, 'Stubborn' implies a positive reaction.

ERIKSON:

This is a good example of how such modalities can be related to vices and virtues alike. When 'Trotz' leads to 'Trutz', you have a warrior who won't let anybody pass. When you say 'obstinate', then you have something entirely different.

MEAD:

Well, maybe you have moral courage. When we want to describe New Englanders in America, for instance, in a way that would be acceptable to New Englanders, or to people who live outside New England, you have the choice of saying they are stubborn, or they have great rock-like integrity!

ERIKSON:

So this whole stage is one in which the child learns to control himself in accordance with certain regulations demanded in the culture. If the regulations are transmitted in such a way that the child receives a good impression of the self-control of those who are delegated to control him, he should end up with a sense that all in all, given regulations and rationales, one is able to regulate oneself more than being regulated. Otherwise a deep sense of shame over being so weak and uncontrolled in comparison with other people, and a sense of doubt either in his own mechanisms of self-regulation or in the methods of regulation and self-regulation in his regulators will arise. This, of course, remains a life-long problem, reflected in our laws and liberties. Their first battleground is the autonomy stage.

HUXLEY:
Up to what age do you think that stage would continue?

ERIKSON:
I should think it includes all of early childhood. In contrast to the things you might learn to *complete* in school later, the child is here primarily preoccupied with the question—who does it, and to whom is it done, am I doing it myself, or is somebody doing it to me or for me—that is the power and extent of one's *willing* something. All of this is related to sitting up, to standing up, to being able to control first a sedentary kingdom, and then a perambulatory one. Psychosocially speaking, shame has something to do with the fact that the individual who sits up and stands up has space all around him; he can suddenly be seen and judged from all sides. An increased awareness and sensitivity to the environment goes with this. In many societies this is exploited by intense shaming—laughing when the child falls down, and so on, all of which causes a very particular rage in the child, a mixture of the rage of shame, and shame over rage. This is why shame has, at least in the English language, such connotations as that one wants to sink into the ground, which means one does not stick out in space, or one wants to hide one's face, because one may not be able yet to manage the expression on one's face. I would think that blushing has a lot to do with it. I would be interested to know when children begin to blush.

LORENZ:
And then one 'loses face.'

FREMONT-SMITH:
Would you call that paranoid?

ERIKSON:
Yes, exactly. It is the origin of lifelong paranoid trends such as are present in everybody. I could relate each stage to extreme psychopathology. Paranoia itself is the extreme accentuation of obsessive doubt of what one has 'left behind', suspicious doubt of what people would do to you behind your back.

RÉMOND:
What would be the age at which children would first show shame?

ERIKSON:

I would like to have you discuss this question.

REMOND:

Personally I had the impression that this period of 'doubt' and particularly feelings of shame came later, probably after three years.

MEAD:

I should think the shame-response could appear at about nine months, but the most likely age would be around two years.

LORENZ:

I myself recall early shame, which was the shame combined with soiling. All children in our family including myself were perfectly clean at nine months. The most shameful thing that can happen to an adult is this, and after all it is no sin, it is nothing to be ashamed of. You may be ill and not at all responsible really but still, if it happens to you, it's worse than murder. There is a sense of guilt which is absolutely awful—I couldn't find an example of such an absolutely shattering sense of shame—and this is definitely acquired at less than twelve months.

ERIKSON:

In this sense shame has something to do with the feeling that one lost self-control under 'everybody's' eyes.

LORENZ:

Yes, of course, and if you find people under extreme circumstances, undernourished and so on, who start to soil themselves, it is a sign that they will die very soon because they have completely lost control of themselves.

ERIKSON:

This is very important because in children there is a corresponding experience of absolute despair.

HUXLEY:

Could you tell us approximately when children start blushing?

ERIKSON:

I do not know.

175

GREY WALTER:

There have been studies of blushing and change of skin resistance and acceleration of the pulse and so forth as signs of autonomic responsiveness, and it is surprising how late these autonomic displays arise, at least in English children. It is probably not before four or five.

ERIKSON:

I would emphasize here again the systematic point that probably blushing appears when the child has already learned to internalize a particular type of rage which is a response to being ridiculed or looked at.

FREMONT-SMITH:

I think internalization is crucial in the whole business of conflict and I suspect that until a certain age inhibition is not possible because the cortex isn't developed sufficiently. I believe that the exaggerated autonomic responses which are the basis of psychosomatic syndromes are present only when there is an inhibition of cortical control.

ZAZZO:

I remember a discussion we had during the previous meeting where we came to compare one of my sons with one of Grey Walter's tortoises. I had stated that my son at the age of fifteen or sixteen months, as far as I remember, had a disorientation reaction in front of the mirror, with flushing and turning away from the mirror. This corresponds moreover to one important stage of development. Up to then he had not recognized himself in the mirror. Blushing, then, appeared in connexion with a recognition of an image of self, with a sudden realization.

ERIKSON:

Skirting the question of later internalization, I would say that psychosocially speaking blushing as a primitive reaction contains an affective turning against oneself and at the same time as against others.

Now the next stage I call the play age. Psychoanalytically, we would speak here of the phallic-ambulatory stage, and I would like to emphasize again that each stage is related to a pair of organ systems, one of the pair being an orifical, the other a peripheral-contact system: in stage one it was the oral area and the sensory surface, in stage two, eliminative organs and the musculature. It is here that psychosocial and psychosexual development overlap. If

176

in psychoanalysis we call this the phallic stage it is because interest in the genitals would at this time be aroused by sensations in the sexual organs, by a general awareness which is intensified by cultural ways of counterpointing the sexes at that age, and maybe, by the experiences of shame. Psychosocially speaking the main emphasis is now on motion toward goals, many of which for the child have to be play and fantasy goals. The emphasis is on initiative in the sense that the child is passionately preoccupied in reality and in fantasy with what he wants to get at, where he wants to go, what he wants to see and touch, what question he wants to understand. The selection of goals and the persistence in approaching these goals vastly outdoes the child's actual ability to gain access and to master these goals. Many of them are transferred into the area of play. Then either the goals themselves become playful goals or else toys represent the child, and the question is where can the toy automobile go.

Children at this stage take things apart, even though they can't put them together. They gradually leave the mother's house and are taken along to be shown how to fish or shoot a small bow and arrow. In primitive societies such play has a much more direct connexion with the technology than in our lives, where play has often lost its connexion with the technological world. Yet, even here you can still see the preoccupation with what are considered the outstanding tools and roles. In any given family or culture the child here has to learn somehow who may take the initiative and when and towards whom; who has access to the tools with which you get at things. He will be at this time intensely aware of the hierarchy of ages in children. Jealousy of the younger children and rivalry with the older ones is very strong. He cannot use the helpless approach of the younger ones and he cannot as yet master the approaches of the older ones. I would think this is the most common source of impotent rage at this time.

There is a great expansion and intensification of fantasy at this time, and also a great development of guilt over fantasies in which one 'approached' people or goals which belong to others, or 'approached' them in ways strictly reserved for others. This, of course, is an important aspect of what in psychoanalysis is called the Oedipus complex. One cannot return to the mother as a baby, so one now wants to, as we would say, in American at least, 'make' her in some way as a woman, or, in the case of girls, be like her and 'make' father. The same is true for the boy's relationship to the father, whose executive organs and tools, capacities and roles he does not even approach at that time and with whom already he wishes to identify. In fantasy the boy does all kinds of things as the father does them, or as he fantasies the father does them. This then becomes the soil for sinister and hidden guilt feelings, guilt feelings which must balance a secretly wild sense of unlimited initiative. This has eminently to do with the superego development, which was discussed here at a previous meeting. This guilt is already something much more internalized than shame and doubt were at the beginning, before they were linked with guilt. But I think the differences both in different cultures and in individuals are great, and my psychoanalytic colleagues will agree that for a long time we have called too many things guilt which are pre-guilt.

FREMONT-SMITH:

Could you say that there is a progressive internalization with development?

ERIKSON:

Yes. If I were talking about the development of the ego, I would use those terms, but I am talking about psychosocial development on a rather phenomenological level. The psychopathology corresponding to this stage, in general, is based on hysterical mechanisms of denial or repression. One denies goals. One represses impressions, effects, and drives. Later, paralysis may disarm an organ as an organ of aggression or reaching out, or the individual may otherwise restrict his awareness, initiative, or techniques. There are, again, both extreme pathological forms of this and those which are very close to the norm and appear as collective self-delimitations. Probably certain psychosomatic diseases which would express a greater degree of internalization of self-restriction belong here. What also belongs here is regression. Everybody who has grown up with children knows it is at this time that you have violent shifts from victorious progression to meek or demanding regression, for example, when the child becomes sick and wants to be very much a baby again. But there is also an over-compensatory exhibitionism, where a shaky initiative expresses itself in being a he-man, in self-advertising, but always with an underlying sense that one is not quite as one advertises oneself to be.

INTERVAL

ERIKSON:

Huxley reminded me of William Blake in the intermission and of Blake's saying 'The child's toys and the old man's reasons are the fruit of the two seasons'. We are now at the end of the first season. The positive outcome of this play age would be that the child has enough initiative left from his disappointments and from his guilt feelings that he vigorously enters the school age and the learning of actual techniques leading to his people's technology. This next stage I call the stage of industry, or of workmanship. It is the stage at which the child forgets most of his earlier experiences, 'forgets about' much of his relationship to his family and what he wants from them, can turn to tools, objects and work situations; he can learn with others to do competitive tasks and the tasks of finishing things. The difference between initiative and workmanship would be that, in the period of initiative, the emphasis is on the goal, but very little actually gets finished. So now the child begins to manage the smaller steps which in his particular technology lead to observation in work situations. In literate society that begins with learning to write and read; in other societies it might mean being taken along by selected teachers into fishing situations or hunting situations. I think there are certain aspects of this stage which are world-wide also; though some societies would handle it in ways almost unrecognizable as similar to our own, still there are selected adults who are gifted as teachers and who are more or less chosen and entitled to take a group of children together, and show them certain important initial steps in the management of technology. In our world, literacy has to be learned first, which poses particular problems because you enter a separate school world, while of course in many societies the school is not separated from the rest. In the eastern Jewish settlements there is probably the most extreme accentuation on literacy taking you from home and mother. In certain American Indian societies there is extreme accentuation as between the mother's house and the bath house of the men. In most cultures at this time a differentiation of masculine and feminine takes place, in that these measures are primarily for the boy. There is a marked pulling away from the home, away from the mother, and towards the tools and the techniques of the particular culture. Now, some children are not quite ready for this. For any number of reasons they want to go back home as if there was something they have forgotten there. They daydream; or a guilt feeling over something they have not settled at home may keep them from enjoying the tool situation and from becoming absorbed in work completion. This, then, is the period during which the sense of inferiority (see chart) can become strongest, in that the mastery of both the preceding and the present stage has been missed. This, very often and in fact mostly, has nothing to do with the child's actual capacities or with his real intelligence, but

179

is rather a sense that as a whole person somehow one does not deserve to do, to achieve, and to succeed. As was first pointed out by Freud, this can go back to a very marked sense of sexual inferiority in comparison with the man or men at home. But then early school failure throws the child back to the guilt-problems of the initiative stage.

In psychoanalysis this is the particular period called 'latency', meaning a relative latency of psychosexual drive. In following here the psychosocial line I must consider what Freud called libido development almost as subsidiary, while if I would speak of psychosexual development I would have to consider psychosocial development subsidiary. This is a matter of the point of departure in any particular discussion. But I do feel that both points of departure are relevant and that the originally purely biological ideas of Freud have to be restated in psychosocial terms—humanized as it were—because it seems obvious that what he described as a latency and delay of genitality is to some extent the utilization by psychosocial development of certain quantities of libidinal energy.

We have already discussed the matter of *identity* (see chart). I may just add here that in identity development, what one has learned to do well counts very much. When one approaches the identity crisis one is already somebody who does such and such things well, and one is already one whom other children have called such and such a person, maybe even by a nickname or two. At the same time, secret mistrust, shame, and guilt have set into a negative inner image. In other words, a differentiation has taken place already. Secondly, the length and intensity of the identity crisis depends to a very large extent on the technological circumstances into which one is growing. In societies with a primitive technology people have a much shorter way to the full development of the sense that they know who they are within their culture. By the same token in more complicated cultures, it may be easier psychologically for certain unskilled classes, because they remain closer to the technological pursuits which a twelve-year-old and a thirteen-year-old can already manage.

Depending then on the degree of civilization, identity development in certain specialties and in people who because of inner complications can only survive in the specialties, is tremendously prolonged, maybe all the way up to twenty-five or more. What I call the school-age here, therefore, includes everything that you learn in a preparatory way, all kinds of apprenticeships and psychosocial moratoria of other kinds—graduate studies, and after-graduate studies. Some people prolong this (Veblen, for example, after college went home for seven years, just to read by himself) and the age-range is, therefore, almost impossible to state.

I think I have indicated that the identity development itself is sub-divided into a number of part-identities, such as sexual identity (what kind of a man, what kind of a woman one is), age identity (younger adolescent and older adolescent), and occupational identity: these divisions can grow at different rates, and this also depends on individual patterns as well as cultural ones. As for the sexual moratorium, it can consist of early promiscuity without personal commitment, or of a long-drawn-out period of abstinence. I think my psychoanalytic colleagues would agree that in our field we have emphasized too exclusively the mechanical consequences of either abstinence or promiscuity for the individual, and have underestimated the role and status factor in sexual behaviour. In some classes, and in some cultures, early promiscuity is so much the rule that the child has to act it out whether he is otherwise particularly motivated or not, just as in another culture or class, abstinence would be the rule. The demands can vary from sexual licence with a total lack of personal commitment, to a deep personal commitment without sexual liberties. The individual's motivations must be evaluated within such patterns.

While the vicissitudes of genital drives must be accounted for under all these conditions, we cannot simply assume that what young people 'really' want is to have intercourse. Very often what young people want from one another—though it is obviously hard to say what a person 'really' wants—is mutual delineation. The young man becomes more differentiated as a man if he mirrors himself in a girl who, at the same time, through him tries to become more of a girl, and in this sense a polarization takes place which is a necessity whatever the sexual mores.

I would especially emphasize that psychiatric ideology has done at least as much harm as it has done good by suggesting to young people who were in the process of such mutual delineation that maybe intercourse or early marriage would be the thing that would solve it all. The fact is that only two people who have learned already to delineate themselves in relation to the other sex are psychologically ready for genital mutuality. Thus sexual activity as such is not the royal road to maturity.

Identity diffusion is the item from which I took my departure yesterday morning. In horizontal V, in the chart (page 168) you will find those elements of identity diffusion which we discussed yesterday. But let me point out another principle represented by this kind of epigenetic chart. It is apparent that V.1, *time-perspective*,

181

is really a late development of what in I.1 is called *basic trust*. In other words, if young people are inclined to believe that time and history are benevolent, that there is a whole lifetime before them, space to go somewhere, and historical tradition: this would be basic trust in the form of a more differentiated time perspective. Time is not going to crush you, and time is not going to be more than you know what to do with.

MEAD:
Time is on your side.

ERIKSON:
Time is on your side, and history is on your side. It is for this reason that ideology is important for this particular age. By ideology I merely mean a coherent system of images and ideas which, among other things, gives the young person at this stage a sense that history is on his side. *Self-certainty*, V.2, would be a later development of the sense of *autonomy* (II.2). It means that now one is not only an autonomous person, one is also a person with a particular social identity. In this way, each item of the chart is related horizontally and vertically to an item that developed earlier and to an item that is developing now. So that self-certainty is determined both by the earlier development of autonomy (vertical) and by the over-all identity development (horizontal).

But here the chart should be three-dimensional, with a social dimension providing depth. For the young individual is unable to have self-certainty of his own. He must join a subculture, a movement, an organization, a clique, or a circle of the like-minded. That is why at this time fraternities, secret societies, delinquent gangs, and ideological movements give young people a sense of self-certainty which we as clinicians know they would not have reached alone.

Role experimentation (V.3) is another part aspect. Young people, depending on where they live, will try out a number of gangs, or cliques, or organizations, or movements. It is very hard for their parents to understand what makes them change from, say, a pacifist to an extreme militarist organization. The necessity to totalize one's outlook and one's associations at any given time is an adolescent trend.

Then in V.4—we have the *anticipation of achievement*. It means that whatever is one's apprenticeship one must be promised a mastership. One over-identifies with the people who teach particular achievements, and while one has to learn still to be a student and still to be an apprentice, one already learns 'wie er sich räuspert und wie er spuckt'. Then we come to V.5, i.e., *identity*, and V.6, *sexual identity*. Adolescence is at an end when one's sexual maturation is completed, *and* one's psychosexual role defined and accepted. I do not think VI.7, *leadership polarization* needs to be explained further, but it should be said that this is a further development of conscience formation. In any culture, the young person has to learn to be a leader of some and a follower of others. I call it a polarization, because these two roles are systematically related in any human society. That is why I get annoyed when questionnaires in America ask you about a particular child—'Is he a leader?' I always want to ask what kind of a follower is he, because that one has to learn also, and nobody can be a leader who has not learned to be a follower.

LORENZ:
Unless he is a megalomaniac?

ERIKSON:
That alone would not make him a leader. At the same time, I don't think anybody can be a follower who could not at any given time take over the command, at least in a small unit.

FREMONT-SMITH:
Even Hitler was a follower at one stage.

ERIKSON:
The only friend that Hitler had between the ages of sixteen and twenty has written a description of Hitler in those years, and if you want to have a ludicrous example for everything that I have been saying about adolescence you will have to read it. Hitler went through a very prolonged psychosocial moratorium during which for four years he had only this one friend, and then for two years not a single friend anywhere who could remember ever having seen him. In those four years he went around rebuilding Linz, in Austria, in his imagination. This friend not only describes him, but has sketches in his possession that Hitler gave him. He lived in Linz at that time, and as he went around rebuilding it, his friend wondered whether the more important thing for him was to tear down the houses or to rebuild them. At any rate, Hitler called this his work. He hungered, he abstained from the pleasures of life, and he abstained from friendship, and rebuilt Linz. This friend who is a very naïve—but I think, if I am a psychologist at all, a trustworthy—individual was a musician, and he felt that Hitler needed a public,

and he was his public. Then even that much public was too much for Hitler. He suddenly disappeared, and apparently he lived in homes for itinerant workers. When the friend later met Hitler again, Hitler was the 'Fuehrer' of the German nation which included Austria, and he had started to rebuild Linz exactly according to the plans he had drawn up as a young boy of eighteen. Indeed, one of the last things Hitler did in his bunker and in the days preceding his suicide, was to complete his plans for the opera house in Linz. Leadership polarization for a man like Hitler meant from the beginning only to be an absolute leader.

LORENZ:

You know that one can produce leadership in fish? There is chronically a strong.followership. If you cut off a minnow's fore-brain the fish can still eat and see, but the schooling reactions are somehow destroyed. Paradoxically, this fish becomes automatically the leader, just because it moves without any regard if someone follows him or not.

GREY WALTER:

We had a whole collection of our models at one time and several of them would go round and round the room in procession. We found that one was always in front; it would lead the procession round the room and keep them together. The one that was in front was always one that was faulty—he couldn't see. That one couldn't see the others, but they saw him and followed him. It was a very impressive demonstration of a delinquent appearing an ideal leader.

ERIKSON:

I have always felt that psychosocially speaking these two things come out of the same matrix.

LORENZ:

That just shows how perfectly fitting your expression of leadership polarization is.

ERIKSON:

Now as to *ideological polarization*—V.8. By polarization, I mean that the ideal ideological position should be sufficiently separated from the undesirable position. Here it is important to understand that identity development at its height presupposes the repudiation of otherness, at least for a period. We must understand that a young person may need something at one time which he can relinquish at

184

another. Prejudice of some kind cannot be ruled out by decree or by pious wishes. If ideological evil is not clearly defined in accord with the prevalent identity young people will turn against all kinds of things. Some of them are innocent enough. In one area of California at one time the left back hip pocket of boys had to be torn, and anybody who had not torn his hip pocket—well, what could one expect from a guy like that?

HUXLEY:

At Eton it was obligatory for all the boys to leave the lowest button of the waistcoat undone.

ERIKSON:

Little items like this can become the expression of distinction and repudiation, and this has a lot to do with the development of snobbishness.

HARGREAVES:

In Fighter Command during the war, the fighter pilots distinguished themselves from bomber pilots by leaving the top button of their jacket undone.

BUCKLE:

Where do you fit in the phase of change from feeling that one is a child to feeling that one is an adult, and the expectation often given by the adults for some kind of initiation into their group?

ERIKSON:

I know a few fraternity rites in America where the individual has to go through a harrowing experience for a few days, in many ways quite analogous to primitive puberty rites: he has to starve, is kept from sleeping, and gradually is scared into a kind of twilight state in which almost anything seems possible, in which he really begins to have the feeling (as the student describes it) that something is going to come to an end or a new beginning is going to be made. Such organizations share this with large ideological movements which also emphasize that one kind of world is coming to an end, and a millennium of another kind is going to start. But the important thing is that through some experience of this sort, the individual comes to feel that he is wanted, that he is reborn into a particular ideological brotherhood which is from then on more important

185

than his family. The victimization by ritual has the peculiar consequence that he feels that he has actively adopted the new way of life with all his will.

BUCKLE:

I was thinking not of the sense of ideological or sexual identity, but the way in our culture in which a child grows up by learning to do the things that men do, which operate very strongly in a purely homosexual channel; for instance drinking patterns and drinking habits. This is not a work role, it is not a sex role in the sense of sexual differentiation; it seems to be another system.

ERIKSON:

Now as to the next item, *intimacy* (VI.6): besides sexual intimacy, I think what is important here is intimacy with one's own drives and excitations as well as with the body of other people. Transitory masturbation in adolescence may thus be a step not only towards identity but also toward a sense of intimacy in the sense that the individual becomes able and willing at one time or another to face the quantities of his sexual excitement. The next step is to fuse it with the sexual excitement of others. This sexual intimacy in the psychosocial sense obviously depends on one's identity, in that only two people who are pretty sure of their own identity, can bear completely to fuse genitally with another person, and this because of the climactic nature of genitality and the loss of consciousness in the climax. All this seems tremendously dangerous to young people who have not found their identity. That is why they may be either crushed by sexual experiences, avoid them altogether, or sometimes try, as it were, to crash through to genitality, without real success.

LORENZ:

May I add this point—I am not so sure that intimacy, I mean to say, non-sexual intimacy, always comes so comparatively late in life. I think that very often character traits determining identity may develop quite early. A great percentage of my friends are people with whom I got intimate at the age of nine or ten.

ERIKSON:

With regard to young friends, that is an early selection, which must be verified and made final in late adolescence. But in some individuals and in some cultures, all of this may start much earlier.

186

LORENZ:

It has, I feel, very much to do with identity. If two boys develop a real friendship as early as that each must remain very identical with himself if they are to keep up their friendship. Indeed, the earlier-made friends give you the highest reassurance of your own identity if they endure. The highest reassurance your own identity can have is that if you meet a friend again after thirty years, you find him identical.

ERIKSON:

Yes, indeed.

HUXLEY:

May I interrupt for one moment: couldn't you have in addition to the types of intimacy you have mentioned, what might be called team intimacy or companionship intimacy, which may be very important?

ERIKSON:

Team-intimacy belongs here most definitely. Even intimate enmities and rivalries.

Now comes a word which I always apologize for—*generativity* (VII.7), which I merely use because I do not want to use the word creativity, and I don't want to use the word productivity. This designates anything you generate—your own children, the whole next generation, goods, objects or ideas. I would say again that in psychoanalysis we have omitted this further development of the libido because of our preoccupation with neurotics who could not even become 'genital' because of their infantile psychosexuality. We have, I think, understated this further development, such as the love for what one generates, which is an independent matter, not just something like—well, to mention an extreme—a transfer of anality to the organs of conception. *Self-absorption* (VII.7) doesn't have to be explained, I think, as the opposite of generativity. People who do not develop generativity of one kind or another treat themselves as children. They go on spoiling themselves, being hypochondriacally concerned with themselves, building up their whole lives as if they were their own children to be taken care of.

HUXLEY:

The pathological side of it would be narcissism.

ERIKSON:

Yes, it is a regression to narcissism. Now we come to *integrity*,

187

the final step, a difficult thing to discuss, and I am sure Huxley could find a quotation from William Blake which would say what I can only indicate poorly. It means really something beyond generativity, something beyond intimacy, and most of all something beyond identity. This I want to emphasize particularly, because you may come to the conclusion that I would consider the definition of one's identity the final step in life. Maybe the simplest way for me to indicate integrity would be to refer back to that very nice short phrase of Shaw's, when he looked at his own identity formation, called himself 'an actor on the stage of life', and said 'This I learned only too well'. There is something in the ageing person because of which he has to recognize the relativity of his own identity, as against that of all others, and yet has to accept his own life cycle as the only life cycle that he will ever have. For the ageing person this is not an easy thing to accept, but maybe you will agree that it is the perfection of maturity, which is supported by a universal social institution, here wisdom.

MEAD:

His own life cycle as the only *remembered* life cycle he will ever have, because half the human race feels that there is another life cycle with continuity.

ERIKSON:

Yes. You might say the individual accepts his own remembered life cycle as the point from which he looks at the great variety of other life cycles known to him, being able to encompass their relativities, and this is one aspect of wisdom.

* * *

GREY WALTER:

While Erik was speaking and describing his chart, I was trying to see whether one could translate his terms into the terms in which I try to think about this problem of maturation. This is in terms of a rather probabilistic approach to animal—or human—experience. I jotted down a set of headings, which correspond to Erik's I to VIII, and I should like to see what impression it would make on Erik in particular and on my psychiatric colleagues. I suppose, to make sense, it ought to give one an idea of what to look for in children— we see an enormous number of children, some suffering from exactly the sort of disturbances Erik has outlined, some of them normal controls. Our difficulty at the moment is to know just what observations are worth making, let alone what experiments to plan.

The scheme that Erik has suggested has brought to life some notions of my own which before have appeared quite lifeless.

The first stage that Erik outlined for us involved the question of giving and getting, getting to give and getting to be given—the trust-mistrust stage. It seems to me that from the neurophysiological standpoint, the answer which a nervous system, if it were a computer, would give back in reply to the environment at this stage, would be 'insufficient information'. That is, I am considering that in the baby-world situation the environment is questioning the nervous system: the observer or the environment is testing the baby, and the baby-computer is giving back the answer, 'not enough data' which is, of course, the answer one should get when there is not enough information supplied.

You would expect that in a recently born nervous system there would be an insufficient number of complete circuits to handle anything but the simplest situations. The simplest situation for the baby is this question of getting and giving, getting food and comfort in small quantities at regular intervals and giving signs of distress and satisfaction. Now this seems to me to produce just that state of mind, if you like, or state of brain, that one can understand by the 'trust/mistrust' contrast. Let us now reverse our point of view and think of the situation from the standpoint of the baby-computer trying to solve problems for which there are insufficient data or for which he can't handle the mass of data. It is difficult to force a computer to give an answer for which it hasn't got enough data, but you can do this for certain types of machine—you can turn a knob which makes the system less and less accurate and more and more 'trusting'. It can be persuaded to give you an approximate answer, to guess. If you ask it 'What are two and two?' it doesn't really know the answer but it can be forced to admit that it can't be more than five or less than three—it will give an approximate answer to a precise proposition. This is what one would expect to happen in a statistical theory of learning in a nervous system that was not primed with information and had not had time to collect the required data.

FREMONT-SMITH:
It was not only not primed, but it was also insufficiently developed.

GREY WALTER:
That's true, of course: if we take an anatomical analogy, for example, if we associate walking with the anatomical size of a child's legs—you still won't get him to walk before the age of, say, eight

months, and it won't matter what you do, the white matter just isn't there in the nervous system, whatever the size of the legs may be.

In stage II, where the antonyms are 'autonomy' against 'shame and doubt', that seems to me to be the equivalent of the use of tentative statistical criteria derived from stage I. In other words, the computer is, all the time, building up a stock of statistical criteria from experience but at this stage it can't really act on them with any confidence. It has got beyond the stage of pure trust or guesswork and has accumulated enough data to make a tentative calculation. In the simple model of learning which I presented at our last meeting—and which I maintain is the simplest possible one—there is also a stage at which data have accumulated but cannot readily be used. There is a store of information but this store is, in any useful mechano-physiologic sense 'unconscious'. It certainly has no overt effect in normal circumstances and is quite hard to detect in the machinery, but it is there, and it has the effect of giving the mechanism some degree of autonomy and of freedom of action in an emergency, because there is sufficient information for it to make trial essays of behaviour. This corresponds in stage II to the question of holding on or letting go: it is in the nature of a set of hypotheses being built up.

Here I should like to ask a question to which the answer would be very important to my theory: do you recognize an important difference, at stage II, between behaviour patterns which are based on or grow out of appetitive activity, as compared with those that grow out of defensive activities? The reason that this is important to my theory is that a purely appetitive activity, which is built up as a result of experience in the newly hatched or born creature of this type, is very easily extinguished: it has the clear characteristics of the simple Pavlovian conditioned reflex, being liable to extinction by the withholding of a reward or by the lapse of time, and it may leave no trace at all. In other words, a situation of conflict between autonomy and shame that is developed from the irregular satisfaction of an appetite, could be relatively harmless, and it could die away without treatment or insight. On the other hand, one based on irregular punishment, the exploitation of a defensive process, could be permanently dangerous, and give more sensational effects—perhaps long-term compulsive, obsessive, even paranoid states. This is according to my theory—which is a very rough one.

LORENZ:

Didn't Howard Liddell show that he could create obsessions with only negative stimuli?

GREY WALTER:

Yes, I believe that at the last meeting that was agreed to by Howard Liddell, and I think that in the case of animals there is support for it, but the situation as regards human beings is not so clear. It is not obvious to the human that defence is not an inhibition. There are all sorts of paradoxes that might arise in the human being which would make hay of this rather simple explanation, which is crucial to my particular theory.

BOWLBY:

In the psycho-analytical literature the view has frequently been expressed that fixation could be due either to over-indulgence or to frustration. I confess that I have never seen a patient in whom I thought that fixation was due to over-indulgence, and I don't share that particular view. So I agree with you.

ERIKSON:

Prohibition after over-indulgence certainly may be fixating.

GREY WALTER:

Yes, it's complicated, of course, in the human being in that sort of way. I imagine that if you let a baby over-indulge and then punish it later, something might happen which would complicate the issue. Cyberneticists have discussed the situation in which a correcting system says in effect: 'You have gone too far—go further'. There might be simple cases in which it might be effective, perhaps— the Road of Excess leading to the Palace of Wisdom.

Another question that is running through my mind all the time as I look at diagonal squares in the chart concerns the abruptness of change between these phases in the individual. Statistically, in a population, of course, you wouldn't expect a very abrupt transition, but in individuals a very rapid transition should, on the whole, have survival-value in an organism with a prolonged childhood. If there is, in fact, a fairly abrupt transition from stage to stage, in an individual, then he is less vulnerable, because the time taken to change over is shorter. This again comes out in the study of Ashby (1952), or in any cybernetic approach to the problem of maturation; if a step-function exists, then during the time when it is just about to change, to switch over (like a thermostat that's heating up and is just about to turn the heater off) it's very vulnerable—a bit of vibration and it will just go over or just go back again. What is very interesting psychiatrically is that during this period of change-over, when the contact, so to say, is just wobbling between phase I and phase II, or phase II and phase III, it can easily get into an unstable vacillating state, with anticipation and regression back again. In other words, the effect of some catastrophe in the child's life, in one of its short vulnerable periods of change-over might well be mainly a regression to an earlier stage. It might even go right down through the sequence again, like Snakes and Ladders.

HARGREAVES:

The speeding up of the phase of transition reduces the period of vulnerability but makes it more dangerous while it lasts, doesn't it?

GREY WALTER:

It reduces the number of casualties, but increases the risk of serious injury in those to whom something unlucky happens. This, as Ronald Hargreaves implies, should produce in the population a very skew distribution of neurotics; instead of having a normal distribution of neurosis (like the distribution of stature or weight) in which most people are slightly neurotic, a few are very neurotic, and a few are not neurotic at all, you get most of the population untraumatized, but the minority very heavily traumatized. These are the ones that are unlucky enough to get hit when they are running from one trench to the other, so to speak. Study of the population statistics of neurosis might throw some light on the very important problem of whether or not there are abrupt changes in the neurophysiological and psychological behaviour of children. If one compared the distribution of the various types of neurosis, one might get some idea whether some types were due to conflicts experienced during the vulnerable change-over phases.

If you have a number of smooth changes that follow an S-shaped curve, each rising slowly but influencing each other, it is easy to show that the effect of the combination is to produce an abrupt step-function. If you have a very large number of fairly slow changes, all working together, the effect is to produce a sudden change. Fessard (1954) illustrated this very nicely in the Proceedings of the Laurentian Symposium on Brain Mechanisms and Consciousness. One doesn't have to suppose that anything terribly romantic happens, like millions of neurones suddenly being myelinated at the same time, but simply a few processes of gradual change connected in series would produce, in fact, a very abrupt change in behaviour, with all the possibilities for vacillation and regression, which would be diagnostic of this process. Of course, from the point of view of the theory of learning, that would be extremely important, because it means that the system would change its law, that as you go from square to square in Erik's schema, in between the two would be a vacillation of law.

This is very difficult to put in words but it is clearly defined in Ashby's book (1952) where there are diagrams, showing what is meant by an ultra-stable system, in which the representative point in the system may run off the edge of its stable platform and can then find another platform, another system of operation, and quite new laws. You cannot have a smooth transition from one to the other, because the two together may be totally unstable. This again might be a point in child behaviour; if a child is, for some constitutional reason, or as a result of an illness or accident, trying to make too smooth a transition from one stage to the other and finds himself operating under two laws at once, life may be quite confusing and, as Ashby shows again, such a state may produce very dramatic, violent vacillation or oscillation of the whole mechanism.

The third stage, shown on the chart as 'initiative' as against 'guilt', represents in my terms the stage when a creature is acting on hypotheses which have now been built up during the first two stages, but which have still to be confirmed by test. I suggest that the initiative phase in development, assuming that it is a healthy one, is a stage where there is quite a bundle of home-made hypotheses in the brain, which are still to be tested, and this is the testing time of these hypotheses. In other words, the brain computer has extracted from experience a contingency rating high enough to permit action, but it is not yet a 'natural law', it is only a notion, a limited theory. The baby computer, or now the child computer, in the play age, is testing out the hypotheses which it has built up, still, most of them, not at all conscious—or not in any useful sense conscious. It is playing with these ideas and making experiments which, later on, if we go down column 3, become role-experimentation, the rehearsal stage. The rehearsal stage is really a development of the essential activity, of play. Play as a whole is a test of initiative combined with rule-keeping, even in sub-primate species. What we call 'make-believe' is synonymous with 'als ob' reasoning.

I think the rate of change gets less abrupt here: and this is what intrigues me in this whole system: if there is an advantage in rapid transition, if there is a survival value in terms of a diminished probability of being hurt, then why is it that mankind has done so well with such a long period of infancy? It would seem possible that one of the compensatory factors is the existence of step-changes within this long period of development. Although there is a long period of immaturity, at each stage the system is fairly stable, so that the person climbs to maturity, not up a long slope but in a series

193

of fairly abrupt steps, and the advantage for anyone standing on a step is that within its limits it is level, whereas if you are standing on a ramp it is all sloping.

That seems a possibility, because in the next stage, stage IV, where we have the industry and inferiority contrast, there an entirely new thing is happening, which interests me very much in relation to learning theory, the organism at this stage is having to accept *predigested statistics* at school. This is the school age and he is dealing with preselected contingency computations, with the 'facts of life', the facts of the three Rs, history and geography; it seems to me the acceptance or non-acceptance of this is exactly what is important in the school age; consistent failure on the part of the organism in its earlier phases to work out the later parts of the statistical sum will mean that it will be unable to accept the predigested material at a later stage. It can only either accept or reject, it has no way of making a tentative judgement. In the case of human children a schoolchild who has not acquired his statistical criteria in play or whose brain has not developed normally is still forced by the culture to go to school or to accept instruction or initiation which it can either accept or reject. It cannot make a tentative judgement; so you may get a child who is in love with school and authority, accepts every-thing he is told, is completely taken in by any sort of doctrine or myth and in the extreme is the fanatical member of a party. On the other hand, the same situation may result in a child who is com-pletely, profoundly, sceptical, rejects every attempt to instruct or teach him, irrespective of so-called intelligence, and becomes the pariah, the outcast, the cynic who will not accept anything and who later on refuses to accept any ideology or general notion at all, and becomes the desperate nihilist. In case this approach should seem really too naïve, remember that at this stage I must postulate that the child has accumulated a colossal number of hypotheses about the world and it is this gorgeous network of ideas of inter-relation-ships between things and events that seems to me to enfold the idea of self, to be weaving the identity. On this web I suggest there is im-printed the identity of the individual who has gone through these experiences. At this stage approaching adolescence, one can imagine that the system will begin to extract general laws. A complicated model would do the same thing, but it would have to be quite an elaborate one. This seems to me then to be the stage of abstraction and the formulation of some 'laws of nature'.

The notion of causality will arise here too; and the connexion between experience and notions of causality seems to me to be of paramount importance in understanding young people. We regulate our lives very much on notions of causality, and at some stage of his development every sane individual has to build up and accept for himself or take over from somebody else an elaborate system of causal relationships. But this can only be achieved if the foundations have been laid in the earlier stages. Of course, as a corollary of the development from a statistical to a causal world, in the model or the child one would see the elaboration of *dei ex machina*—gods outside the machine—of common causes and first causes and so forth. This too is an effect that one might observe quite easily with a very simple set of models; one would begin to find the machine giving out little chits like you get from a weighing machine—it would be easy for the machine to issue apt little aphorisms about the world in general, because if it were forced to give a short answer to a really complicated problem, it could only give an aphoristic answer. This stage is then the age of aphorism too, when the child is beginning to quote proverbs and carry around little tags, and put mottoes up on its wall, feeling they must contain secrets of the universe.

Another characteristic of this phase would be constant testing by excess. This seems to be an interesting point about, perhaps, most animals. Certainly mammals show this constantly going to extremes in everything, of testing ideas to breaking point. This is sometimes called the scientific method, but it's really the method of the adolescent who goes through a score of crazes before settling down. If you want to know how a toy works, you can go on fiddling with it until it breaks—and any scientific hypothesis has to be tested to destruction, or should be testable to destruction.

It is only up to stage V that I have developed this notion from the point of view of statistical neurophysiology. From that stage the brain is full, so to speak, and after that what happens is determined more by the fullness and effectiveness of the brain pattern, and the interaction with cultural influences. This is just an essay in the transposition of these notions of development to the general theory of learning by association. There may well be objective physiological correlates of these stages which one can measure and record and contrast and, as a matter of fact, this is what I propose to try to do; to use this sort of schema to grade the children we see and try to construct some correlative objective table, bearing in mind that we tend to see more psychopathological than normal material. This may really be very helpful, because pathology takes processes to extremes, and you can see these conditions almost in a pure culture sometimes. This schema of Erik's is about the first realistic diagram that we have seen that tells us anything about the psychobiological development of the child.

BUCKLE:

Perhaps Grey could continue the account into what would happen to people when they got a little older; some psychological data suggest that the brain begins to deteriorate in certain ways from thirty or forty years onwards. What would be the analogy to that in your models?

GREY WALTER:

Well, that's rather difficult to say for certain because even the simple models have a large number of possibilities—a great many things might happen in the way of wearing out or deteriorating. There is one effect, though, that I should expect to find regularly if the model I am considering would include reflexive processes, instinctive or IRM ones and associative ones as well—something like a combination of the three models Olga, Irma and Cora I demonstrated at our meeting last year. This compound model contains several series of relay elements leading to one another and would exaggerate the effect of any *general* process such as illness or ageing. Consequently, a slight change in general conditions must have a dramatic effect both on the pattern of instinctive behaviour and on the criteria for the adoption of novel conditioned modifications. In the living brain, I should expect that the effect of age would be seen first and most as a specific action on any functional region or system of the brain in which there is a cascade or series of nerve elements. The diffuse projection systems in brain-stem and thalamus are such an arrangement of elaborate filters in series connexion. Any general change in metabolism which affected them would have an exaggerated effect on behaviour since it would seem that all sensory information must pass through these filters. The reason why general effects are exaggerated in these conditions was discussed at our meeting last year; briefly it is because the number of elements appears as the exponent in the equation. For example, if some general change, such as arteriosclerosis, reduces the transmission probability or the efficiency of synaptic transmission by one half, then in a series or cascade system the overall reduction is a half of a half of a half and so on. If there are ten relays the overall reduction would be by a factor of 1024. Similar effects would be seen with any neurotropic hormone or dietary change. Konrad reminded us once of the effects of artificial but apparently adequate diet on the elaborate instinctive feeding behaviour of shrikes. In humans too, dramatic mental changes occur with inanition. Helweg-Larsen et al. (1952) described the specific effects of starvation as: impairment of memory, reduced spontaneous cerebration, disappearance of libido, in-

196

difference. This even in a German concentration camp where there was still some chance of survival, and morale was otherwise surprisingly high. These are precisely the changes one would expect if the chain of diffuse relays were affected. So the first sign of ageing might well be to simplify instincts and to restrict the ability to learn. These effects might not always be seen as social deterioration—in the early stages, behaviour would seem more austere and discriminating—but in the extreme it would be dull and dirty. I would suggest that a sufficient explanation for these changes is the metabolic endocrinological and vascular decline which is so common from middle-age on.

FREMONT-SMITH:

There is some indication that, as the central nervous system ages, cells drop out. If we go back to your computing model, supposing you have given your model all its information, and then supposing you were to take out, in a random way, every tenth or hundredth tube, how would this affect the computing apparatus as compared to taking them out before information was fed in?

GREY WALTER:

Well, it would make very little difference in maturity until you cut it down to nearly fifty per cent.

FREMONT-SMITH:

Well, that I think corresponds to reality in a very interesting way.

HUXLEY:

I was very much interested in Erikson's chart. We may disagree with this or that detail, but we have now a comprehensive statement of the method of psychobiological development and the possibility of its continuity. It is not uniform but epigenetic, as you rightly said, in that novelty arises during the process. Novelty arises through two methods—first of all through the development of new mechanisms of change, and secondly through the effects of the environment becoming incorporated into the process. To take a parallel from biology, new mechanisms arise during the development of the sea-urchin or the frog, or indeed, almost any organism. First of all, there is the action of the genes in relation to a polarized gradient-field. Then there is the stage of mosaic determination well illustrated in vertebrate embryology, in which each part is chemically pre-determined to do something precise and specific. And then there are the mechanisms of interrelations—the endocrine system and the

197

Z

influence of one part on another. Further, all these mechanisms operate in relation to the environment. For instance, environmental influence may distort the gradient-fields; once they are distorted beyond a certain degree then you will get permanent structural distortion. Thus in Stockard's experiments with lithium, the head of the gradient is depressed, and so you get microcephalous or cyclopic embryos.

Another interesting analogy is this: in psychological as in biological development, as Erikson stressed, the structuring which arises in each of his phases persists in some measure into the later ones. So in a sense the first stage is the most important; in psychiatry it is useful to go back to the past, though you can often detect it by looking at the present state of affairs.

That marked changes in personality structure can be imposed upon one from without, is obvious from all our experiences; for instance, there is the way in which so many of our acquaintances have had a really very different type of personality structure imposed on them by having to go to fight in the army or navy or air force. Again, many people have had a different personality structure imposed on them through sexual love—by falling madly in love, with emphasis on the word 'madly'. This brings up an earlier point, namely that in this madness of love, you often find the analogy or metaphor of surrender being used by the lover. The man or the woman feels that he is surrendering his will or his identity to somebody else, and that does mean a real personality change. Even when you get over it, something new has got incorporated in your personality structure.

Then another point: I have just been reading Bronowski's (1943) very interesting book on William Blake, in which many things seem to me to be highly relevant to what various people here have been saying, and especially, perhaps, Erikson.

For instance, Blake began one of his books with a statement that 'Without contraries is no progression. Attraction and repulsion, reason and energy, love and hate, are necessary to human existence. From these contraries spring what the religious call Good and Evil' (here we have Blake hitting on the idea of the dialectic long before Hegel expressed it in formal terms). A further aspect of this is his constant emphasis on the two opposites of Innocence and Experience. Bronowski gives a penetrating analysis of Blake's treatment of these 'two contrary states of the human soul'. 'The symbol of innocence, up to this time in Blake's career, had been the child; the symbol of experience, mazy and manifold as Blake's symbol of the hypocrite, and as fascinating, is the father.' The

198

innocent child has to grow up and experience what it means to be a father, but he can only do so by killing something, either within or outside himself.

This passage too is extremely illuminating, where he speaks of the way in which, somehow, man has got to combine innocence and experience: 'Although the life of the senses is one-sided, it is part of the whole life, innocence and experience together; and only by way of this life can we enter a whole life. The tree is the knowledge of good and evil. The child is freed from the tree only when these are become one. For he is freed by murder.' The deepest meaning of the particular poem which he is analysing is, he writes, 'that innocence becomes experience by energy; and to that end must submit to becoming guilty, because it must work in the flesh.' I think this is very illuminating because it makes nonsense of many statements about sin. For instance, that you can get rid of evil and pain by denying their existence, like the Christian Scientists; or the conclusion implicit in my brother's book *Grey Eminence* (Huxley, 1941) that Père Joseph was always animated by the best motives, but because he had to put them into action they always went wrong; so the final moral to be drawn was that you ought never to act at all. In Blake you have a reconciliation of that dilemma. You must act if you are to live and grow, but you can't help sometimes acting wrongly; you can't help bringing in evil; you can't help causing pain, either to yourself or somebody else, but this is necessary for life and growth and the fullness of experience. Good and evil find their reconciliation in progressive development.

Also Blake brought in the psychosocial aspect. For instance, Blake often speaks about how society was imposing limitations and frustrations on man's free activities, and how it eventually becomes necessary to have some sort of a revolution, which would lead to a new type of society. Such a process could go on *ad infinitum* in a series of cycles; but, as Bronowski points out, Blake saw that beyond Society is Man. Society, up till now, has been either something which we just have to accept and which does put a brake on our activities; or else it has been exalted into a kind of super-individual, something more important than the individual man, as in certain aspects of Marxist Communism, Nazism and Fascism. But in the long run we shall find out how to make society not an end, but a means to an end, and the end will be the fulfilment of man. So, as he says somewhere, no revolution is the last: you always have to go on toward greater and further possibilities.

This interests me a great deal because it links up with what people like Simpson, and myself, and Rensch are gradually getting at in

199

modern evolution theory. Simpson (1953) points out in his latest book, *The Major Features of Evolution*, that at least ten times as many species have become extinct in the course of evolution as have survived. I would add that of those which have survived, at least ten times, perhaps one hundred times, as many have become stabilized at a certain level of organization, apparently indefinitely and inevitably, as those which have continued to advance. Only a very small minority has been able to progress to a new and higher form of organization. Even of those which have been capable of advance to a higher level of organization, most are self-limiting or self-limited. Thus all specializations inevitably, so far as we can see, come eventually to an end. You can't have a horse which is more horse-like than a modern horse: you can have a zebra and an ass, but they are all modern horses. As far as we can see there is no way of continuing that trend towards further specialization. Or you can have something which eventually introduces some limitation which was unsuspected at the beginning: the most striking example is that of insect respiration, pointed out by Krogh many years ago. Insects adopted the method of breathing by tracheae. This is more efficient than breathing by lungs, so long as you remain small. But it becomes completely inefficient when you get large, so that it is physiologically impossible to have an insect as big as a rat. As they never could grow large, they could never have large brains, they never could have a large number of brain neurones, and therefore, could never have so many possibilities of combination, and had to rely more on instinct and less on plasticity and intelligence of behaviour. And if it hadn't been for that, none of us would have been here now!

This leads on to the fact, which I think is relevant to our discussion, both from the individual and the psychosocial point of view, that in Blake's words, no revolution is the last. Every now and then in biological evolution you get a type which is capable of achieving large-scale biological improvement by evolving to a higher level of organization. Furthermore, the only satisfactory definition of biological process that I have ever been able to find is this: biological improvement or advance, which does not stand in the way of further general improvement of type. This is very much in line with Bertalanffy's (1952) ideas about open biological development, with Charles Morris' (1948) ideas about personal development, in his book, 'The Open Self', with ideas about the Open Society, and with the general idea of unlimited possibilities still open before us. This in turn brings up, I think, something very relevant to what you were saying about ideology.

In the past, most ideologies have definitely been backwardly directed, resistant to the idea of change. Our problem today is whether we can get ideologies which are either partially or wholly change-promoting. The answer is yes, of course we can. For instance, in regard to scientific method, we have long adopted the idea that change is possible and desirable, and we practise and encourage it. So far, however, this is mainly in the field of the natural sciences, though of course it is beginning in the social sciences too. Then it has been done on a larger and more extensive scale, in ideologies like Marxism, where the whole emphasis is on change: but the possibilities are still limited by the authoritarian nature of the system, and secondly by the fact that Marxism is an apocalyptic or millenary ideology, envisaging an ideal final state beyond which there can be no further progress. In both these ways it ceases to be an open system. An open social system would be, I should imagine, one which would provide the best environment for the open personality to develop.

The question arises, can you get a cultural ideology which would be an ideology of change, and which would apply to all aspects of human activity, and still be open in the sense that it does not contemplate any final state? In little groups such as ours here something of the sort can certainly be achieved. Such groups can be self-moving systems, dynamic, but reasonably stable with a self-regulating equilibrium of change towards some sort of improvement in knowledge—which, however, is unknown to their members at the time. This linking up of the assurance of possibilities to be realized with the idea that we don't know precisely what is coming, and yet trying to define it a little more, is extremely relevant. Whether you can make an ideology of this sort have as much compelling force as an ideology which claims certitude about everything, I don't know. But we ought to try.

Finally, you said that history is on our side. I agree, but would prefer to enlarge that view. We can be on the side, not merely of history but also of destiny in general, using destiny to include history in the past and possibilities in the future.

There is one other point. We discussed the matter of personality distortion imposed by society, or by social relations, or by frustration, and also the idea of supernormal stimuli in animals. It is quite clear, I think, that you can get a cultural distortion which produces a totally abnormal or subnormal result, but it is equally clear that you can have a cultural milieu which acts as a supernormal stimulus to totally new degrees of achievement. As Konrad Lorenz knows, jackdaws and ravens can count just as well as human beings, provided that the human beings don't have the use of verbal symbols.

201

But the possession of verbal symbols and then a long history of people using those symbols to build up mathematical systems, together with an educational system encouraging the learning of them, has led to the development of higher mathematics out of something that was originally no higher, so far as we know, than the capacities of a jackdaw. Much of Kroeber's work points in the same direction. He showed that the cultural milieu is necessary to bring out genius. A genius doesn't just happen anyhow: he is somebody who is capable of being stimulated by a particular cultural milieu to do something exceptional in it.

LORENZ:

May I just say one word. You will find a paper by a Swiss psychologist and sociologist, Jean Gebser (1954), on the ideology of the Western world, which says that our ideology is and ought to be that we don't have an ideology. You will find there very nearly exactly the same thoughts about ideologies which you have just propounded.

FREMONT-SMITH:

There is one other element which comes into the concept of an ideology which accepts, favours and encourages change, that is that it has got to accept, favour and encourage change at a progressively accelerating rate.

HUXLEY:

Well, not necessarily. Change could go too fast. You might have, and I am sure Grey Walter would agree with me, a system which promoted change at such a rate that human beings couldn't keep up with it. You have got to aim at an optimum tempo of change.

FREMONT-SMITH:

Well, isn't everything that is happening now happening at a progressively accelerating rate?

HUXLEY:

Yes, but I think there is bound to be a limit to such development sooner or later.

GREY WALTER:

I think we are reaching the limit now in the communication of information. If you discover two facts, there are three possible classes of relation between the facts, but if you discover one hundred facts, the number of possible relations becomes impossibly large. I think the evolution of scientific thinking is already slowing down.

HUXLEY:

You will find that with every major evolutionary improvement or advance you get a sudden change (or rather a relatively sudden one, for it may take millions of years) producing a new type and its radiation. Then you get the improvement of each of those types, which we call specialization; this trend goes more slowly and eventually bends over and becomes asymptotic to stability. The same thing seems to happen with human activities. For instance, it happened with ploughing by primitive methods. After a series of improvements, ploughing ceased to change in essentials: it became stabilized. Today, though, we are getting new mechanical methods, which are superseding the original type of plough.

HARGREAVES:

I think Dr. Huxley really has brought us round to the idea that Erik mentioned yesterday, when he talked about the individual having the capacity to establish his identity if the culture gives him room for it. Really, I feel that we have been talking about what kind of culture gives people room to establish an identity—but the trouble about the sciences is not only the vastness of its mass of facts, but also that to some extent scientists are all 'zoot suiters'. One characteristic of the zoot suiters or the teddy boys is that there is a lot of gang warfare between the different groups, and the shared ideology, say of biochemists, includes the idea that all psychiatrists are mad. And the shared ideology of all psychiatrists includes similar ideas about other groups, so that there isn't at present, except in comparatively few people, a wider shared ideology about the future of the human race. It seems to me another element that is important is a culture which is 'open-ended'—having a loyalty to the unknown future of the human race, which includes not only the idea of change, but the idea of heterogeneity, because homogeneous change seems to me to be no change, in that everybody has to change together, like a flock of birds that all take off at once.

HUXLEY:

That was really implicit in my remarks. When I spoke of realizing possibilities, I should have said realizing *more* possibilities, which implies greater variety. This is just what biological evolution has achieved—a richer as well as a more intensively efficient manifestation of life.

MEAD:

I think that perhaps this particular chart of Erik's raises more complications than the equivalent psychosexual chart, in that he is using words here that have been arrived at deviously and perhaps, in some instances, dubiously, as compromises out of the common stock of our information. Now in Erik's chart of pregenital psychosexual development (see Vol. IV, in press), when one uses only diagrams of zones and modes which can be handled formally, and does not have to include such words as guilt or autonomy, it is considerably easier to see the way in which these modes are grounded in stages of development of the organism. It is not awfully difficult to see why the oral stage comes before the stage that involves locomotor mechanisms, or why a stage that involves taking in receptively precedes the stage of going out and getting. But the interest of this conference has been centred on the problem of identity and the psychosocial chart includes many descriptive literary words that we should not lose sight of. But this scheme is based on a definite relationship to the structure of the organism and to the types of behaviour which show formal relationships to, say, taking in, receiving, grasping, moving towards, relinquishing, which do not have to be handled in terms of words which have philosophical connotations, such as the autonomy that comes after getting rid of guilt or the autonomy that comes before one is capable of it.

ERIKSON:

I may add that I would be more than grateful to any member of this group who wants to suggest to me that the use of a certain word is undesirable, because of its connotation either in another language or in a neighbouring field.

GREY WALTER:

There is a term that is very current in England just now in circles concerned with delinquency and that is the term 'responsibility'. There is a great deal of discussion as to whether a given criminal is responsible for his actions. A Royal Commission is considering whether a lay jury could decide whether an individual criminal could be regarded as being fully responsible, or to what degree he is responsible—in the most difficult case, for murder. I wonder whether that might be a word that could find a place on your chart—the sense of responsibility or irresponsibility is obviously associated with feelings of guilt and seems to play a large part in normal social development. There is also the general question, which is high-lighted by capital punishment, as to whether societies are responsible for their criminals. Very vague and unsatisfactory discussions are held around this, but there is a general cultural feeling of joint and universal responsibility and/or the difficulty of deciding whether a person is uniquely responsible for his actions.

We know that in fact clinically there are various degrees of responsibility, it is a state that develops slowly and isn't born in a baby. It would be hard to say whether a child of a certain age is responsible for any particular class of action. Do you think that there is a term which could find a place somewhere here?

ERIKSON:

I am not sure I can answer you sufficiently. This matter of the responsibility of the young delinquent is, of course, primarily a legal question. Psychologically speaking, he is at a stage where he is both still a child and already an adult and it would be hard to test how much he is one or the other. The only contribution that my formulations would make to this is the question as to whether we, as representatives of society, could recognize an individual who chose delinquency or criminality as a negative identity and a perverse kind of psychosocial moratorium, as it were. There must be more definite criteria which differentiate between a state of identity diffusion of a schizophrenic, a hysterical, and a delinquent type. Once we come to understand this and can specify the criteria and find tests or find criteria in existing tests, we should be able to establish to what extent a young person made a choice of a negative identity.

GREY WALTER:

So many of our young delinquents, as everyone knows, don't blame themselves for their offences. They say they are sorry they are caught, but the recidivists have a very general character of blaming something else. They are often told what to blame by the psychiatric social worker! They blame their family or a broken home; they can read now, so they know what the causes of delinquency are supposed to be. But, apart from that, they have a fairly spontaneous sense of irresponsibility. They haven't got any degree of autonomy, they haven't got a feeling of personal guilt. They don't consider that freedom of action implies responsibility for action.

ERIKSON:

I would rather speak of a miscarriage of the development of the sense of guilt. From what we know from working with young criminals, which for me is only a very occasional occupation, I do not think one could ever say that they really have no guilt feelings. It belongs to the negative identity which they show to society, that they must insist they have no guilt. I would not even say the so-called psychopathic delinquent has no sense of guilt, but he has lost all trust that any show of guilt would get him anywhere. I think that a sense of responsibility if put on the chart would be part of the resolution of the alternative of initiative and guilt. This is related to what we call super-ego development, quite obviously, because it is the super-ego which will tell you what goals you may still go after or even fantasy about, or what intentions and acts will call forth inner signals of guilt.

GREY WALTER:

The reason I am particularly intrigued by your placing it just there is that we have plenty of evidence that the majority of recidivist juvenile delinquents, who have on the whole a *good* attitude to their mother and to their leisure occupations, their companions, their social relations, have a brain activity which would put them in a much lower age category than their chronological, endocrine, intellectual or anatomical age. Some people call this 'immaturity' or retarded development of the brain activity but I am not sure it is just immaturity. It is something a bit more subtle than that. Perhaps one should use the term suggested for other types of infantilism: ateleiosis. It looks as though there is quite a large group of young delinquents, perhaps 60 per cent. to 70 per cent. of them, who have some disturbance around about the period which you describe as the play age, in which their sense of responsibility should be developing; post or propter hoc the previous stage, which you call the doubting stage, remains the most prominent feature of their lives. They are full of doubts and vacillations. We call the result ductility, because socially these people are easily led. Any influence that comes to bear on them will direct them to crime or reform. When one influence is removed, then they will revert again to some other influence. They are recidivists because they are constantly being tempted to delinquency, and constantly being reformed. Their whole juvenile existence is a history of vacillations from one mode of behaviour to the other, even after the age of eighteen, and it seems that here we may find a close correlation between this tentative scheme which you developed by impressionistic methods, and the objective results of the measurement of brain activity. Non-criminal adults of this type seem to retain a love for episodic adventure sandwiched between periods of withdrawal and seclusion.

BOWLBY:

It seems to me that the sense of responsibility is related to self-identification: you cannot be responsible for yourself unless you know all major aspects of yourself. The characteristic thing about the psychopathic delinquent and other disturbed personalities is that there are large parts of himself which he does not know. A conscious sense of guilt is dependent on a conflict both aspects of which are in some measure conscious. The psychopath keeps part of his feelings out of consciousness. Many psychopaths identify only with their greedy, hostile and cruel feelings and deny the existence in themselves of any kindly feelings. I have treated such a person myself. It was apparent to me that she was really very shamefaced towards me: she regarded me as good and she regarded herself as someone who was so unbelievably bad that there were no prospects of her ever being accepted by me—indeed, of her ever being an acceptable member of society. She managed to avoid conscious guilt by the simple expedient of claiming that her way of life was was much better than anyone else's. She was, in fact, a prostitute, a Lesbian and a thief and she did all these things in a big way claiming that she was not in the least guilty about them. The problem with her was to help her recognize her own feelings of generosity and kindness and love, all of which she had the utmost difficulty in tolerating because, of course, they came into such acute conflict with greedy and sexual aspects of herself.

And that brings me to identification. In the problems of identification which one meets in adolescents, the question is why they can't help swinging from one extreme to another—why their identifications are so incompatible. Erikson's boy wanted to be both a monk and a trumpet player and you cannot easily be both: these two identifications represent two incompatible ways of life. It seems to me that the main problem with which we are all faced in the process of growing up is that of making a tolerable and compatible synthesis out of a number of manifestly incompatible components. We hate and we love, we are greedy and we are generous, we are kind and we are cruel. These things are literally incompatible and it is only by making some tolerable synthesis out of these incompatibilities that we develop any sort of unity. The task for the individual as he grows up is not only to own to all these different parts of himself but gradually to relate them in some self-balancing unity.

The question then arises as to why some people are unable to relate and unify these different parts of themselves in a satisfactory way. I think we know of at least two main reasons why people find this difficult or impossible, and I daresay there are many others besides. One set of conditions is when the strength of these conflicting impulses is persistently above a certain threshold. If a child is deprived, his need for his mother's company may be persistently and embarrassingly high over a long period; similarly his hatred of her may also become persistently and embarrassingly high over this same period. Obviously, the higher the intensity of these impulses, the more they conflict with each other and the more difficult are they to integrate. Another common way in which an important component comes to be omitted from the developing personality is through a parent disapproving very strongly of a particular aspect of a child. If a parent regards sexuality, for instance, as being an intolerable, disagreeable thing, the child doesn't accept his sexuality and doesn't identify himself with it and thus sexuality becomes a non-integrated part of his personality. As a result he may grow up with the incompatible identifications of being a prude and a peeping-Tom. Naturally, we all develop manifold identifications. Provided they are compatible it is all right; it is the incompatible identifications based on unresolved conflicts that lead to disunity of the personality.

MEAD:

What are the conditions of disassociation in which you do or do not own to this part of your personality?

BOWLBY:

I think one could refer to the notions of forgivability and unforgivability. Provided something is forgivable one can own to it, but if it is unforgivable one cannot. It is characteristic of neurotic patients that they regard something or other in their own impulse-life as being unforgivable, unmanageable, uncontrollable, and this is why it has to be divorced from the rest of their personalities.

HUXLEY:

Isn't it a fact, John, that sex is rather peculiar among all these factors in that at puberty suddenly something happens to you, apparently from outside your ego, though actually from inside your body from the circulating sex-hormones, and a change is imposed on you?

BOWLBY:

I don't want to give the impression that I think these dissociations are entirely due to adult disapproval. That, I think, is only one source of them. The other source is that the powerfulness of the drive is so disagreeable and frightening that we are inclined to say that we don't want to have anything to do with the drive, and to disown it.

MEAD:

Unmanageable within the full framework of the society—the

208

child, for example, who has an enormously greater than usual greed, even though the adults might be kind, would nevertheless, feel it as much more exaggerated than its companions and other people around it.

BOWLBY:

Not only that, but the magnitude of his greed creates an even bigger conflict with his own love and concern for the object—say his mother. If both impulses are at high level, the clash which results is much more unmanageable than if they are both at more modest levels.

HUXLEY:

Dr. Bowlby started off by talking about the incompatibility between being a monk and being a trumpeter in most societies, and then went back to the incompatibility between different inner urges. This is to my mind something very different. There are two different kinds of incompatibility—the incompatibilities between your own impulses which arise automatically, and the incompatibilities between different possibilities of identity. There is a point which I wanted to bring up before and forgot—on the subject of hobbies. I think it is very important, in any complex society where there is a high degree of specialization, to provide the possibility of really satisfying hobbies. When this is not forthcoming you may get the most extraordinary phenomena, one of the most remarkable of which happened in England during this century. A rather dry, meticulous civil servant, William Sharp, invented a second personality for himself whom he called Fiona Macleod. 'She' wrote remarkable poems all full of Celtic twilight, and he actually corresponded with her—he corresponded with the other half of his dual personality. This was an extreme, almost pathological case—but many people can increase the variety of their identities, which is probably a good thing. I know a very distinguished man, I won't mention his name, who behaves and looks quite differently when he is in the Athenaeum Club from when he is in the Savile!

ERIKSON:

I would like to have seen the handwriting of the 'two' correspondents.

HUXLEY:

I believe it is possible to do so.

LORENZ:

Before I put a question I want to make a statement, which may be very much a matter of course, but maybe other people feel like me. Erikson's statement about negative identity suddenly makes comprehensible to me the hitherto incomprehensible fact that there are villains. You see, in my religion, there is a God but no devil—evil is just lack of the creative and not something negative trying to create in the opposite direction.

I was confronted repeatedly in my life with people who actually did the contrary of good, which we call evil, which didn't make sense at all, but now I suddenly understand that there are fixed personalities who know and feel perfectly what is 'good' but are forced, by the mechanism which you demonstrated, to do the opposite.

HUXLEY:

'Evil be thou my good!'

LORENZ:

And the other thing—I have been for a long time greatly intrigued with the question of the hysterical character that has, if I may use Grey Walter's terminology a specially high ductility of identity. It is characteristic of the hysterical character that he can identify successively with incredibly different people, and be comrades with people in speech and thought and gesture and outlook. Of course, this is not the only characteristic of the hysterical character, but it is one of the most important, and I was struggling in vain with the question, 'How does the conception of hysterical suggestibility, of hysterical lack of backbone in time, overlap and coincide with your conception of identity diffusion?' Is the hysterical character a special case of identity dispersal or diffusion, or is identity dispersal as a special phenomenon one condition for the appearance of what we call a hysterical character? The two syndromes must meet somewhere. What happens when an hysterical character gets a good and well-marked identity dispersal?

ERIKSON:

I can only take refuge in the position that there are different preconditions for identity conflicts, and one of them is an hysterical

210

personality. The hysterical identity conflict is different from a paranoid or other one, and the hysterical one is, indeed, characterized by what you called the ductility of identification. The hysteric has a collection of identity fragments, each of which he can display as complete at different times. Very often the hysterical character has a histrionic quality, and if everything works out nicely, that is if he lives at the right time, and finds the right profession, then he can elaborate what you call the ductility of identification into being different people at different times, let us say as actor, orator, politician, psychiatrist, etc. So what comes first? I don't know. In every such question so much depends on what kind of individual he is, and at what time of history he lives, and in what part of his society. In a primitive tribe a woman with an outstanding hysterical character may be a medicine-woman, because she is the one who can identify with conditions in other people and always can quickly guess what is wrong. To utilize such a gift, however, it is important that, in addition to the ability to identify quickly with somebody else, one must be able quickly to regain one's own identity. This is really the art of diagnosis, and of all empathy—psychological, artistic, and histrionic.

LORENZ:

Now it is characteristic of some hysterics, of these role-playing characters, that they can play the role so long as they have an audience, and not before themselves. These people are happy as long as they have an audience who believes in them, but have to change their milieus because after one audience has seen through them and does not play up to them any more they have to turn to a new milieu, which is not yet warned against the different roles of their façade. As they are out for approval they have to adapt the whole identity to each new audience and so the poor things have to change from one identity to another.

DE SAUSSURE:

Charles Odier considered that one of the criteria of maturity was what he called 'endogenous securization'—the ability to achieve for oneself a feeling of security, that is to say, a security which would come not from outside but from inside. Do you not think that this criterion of 'endogenous securization' would be a fairly important criterion in one of your diagonal squares? It seems to me that it is also closely linked to the problem of responsibility and to that of identity. One can only achieve identity once one has a feeling of inner security.

ZAZZO:

According to you, what are the conditions of this endogenous securization, of this feeling of internal security? There are probably conditions which are exogenous?

DE SAUSSURE:

Of course, in order to achieve endogenous security one must have a certain exogenous security. But let us say that for a long time the child feels himself to be secure if he is in tune with his environment; but there comes a time when the child has had sufficient experience to be able to rest on this experience and to feel himself in security even if he is out of tune with his environment.

It is a process of interiorization, a process where Piaget's ideas of socialization experiences, etc. are probably very much concerned. I think this would be a fairly descriptive term for one of these stages— internal securization.

ERIKSON:

I would say that security after all can be expected during childhood and adolescence only in relation to a particularly restricted group of people. The baby will certainly feel secure only with one or two persons, especially at critical times. Each of the stages which I outlined coincides with an extension of the social radius of interaction: from the family to the known 'world'. Therefore, with each crisis, security has to be re-established within a wider radius, from a mother or maternal person to that of parental persons in general, which would include two polarized people like father and mother, to the basic family, to the neighbourhood, to the peer-group, to the apprenticeship organization and so on. Each of the early securities is basic for the later one, but it has first to find its own establishment in its own social radius, and in that sense I believe the security problem continues all the way through and is not added at any particular time.

RÉMOND:

Mr. Erikson, I have the impression that I have not heard your explanation of the succession of ideas which you have in column 5 in your table, from 'bipolarity' to 'identity'. Could you go over again what you wanted to show in this vertical column?

This column is really very tentative. But I will do the best I can.

In I, 5 I have the term *unipolarity*. I mean by that the great and as yet undisturbed security of the baby in his complete dependence on the maternal environment, which will be disturbed only if he prematurely feels the loss of and thus the dependence on the mother. It looks as if this unity gave him an inner pole which does not make it necessary to differentiate himself from that original matrix. That is why I contrast premature differentiation of self, a premature sense of being separate, with a sense of unipolarity. Gradually, however, he does differentiate himself, for any number of reasons, which culminate in the sense of autonomy. During this process he has to establish with his mother what I call a *bipolarity*, because once he has lost the feeling that he is one with her, there have to be two that interplay in a way of mutuality. And his security lies in his ability to interplay with her.

I know that I should make a string of quotation marks around the word '*autism*', (see III.4) but I do believe that children who do not develop a bipolarity with their mothers and selected other people withdraw and develop a bipolarization with their own fantasy life which I call 'psychosocial autism' which some children develop for some time without ever being autistic in the psychiatric sense. In extreme cases you can observe that autistic children play with their own vision, or their own hearing. In other words, they would not use their eyes to bipolarize with an object outside, but act as if they were looking at their own vision; or they go around with fingers in their ears, and, as it were, play with their own audition. There are all number of gradations from what you might call psychosocial 'autism' to what would be a psychiatric 'autism'.

Then the third step, *play identification* (III.5) would be the kind of security a child can develop after he is able to interact intensively with a number of people. I would think that during the initiative stage great security is derived from identification in play with others, and identification with others in playing. By *Oedipal fantasy identifications*, I mean that the child would in his fantasies identify, for example, with a very dangerous or very powerful father, or a very endangered mother. This would be alleviated by the child's ability to have a rich play-life and to identify playfully with a great number of people and to measure himself and his own strength versus their strength in play. But if this fails, then we have a child who has to fight giants in his own fantasy, and there is no corrective, except an unrealistic identification with them. There is no testing of reality, and no convincing experience of the fact that most adults are rela-

213

tively benign people and do not annihilate you if you fight them playfully.

Then the next stage would be *work identification*, which probably is in itself already somewhat clearer, because it means an identification with people who know how to do certain things and to complete them. That has an enormous importance for the child's anticipated place within his technology and therefore is a more direct precursor of identity. In work identification you can see the special problem of children to whom the plumber or the gardener or the policeman are more tangible people than the father who, say, every morning, takes a brief case and goes to work, where the child has no idea what he does all day. *Identity foreclosure* would be any development, such as precocity or gifts or character development, which 'types' the child so early, that he does not develop even a normal and necessary amount of identity diffusion.

There is one aspect about the juvenile offender I want to come back to. In juvenile offenders you find a strange combination of an extreme sense of social sensitivity and of a 'lack of guilt'. In other words, the people you are talking about (whenever it was that they started to offend) regressed, I would say, in psychological terms to the state of shame, and cannot manage it. There is an interesting American ballad, of the man who is on the gallows, and is to be executed, and people mill about and want to watch the spectacle. In this ballad he repeats the refrain, 'God damn your eyes', meaning 'You cannot damn me with your eyes—God damn all of your eyes for looking at me'. Now this is, I would think, one of the basic criminal positions and often has to do with an intense shaming of the small child before the guilt stage, in which case the guilt stage never fully develops. Maybe this is one of the conflicts in the kind of person you have in mind.

HUXLEY:

Erik, you said that you find your own assurance by finding out what you mean most to others. But surely you've got to think of 'others' in a highly abstract way when you are dealing with the solitary genius—I mean a man like Spinoza, or Leonardo, who never communicated the contents of his notebooks to any actual others, or the artist who paints pictures merely to satisfy himself. I quite see that such cases can be brought into your schema, but you have got to transcend all crude or simple formulations of it.

I spoke of young people, and I don't know Spinoza's identity problems as a young person. You will find in Shaw's autobiography, that he admits to having 'always been a stranger in this world and . . . at home only with the mighty dead'. Rare people can afford to establish an identity in their historical time and then move on to a position where they may really feel solidarity only with those very few who sit on the lonely mountain tops of history basing their final identity on a common integrity. These are often people in whose late adolescence a kind of premature integrity arises, which makes them in many ways old, and yet preserves a certain child-likeness. But even the people on mountain tops maintain some kind of identity based on a sincere sense of tradition, and most of all, on the deepest solidarity with the human race.

REFERENCES

ASHBY, W. R. (1952). *Design for a brain*, London.

BERTALANFFY, L. VON (1952). *Problems of life: an evaluation of modern biological thought*, London.

BIRCH, H. (1954). In: *Josiah Macy Conference on Group Processes*, 1954, New York.

BRONOWSKI, J. (1943). *William Blake, 1757-1827; a man without a mask*, London.

ERIKSON, E. H. (1950). *Childhood and society*, New York. Swedish Edition: (1954) *Barnet och Samballet*, Stockholm; Japanese Edition: (1954) Tokyo; German Edition (in press) *Kindheit und Gesellschaft*, Zürich.

ERIKSON, E. H. (1950). Growth and Crises of the 'Healthy Personality'. In: *Symposium on the Healthy Personality*, Supplement II to the Transactions of the Fourth Conference on Problems of Infancy and Childhood, June 8-9 and July 3-4, edited by Milton J. E. Senn. (Prepared for the White House Conference, December 1950). Josiah Macy, Jr. Foundation, New York. German Translation: (1953) *Wachstum und Krisen der gesunden Personlichkeit*, Stuttgart, also in *Psyche*, Heidelberg, 7, 1, 112.

ERIKSON, E. H. (1951). Sex differences in the play configuration of preadolescents. *Amer. J. Orthopsychiat.* 21, 667.

ERIKSON, E. H. (in press). *The problem of identity*.

FESSARD, A. (1954). In: *Brain mechanisms and consciousness*, Oxford.

FRANCK, K. and ROSEN, E. (1949). A projective test of masculinity-feminity, *J. Consult. Psychol.* 13, 247.

GEBSER, J. (1954). *Strukturwandel Europaïschen Geistes*, Essen.

HART, C. W. M. (1955). *Contrasts between prepubertal and pubertal education*. In: *Education and anthropology*, Stanford, p. 271.

HAYES, C. (1951). *The ape in our house*, New York.

HELWEG-LARSEN, P., HOFFMEYER, H., KIELER, J., THAYSEN, E. H. THAYSEN, J. H., THYGESEN, P. and WULFF, M. H. (1952). *Famine disease in German concentration camps*, Copenhagen.

HENRY, J. (1941). *Jungle people, a Kaingàng tribe of the highlands of Brazil*, New York.

HERSEY, R. B. (1931). Emotional cycles in man. *J. ment. Sci.* 77, 151 (reprinted in 1944 by the Foundation for the Study of Cycles, New York).

HONZIK, M. P. (1951). Sex differences in the occurrence of materials in the play constructions of preadolescents, *Child Development*, 22, 15.

HUXLEY, A. (1941). *Grey Eminence*, London.

KESTENBERG, J. (in press), *J. Amer. psychoan. Soc.*

MANN, T. (1948). *Joseph and his brothers*, New York.

217

MEAD, M. (1935). *Sex and temperament in three primitive societies*, New York (reprinted in: *From the South Seas*, New York (1939) and as a Mentor Book, New York (1950); English edition: London (1935); Spanish edition: *Sexo y temperamento*, Buenos Aires (1947); Swedish edition: *Kvinnligt, Manligt, Mänskligt*; Stockholm (1948)).

MEAD, M. (1947). On the implications for anthropology of the Gesell-Ilg approach to maturation, *Amer. Anthropol, 49,* 69.

MEAD, M. (1949). *Male and female*, New York (English edition: London, 1949; German edition; *Mann und Weib*, Zurich, 1955).

MEAD, M. (1955). *The implications of insight. II.* In: *Childhood in contemporary cultures*, ed. Mead, M. and Wolfenstein, M., Chicago, p. 449.

MOLL, A. (1889). *Der Hypnotismus*, Berlin.

MORGAN, L. H. (1907). *Ancient Society*, Chicago.

MORRIS, C. (1948). *The open self*, New York.

PIAGET, J. and INHELDER, B. (1948). *La Représentation de l'espace chez l'enfant*, Paris.

RICKMAN, J. (1951). Methodology and thought in psychopathology, *Brit. J. med. Psychol. 24,* 1.

SAUSSURE, R. de (1929). *La Méthode psychanalytique*, Paris.

SAUSSURE, R. de (1939). *Le Miracle grec*, Paris.

SAUSSURE, R. de (1950). *Psychoanalysis and history.* In: *Psychoanalysis and the social sciences*, 1949; New York, vol. 2, p. 7.

SEARS, P. S. (1953). Child-rearing factors related to playing sex-typed roles, *Amer. Psychol. 8,* 431.

SHANNON, C. E. and WEAVER, W. (1949). *The mathematical theory of communication*, Urbana.

SIMPSON, D. G. (1953). *The major features of evolution*, New York.

STRACHEY, J. (1934). The nature of the therapeutic action of psychoanalysis, *Int. J. Psycho-Anal. 15,* 127.

WINTERBOTTOM, J. M. (1929). Studies in sexual phenomena, *Proc. zool. Soc.*

WOLFENSTEIN, M. (1945). *The impact of a children's story on mothers and children*, Washington.

Index

DISCUSSIONS ON
Child Development

VOLUME FOUR

*The Proceedings of the Fourth Meeting of the
World Health Organization Study Group
on the Psychobiological Development of the Child
Geneva 1956*

MEMBERS OF STUDY GROUP

DR. JOHN BOWLBY
Psychoanalysis
Director, Department of Children and Parents
Tavistock Clinic, London

DR. FRANK FREMONT-SMITH
Research Promotion
Chairman
Josiah Macy, Jr. Foundation
New York

PROFESSOR G. R. HARGREAVES
Psychiatry
Professor of Psychiatry
University of Leeds
Lately Chief, Mental Health Section
World Health Organization

PROFESSOR BÄRBEL INHELDER
Psychology
Professeur de Psychologie de l'Enfant
Institut des Sciences de l'Education
de l'Université de Genève

DR. E. E. KRAPF
Psychiatry
Chief, Mental Health Section
World Health Organization

DR. KONRAD Z. LORENZ
Ethology
Director, Max-Planck Institut
für Verhaltensphysiologie
Seewiesen, Bavaria

DR. MARGARET MEAD
Cultural Anthropology
Associate Director, Dept. of Anthropology
American Museum of Natural History
New York

DR. KARL-AXEL MELIN
Electrophysiology
Director, Clinic for Convulsive Disorders
Stora Sköndal, Stockholm

PROFESSOR MARCEL MONNIER
Electrophysiology
Professor of Physiology
University of Basel

PROFESSOR J. PIAGET *Psychology*
Professeur de Psychologie
à la Sorbonne et à l'Université
de Genève

DR. J. M. TANNER *Human Biology*
Reader in Growth and Development
Institute of Child Health
University of London

DR. W. GREY WALTER *Electrophysiology*
Director of Research
Burden Neurological Institute
Bristol

DR. RENÉ ZAZZO *Psychology*
Directeur de Laboratoire de
Psychobiologie de l'Enfant
Institut des Hautes Études
Paris

GUESTS

DR. L. VON BERTALANFFY   *General Biology*

Visiting Professor of Physiology
Univ. of Southern California
and Director of Biological Research
Mount Sinai Hospital
Los Angeles

PROFESSOR ERIK ERIKSON   *Psychoanalysis*

Austen Riggs Center
Stockbridge, Mass.
and Dept. of Psychiatry
University of Pittsburgh
School of Medicine

PREFACE

This volume gives an account of the fourth and last meeting of the W.H.O. Research Study Group on the Psychobiological Development of the Child and also includes the extensive correspondence which preceded and prepared for the meeting. The editors, as they explain in their foreword, have wisely decided that this preparatory correspondence forms an essential part of the record of the meeting. Hence its inclusion.

It is difficult to write a preface to this volume. Indeed, it should be emphasized for the benefit of the reader that the only adequate preface available to the volume is to read the three volumes which have preceded it. Each of the three previous meetings was devoted to a discussion of data presented to the Group from the point of view of a specific scientific discipline, whereas at this last meeting the data which the Group examined and discussed was its own previous meetings. The account of this examination and discussion can be fully understood only by the reader who has shared, in as far as the printed word permits, the previous shared intellectual development of the members of the Group. But for the student of human development who comes to this volume prepared for it by its predecessors there will be a rich reward regardless of the particular scientific discipline to which the reader belongs.

The meeting was, in effect, a search for a synthesis of all the data that had been presented and discussed at the previous meetings but, as Professor Piaget says in his opening presentation, 'a synthesis which will not be one of doctrine, but which will consist of an arrangement in order of possible questions and explanatory models, so as to delineate the field of interdisciplinary research which will be most usefully followed in our subsequent work'. In its search for a synthesis the Group was aided by a presentation on General System Theory from a new guest—Professor Ludwig von Bertalanffy.

In previous volumes I have acknowledged the Group's indebtedness to many people who contributed to the success of their meetings, but in three directions our indebtedness is so great that it should be re-affirmed. Firstly, to our Chairman—Dr. Frank Fremont-Smith—who enabled this Group to become an effective instrument of scientific exploration; secondly, to our editors, who have so skilfully preserved in written form the essence of our discussions; and finally, to the Director-General of W.H.O., Dr. M. G. Candau, to his predecessor, Dr. Brock Chisholm, and to the late Dr. Norman Begg, W.H.O. Regional Director for Europe.

As the only member of the Group who had the opportunity of seeing, while serving with W.H.O., the extent to which the setting up of the Group and the continuation of its work depended upon the support of these three officials of W.H.O., I feel a strong sense of personal gratitude to them. At a time when the climate of opinion in the governing body of W.H.O. was biased in favour of 'action' and 'quick results' and against 'research' and 'theory', they were among the few who never forgot that the future development of medicine in general, and preventive medicine in particular, depends

ix

upon current research in the present—that the future technology of preventive and clinical medicine will rest upon the findings of pure science. The climate of opinion has now changed and the World Health Organization has now recognized the importance of fostering research. This is due in large part to their leadership. Perhaps also the success of the work of the Research Study Group itself has contributed in some small degree to that change.

Leeds   G. R. HARGREAVES

FOREWORD

A word of editorial explanation concerning the structure (if not the equilibrium!) of this volume may not be amiss, particularly to readers of the previous three volumes, accustomed to *Discussions* opening, as it were, with a bang. Prior to the fourth meeting Professor Jean Piaget was prevailed upon to precirculate to all members and guests of our group a paper containing his views of what were the basic questions to be answered, or rather asked, by all those of whatever discipline who were investigating the development of the child. He ended this paper by addressing a series of specific questions to each member of the Group, as well as a series of general questions to us all. It is a measure of the intellectual weight of Professor Piaget's paper that the replies that came back were prompt, lengthy, and deeply considered. They were in turn precirculated.

The meeting followed with a further thrashing out of the issues raised. Then, at its close, Professor Piaget was asked to draft a short summary statement following on his opening paper, but taking account of our comments and our discussions upon it. Once again, at great pains to himself, he complied.

We have now placed this opening paper, the replies, and the post-discussion paper all as Part I of this volume, and followed it with the usual edited discussion as Part II. We have been in some doubt whether the post-discussion paper should appear where it does, or at the end of this volume after the discussion, and warn readers that they may be best advised to read the precirculated papers first, then the discussion of Part II, and finally this last section of Part I. At least this may be the best course for a first reading; for we make bold to suggest that many readers may feel rewarded by a second journey, one way or another, through some of the papers of Part I.

As this is the last volume, at any rate of the current series, perhaps we may be allowed a few words in a more personal vein. As editors, charged with the task of reducing the original table-talk to an integrated discussion shorn of the ethology of the red herring, we have had more opportunity to view the texts, total and condensed, than any other of our members. We have seen at first hand the growth of mutual comprehension amongst our Group. We have seen many times how remarks identical in content in the first and fourth meetings were on the first occasion passed over in uncomprehending silence by the Group and on the fourth handled easily and accurately as part of the common fund of knowledge. We have watched the gradual and painless assimilation by each member from year to year of ideas and attitudes at first foreign and, perhaps, even uncongenial to him. We wish to make a sweeping and general claim: that Study Groups of this sort—containing a dozen or so people, each eminent in his own field, but each or nearly each drawn from a different field, meeting at yearly intervals for not less than three years, generating a discussion whose form is determined as much after the event as before it—such Study Groups are the means of education, not at the postgraduate but at the truly professorial level. All of us deplore our increasing specialization; all of us deplore our lack of acquaintance with fields other than our own; all of us deplore the absorption in our own ideas that gradually overtakes us unless we learn continuously as well as teach. The experiment of this international Study Group has, we believe, given us a glimpse of what might become a general pattern for maintaining those precious and precarious possessions, wide horizons and flexible minds.

J. M. TANNER

BÄRBEL INHELDER

CONTENTS

PART I
PRECIRCULATED PAPERS

JEAN PIAGET

The General Problems of the Psychobiological Development of the Child[1]

Having given most of the time at our previous meetings to the study of special problems of child development, we agreed to devote this fourth and last meeting to a discussion of the more general problems, such as the identification of the factors affecting development, of the stages of development and particularly of the mechanisms enabling the transition from one stage to another to be explained.

Each of us has already contributed a large number of data on these different points, but what is now required is a synthesis, harmonizing as far as possible the different viewpoints presented. I shall try to formulate this synthesis in such a way that each member of the Group can add to this preliminary paper, so that in the end a more complete picture can be obtained.

I. FACTORS AFFECTING DEVELOPMENT

Immediately on approaching this first great problem, it can easily be seen, on re-reading the discussions of the Study Group (*Discussions on Child Development*, Volumes I-III), that we did not keep to the simple and traditional distinction into three main factors of development:

(*a*) Hereditary factors, manifested in physical growth and especially in the maturing of the nervous system;

(*b*) The action of the physical environment (nutrition and the experience of handling objects), and

(*c*) The action of the social environment.

On the contrary, we constantly tried to overcome this dangerous partitioning and, if our respective contributions are carefully examined, it can be seen that we did so in three ways:

[1] This essay, not originally intended for publication, was contributed as a starting-point for the discussions of the fourth meeting, with the particular hope of helping to synthesize the views of the several members.

3

(1) by searching for interactions between these three factors;
(2) by searching for a common language making it possible to describe all three and to formulate their interactions more clearly;
(3) by recognizing either implicitly or explicitly the existence of a fourth factor, (*d*), additional to factors (*a*), (*b*) and (*c*), introducing new elements, while at the same time making it possible to co-ordinate them.

1. *Search for interaction between factors* (*a*), (*b*) *and* (*c*)

It might have been expected at first glance that the position taken by the members of the Group with regard to factors affecting development would be determined chiefly by the field in which they had made their own discoveries; for example that Lorenz would explain everything by innate mechanisms and the spontaneous activity of the nervous system; that Margaret Mead would explain everything by social factors and that Zazzo (as a disciple of Wallon) would base everything on the maturing of the nervous system and social factors, while underestimating the importance of the individual's actions in dealing with his experience.

However, the first result of the discussions of the Study Group, the first concrete element of the 'synthesis' which you have asked me to make, is that we are unanimous in considering that the three factors (*a*), (*b*) and (*c*) *never* occur independently of each other and that their *interactions* are consequently at least as important as their respective actions.

Below are some examples of this:

For the discussions on cerebral activity (EEG, etc.) I shall restrict myself to a quotation from Grey Walter (1953):

'The crude division of all human attributes into "inherited" and "acquired" is excusable but quite unreasonable. Even in the simple models of behaviour we have described, it is often quite impossible to decide whether what the model is doing is the result of its design or of its experience. Such a categorization is in fact meaningless when use influences design, and design use.'

As regards Lorenz, I would recall the moment (which appeared decisive for him and myself) at the end of the discussions during the London meeting (see Volume II, p. 260 ff.) where he accepted and stressed my remark that there is no genotype which is not linked to a phenotype, where he discovered with surprise that I was by no means an empiricist (in the sense of explaining development and learning by experience alone) and where he briefly described what he termed his 'dynamic apriorism'. Lorenz's dynamic apriorism, i.e. the concept of an internal activity of the organism developing in constant interplay with acquired experience, is not very far from development through constant interaction of internal and external factors which we ourselves describe as a continuous formation of structure by successive equilibrations (see Inhelder & Piaget, 1955).

As regards the psychoanalysts who, following Freud's early opinions, explained so much by instinct, I do not need to remind you of Bowlby's flexible and delicately inflected attitude, based on continued interaction between instinctive factors and individual experience as well as interindividual or social relations.

As regards the cultural and social aspect, we may recall how Margaret Mead, who proposed repeating in New Guinea certain of our intelligence tests (conservation, spatial relations, etc.) was in agreement with the theory according to which the stages of reactions to these tests might be the same as regards the order of succession, but might be very different as regards average ages or even the non-attainment of higher levels. And this implies that social factors are constantly interacting with other factors (physical experience, etc.) even in such a sphere as the organization of concepts, which is sometimes interpreted sociologically in a rather exclusive and rigid manner (Durkheim, etc.).

However, all this is self-evident. What is more exciting is to trace how the members of the Study Group, who are unanimous in considering the interactions between facts (a), (b) and (c) to be as important as the factors themselves, endeavoured to co-ordinate their viewpoints and to describe these interactions.

2. Search for a common language

In order to describe development 'synthetically' and, above all, to make some progress in the explanation of these general mechanisms, it is essential to have a common language. Indeed, without a common language we shall never succeed in analysing the actual interactions between the factors and will always return, despite ourselves, to a description by juxtaposition (or accumulation) of influences.

Let us imagine, for example, that some poor child has been studied by each of us for a month or a year and that we then meet to co-ordinate our results. We would know its brain rhythms, rates of physical growth, family conflicts, relations with its social environment, its reactions to problems of intelligence and to the 25 perceptive laboratory tests which my co-workers have already studied in children, the extent of its vocabulary, its drawings, etc., etc. However, and this is the tragedy of present studies on development, we would be incapable without a common language of achieving anything other than an enormous dossier consisting of a series of small mosaic-like chapters, complete with a concluding essay on the

5

'personality' of the child (with photographs) linking together with varying degrees of imagination a few facts taken from each of the preceding chapters. We would naturally make films and sound recordings to show how 'alive' all this is, but we would nevertheless continue, in the absence of a common language, each to tell his own separate little story in his own language, without making a real synthesis.

Of course, we have often worked like this during the meetings of the Study Group, but we also did something else and your unfortunate colleague given the task of making this synthesis had the great pleasure to find, on re-reading our reports, that very often we also made an effort to translate from one viewpoint into another and that at certain particularly decisive moments we even glimpsed what might be our common language, or the new language of the future. . . .

I shall start with an example. During the last meeting, Erikson gave us a table of the elementary affective stages, going beyond a narrow Freudian framework, and endeavouring to characterize general forms of behaviour by bipolar links such as 'giving-getting', 'autonomy-shame and doubt', 'initiative-guilt', etc. (see Volume III, p. 168). It is clear that such a table, although it may be immediately usable by all those who have specialized in the affective development of the child, represents to those who have limited their field of study to questions of intelligence or thought only a collection of problems without any solution at present. Each of the criteria employed by Erikson could, naturally, also be applied to the field of learning and the structuration of knowledge. But instead of remaining well-defined, as in Erikson's field, they run the risk of becoming more and more vague the more general they become. Consequently, what we require is not a mere extension, with the risk of increasing inexactitude, but a translation into a common language. While Erikson was speaking, however, Grey Walter was looking for such a translation, of which he gave shortly afterwards a series of examples. Speaking from the viewpoint of 'statistical neurophysiology' he endeavoured to re-interpret Erikson's stages in the context of information theory and, even if we do not accept this parallelism in detail, we cannot help recognizing the fact that he made use of a much more general language, enabling more precise comparisons to be drawn between the various aspects of behaviour and in particular between its affective and cognitive aspects.

For example, the stage of 'giving-getting' with, as poles, 'trust' and 'mistrust', would correspond to an initial insufficiency of information, such that the elementary exchanges 'giving-getting' are accompanied from the viewpoint of the 'baby-computer' by a degree of approximation large enough to make the system less precise and consequently more 'trusting'. Similarly, a certain particular type of learning would correspond to the next of Erikson's stages and so on.

The details of such analogies produced on the spur of the moment by Grey Walter are of little importance. Their great significance is to show that one of us who works continually with mechano-physiological models was able to give, in terms of probability of information, an immediate translation rendering the stages of affective development still clearer for those of us concerned with intelligence or with learning.

In fact, this probabilistic language is clearly the common language that we are looking for, provided that the information and communication schemata are supplemented by introducing the concept of 'strategy' and the terminology of the theory of games. In this broadened form the probabilistic language may be suitable for all of us. In the first place, its generality makes it possible to establish fairly direct correspondence between the mechano-physiological models and the various forms of behaviour observed in the psychology of the cognitive functions. In the second place, it is not restricted to describing the information as such, under its cognitive aspect, but, by introducing the concept of gain and loss it provides a means of analysing the 'economics' of forms of behaviour. It is without doubt this 'economics' of forms of behaviour which constitutes the most natural transition between their affective aspect (which can always be translated in terms of enrichment and impoverishment) and their cognitive aspect. In the third place, it enables certain isomorphisms to be found between models of intra-individual operations and inter-individual or social ones and this makes it possible to by-pass the over-simplified and crude antithesis of the individual and the social factors, which is as much a drawback for the theory of development as the distinction between 'innate' and 'acquired'.

3. *Recognition of a fourth factor (d) of development*

As soon as we adopt this broader viewpoint, as imposed on us by the search for a common language, we perceive that there exists a fourth factor, more general than the three classic factors of innateness, physical experience and social environment, and obeying its own special laws of probability and the minimum: this is the factor of *equilibrium* which is found associated with each of the three preceding ones, but which governs particularly their interactions and which, moreover, reveals itself frequently in an independent manner.

To give an idea of what such independence may signify, let us take an entirely theoretical example but one which has the advantage of posing the problem in one of its most general biological forms. We may suppose that in the course of development certain sectors of the organism can be considered as a closed system and are found to obey the second law of thermo-dynamics. In this case the constant increase in entropy, tending towards that state of equilibrium which is maximum entropy, would constitute neither an innate mechanism nor an acquisition in terms of environment, but the result of a purely probabilistic mechanism. We may suppose, on the contrary (like Helmholtz, Guye, etc.) that physical development does not obey the second law. In this case the state of equilibrium towards which growth tends would be characterized by a system of regulations controlling chance; and the overall form of this system would constitute a factor leading to a better understanding of developmental theory than any number of details of various hereditary, acquired or social factors.

To return to concrete problems which are apparently completely different in each of our many fields of investigation, it is very striking to observe how the equilibrium problem constantly recurs, either explicitly or implicitly, in each field which we are studying.

To begin with social factors: even if we accept the great plasticity which Margaret Mead attributes to mental characteristics under the influence of various communities, nevertheless society is not the source of the nervous system, and consequently the many more or less stable reactions which we observe in the different communities constitute more or less complex forms of equilibrium between the psycho-physiological aptitudes of the individual and the actions of the environment. Thus it is not by chance that in the book entitled *Family, Socialization and Interaction Process*, Parsons & Bales (1955) particularly stress states of equilibrium and of disequilibrium, and the double equilibrium peculiar to the internal system of the personality and the system of social exchanges (see in particular a formalized diagram of these equilibrium systems in Appendix B of above, by Morris Zelditch, Jr).

In the field of affective development it would be particularly interesting to translate social and dynamic psychoanalysis, as understood by Bowlby or Erikson, into the language of equilibrium. It is clear, for example, that the Oedipus stage represents a certain form of affective equilibrium, characterized by a maximization of the 'gains' expected from the mother and by a minimization of the 'losses' expected from the father. In this connexion it would be of interest to examine whether the equilibrium point corresponds merely to a Bayes strategy, the criterion of which would be a simple maximum of 'gain minus loss', or whether it corresponds to a 'minimax' strategy, with a search for the minimum or the maximum loss which the subject supposes a hostile environment is trying to inflict on him. It is evident that a problem such as this cannot be treated in general since it depends for its solution on the overall environmental conditions for each child.

Besides these problems of 'cross-sectional' equilibrium at any given moment raised by each of the essential phases of affective development, there remains also the essential problem of the equilibrium between the *previous* affective schemata of the subject and the exigencies of the *present* position.

From the mechano-physiological viewpoint, the part played by the concept of equilibrium, and especially progressive equilibrium, is particularly important. This is because of the perspectives it opens up not only as regards the process of problem-solving and of what Ashby calls the 'finalized mechanisms', but also as regards the general lines of development of the cognitive functions. An apparatus which solves problems by a succession of approximations based on a series of feedbacks shows in the most decisive manner the part played by the concepts of disequilibrium and of progressive equilibration. As long as there is disequilibrium, i.e. while the problem still remains unsolved, a new negative feedback is set off, whereas the attainment of the correct solution is marked by the production of a state of equilibrium. Furthermore, successive approximations to the solution correspond to a progressive equilibration in accordance with a series of steps. These steps can be thought of as corresponding to phases in the processes of adult problem-solving ('Aktualgenese'), or even to stages in the developmental capacity of the child.

It is in fact very suggestive to compare such an equilibration mechanism with the processes of solution of a conservation problem in the child, since this last class of facts is of such a nature as to show the fundamental part played by the concept of equilibrium, not only in the mechanism of solution of problems but also in the development of cognitive functions in general.

From the first of these two viewpoints, if we study a child aged seven or eight years who begins by denying that there is conservation of matter when a ball of clay is moulded into a progressively longer and longer sausage and then discovers during the actual experiment the need for such conservation, we can distinguish the following phases:

1. During an initial phase, the child perceives perfectly well the lengthening and gradual thinning of the sausage, but he chooses the simplest strategy and reasons only on one of these two properties: he will say, for example, that the sausage in state A contains more modelling clay than the ball because it is 'longer' and that the sausage in state B contains still more because it is 'still longer', etc.

2. During the second phase, the error is corrected by its very exaggeration (negative feedback): when the sausage has become too long (state C or D) its thinning, which up till then was forced into the

9

background, reappears in the foreground by a kind of backward step or regulation and the child says: 'Now there is less clay because it is too thin.'

3. During the third phase, there is a sudden change in strategy and an arrival at the equilibrium point: instead of reasoning as before on the properties of the states ('longer' or 'thinner') the child begins to reason about the transformation itself: the ball is drawn out, consequently it is lengthened and made thinner at *the same time*, thus one of the two changes compensates for the other, consequently there is *conservation*.

This small example reveals the development of the cognitive functions as a whole, since equilibration plays the part there of a fourth fundamental factor of evolution. Indeed, the clearest result of our researches on the intelligence of the child is that intelligence in course of formation is oriented in the sense of a progressive *reversibility*. Thus the act of intelligence consists in grouping or co-ordinating operations: however, operations are actions which are interiorized and have come reversible, like addition which is derived from the action of bringing together and which can be reversed in the form of subtraction. On considering the evolution of operational systems, one finds three stages, corresponding in outline to the phases of the 'Aktualgenese' in adult problem solving.

1. During an initial stage, which marks the commencement of early childhood, we find rhythmic-activity actions tending towards a material aim or success are only uni-directional or irreversible. It is because of this irreversibility that the child lacks the notion of the persistence of material objects.

2. During a second stage, this initial irreversibility, which characterizes intelligence or thought in course of formation as well as the most general cognitive functions (from perception to habits, associations and memory) is tempered by a more and more complex system of regulations, which constitute a state of semi-reversibility.

3. At a third stage there is the development of operational structures which are characterized by their strict reversibility. The most direct result of these operational mechanisms is then the formation of concepts of conservation: the invariants or conservations (of geometric or physical properties of objects, or of whole or discontinuous quantities, etc.) always, in fact, appear as the product of a particular form of operational reversibility.

This reversibility, which may usually be considered as the most specific characteristic of intelligence, is nothing other than an expression of a law of equilibrium. Whatever the relative contributions made to the formation of reversible operational mechanisms by the maturing of nervous co-ordinations, by physical experience, and by social relations, the principal property of such mechanisms is that they are systems which are both mobile and stable, characterized by virtual transformation and by exact compensation. This makes it possible to conceive of the development of intelligence as being directed towards various forms of equilibrium.

To summarize: it is found that if, in order to describe the classical factors of development, one adopts a common language consisting of the modern applications of probabilistic language (theory of information, games theory), then one is forced to recognize the existence of a fourth factor of development, a factor of equilibration. Moreover, it is seen that this fourth factor is common to all our respective fields of investigation, since it is found in the social field, the affective field, in the mechano-physiological realm and in the sphere of the cognitive functions.

II. THE PROBLEM OF THE STAGES OF DEVELOPMENT

Although we are specialists on development, we still have not found out whether we understand the concept of stages in development in the same way and whether we can hope some day to establish some relationship between our respective stages! Indeed it is not clear whether all of us would subscribe even to the existence of stages. Tanner particularly stresses in his field the continuity of physical growth. Nevertheless, this problem was the starting point of our first meeting; thus it would seem essential to revert to it in the final synthesis.

The first problem confronting us is that of the actual concept of stages, regarding which our respective positions diverge rather considerably. Certain schools, for example, limit the characterization of the stages to a consideration of 'dominant characteristics'. Thus, Freud speaks of an oral stage at a period where the child already makes use of his anus and of an anal stage at a period where he still makes use of his mouth. Similarly, Wallon, represented in our Group by Zazzo, speaks of an emotional stage at a time where the infant is already exercising all kinds of sensorimotor functions and of a subsequent sensorimotor stage during which emotions are by no means absent.

Others among us demand more complex criteria. For example, Inhelder and I, when considering the development of structures and of thought, speak of stages only in connexion with the formation of total structures. We include as special cases all structures observable during a given stage which integrate with the structures of the preceding stage as necessary sub-structures. In this way the logical operations of the 'stage of formal operations' (from 11-12 to 14-15 years) constitute a total structure whose two complementary aspects are the formation of a 'lattice' (combinatory aspect) and the constitution of a 'group' of four transformations (double reversibility). However, this general structure covers, on the one hand, all the operational schemata of this stage (combinatory operations, proportions, double systems of reference, etc.) and, on the other hand, implies as sub-structures the general structures of the preceding stages (in particular the characteristic 'groupments' of the 'stage of concrete operations' from 7-8 to 11-12 years: classifications, seriations and correspondences). If we wish to aim at a synthesis in the fundamental problem of stages, we must first agree on the criteria of the stages. We have just indicated two possible criteria (dominant characteristic or total structure) but there may be many others. However, even if we limit ourselves to these two possible criteria the problems which they raise are immediately visible.

1. If we restrict ourselves to dominant characteristics, then by what objective signs can we recognize a characteristic as really dominant? Can we hope to furnish statistical criteria of frequency, or must we be content with a clinical impression, which runs the risk of being subjective? Does dominance imply a tendency towards integration of the other characteristics under the dominant characteristic (which would bring us close to the concept of 'total structures') or shall dominance be defined only in terms of relative importance from the viewpoint of frequency?

2. If the requirement of general structures is imposed, then what would be the field of application of such structures, and, in the case of several distinct fields which one wishes to interconnect, what language should be used to describe these structures? Inhelder and I have restricted ourselves to the study of intelligence and of thought and in this field—perhaps a special one as regards stages—the concept of total structure takes on a precise sense which can be defined in terms of general algebra and symbolic logic. But these concepts no longer apply when we come to perception and we have not found stages of the development of perception, at least in a form as simple and clear as our stages of the development of intellectual operations. Can we, then, hope to apply the criteria of total structure to the stages of social development, affective development, or psychomotor development, and, if the answer is 'yes', in what language should they be expressed, since affectivity, for example, characterizes the energy component of behaviour rather than its structure?

It can be seen that this initial problem in the delimitation of stages brings us back to questions very close to that of the part played by equilibrium discussed above. To the extent that objectively certain stages exist (and this is indisputable in certain fields), they cannot be considered as a product of subjective cuts arbitrarily made by the research worker in a rigorously continuous development. If stages do exist objectively, they can only consist of successive *steps* or *levels* of equilibrium, separated by a phase of transition or crisis, and each characterized by a momentary stability. The criteria employed to characterize the stages would then reduce to criteria of equilibrium: the 'total structures' are 'equilibrium forms' and the 'dominant characteristics' are linked to a certain property of equilibrium, existing at least momentarily. Generally speaking it would thus be again the language of equilibrium, which would be most suitable for reaching co-ordination between our different viewpoints on this problem.

Consequently, it is essential for us to begin by establishing a series of criteria of what we call stages (see Inhelder, First Meeting, Vol. I, p. 84) by proceeding systematically from what could be termed a *minimum* programme to a *maximum* one:

1. The *minimum* programme for establishment of stages is the recognition of a distinct chronology, in the sense of a *constant order of succession*. The average age for the appearance of a stage may vary greatly from one physical or social environment to another: for example, if the children of New Guinea, studied by Margaret Mead, manage to understand, like those of Geneva, certain structures of Euclidian geometry, they may do so at a much later or much earlier age. Whether older or younger is of little importance, but one could not speak of stage in this connexion, unless in all environments the Euclidian structures were established *after* and not before the topological structures considered as primitive.

2. A further step is taken in establishing a programme of stages when one succeeds in finding the equivalent of an *integration* in the transition from a lower stage to a higher one. As regards intellectual operations it is clear, for example, that the initial sensorimotor structures are integrated into the structures of concrete operations and the latter into formal structures. But can one say as much of the classic Freudian stages, and is it possible to agree that the elements of oral and anal stages are integrated at the level of the Oedipus stage? The great merit of Erikson's stages (Vol. III, p. 168) is precisely that he attempted, by situating the Freudian mechanisms within more general types of conduct (walking, exploring, etc.), to postulate continual integration of previous acquisitions at subsequent levels, and it seems to me that Bowlby, while laying greater stress on the essential reality of conflicts, both internal and external, is nevertheless in search of an ideal not very far from such integration.

3. The integration of the elements of a stage n into the achievements of stage $n+1$ gives rise to the supposition that if the stage $n+1$ is really new with respect to stage n, then in any stage n it should be

possible to distinguish an aspect of *achievement* with respect to the stages going before and also an aspect of *preparation* with respect to the stages coming after. Naturally it is possible for both achievement and preparation to be promoted or hampered by favourable or unfavourable external situations (hence the possibility of crises as natural transitions between one stage and the next).

4. We advance further towards the *maximum* programme of criteria of stages if we then say that it is justifiable to ascribe all the preparations leading to a stage and all the achievements characterizing this stage, to the existence of a *general* (or total) *structure* in the sense defined above.

5. However, as the concept of structure is perhaps peculiar to certain aspects of development, particularly cognitive functions, and as the corresponding affective aspect is ascribable more to an energy principle than a structure, the most general and the most elaborate programme for a theory of stages doubtless consists in representing the stages in the form of a series of equilibrium levels, the fields of which would be always more and more extensive and the mobility always greater, but whose increasing stability would depend precisely on the degree of integration and of structuration just discussed.

The first problem in our synthesis of stages would consequently consist in deciding whether we accept such a programme and if not, why not, and in the event of our accepting it, which of the five aims of this programme we believe it possible to reach at present in the different disciplines which we represent. To start with it would be a considerable advance in the study of development if we could agree on the actual concept of stages. At present almost all authors interpret this concept quite differently, as was revealed, for example, in the examination of this problem by the third meeting of the *Association de Psychologie scientifique de langue française*, at Geneva in 1955 (*Association, 1956*).

Next, however, comes the second question, which is much more serious: to what extent can we establish co-ordinations, not only between our concepts of stages, but also between our stages themselves? This leads to a still more fundamental problem: do *general* stages exist, i.e. stages including at the same time, for a given level, the totality of the organic, mental and social aspects of development? I would like to submit to the Study Group the following hypotheses, which seem to be the most cautious expression of the degree of synthesis which we may hope to attain.

1. There are no general stages. Just as, in connexion with physical growth, Tanner showed us that there was an absence of close relationship between the skeletal age, the dental age, etc., similarly, in the various neurological, mental and social fields, we see an intermingling

14

of processes of development which are evidently interrelated, but to different extents or according to multiple temporal rhythms, there being no reason why these processes should constitute a unique structural whole at each level.

2. The unity of the 'personality' is a functional unity, i.e. a unity which is in search of itself and builds itself step by step, but for which it has never been possible to give an adequate and verifiable structural expression; consequently we cannot take such a concept, which conceals an indefinite number of interacting biological, mental and social factors, as a starting point for postulating the existence of general stages.

3. On the other hand, to the extent that the unity of the body and the personality is built up by successive equilibrium levels and through an innumerable series of disequilibria and re-equilibria, it is possible, by following the various developmental series which each of us is studying, to establish groups of *particular* convergences all the more instructive in that they will be better delimited and more advanced in their detailed analysis.

4. It is not only in the correspondence of the stages, or perhaps not even in such correspondence, that one can hope to find the convergences sought for. It is, perhaps, rather in the mechanism of the transition from one stage to the following, i.e. in certain characteristic processes of the actual mechanism of development.

III. THE PROBLEM OF THE TRANSITION FROM ONE STAGE TO THE FOLLOWING: THE MECHANISM OF DEVELOPMENT

In this part we shall proceed by discussing a few examples:

1. *The construction of the sensorimotor object and 'objectal' relations*

As I showed long ago, the infant begins by not believing in the permanence of objects when they leave his field of perception. He does not look for a toy which he was going to grasp when it is covered with a cloth. When, at feeding time, I hide his feeding bottle behind my arm a few centimetres from his hand, he screams (even at seven months) instead of trying to grasp it or instead of trying to see it behind my arm, by bending slightly forward (whereas he immediately grasps it if an end of the object still remains visible). Towards the end of the first year, on the other hand, he looks for objects which have disappeared and finds them in accordance with their successive displacements (Piaget, 1950).

In the field of psychoanalysis (with which our researches have had no direct connexion) Freud described how the infant, at first interested only in his bodily functions, ends by objectivizing his

15

affectivity on persons, and Spitz has devoted a recent series of studies to these 'objectal' affective relations.

In such cases it can be seen straight away how we are faced with the question of the correspondence of stages. At almost the same ages and in both fields one witnesses a parallel transition from an initial state of centration on the subject's own activities (reality is reduced to a dependence on perceptual pictures as related to the momentary actions of the subject) to a final state of decentration wherein the subject becomes conscious of his subjectivity, 'places himself' with respect to a world of external objects and persons. The problems are, then, to know whether one will come across the same intermediate stages at the same ages, or whether the affective stages precede the cognitive stages, or vice versa. On this will be based hypotheses on the interaction, or rather the indissociable complementarity, of the affective and the cognitive, or on the primitive and causal character of one of these two factors with respect to the other. I personally believe in the indissociable complementarity of the cognitive structuration and the affective energy principle, but this is a personal opinion only.

A still more interesting problem is that of the mechanism of the transition from one stage to another (even if the two series of stages do not exactly correspond) for this is a fine example of those general problems of strategy and equilibrium which were discussed in Part I.

A. From the *cognitive viewpoint* the problem is to explain by what strategy a baby, who begins by reducing everything to itself, and by not comprehending the existence of changes outside its own actions, eventually succeeds in objectivizing these changes and attributing them to causal sources independent of itself. It is clear that this discovery is not innate since it results from a long construction. Neither is it due to the teaching of experience alone, since experience itself, which cannot even contradict a radical solipsism, is quite inadequate to correct this kind of egocentric perspective linked to the absence of consciousness of the self which characterizes the initial actions of the baby. This discovery is due to a decentration or inversion of the sense of cognitive perspective, i.e. to a new structuration or to a general equilibration of the spatial, temporal and causal relationships involved, and not to an acquisition based solely on experience. In fact, this equilibration is produced fairly clearly by a combined mechanism of least action and sequential probability:

(*a*) In the first place, the strategies of the infant may be classified in accordance with an order which is simultaneously chronological and of increasing complexity: (i) the infant localizes the object only in its perceptual field without paying attention to its movements or to

16

its localization at the moment it disappears; (ii) the infant begins to look for it after its disappearance, but in relation solely to previously successful actions (consisting in finding it in a given place) and not in relation to the successive displacement (although visible) of the object itself; (iii) the infant looks for it in relation to visible and successive displacements, co-ordinating the latter according to a group structure, etc. (The next step consists of an extension to certain invisible displacements.)

(*b*) It is next found that these strategies are more and more costly to construct but give more and more remunerative results: to be concerned only with perceptual localizations is very simple, consequently costs little, but is profitless, since the object which had disappeared becomes non-existent and is no longer to be located; to localize in relation to previous successful actions is already more costly, since this calls for more complex co-ordinations, but the result is a little more fruitful, although not always. To localize in relation to a 'group of displacements' is much more costly, since this consists in *adding* to the direct perceptual experience new relationships of a temporal nature, spatial references, etc., but the result is much more remunerative, since it makes it possible to foresee the successive positions of moving objects according to a system of localizations and reversible displacements.

(*c*) Consequently, equilibrium is attained when reality is understood in relation to a system of *minimum* changes (a system of displacements instead of the initial system of continual creations and annihilations) but supplying the *maximum* information (on utilizable objective relationships).

(*d*) From the viewpoint of strategies, equilibrium is consequently attained with the strategy furnishing the *maximum* of 'gains minus losses', which was the most costly to construct but which has become the simplest to apply (=*minimum* losses) and which gives the *maximum* results.

(*e*) From the viewpoint of probabilities, one may consider each new strategy as being the most probable, once the results of the preceding one have been obtained (and once the inadequacy and indeterminateness of the information to which it led has been observed). The final equilibrium is consequently not the most probable product *a priori* (at the outset), but is the end result of a series of reorganizations, each of which is the most probable one after observation of the failure of the preceding ones (a series of feedbacks finally culminating in stable equilibrium).

B. *From the affective viewpoint* we believe, despite the surprising and paradoxical nature of this opinion, that the procedure followed is not very different! In short, it is not entirely unreasonable to believe

17

that the fact of maintaining 'objectal' relations with the persons about him is, for the infant, a much more costly strategy, although much more remunerative in affective values of all kinds, than to be content with merely giving play to his sucking reflexes or even his sphincters. What is required is once more to analyse, in terms of *minimum* and of sequential probability, the successive strategies leading from one of these extremes to the other.

We should note, however, that an explanation in terms of profit and loss of the phases of affective development does not signify that the subject (the infant) has himself made a calculation of his interests in each situation lived through. This calculation is made solely in the sense that the fact of experiencing positive or negative *values* (an affect consists essentially in attaching value to a given action) amounts precisely to enriching or impoverishing oneself, from the viewpoint of functional exchanges with surrounding persons. P. Janet has already reduced the elementary feelings (joy and sadness, effort and fatigue, etc.) to the rules of an internal economy of action. This point can be extended to form a theory of values considered as the external economy of the action, and to deduce from it a theory of affective equilibration. From this point of view, the achievement of objectal relationships as enrichment, but also as a more costly strategy, probably marks the arrival at a certain level of equilibrium, which is, however, at the same time a point of departure for numerous and profound disequilibria.

2. The problem of affective schemata (*in particular of the superego*) and of representative and operational schemata

A series of convergences between the work of Bowlby and that of the Jean-Jacques Rousseau Institute at Geneva seemed possible during our last meeting and I should like to indicate in a few words how the second example could be developed.

Despite the absence of all direct relationship between our work and psychoanalysis, there exists a certain similarity in the way in which we pose our problems. This common point of departure consists in accepting that all feelings and knowledge have a history and consequently in considering that no external influence represents an entirely new beginning, but is always *assimilated* to all that has gone before, and may modify the subsequent course of the history by giving it an impulse in a partly new direction. The problem then is to understand how this assimilation takes place and in what form the organization of the old and new factors exists.

To this problem, Freud replied that, in the affective field, we retain in our subconscious all our experiences of the past, particularly infantile or early conflicts, and that our subsequent affective life always consists, to some extent, in the identification of new situations with previous ones, by a kind of fixation of initial images and complexes.

The history of the individual development of knowledge, on the other hand, gives a rather different picture. In general it is not the memories as such of things we know which are retained but rather schemata of actions or operations derived one from the other. These have a constant adaptation to the present and a structuration which is continuous (or in steps), orientated in the direction of equilibration.

However, during a very instructive discussion on the search for common mechanisms of development, Bowlby seemed to admit, if I am not mistaken, that the history of affective schemata and of conflicts was not so far distant from such continuous structuration. He appeared to feel that there is dynamic assimilation rather than strict identification, and that such assimilation proceeds by analogies and transfers and not by any exclusive fixation, in the course of adapting a perpetual reconstruction of the past to the present in various conflictual or equilibrated ways.

The problem of choosing between these two interpretations arises notably in regard to the superego. This may be conceived of either as a simple fixation on past images and imperatives or else as a group of schemata of affective reactions presenting the same factor of continuity in the presence of each new situation but with a progressive flexibility of accommodation in regard to the particular data presented.

It is clear that this problem lies at the root of the question of convergences or of divergences between the affective and cognitive forms of equilibration. One must be very careful, of course, in using a term such as 'equilibrium' which is too convenient and so often merely verbal or literary. The strict rule should be followed of using it only in situations where one has objective criteria such as the indices of *minimum* (including the minimax) or of fairly convincing probability schemata. However, it seems impossible to express affective conflict situations in this way, and especially, the various modes of solution of the conflicts, without in the end adopting a rather precise terminology using the language of equilibrium. Even in a conflictual situation where one is losing all round, as in the case of an individual whose superego prevents all adaptation and whose liberation from his superego would represent, moreover, a definite privation, one might still ask whether such an individual would not finish by choosing, out of all these possible losses, the solution consisting in minimizing the *maximum* loss inflicted on him by his history and environment; and, this would constitute a point of equilibrium according to the minimax strategy.

Consequently we feel that a discussion on these basic problems would lead to appreciable progress in our projects of synthesis in the interpretation of development, according to whether there is a possible convergence or a necessary divergence between the processes of the history of affects and those of the history of intellectual operations and representations.

3. *The forms of social interaction and the development of the child*

Let us agree to distinguish in social life between molar phenomena (general form of society and transmission of community culture from one generation to the next) and molecular phenomena (interaction between individuals on various levels). It is evident that there are all kinds of transitions between the molar and the molecular and that the general molar forms influence to a high degree the molecular interactions. However, this very fact makes it all the more interesting to consider whether among the modes of molecular interactions there exist certain tendencies towards equilibrium and, if so, what their relationships to mental development may be.

In European societies such as the one in which we live, it is very interesting to follow up step by step the spontaneous forms of collaboration between children in well-defined situations, such as a constructional game, which can remain individual with various imitations, or become collective to different degrees. Mlle Inhelder, who has recently made such studies, with the collaboration of G. Noelting, will be able to give us more details; for the time being I will simply point out the fact that there is a remarkable convergence between the stages of this social collaboration and that of the formation of intellectual operations, to such a point that one has the impression that there are here two complementary and inseparable aspects of the same process of equilibration.

To cite only one example: the social relation of reciprocity, which gradually imposes itself as a form of equilibrium between individuals considering themselves as equals, assuredly corresponds to the logical and operational transformation of reciprocity which dominates the logic of symmetrical relationships (a=b therefore b=a) and certain equations in the logic of propositions ($p \supset q = \bar{q} \supset \bar{p}$ and $\bar{p} \supset \bar{q} = q \supset p$). Developmentally speaking the progressive organization of inter-individual reciprocities and that of operational reciprocities in the field of thought certainly constitutes two correlated phenomena, without mentioning moral reciprocity which is of importance in the organization of normative values and which is, in the opinion of all authors, simultaneously social and relative to 'practical thought'.

This being so, a clearly circumscribed problem of possible synthesis between the researches of cultural anthropology and those of child psychology would consist in determining up to what point a molecular tendency to reciprocity is found, considered as a most probable form of equilibrium between equal individuals, ensuring the *maximum* of performance compatible with the *minimum* of change, and this whatever the molar form of the situations in question. Margaret Mead has described social situations in which a baby sucks anything except his thumb, others in which he does not smile because he passes his existence on his mother's back, without seeing her face, etc. But are there societies without any reciprocity? Sociologists have described primitive forms of exchange, finding them in gifts or presents which sooner or later give rise to reciprocal reactions. These are institutional reciprocities which have become molar. What are the transitions between these molar reciprocities and the many possible forms of molecular reciprocity?

4. *Perceptual activities, intellectual operations, and the EEG*

My role in drawing up this draft for discussions directed towards the synthesis of our results is certainly not to appear to have an extensive competence in all our fields of study, but on the contrary to provoke the reactions of each specialist by simply imagining problems of general interest capable of linking together the fields which he knows and those with which he is not familiar. In other words, Part III of this paper, devoted to problems of the mechanism of development, brings us quite naturally to Part IV, devoted merely to a listing of the problems to be discussed, as the author leaves his own field further and further behind and approaches what for him appear merely to be 'promised lands'.

This is the spirit in which I would like to conclude Part III, by describing with some degree of naïvety what I would expect from a theory of the change in the EEG with age if I wanted it to link up with the problems of equilibrium which seem to me most general and most 'synthesizing' in relation to the mechanism of development.

On considering in their most general form the equilibrium of patterns of behaviour (it being understood that the affective factors corresponding to the energy principle of such forms of behaviour and the cognitive factors corresponding to their structure are always complementary and indissociable) I would say that such forms of equilibrium comprise three types:

1. A progressive extension of the field of equilibrium, i.e. of the objects to which the forms of behaviour apply. This extension of the field may be expressed in terms of the 'probability of encounter'. We have endeavoured to give a very simple mathematical model of this probabilistic mechanism in the case of perceptual centrations and in the explanation of elementary perceptual illusions, but the process of 'probabilities of encounters' may be generalized on all

levels, on the understanding that 'encounters' on the higher levels may themselves be functions of a continually more complex schema dependent on the mechanisms which follow.

2. An increasing mobility of the equilibrium, since the equilibrium of behaviours is an equilibrium between actions and movement; actions may be described in their most general form as a system of 'couplings' between the elements 'encountered'. Here again one can assign a probabilistic form to the couplings in order to take account of their complete or incomplete character with respect to a given field of extension. This form is very simple when the couplings are independent (one can interpret in this way the well-known Weber's law for example), but more complex in the case of sequential probabilities, as in successive strategies applied to the solution of one and the same problem (such as the problems of conservation or of construction of the permanent object, examples of which we have given above).

3. An increasing stability of the equilibrium (which does not contradict its mobile character). This will tend to the *minimum* characteristic and to exact compensation (reversibility) of the virtual transformations involved in the system, these transformations being on a higher level than that of the couplings, and consisting in co-ordinating the couplings in various ways.

If we examine by means of such schema, but in full consciousness of our ignorance, present EEG data on the development of the child, we cannot but be struck by certain analogies, which may be superficial or profound. First of all, it is evident that in passing from the slow waves, which are the earliest ones, to the rapid waves, which do not become general until 10 or 11 years of age (at the commencement of the level which we characterize by 'formal operations') we see an advance in mobility; it is, however, correlated with and not contradictory to an advance towards stability and regularity. On the other hand, if we agree with Grey Walter that the alpha rhythm is the manifestation of an exploratory or scanning activity, corresponding to the principle of what we call 'encounters' and giving rise to 'couplings', the progressive extension of the field of this activity from the visual occipital regions towards the temporal and frontal regions is very striking. If one first considers the level of visual perception: we have been able to establish at the Institute, on the basis of the probabilistic schema of encounters and couplings, using over-estimations (and consequently the correlated under-estimations) of lengths, that the lengths perceived are a function of the centration of vision. It is suggestive to compare these facts with the results observed by Grey Walter on the manner in which a perceptual excitation extends further and further into the brain and quickly goes beyond the frontiers of the visual cortex to reach the motor regions and beyond; this irradiation may thus be related to the opening of pathways by centration. It is very interesting, on the other hand, to note that if, in behaviour, the perceptive couplings are gradually supplemented by representative couplings, bringing about between 12 and 15 years of age a combinatory system proper (commencement of formal operations), we see a correlated extension of the alpha rhythm to regions of the brain which are increasingly more extensive and closer to the paths of association.

In short, even if these attempts to establish two corresponding series of stages for intellectual operations and for the EEGs have so far failed (which may be due, moreover, to the inadequacy of the means of detection used for the latter) nevertheless one may hope to establish more general convergences between the dimensions of the organization of the rhythms and those of the equilibration by successive steps of cognitive links, ranging from perceptual couplings to the combination characterizing formal operations. It would, moreover, be surprising if it were otherwise. For although the EEGs do not of course represent the expression of operations proper, they seem to translate attitudes arising in the cerebral activities of the subject, attitudes ranging from mere watchfulness to active exploration, and becoming differentiated in the field of such exploration into a multiplicity of forms as varied as those seen in observing behaviour. Indeed, if it is legitimate to bring together all types of exploration into a single general schema of encounters, couplings and transformations (or couplings raised to the second power), then one can count on refinements in the analyses of the multiple varieties of alpha waves leading sooner or later to a picture corresponding in broad outline to that of the different types of behaviour.

IV. QUESTIONS TO MY COLLEAGUES IN THE STUDY GROUP

The preceding pages (Parts I, II, III) represent an attempt to propound, in a common language, a certain number of common problems, discussion of which could serve as a synthesis for our work on development. Of course, each of us remains free to declare that the problems are ill-chosen and that their discussion will lead to nothing, but showing why they are ill-chosen or will lead to nothing would itself bring about a synthesis.

However, it may be useful in concluding this essay to put a few questions personally to members of the group in the hope of systematic replies. I shall not put such questions to Inhelder or to Zazzo, who are too close to the way of thinking embodied in the essay, and I shall consider Melin, Monnier and Rémond as sharing in the questions put to Grey Walter.

I. Questions to Lorenz

1. Static apriorism is only an over-simple preformism, which Lorenz rightly rejects and replaces by a 'dynamic apriorism'. However, is there not a risk that the latter will bring us back indirectly to vitalism, i.e. to the convenient theory that 'life' can always arrange everything? Is not the only way of escaping from vitalism, if one is not an empiricist, to have recourse to probabilistic equilibration processes?

2. Lorenz has shown us (Vol. I, p. 197) various compromises between the IRM and learning and above all he has shown us (Vol. II, p. 264) that a characteristic may be innate in the case of one species and based on individual learning in another. Does not this show that the appearance of this characteristic is necessary as part of a certain functional process of equilibration which is more general than the innate or the acquired? This appears to me to be the case, for example, in behaviour entailing search for an object which has disappeared, behaviour which is acquired in the baby (see above III 1 A), but is innate in many animals (digging instinct, etc.).

3. 'Logical necessity does not exist *per se* but corresponds to laws of the nervous system' (Vol. II, p. 264). I agree if these are laws of equilibration such as the law of 'all or nothing' in which has been seen the starting point of binary arithmetic (one or zero), which is isomorphous with Boolian algebra, and consequently with logic. But otherwise we fall back into preformist apriorism.

4. Are there objective criteria for distinction between compromise solutions and more stable equilibrations in cases of conflicting activities (Vol. I, p. 198)?

II. Bowlby

1. Are there at present any psychoanalytical attempts to explain the *transition* from one stage to the next? Has Bowlby himself considered how to solve this problem? Would he agree with the hypothesis that the reactions pertaining to a stage *n* are set off by dissatisfactions, conflicts or disequilibria pertaining to the preceding stage *n*–1, which hypothesis would favour the interpretation of such transitions on the basis of an equilibration process?

2. What in particular is his attitude to the 'latency' stage? Can one interpret it in terms of equilibrium or is it only the manifestation of a phase of maturation?

3. Does Bowlby agree that all behaviour is *always* simultaneously affective and cognitive, in accordance with two inseparable but distinct aspects, one of which constitutes the *energy component* of this behaviour (affective aspect) and the other the *structure* of the same behaviour (cognitive aspect)? Would he agree in drawing the

24

conclusion that an affect is never the cause of a cognition, nor the reverse, since both are built up together in an indissociable manner (for example, the cognitive 'permanent object' and the affective 'objectal relation')?

Odier, who dealt with this problem, accepts in all cases the priority and the causal action of the affective on the cognitive which seems to me to complicate matters without yielding any advantage. On the other hand, no one supports the view that the cognitive is the cause of the affective.

III. *Margaret Mead*

1. Everything varies from one society to another, in particular the systems of numeration and the circumstances under which one learns to count. But why is it generally accepted that $1+1=2$ or $2+2=4$? This is not innate. It is not learned from experience, since two objects are not equivalent to 'two' unless they are counted (=activity of the subject). Is it 'social' as thought by Durkheim? But he was then obliged to suggest that 'under all civilizations lies *the* civilization' and consequently to postulate a certain common functioning which seems to me characteristic of the laws of equilibrium (which apply equally well to operations between individuals and to the operations of the individual himself). Does Margaret Mead accept the possibility of arriving, thanks to the mechanisms of equilibration, at such common elements despite the diversity of the cultural points of departure?

2. When an individual is transplanted from one civilization to another or subjected to a new *training*, can any similarity be perceived between the order of things learned during this kind of 'Aktualgenese' and the developmental order observed in the growth of the child as studied among us? Example: the acquisition of the operations of measurement?

IV. *Grey Walter*

1. Grey distinguished between six possible forms of psychobiological development: (1) evolution (mutation, etc.), (2) tropisms, etc., (3) instincts (IRMs, etc.), (4) learning by repetition, (5) learning by association, (6) social communication (Vol. II, p. 21). I feel that the construction of logical relationships by the child aged 7-8 years (for example, the previously unrecognized relationship: $A=B$, $B=C$, therefore $A=C$, which presupposes the retention of A, B and C during the process of reasoning) does not enter into any of these six forms, and that we must accept a further category (7) *learning by successive equilibrations* (individual, or social in the

sense of inter-individual). The examples of cognitive equilibration mentioned in this paper all come within this category (7) and cannot be explained by categories (1)-(6). I should be glad to have the agreement or objections of Grey Walter on this point, since I was not able to make myself understood in London in this connexion (Vol. II, pp. 58-60), when I stressed the fact that, in this kind of learning, knowledge is not drawn from objects but from co-ordinations between the actions of the subject. Consequently, it was my fault that Grey Walter did not reply precisely to my question (Vol. II, p. 60). However, if one is to hope for convergences between the development of the EEG and the evolution of intellectual operations, it is fundamental to know whether such learning by equilibration (of which the finest mechano-physiological model is Ashby's homeostat) reduces to the six forms of Grey Walter or not.

2. The most important critical age for our cognitive stages is, on the average, 7 years. Now Grey Walter has shown (Vol. II, p. 71) that 'elaboration' appeared in the EEG only towards 6-7 years. Could not this 'elaboration', of which there is no trace before 3-4 years, which increases from 4 to 6-7 years and takes on a more general and more stable form from 6-7 years of age, be related to the type of structuration to which we have just drawn attention?

3. Generally speaking, is the inadequate correspondence observed so far between the EEG and the cognitive structures, thought by Grey Walter to be due to gaps in recording, due to the nature of the EEG, or might it not also be due in part to the inadequate theoretical development of possible common mechanisms (I have in mind the development still called for in connexion with a theory of equilibration)?

V. *Tanner*

1. In the absence of stages of growth, Tanner recognizes the existence of 'phases of acceleration'. Could these be characterized by the causal mechanism of this acceleration, for example, by a more or less regular interaction between the nervous and endocrine mechanisms, or should one restrict oneself to observing this acceleration as such?

This question is indirectly related to the one which seems to me the most important of the general problems: the mechanism of the transition from one stage to another, the mechanism of continuous transformations.

2. What outstanding transformations in the nervous system might it be possible to relate to the levels of $1\frac{1}{2}$-2 years (beginning of language and of symbolic function in general), of 7-8 years (beginning of

complete operations) and 11-12 years (beginning of formal operations, linked with the functioning of the frontal lobes)?

3. Organic embryogeny (which is continued in physical growth) has often been thought of as directed towards the form of equilibrium which constitutes the adult state of the corresponding species. Could one at the present time say something positive regarding the criteria of this equilibrium (*minimum* and compensated virtual transformations), its mechanism (regulations) and above all, the mechanism of the successive equilibration phases (other than the final stage), which might be compared with analogous problems in other sectors of development?

VI. *General questions (for all)*

Discussion of this attempted synthesis cannot be fruitful unless each of us, in his own field, supplies a few well-defined and well-analysed facts relevant to the passage from one stage to the following or to some particular continuous transformation occurring in the course of development. It is by comparing such facts that we shall be able to decide whether it is reasonable or whether it is definitely premature to attempt to characterize certain *general* mechanisms of development. I am almost certain that the equilibration mechanisms explain the development of the logico-mathematical operational structures, because these structures are themselves nothing more than the equilibrium forms peculiar to the intellectual operations. But only a general discussion would show whether we have here a possibility for a general or only for a particular explanation.

KONRAD LORENZ

Comments on Professor Piaget's Paper

I think it advisable to answer Professor Piaget's questions to myself first, and then to proceed to what I have to say on the conceptions of 'development' and of 'stages' as well as on the urgent necessity of a 'common language'.

1. Professor Piaget's first question to me was whether there is not a danger of vitalism surreptitiously introduced by my attitude to the 'prioric' forms of thought and categories. He calls this attitude 'dynamic apriorism'—and I think that this term is entirely misleading: I am profoundly thankful that it is so, because any sort of apriorism, however dynamic, would indeed lead to the danger Professor Piaget fears. I am quite convinced that things that conform to Kant's definition of the *a priori*—e.g. things that exist in our mind before any experience and which must be there in order to make experience possible—are not things that exist in the absolute. Nothing is really there *a priori*. All the forms and functions of our mental processes that really exist independently of experience are related to the form and function of our central nervous system and have developed in phylogeny just as have the form and function of any of our other bodily organs. All structures and functions have attained their present form in an age-long interaction between the organism and its environment. Nothing whatsoever is preformed, unless it be the basic properties of the smallest known physical units. Nobody in the world is less of a preformationist than the phylogeneticist. If I may widen the concept of the empiric so far that it includes not only what the individual derives from personal experience, but everything that the species gains out of its interaction with outward reality, then I should definitely call the attitude assumed by ethologists towards the problem of the 'a priori' one of an extreme 'phyletic empiricism'.

2. The second question, if I understand Professor Piaget rightly, is whether a process of functional 'equilibration' is not much more general and primary than the function of innate releasing mechanisms and learned responses (see page 24). If I may substitute 'adaptive interaction' for 'equilibration', as I assume I may, the answer is

28

simply and emphatically yes. (I agree with Professor Bertalanffy's objection to the term equilibrium: see on page 94 below). There definitely are organisms which do not have any instinctive movements or innate relasing mechanisms and also are quite incapable of learning. All organisms are open systems and all of them live only by achieving a regulative equilibration between their inner processes and the requirements of their outer environment. The functions of innate releasing mechanisms and of learning are those only of very highly specialized organs that higher animals have developed under the pressure of natural selection in the service of that general regulative equilibration. The same applies to searching behaviour, to all cognitive functions, in short to all structures and functions which develop a survival value. I do not think that the term 'compromise' (p. 24) is very descriptive for the co-operation of the innate and the acquired. An organism can be 'constructed' in very different ways by all the factors affecting evolution, of which I still think natural selection to be the most effective. A grebe is 'so made' that it needs to learn very little in order to survive, having beautifully specialized innate responses and organs. But a raven needs a lot of learning and correspondingly is furnished with an inexhaustible source of exploratory behaviour: both 'constructions' are equally successful in surviving.

3. The third question concerns my statement that 'logical necessity does not exist *per se* but corresponds to laws of the nervous system'. Professor Piaget fears that the acceptance of existing 'laws' may lead back to preformist apriorism. It does not, though, because the 'laws' in question are by no means logical necessities. None of the biological 'laws' are. Mendel's 'laws' would be entirely different if the structure of chromosomes and the processes of fertilization were not exactly as they are, which might easily have happened if evolution had run a slightly different course. Exactly the same applies to all the 'laws' prevailing in the function of our brain.

4. The last question is whether there are any objective criteria for distinguishing, in cases of conflicting motivation, mere compromise solutions from more stable equilibrations. It is one that is occupying ethologists most seriously. Indeed, the distinction between a mere epiphenomenon and a function which serves 'equilibration', in other words one that develops a definite survival value, is, in many cases, of the utmost importance. It can, however, only be answered for each single case separately and only by a thorough experimental investigation.

I now come to the question of common language which is more or less identical with the problem of synthesis. I confess that I heard of general system theory for the first time when I read Professor Bertalanffy's comments (see page 69), so I know no more about it than what he said in his first three pages. My question to Professor Bertalanffy may therefore be quite beside the point: but is there not a certain danger that, in order to make different systems comparable and describable in the same 'language', we strip them of characters which seem to be non-essential frills from the point of view of theory, but which are highly characteristic and essential to the proper understanding of each of the systems separately?

On the other hand, the study and comparison of extremely different systems may reveal the surprising fact that they contain mechanisms that *are* directly comparable. Modern physiology of perception in particular and neurophysiology in general have discovered processes which are not only comparable, but essentially identical with those known to cybernetics. I entirely agree with what Bertalanffy says about the danger of using fashionable words in a loose way, but this is certainly not the case when Mittelstaedt or Von Holst use cybernetic terms in their studies of optokinetic movements or the function of the muscle spindles. Indeed, the processes investigated in these cases are classically simple examples of positive and negative feedback mechanisms, and it would be a great error and hindrance to mutual understanding not to use such terms.

Another example: at our last meeting I was trying to explain the controlled use of Gestalt perception in the study of animal behaviour (Vol. III, p. 122). I am afraid it took me a very long time to expound how very many repeated observations of the same process are necessary before our Gestalt perception at last succeeds in disentangling the essential lawfulness from the 'background' of inessential, accidental sensory data. Grey Walter was sitting beside me and, looking over his shoulder, I was slightly taken aback to see that he had compressed the whole symphony of what I had been trying to explain into one sentence. He had written: 'Redundancy of information makes up for noisiness of channel'.

This is an example of a *perfect* translation of the kind that general system theory should strive for. But we must keep in mind that this kind of mutual understanding is only possible wherever two independent investigations have reached a comparatively high degree of insight into the process investigated. Gestalt perception is a function dependent on a neural organization that is very much akin to a true computer and which consequently lends itself particularly well to a description in the terms of information theory.

In the majority of cases, however, our insight into what really happens in an organism is much too superficial to permit a translation that is similarly fundamental. We must never forget that the words we use are connected with conceptions of vastly different degrees of clarity. If I speak in the same breath of instinctive movements and of innate releasing mechanisms, I cannot help suggesting,

30

in a most insidious manner, that the conceptions symbolized by these two words are of approximately equal value. They are not. We can make, to say the very least, a pretty shrewd guess as to the physiological nature of instinctive movements, while we have but the haziest ideas concerning the physiological mechanisms underlying the function of an innate releasing mechanism. Therefore, what ethology calls instinctive movements can be described tolerably well in the terminology of Von Holst's studies on central co-ordination, while the conception of the innate releasing mechanism which is only functionally determined cannot be translated into anything at all until we know much more about it than we do at present.

Nevertheless, these hazily defined conceptions correspond to something real. I have much confidence in the ability of our Gestalt perception to pick natural units out of the immeasurable chaos of sensory data. If an observer like Piaget calls something 'affectivity', I rely blindly on the assumption that there is a natural unit corresponding to that term. But I find it very difficult to ascertain what exactly that unit is. All conceptions of this type are what Hassenstein has called 'injunctive'. *Injungere* means to enjoin. A number of characters are 'enjoined' in order to make a special case fit into the contents of the conception. A number of constituent properties go into the making of the conception, but none of them ever is 'constitutive': they constitute the conception only by a process of summation. A special case may lack one or even several of these properties, and yet not be excluded from the contents of the injunctive conception. Metabolism and reproduction are indubitably constituent characters of life, yet a cooled anthrax spore which has no metabolism, or an ox which cannot reproduce, are unquestionably alive. Symbolic speech is a constituent character of Man, yet a patient with total aphasia still is human, etc., etc. All injunctive conceptions merge, without any clear boundary-line, into neighbouring ones which have one or several part-constituent characters in common.

All the words which we coin to describe natural units, of whose existence we are told by our Gestalt perception, necessarily refer to injunctive conceptions exclusively. When we first say 'bow-wow', we do not ourselves know whether we mean this dog, any dog, any mammal, any four-legged animal or perhaps anything alive. It is quite difficult to find out what part-constituent properties one enjoins oneself, if one wants to place a special case under the heading of an injunctive conception. And it is still harder to know exactly what another man is enjoining when he uses the same term. Injunctive conceptions may not only vary as to the size of their contents, but their contents may overlap. The trouble is that real natural units may overlap. Take a zoological example. Every naïve person seeing a lamprey for the first time would say it is a fish. It has eyes, gills, a silvery surface, etc., just like any other fish: but it has no jaws. Anybody with an inkling of comparative anatomy would see in an instant that a shark, a frog and a man are more closely related to each other than all of them are to a lamprey. 'Fish', including the cyclostomes, are a natural unit, and 'fish', as a class of gnathostomes, excluding the lampreys, are also a natural unit. Which sort of unit is reported to a given man by his Gestalt perception, and what he consequently subsumes under an injunctive conception, depends on the man.

Consequently, you have to know that man and his whole way of thinking and observing just in order to know what he means when he uses one single word. And the more of an observational genius the man is, in other words, the more unexpected natural units his Gestalt perception makes visible to him, the more difficult we shall find it to get hold of the part-constituent characters that make up his injunctive conceptions. Indeed he will find it so himself! I am sure that Professor Piaget will take it as the compliment which is meant when I say that he is a *very* difficult man to understand—in the respect just discussed! I do *not* know what he means, for example, by the word 'affectivity'. John Bowlby, in his comments, has attempted to translate it into ethologese, defining the conception exactly as I would, but I do not expect Professor Piaget to feel himself very deeply understood.

On the whole I think that we have done marvellously well in learning to understand each other. A good symptom of this is if one finds oneself adopting another person's concepts—not the word, mind, but the concept. Speaking for myself, I have done that extensively. The conception of the case-history, which formerly did not play any role at all in our daily work, now looms very large indeed. Conversely, I find some of our study group, particularly Bowlby, using ethological terms naturally and correctly.

Correct mutual understanding, in other words, exact coincidence of conceptual contents correlated to the words used, is, of course, the primary condition without whose fulfilment there is no hope for a real synthesis of several people's work.

Synthesis of several people's work is nowhere more necessary than in the study of development. This term is, of course, again correlated to an injunctive conception of immense complication. But in the case of words used in common parlance it is, on principle, not necessary to go into a detailed conceptual analysis in order to achieve mutual understanding. We are, I think, all agreed upon what development is and I may start what I have to say about the synthesis of our work by quoting Goethe's old definition: 'development is differentiation and subordination of parts'. The two hemispheres of a globular, blastula- or volvox-like creature divide the functions of

32

nutrition and defence between themselves, each of them specializing for one of these tasks and consequently becoming as different from the other as ectoderm and endoderm are. By the same act, they become more 'subordinated' to the whole system, as they become dependent on each other, each being incapable of fending for itself. This clearest and most primitive division of labour that ever took place in a metazoan ought to furnish a good example of what 'development' is like and how it ought to be approached in theory. The change of each part has a counterpart in the change of all the others. 'Differentiation' always means 'becoming different' and the question 'different in relation to what?' ought always to be in our minds. In the case of the literal and spatial differentiation of the blastula this question is easy to answer, and it is still answerable in the early stages of embryonic development in which a comparatively small number of tissues have become different from each other so that it is still possible to keep track of the interactions of their functions. Physiologists of development have done amazingly well at these particular tasks. We, of this study group, ought to take the work of experimental embryology as a model, if only to make ourselves realize how immensely difficult our problems are. Bowlby has already proposed a view of psycho-physiological development which makes use not only of Goldschmidt's principle of harmonized reaction velocities (page 36 in his comments see on); he has also, without explicitly saying so, introduced another indispensable concept of experimental embryology, that of 'regulative' and 'mosaic' interaction between the developing parts. Luckily for the analytic biologists, organisms are not 'wholes' in the sense that 'everything' is in a regulative interaction with everything else: there are some few relatively autonomous structures which influence the rest of the system far more than they are influenced by it in return. These are the Archimedean points on which to base investigation. These comparatively invariable and autonomous elements are necessarily more often causes than they are effects in the immensely complicated network of interactions taking place in development. For the same reasons for which investigation and didactic representation of the whole organism invariably start from its skeleton, we ought to try first to get hold of the most autonomous and independent processes of structural and functional development.

Another reason for doing this is that the harmonization of reaction velocities is most liable to go wrong or to fail in regard to these relatively autonomous processes. I think that Kretschmer is entirely right in attributing a large number of psychological disturbances to the disharmonization of the velocities with which a number of structures and/or functions develop in an individual. In the greylag goose, that invaluably simplified 'model', we found that practically all disturbances of sexual function are due to disharmonization of developmental velocities in relatively autonomous activities. Oedipus behaviour arises in exactly the way Kretschmer supposes and male homosexual pairs are formed when a certain stage of courtship activities is 'skipped' because of environmental conditions which prevail in a state of semi-captivity but which may also, often enough, occur in the wild. Helga Fischer has recently found a highly interesting mechanism by which these homosexual pairs are broken up later on and the partners brought back to 'normal'.

Even in geese we find it quite unfeasible to describe 'stages' in the development of behaviour *as a whole*. Well defined 'stages', however, are found in the development of single, relatively autonomous activities and well defined types of disturbances can be correlated to the temporal lack of coincidence of stages, particularly in individuals with a certain amount of domestic inheritance. But also in pure-blooded wild birds the variation of developmental velocities in different activities is so enormous that it would need a very forced and artificial abstraction of a type termed 'normal' to make it possible to speak of 'stages' in the development of the whole organism. I confess that I have very strong doubts whether the variability of developmental velocities in the child is any less than it is in the wild goose and I therefore emphatically agree with the objections to the typification of 'stages' in the development in humans. I have no doubt that very real 'types' of personalities can be explained on the basis of coincidence and non-coincidence of stages in the development of relatively independent structures and/or functions.

The 'moral' of all this is perhaps a platitude: each of us ought to be constantly conscious of the fact that he is only investigating the development of a very small part-structure and/or function. Each of us ought to be looking constantly for lawful coincidences and non-coincidences between the 'stages' in the developmental processes he investigates and those that some one else is studying. Each of us ought to be searching constantly for lawful and harmonizing inter-actions between the processes he himself is working on and the most unexpected and far-fetched developments in other parts of the organism, even if the latter do not interest him in the least. But we ought not to postulate *a priori* that any particular interaction exists. We know there are highly independent mosaic parts and whether or not they interact, and if they do, to what extent, are problems that must be investigated singly for every single case.

Comments on Professor Piaget's Paper

Introduction

Piaget has raised some very fundamental problems and in attempting to answer the questions he has put to me I have found it necessary to give some indication of my own position with regard to them. This I do with some diffidence, partly because of the difficulty of the issues raised and partly because I am often unsure how adequately I have comprehended Piaget's ideas. In preparing the following comments I have been much helped by three research colleagues: Peter Hildebrand, whose knowledge of Piaget's writings is far greater than my own, Anthony Ambrose and Robert Hinde.

Though I find myself in close agreement with the early passages of Section 1 of Piaget's paper, I find difficulty over his concept of affectivity and I expect to find much more autonomy in the development of different structures and their related activities[1] than Piaget seems to expect. However, before commenting on this I think it would be best for me to deal with the problems of stages of development since this is where ideas derived from psychoanalysis are much concerned.

Problem of stages of development

In discussing this topic I want to bring out rather fully a distinction which is clearly present in Piaget's discussion through not always very explicit. I do so because I think there is always a danger of confusion arising if we do not clearly distinguish:
(*a*) phases in the development of the whole organism,
(*b*) phases in the development of particular structures and activities of the organism.

Some of the most dramatic examples of phases in the development of the whole organism are apparent in insect life, e.g. larva, chrysalis,

---

[1] To describe the growth of any particular part of the organism, I am referring to the part as a 'structure and its related activity' to make it plain that structure and activity are indissolubly linked. To avoid clumsiness in the text I have often contracted it to 'structure and activity' or even to 'activity'.

imago. In mammals one can easily discern the intra-uterine and extra-uterine phases, but when one tries to find substages within the extra-uterine this type of classification quickly breaks down. The second concept—phases in the development of particular structures and activities—seems to me far more valuable than the first.

In the field of physiological structure and activity, development, though in some respects gradual, often proceeds in steps, e.g. when the foetal heart begins to beat or when the child starts to walk. Tanner has emphasized, if I understand him aright, that in the physiological field different structures and activities often develop at different rates and that a major step in development in one area may not be contemporaneous or even in any obvious way co-ordinated with one in another area. Perhaps a partial exception to this in mammals is birth, where several activities change in character simultaneously, though even here I imagine those which change constitute only a small minority of all the activities operating. Thus in physical growth the picture appears to be one of a multiplicity of developing activities each progressing at its own pace and passing through major phases which may not be closely co-ordinated with the phases passed through by other activities. As a result it is not possible when we consider the organism as a whole to discern overall stages of physical growth.

It is my impression that exactly the same picture will be found in the development of psychological structures and activities. Piaget clearly postulates multiple psychological activities; I am not clear how many he expects to find but I have the impression it may be only a few. My own expectation is that we shall identify very many. Furthermore, whereas Piaget seems to expect to find fairly close parallelism and interconnexion in their developments, I do not. In so far as development in any one area is influenced by the total field of forces in which it is occurring there must be interconnexion, but I expect it to be complex in its manifestations with each structure and activity developing at its own pace.

It seems to me that the view that psychological development is the product of the relatively autonomous development of a fairly large number of different structures and activities agrees with clinical experience of the ordinary child: the development of each child is extraordinarily uneven in respect of different activities and every child differs from every other in the order in which they develop. This is a view of psychological development which makes use of Goldschmidt's principle, derived from embryology, of harmonized reaction velocities; this principle he advanced to account for physiological development and the differences in its outcome displayed in the mature form reached by each individual organism. Just as, according to Goldschmidt, differential variations in the velocity of

36

development of different structures and activities account for differences in the mature physical form of organisms even as far as the differences between the sexes of one species, so would I expect variations in the velocity of development of different psychological activities to account for differences in the psychic form or personality of individuals, including differences which tend to be characteristic of the two sexes. In other words I am pinning much hope to the systematic application of Goldschmidt's theory to psychological development.

Let us now turn to the various theories of stages of development which have been advanced in regard to children. Wallon's stages seem to be concerned with the organism as a whole and are therefore in my view of limited use. The stages described by Inhelder and Piaget are concerned exclusively with cognitive structure and activity, where they appear to be of the greatest value. As indicated earlier, however, I do not share Piaget's hope that they will be found to run closely parallel to the development of other activities. Finally, there is Freud's formulation of the theory of libidinal phases.

Stages in the organization of the libido

First, it seems plain that in advancing his hypothesis Freud is referring to the development of a particular function, namely the sexual. Any attempt to extend these stages to characterize the whole of the psychological development of the child would seem to be wholly mistaken.

However, with Piaget, I think Freud's libidinal phases differ materially in their nature from the cognitive phases of Inhelder and Piaget. The latter are characterized by true steps, namely the condition of progress from one phase to another is that the prior phase is a necessary precondition for the emergence of the subsequent one. At the most Freud's libidinal phases are, as Piaget points out, only phases with dominant characters. Freud (1949a) himself remarks: 'It would be a mistake to suppose that these three phases succeed one another in a clear-cut fashion: one of them may appear in addition to another, they may overlap one another, they may be present simultaneously'. Such an assessment seems to me to rob the notion of libidinal stages of most of its usefulness. It happens that in contrast to many psychoanalysts, I have never found the concept of libidinal stages useful and I regard the elaboration of hypotheses which seek to relate particular psychiatric syndromes to particular libidinal phases as mistaken. For all these reasons I recommend we do not spend too much time on them.

It happens, however, that mixed up with Freud's concept of libidinal phases there is what in my opinion is a far more valuable idea; this is his notion of 'individual component instincts' which are at first 'disconnected and independent of one another' but which later 'under the primacy of a single erotogenic zone, form a firm organization directed towards a sexual aim attached to some extraneous sexual object' (Freud, 1949b). The theme here is that the sexual responses of the mature adult are to be seen as the result of a special synthesis of a number of component behaviour patterns, some of which first make their appearance in infancy and early childhood. Freud's further point is, of course, that sexual disturbances including perversions are to be understood as resulting from a faulty synthesis of these components. These ideas of Freud seem to me to be almost identical in character with ideas now fairly widely accepted by ethologists in accounting for the complex behaviour of other species, e.g. nest building or courtship in birds.

If we select this aspect of Freud's formulations, we see that the phases of sexual development which would correspond to Piaget's phases of cognitive development would be not the manifestations of component patterns, but the various steps in the synthesis of these behaviour patterns into a more complex whole. I am not aware that any systematic work has been done on this though I may well be wrong. If the orientation I am recommending is a useful one, the tasks before the research psychoanalyst are (a) to describe more carefully the component 'part-instincts', (b) to study the stages in their synthesis to form mature sexual behaviour in its varying forms, normal and 'abnormal'.

Here I would like to say a word about the terms fixation and regression. Both are used in at least two different senses.

Fixation can refer either to a pattern of behaviour or to the object towards which the behaviour is directed. In the second usage it seems to me fairly satisfactory, though it tends to be used to refer only to 'abnormal' object choice, whereas a neutral term referring to the selection of any object, normal or 'abnormal' would be better. The term when used to refer to the persistence into adult life of behaviour patterns characteristic of infancy or childhood can be misleading and smacks too much of a static tethering to the past. Instead, as Piaget and I have agreed, it is far more fruitful to think of present behaviour as being due to the ongoing dynamic assimilation and restructuring of the past in terms of the present.

The term *regression* is often used by psychoanalysts in rather the same sense as the first usage of fixation: but, whereas fixation usually refers to the *persistence* into mature life of patterns of behaviour characteristic of the immature, regression is often used to describe a *recurrence* of such behaviour after it has been discontinued. This usage should of course be distinguished sharply from the usage such as that which Lewin (in Barker *et al.*, 1943) adopts in discussing

38

his experiment on Frustration and Regression. Here it is used to describe a return to less differentiated behaviour by children capable of more differentiated behaviour. It is imperative we find two terms to describe these two different processes. My own inclination would be to coin a new word for the concept denoted by the psychoanalytic usage; in coining it I would strive to convey the meaning of 're-arousal'. Unfortunately, however, it would hardly be easy to persuade psychoanalysts to forego their traditional use of the term.

Piaget (p. 19) is still not quite convinced that I share his belief that present behaviour is a result of the ongoing dynamic assimilation and restructuring of the past in terms of the present. Actually this is a view which many English psychoanalysts have emphasized for ten years or more as a result of being influenced by Lewin's field theory. The late John Rickman (1951) (President of the British Psycho-Analytical Society, 1947-50) was an ardent exponent of it and most of the analysts associated with the Tavistock Clinic and Institute share this view quite explicitly.

Having lived in this intellectual climate for some years I at first found the delighted incredulity with which Piaget has greeted my agreement with him a little puzzling. However, I have recently come across a passage in one of Freud's later papers which makes it plain that Freud never reached this view himself but, on the contrary, was a convinced exponent of the opposite standpoint, which I am afraid a majority of analysts still adopt. In contrasting the work of the psychoanalyst with that of the archaeologist who has to make reconstructions from material much of which has been lost or destroyed, Freud (1950) writes 'But it is different with the psychical object whose early history the analyst is seeking to recover. . . . All of the essentials are preserved, even things that seem completely forgotten are present somehow and somewhere, and have merely been buried and made inaccessible to the subject. Indeed, it may, as we know, be doubted whether any psychical structure can really be the victim of total destruction. It depends only upon analytical technique whether we shall succeed in bringing what is concealed completely to light.'

From this and other passages in the same paper it must be admitted that Freud held the view (a) that analytic treatment was concerned with 'digging up the past'—'we are in search of . . . a picture of the patient's forgotten years that shall be alike trustworthy and in all essential respects complete', and (b) that he believed that accurate reconstructions of the past could be achieved in the course of analytical therapy. As I explained in my contribution to our third meeting (Vol. III, p. 159), I and many English analysts do not share this view of therapy. Moreover, my own research programme is based on the view that data obtained in the course of analytic therapy can only be samples of behaviour (including introspections) which, though much influenced by the past, are inevitably influenced also by the present. For this reason what these data tell us of the influences active in the patient's early years is seen as in a glass darkly. Therefore if we wish to know about the influence of early experiences we have no option but to study the individual undergoing them as and when they are occurring.

Incidentally it is useful to note that we can formulate in two ways the process Piaget and I believe occurs. On the one hand we can refer to present behaviour as due to ongoing dynamic assimilation and restructuring of the past in terms of the present: on the other we can say that the present to which the behaviour is a response is assimilated and structured (or interpreted) in terms of the past.

Affectivity

I find it rather difficult to be clear what Piaget has in mind by this word, which happens not to be one I use. I get the impression that he thinks of something unitary in character in the same way as he thinks of cognition as unitary. My own outlook is probably radically different. I think of affectivity as the accompaniment of an activated behaviour pattern, each behaviour pattern having its own characteristic affectivity. In the following account I realize I am following closely the ideas put forward six years ago by Lorenz (1950).

Behaviour patterns

In putting forward the following ideas I realize I am giving a rough and ready sketch map involving nothing less than a theory of motivation and affect. My ideas are anything but clear and I am only advancing them now in order to give Piaget and others an impression of the lines along which I am thinking. The extent to which I have been influenced by ethological data and theory (much of it culled during discussions with Robert Hinde) will be evident.

Affect laden behaviour I tend to view in terms of structures built of component bricks. The bricks are relatively stereotyped behaviour patterns, e.g. bird song or sucking, which, according to the species, may be built in or learnt or a combination of both. The larger structure, e.g. courtship or nest building, is less stereotyped and a complex synthesis of these components. Although in principle any component is available for any synthesis, in practice each synthesis tends to select a particular group of components. None the less it is probably usual for certain component items to be utilized in more than one synthesis.

A typical example from the bird world is seen in connexion with courtship feeding where, in many species, as part of the courtship the male feeds the female in a way clearly resembling the feeding of the young by parents. There are two patterns to concern us here: (i) the food presentation of the male, (ii) the food begging of the female. Food presentation can be seen as a component pattern of the two more complex behaviour sequences (a) parental behaviour and (b) male courtship behaviour; similarly food begging can be seen as a component pattern of (a) chick behaviour and (b) female courtship behaviour.

It is my suspicion that in humans the same principles hold, though, because of our much greater capacities both for conceptualizing and for learning, their manifestation is far more complex. I suspect we shall find them especially clearly when we analyse the component patterns concerned in the three basic social relationships—the infant-parent, the parent-infant, and the sexual. For instance, I think we can identify a number of component behaviour patterns, largely if not wholly built-in, concerned in these three relationships; examples are smiling, crying, cuddling, sucking, the pelvic thrust. Some of these component patterns, e.g. smiling, are usually utilized in all three social relationships and some are confined to two or perhaps only one.

It will be seen that this theory has much in common with Freud's. The main difference appears to be that whereas Freud appears to think that the whole of the earlier behaviour patterns are organized into later sexual behaviour, I am suggesting that it is only some components of those earlier patterns which are so organized. Though this is not a negligible difference the approach is manifestly the same.

If the view I am advancing is right, one of our first tasks must be to identify these component behaviour patterns and, later, to discover by what means they are selected and synthesized to become parts of greater wholes. As regards the latter we would have to keep in mind the concept of harmonized reaction velocities and the big differences in outcome which would result from even small differential changes in these velocities, whether they were principally the result of the influence of genes or of the environment.

It will have been seen that I do not look on the affective aspects of behaviour as being readily described in terms of gain and loss. I think of behaviour patterns with their corresponding affects as being activated and terminated; from this point of view I am doubtful whether concepts of gain and loss are relevant.

Primacy of social responses

It should be noted that in following an ethological approach in the foregoing exposition I have been making an assumption regarding the primacy of social responses about which I ought now to say a word.

Piaget quotes and seems to agree with Freud in his supposition that tle only reason that the baby makes social relations is because he learns to do so: by relating to his mother he discovers that his physiological needs for food and warmth are met. This can be called 'the cupboard love theory of infant love', or as Piaget describes it, a 'remunerative strategy'.

Although many psychoanalysts, including Anna Freud, continue to adopt Freud's views on this topic, many others do not. In particular it is called in question by Melanie Klein and many other English analysts, including myself. The issue is basic to all work on social development and many debates between clinicians or between research workers can be traced to contrary views about it. Not only are psychoanalysts at variance among themselves here but the same is true of experimentalists. While those who follow the ethological tradition tend to assume that social responses are as primary as physiological responses, those who follow the learning theory tradition tend to assume they are secondary and learnt. Wallon, I gather from Zazzo, assumes them to be primary.

It is my hope that in the work we are doing at the Tavistock on smiling and crying we may gradually accumulate data which will assist in the resolution of this conflict.

Relation of affective to cognitive (see Piaget's third question to me, p. 24)

I find myself puzzled by Piaget's tendency to see the affective aspect of behaviour as dynamic and the cognitive aspect as structural, and I doubt whether this will prove a useful way to look at things. Nor am I inclined to think that 'all behaviour is *always* simultaneously affective and cognitive according to two inseparable but distinct aspects', which is the third of Piaget's questions to me. This is clearly a thorny problem but one which I suspect to be of the utmost importance.

It seems to me that any given pattern of behaviour can, at different times, vary in the amount of emotional and intellective activity which goes with it. For instance at one extreme we know from the work of embryologists (Coghill, Paul Weiss and others) that, at any rate in amphibia, basic patterns of motor co-ordination can develop without major impairment even when the sensory nervous system has been anaesthetized. 'The one fact that has been conclusively established by experimental results is that the central nervous system develops a finite repertory of behavioural performances which are prefunctional in origin and ready to be exhibited as soon as a proper effector apparatus becomes available' (Weiss, 1955). This suggests to me that it is useful to look at the development of behaviour patterns, even affectively toned ones, as being possibly independent of cognitive development in their initial stages.

At the other extreme are cognitive activities, e.g. solving a mathematical problem, which seems to be almost or quite independent of any behaviour pattern.

Furthermore, there are many patterns of behaviour, both learnt and unlearnt, which can vary in their cognitive component from occasion to occasion. An example of the unlearnt is breathing, which usually has negligible emotional or cognitive components but may acquire both if suffocation is imminent. Examples of the learnt are serving at tennis or playing a well-known piece on the piano; both skills have been acquired through cognitively directed effort but both may later be performed almost automatically, the established behaviour pattern taking charge.

I realize that in this context I am using the term 'behaviour pattern' in rather a broad way to include a range from co-ordinated movements like walking or breathing which are to a high degree built in to the CNS during its maturation and are dependent on particular muscle groups, to extremely complex movements which are wholly learnt and which are far less dependent on individual muscles. (A good example of the latter is one's signature which, although usually effected with one's hand, is similar in form when produced by any group of muscles, e.g. those of one's leg and foot when signing one's name in the sand with one's big toe.) It is my belief that this extended use of the term 'behaviour pattern' will prove justified because I suspect that both the unlearnt and the learnt may prove to have basic characteristics in common.

It is clearly one of man's special characteristics that he is able to acquire through learning such an extraordinary diversity of new patterns. Further, as Paul Weiss (1950) has shown, it is one of man's special characteristics that he can suppress an in-built pattern and utilize instead a learnt one. Whereas a polio patient can learn to use a limb efficiently after tendons have been transplanted and the inborn pattern thereby made inappropriate, rats cannot do so at all and monkeys show only a faint trace of such adaptive adjustments: animals of both species are restricted to the original motor patterns despite the tendon transplantation having caused its activation to result in incongruous and maladaptive behaviour.

Clearly the development of all the more complex learnt behaviour patterns is dependent on cognitive activity. Furthermore, although I have not grasped fully the implications of Piaget's notion of reversibility as the special characteristic of intelligence, I imagine that reversibility is always a characteristic of the more complex behaviour patterns which man is capable of learning. I shall look forward to Piaget's views on this.

This leads me to what I suspect is a crucial feature of neurotic behaviour. We know that neurotic behaviour is unconsciously motivated and tends to be maladaptive and repetitive: it is felt as irrational and alien to the personality. Evidently such behaviour is still governed by rather primitive processes. Having, as we know, its roots in infancy and early childhood, some neurotic behaviour may well be due to the activation of almost unmodified in-built behaviour patterns, whilst most of it seems likely to be due to the activation of the kind of behaviour patterns which are partly in-built and partly learnt in the earliest years, and whose cognitive components are therefore still primitive. Piaget emphasizes that during early childhood 'we find only unidirectional or irreversible actions' and that reversibility only develops later. All we know of neurotic patterns therefore suggests that their cognitive component lacks that 'most specific characteristic of intelligence', namely reversibility.

I am wondering what Piaget will think of this suggestion and whether he accepts the corollary that, at all ages, behaviour is regulated by cognitive processes of different degrees of development —that in some of our actions we operate with a fully-fledged intelligence characterized by reversibility and in some with an extremely primitive intelligence or none at all, and that in respect of any one activity we may shift from one level to another?

In this connexion Paul Weiss in his studies of polio patients has demonstrated that, even after a new pattern of functioning has been learnt, 'patients would frequently relapse into the old incongruous pattern', demonstrating that 'the latter remained latent but retained its integrity and reappeared periodically whenever the higher replacement went into recess'. This line of thought is fairly consistent with Freud's conception of psychoanalytic therapy. Making what is unconscious conscious is usually interpreted to mean removing barriers between different dynamic systems; such a process may perhaps also involve raising the cognitive component of a behaviour pattern from a primitive to a more sophisticated level.

The upshot of all this appears to be that, in contrast to Piaget, I am inclined to think of some behaviour as being structured in its own right and independently of any cognitive aspect it may later acquire, though I realize that the more complex behaviour patterns are probably structured cognitively from the start. Whether conversely cognition can ever be regarded as dynamic in its own right I find hard to know. Similarly, I have difficulty with regard to the second part of Piaget's third question to me, namely whether affect is ever the cause of cognition or the reverse. My inclination is to suppose that cognition only develops as a result of behaviour and

44

is therefore secondary to it, but I would like to consider the evidence more carefully before giving any definite opinion. From what I have already said, however, it will be seen that, at least in respect of primitive and more or less built-in behaviour patterns, I do not expect to find any very close parallelism in development between the cognitive and the affective.

Turning to the various hypotheses regarding the degree of synthesis which we may hope to attain, which Piaget lists at the end of his Section II on The Problem of the Stages of Development (p. 13), it will be seen that I favour hypothesis 1—that there are no general stages and that 'we see an intermingling of processes of development which are evidently interrelated, but to different extents or according to multiple temporal rhythms, there being no reason why these processes should constitute a unique structural whole at each level'. I do not favour hypothesis 3, that the personality is built up by successive stages of equilibrium and that it will be possible to establish correspondences between stages in the different studies we undertake.

Before discussing the question of transition between stages, I want to say a word about equilibrium.

Equilibrium

It is plain that the structure and activity of the organism as a whole cannot be understood simply in terms of structure and activities of its parts and that the process of organization of the separate activities into a whole must have laws of its own and that, in so far as the organism persists and develops, there must be an equilibrium of forces. In considering the propositions advanced by Piaget, with which at present I am very unfamiliar, I should be concerned to ensure that they take account of various nonadaptive outcomes which favour the survival neither of the individual nor of the species. Examples from my own field would be suicide, a mother murdering her baby, and the affectionless character following prolonged separation. As regards the latter we know it to have tremendous stability but it is certainly inimical to the individual's capacity for participating in family and social life.

I imagine in considering equilibria we have to distinguish rather sharply between the particular outcomes, some of which may be nonadaptive, and the system of feedbacks and governors which, because they more often than not lead to an adaptive outcome, are biologically reasonably efficient.

Transition from one stage of development to the next (see Piaget's first and second question to me, p. 24)

This is clearly a crucial issue and there is a good deal of psychoanalytic literature on the subject. For instance there has been much discussion of the factors which lead to a fixation at a particular libidinal phase; the traditional hypotheses are:

(a) that a particular part-instinct is innately overstrong and
(b) that environmental factors account for part of it.

Of the latter, both frustration and overgratification have been incriminated. (I believe the evidence that frustration is relevant is strong; I am much less convinced about the evidence for overgratification.)

Moreover Melanie Klein, who has done much to call attention to the crucial importance of ambivalence to the love object, has elaborated hypotheses regarding modes of resolving the conflict of ambivalence and transition from one mode to another (see Klein, 1952). Although I am in close sympathy with her general approach I do not find the details of her formulation very convincing. In particular I think it more likely that some of the processes she described as occurring in the first few months in relation to the breast occur during the second year in relation to the mother as a whole person. Her views are almost entirely based on a reconstruction of what may happen in the first year of life using for the purpose data obtained from the analysis of patients above the age of two years. In my view little progress will be made in the theoretical debates which have arisen around Melanie Klein's hypotheses until systematic observation, and where permissible experiments, are made on infants in their first year.

In respect of first-hand experience the transitions with which psychoanalysts are most familiar are those to be observed during successful therapy. Although occurring much later in the life history than is optimal, such transitions are widely believed by psychoanalysts to resemble, in some measure at least, those which are usually achieved in the early years. A systematic study of the nature of the therapeutic process should cast light on certain important transitions, for instance those concerned with developing more efficient modes of dealing with the conflict of ambivalence. To return to Piaget's questions. I would like further information about the implications of his 'hypothesis that the reactions to a stage n are released by the dissatisfactions, conflicts, or disequilibria belonging to the previous stage $n-1$'. Many transitions in behaviour and psychological function I suppose to be due to the maturation of the CNS and the bringing into use of new groups of cells and new circuits. A case in point would be the transition in the development of motility from crawling to walking. Development of cognition must also be dependent on maturation of the CNS, though experience and learning obviously play a larger part than in the development of walking. I conceive of development in the behaviour patterns concerned with social interaction as being dependent partly on CNS

46

maturation and partly on experience, and in this respect comparable with the development of cognition.

In so far as all growth and development can presumably be traced to biochemical disequilibria I agree with Piaget's formulation. I am doubtful if I agree with it if the 'dissatisfaction, conflict or disequilibria' are conceived of as purely psychological.

As regards the *stage of latency* (Piaget's second question to me) I am inclined to regard it as the manifestation of a phase of maturation which in considerable measure has been built into the human species in the course of evolution. Nevertheless I believe the form it takes to be highly dependent on experience.

As regards Piaget's final question addressed to all of us, there are two areas of transition which I might reasonably attempt to study. One would be the integration into an organized whole of the behaviour patterns which form components of the infant's relation to his mother. I am thinking here of suckling, smiling, crying, the need for physical contact, etc. Before attempting to do this, however, I think it will be necessary to do a good deal more research on the nature of these different responses. The other field would be in the transition from one mode of handling the conflict of ambivalence to another.

MARGARET MEAD

Comments on Professor Piaget's Paper

In replying to Professor Piaget's challenging paper, I find that I must first distinguish between two approaches which appear in his statement. On the one hand he appears to say that in order to have a unified theory of development, itself dependent upon a common language, which will make it possible to bring our various materials together, we must recognize the three traditional divisions of (a) hereditary factors, (b) the action of the physical environment, and (c) the action of the social environment, brought together in terms of a fourth factor, that of development, for which he proposes a formulation in terms of contemporary equilibrium theory. With this general position I am in full accord; I believe the development of such a theory is practicable and that its expression by the use of contemporary mathematical models may be fruitful, although I reserve judgment as to whether the adoption of economic emphasis —calculations of strategy based on gains and losses—is the most rewarding model from amongst the available ones. This aspect of the problem is, however, the domain of General System Theory represented in our Group by Dr. von Bertalanffy, and I shall not address myself to it further.

However, throughout Professor Piaget's paper there appears from time to time a second and quite contrasting approach, in which the recognition of the importance of individual differences—as opposed to 'average' performance of individuals at a given 'stage'—the recognition of the role of the culture in advancing or retarding any of these assumed sequences, and the recognition of continuity rather than 'stages' in physical growth (p. 11)—are all treated, not as providing additional and needed material for a general theory of the development of the child, but rather as opposing theories or disproportionate emphases upon one of these three traditional factors. If this approach were followed it would be tantamount to saying that it is possible to establish stages if one confines oneself to the study of the cognitive and affective behaviour of children in twentieth century Euro-American culture, and leaves out of account material on their physical development, and material on children in other cultures. As such an expectation contradicts the whole intention of Professor Piaget's integrating formulation, I merely mention it here, at the beginning, to stress that I am addressing myself to my alternative understanding of his paper, and not to the assumption that study of the factors of physical growth and culture automatically results in disagreement.

In regard to the question of 'general stages', our present cross-cultural evidence, admittedly very fragmentary, suggests that it becomes decreasingly possible to relate different aspects of the child's behaviour to its age or other measure of development, as age increases. The duration of development may nevertheless be of some significance in explaining different configurations of learning. I say 'duration' to allow for periods of illness or regression, or for extreme differences in the amount of interpersonal interaction in the life of a given child, who may, for example, be said to be equivalent—in this widest developmental sense—to a much younger or older child, because of the intervention of factors of acceleration or arrest of interpersonal contacts. For infants and very young children, the gross developmental conditions of learning to walk and talk also seem to introduce, in all known cross-cultural contexts, a certain degree of generalization into all other types of learning occurring at the same time. It must also be recognized that in regard to such things as walking and talking, different individual constitutions and different arrangements for learning in different cultures—as for example when children are kept swaddled or cradled beyond the period when they could walk, or hear phrases stated in their name long before they could formulate them themselves—may both vary to such an extent as again to make any idea of general stages appear useless.

If a theory of stages is conceived as a progressive series of equilibria, disequilibria and re-equilibria, in which successive equilibrium levels, even of only momentary duration, may be distinguished, but in which in any given process certain fixed sequences may occur, this formulation can be applied, with our present knowledge, to the investigation of human development within different cultures. As Professor Piaget now formulates the problem, such exploration would have to be done in very great detail, using tests which were formally identical and culturally comparable on a series of identified children, whose physical development had also been studied, over a sufficient period of time so that *transitions* might be examined and analysed in the case of these identified children. The question of the average age for the appearance of a stage while useful as a corrective for ethnocentric overgeneralization from studies on children of a particular culture, seems to me to be of only very limited significance. Only when the actual *succession* of stages in the development of any process can be followed in identified individuals, in an identified culture, within an identified social unit (that is a group in which each individual's place in relation to each other individual is known) can we begin to relate together the three factors affecting development. I would maintain this as necessary because if, as Professor Piaget suggests, there are no general stages, then retardation or acceleration—(in terms of chronological age or developmental duration)—in any one process, attributable either to culture or to constitution, may have the most profound effects on the configuration of learning, and thus on the development of the personality. It may be that our most acute understanding of the constant sequences in any process may come in those processes where averaging is possible—a position which has not, I believe, yet been demonstrated fully—but that for the understanding of total development, it will still be necessary to take account of the effects of different combinations among these constant or fixed sequences, which are themselves systematically associated with genetic or with cultural patterns.

The specific study of identified individuals makes the distinction which Professor Piaget (p. 20) draws between *molar* phenomena and *molecular* phenomena less significant, for it makes it possible to address research immediately to the molecular level. When the general system of culture is examined as manifested in the behaviour of identified individuals in their interaction with a new member of the society—a formulation which permits more exact study than a formulation in terms of 'generations'—it is then possible to relate this behaviour not only to the whole system of culture (which may be expected to be sufficiently redundant to allow for the total genetic range of contemporary survival possibilities of *homo sapiens*), but also to the peculiarities of certain stocks within the society which have become isolated by various breeding barriers—such as class, cult, sect, occupational lines, etc. In this way it will be possible to investigate the degree of facilitation or inhibition existent, for example, in cultural systems which make a very slight use of mathematics, or in which the perception of time-space relations are very differently organized.

To address myself to the specific questions of Professor Piaget (p. 25, III):

I would not say (with Durkheim) that 'under all civilizations lies *the* civilization', but that all civilizations express the conditions of being human (la condition humaine), in that *homo sapiens* is dependent for his humanity—his survival as a species in the form we call human—on a system of socially transmitted learned behaviour. This learned behaviour shows certain regularities which can be related to the requirements of man's biological characteristics—long infancy, properties of the central nervous system, etc.—in combination with the rest of the environment on this planet. Without such an assumption of regularities all comparative work between different cultures would obviously take a very different form, and such an assumption does underlie all contemporary work in cultural anthropology.

The way in which children learn natural languages may be regarded as a case in point. As far as is known children learn languages which on other grounds may be classified as easy or difficult, and of many different types of complexity, at the same age in all cultures. This can be attributed to two factors—the redundancy of natural languages and the fact that all first languages are learned in interaction between speakers and those who have not learned to speak at all, in the same way. The nature of speech, and the particular language spoken are communicated together. With the rationalization of the cultural understanding of languages, the development of such ideas as 'a language', 'grammar', 'word', 'alphabet', 'verb', 'predicate', 'utterance', 'phoneme', 'morpheme', the process of linguistic learning is becoming progressively transformed. So, in response to Professor Piaget's second question, if an adult had to learn a language as a child learns it, without the intervention of any categories of linguistic analysis, there would undoubtedly be found many similarities in the order of acquisition. However, in all known societies, a difference occurs because the idea of the existence of different languages has already been formalized, and while the child learns to speak, the adult, having learned to speak, learns to speak a second language. It is quite conceivable that the systematic and very early teaching of the alphabet and of reading and writing might introduce into the first learning of the child a new factor which would make learning language in complex, fully literate societies no longer comparable with learning languages in non-literate or slightly literate societies, and that some effects of this sort may be making themselves felt in the present difficulties which are being encountered in efforts to give a type of early education designed for children of the literate to children of the non-literate.

However—still in response to Professor Piaget's second question— it would appear that every cultural system contains within it the provision for the way in which it must be learned by children during their normal development, including sufficient leeway for a range in this normal development—in such respects as type of imagery, capacity to organize, type of memory, etc. One route to a comprehension of another culture, or some complex part of a culture, such as the language, the legal system, the ritual idiom, etc., is to repeat the steps taken by children learning this system. This contrasts with the way in which a linguistically sophisticated adult masters the 'grammar' of another language in a matter of hours, or a mathematically sophisticated adult masters a new type of mathematics. It would seem that once having traversed the steps necessary to become human, in any culture, one may transfer that learning, at an adult level, to any other culture, but that cultures differ in the developmental levels which they call into play in certain areas of experience. So western culture has now developed to a high degree the type of thinking necessary for scientific endeavour, but leaves in a quite uncultivated state various capacities for introspective experience developed in Indian culture. For members of cultures which have not elaborated our type of scientific thinking, immediate transference of previous learning into understanding of our culture may be possible only for the exceptionally gifted as it may mean an imaginative act of transference covering a whole series of missing stages, in the form in which they have been culturally elaborated in our own society. For the less gifted, it may be necessary to include in any education in another culture a re-experience of earlier stages of learning, in the different cultural form. As I have understood Professor Piaget's discussions in our meetings this formulation is one which he feels is compatible with his material.

In conclusion, I should like to stress the significance of our failure, as a group, to pin down our various conceptualizations in any single set of individually identified real children. The insights which each of us has brought to these four rewarding years of work have all been based on very careful precise observations made, over time, on individual children, or in Konrad Lorenz's case, other living creatures in known social contexts. However much we may have concentrated on cognitive behaviour, or emotional disturbance, on behaviour as part of a group in a primitive culture, on electroencephalograms or physical measurements of growth, much of the background of the children studied, or of the other aspects of the children's development was always known, and always taken, however inexplicitly, into account. Not until this new integration proposed by Professor Piaget and modified by the more formal inclusion of differences among children, and among cultures, can be applied to the detailed simultaneous study of a group of *children*, will we know what we have attained in this new way of looking at the psychobiological development of the child. And as I wrote the last sentence I realized that I should lament this, but not reproach ourselves for it, for our mandate was, after all, only to think about the child, to present an integrated set of abstractions which, one hopes, may be used in the study of children in many different parts of the world.

GREY WALTER

Comments on Professor Piaget's Paper

In replying to Professor Piaget's paper from the standpoint of a neurophysiologist, I must begin by saying that, like the other neurophysiologists of our group, I am eager to see the organism whole and to avoid organ dogma. I think it is as silly to attribute all behaviour to the cerebral cortex (or to the reticular system, which is more fashionable) as it is to the possession or not of a penis. Of course we know that we can never see an organism and its history truly whole, but we must try and try to get a glimpse in 3D if not in the 7D we know we need. Opposite p. 148 of our first Proceedings (Vol. I) is an old record showing the simultaneous recording of ten variables during a psychological experiment. We cannot control the variables when we are studying a complex system, so we must observe as many as we can and make all illuminate all. This is the essence of the cybernetic approach. There are still shadows and highlights and deep ravines of inspissated gloom, but we are beginning to see the modelling of the growing brain in its relation to the rest of the body and to behaviour. As a result, the answer I must give to Piaget's questions will be contingent rather than concise. For one thing we are perpetually impressed by the range of variation between children in a given age group—yet Piaget speaks for example of '*the* child aged 7-8 years'. Of course we can accept a *statistical* norm for some of our physiological variables, but if, as we think likely, development of some variables proceeds by steps, then their time-distribution is not normal in the statistical sense and we must specify whether in a particular child a certain step has been made or not. Paediatricians are always talking of 'milestones' in a child's development, but this gives an impression of an arbitrary scale at the side of a smooth road—what I am concerned with is an actual change of plane or field or climate, where, as in the dark wood of middle life, the straight road may seem to lose itself in the undergrowth, and we have to take to the trees.

The question of use and design, or nurture and nature, and the notion of equilibration are affected by this concept, for implicit in it is the consideration of the organism and its environment as a closely interacting *statistical* assembly. Perhaps I mean rather a probabilistic matrix, or a quantum atmosphere; Bertalanffy includes such systems in his General System Theory and Ashby calls certain classes 'ultrastable'. We are in great semantic difficulty here. I don't fully understand Ashby's equations. I can't write down any better ones and the grandiloquence and ambiguity of the above phrases appals me. Furthermore, I have to postulate what I have called 'speculation' in living systems. My models show what I mean if you can remember them; think of all their components assembled together, receptors, relays, storage systems, motors and all, then imagine wires growing out from one component to the other along the potential gradients, so that at first there are only a few simple reflexes, then the scanner starts up the 'speculative' activity, an IRM is triggered, the probability of significance of some sets of events reaches the threshold of implication, the IRM is incorporated into the new association, the original reflexes are adapted to a more complex application. All this time you could amuse yourself by betting on what would happen next and you might win a little if you knew what was inside the boxes, but the only certain thing is that in the end the batteries would run down; the system would no longer be 'open' but very definitely closed, dead.

Now, if you had been playing with the model since it was 'born' and knew what was inside it, you could give a fairly good account of its state and, as I say, a fair prediction of its next phase. But if you came on it after it had already gone through a few manoeuvres you would be quite unable to describe its internal condition. Obviously you could construct an objective description of its behaviour and if you were allowed to use a few instruments you could also identify some of its internal functions; perhaps relate function to behaviour in a tentative way. But you could not *by any means* discriminate between built-in and acquired features. This is a corollary of the proposition so carefully set out by Wiener in *Cybernetics* about biological or Bergsonian time as compared with Newtonian time. We exist on an irreversible time-scale; we cannot live backwards and cannot even make legitimate retrospective analyses without inside information. This is nothing to do with any mystical properties of Time but is because what we see of living creatures—and models of them—are statistically determined interactions between structure and experience. What we call logical processes, the rules of arithmetic and of games, are very special cases, artificially isolated and enforced for special purposes. It seems to me one of the limitations of the Freudian way of thinking that it assumes a principle of strict logical causality in mental processes.

I suppose Adler is dreadfully outmoded but I have always admired his emphasis on the personal vector. The assumption of orientation need not be coloured with transcendental teleology in thinking about children any more than in watching my models. Artificial goal-seeking mechanisms are novel perhaps, but the essence of cybernetics is to define and analyse the factors in 'purposeful' behaviour which are common to all self-controlled systems, and to suggest tactics and strategy for the study of complex interacting systems—which are beyond the range of classical scientific methods and propositional logic.

What seems to me very important in all our discussions is to recognize that complex behavioural patterns which seem to show intense purposefulness may be the expression of quite simple mechanisms. The elements in the mechanism need not be very numerous either, but of course the number of ways in which they can be combined in permutation is certainly colossal, and as Bowlby mentions, very slight differences in their rate of development or in the details of their connectedness will be grossly amplified by the very operation of the mechanism itself on the environment and vice versa, so that again great differences between young individuals of the same age are to be expected and should be appreciated. Furthermore, these very differences should give us essential clues to the whole problem of animal development, since the permissible range, or 'tolerances' as an engineer would call them, of a component or function often reveals far more clearly than its mean or modal value, what part it plays in the whole organism.

When Ross Ashby asked us to help him build one of his homeostatic analogues, he gave us a circuit diagram with the values of the resistances and voltages and so on. Several of these were unusual values and rather hard to obtain. Our electronic craftsman looked the circuits over and said, 'I'm awfully sorry but I can't get that value of resistance, 63,258 ohms, very easily—would 68,000 ohms do instead?' Ashby replied, 'Oh, yes, it doesn't really matter what the value is—I just measured the resistances I happened to put in and that is the average value—they can be almost anything provided they don't pass too much current.' The craftsman looked as though he had found something slimy under a large stone, and we had to subcontract the job. His reaction was perfectly apt—such a specification is too much like life to please a mechanic who wants his machine to behave exactly according to plan. I should add, to point the moral, that Ashby also specified that certain values, of supply voltage for example, should be very carefully fixed and stabilized. This seems to me very important; in complex systems which are capable of self-control and self-development, whether in flesh or metal, some features must be held constant within narrow limits, others can be—in fact must be—left free to vary widely. In other words, in our study of development we might usefully try to decide which aspects of human psychophysiology are homeostatically controlled and which are liable to vary over a wide range. As a simple example, body temperature varies little (as compared with ambient temperature). We know something of the reflexive or 'negative feedback' pathways that ensure this in health and use the failures of control as an aid to the diagnosis of faults or diseases in the organism. On the other hand, EEG characters (which can be measured with a comparable degree of accuracy) vary over a wide range and this variation makes the diagnosis of brain disorders in children by EEG enormously difficult. Are these two classes of relationship what Ashby means by 'Parameters' and 'Variables'? (A parameter being a variable which is not included in a system under consideration.) This is by no means trivial or academic for, to quote Ashby, 'a change of parameter-value changes the field, and because a system's stability depends on its field, a change of parameter value will in general change a system's stability in some way.'

These notions seem to me very apposite to the discussion by Piaget and Bowlby on 'equilibrium'. I feel bound to add that in our studies of human brains we have quite independently been forced to include 'stability' as a measurable neurophysiological relationship, among our *parameters*, and feel justified in identifying certain mechanisms in the brain as serving to ensure failure-to-safety in conditions where stability is threatened by a change in Parameter-value A. I shall be discussing this in more detail in my replies to Piaget's specific questions to me.

This is saying the same thing as others have suggested about whether a child tends to reach an equilibrium (Piaget), or a steady state (Bertalanffy), or stability (Ashby) or normality, or whether in general organisms are essentially spontaneously active (Bertalanffy) or speculative (GW). I am suggesting that there are indeed reflexive mechanisms (a phrase I prefer to 'negative feedback circuits') which are intrinsically homeostatic and self-stabilizing, error-cancelling. Further, I agree with Bertalanffy that the signals or events or stimuli which operate these mechanisms are in general (and particularly in humans) of such variety and intensity that it is better to think of the outcome as the steady state of an open system. As Bertalanffy says, this is classical but not trivial and an important corollary is that when one studies the internal economy of an open-system-in-a-steady-state one often finds a surprising amount of activity going on because the channels carrying the error-signals are likely to be pretty busy even when the whole organism seems in 'equilibrium'. In fact, the more nearly perfect the 'dynamic equilibrium' the more internal 'activity' there may be. There are plenty of examples of this, of course, in flesh and metal.

A very crude illustration for those who haven't thought in these terms: the humble and hygienic water-closet problem. You want a tank of water to be always full so that it will operate a siphon. You can have a continuous inflow with an overflow pipe—very simple, no moving parts except the water. But very wasteful, and the faster you want the tank to fill after it had been emptied, the more wasteful it will be. This is a closed system in a 'dynamic equilibrium' of the simplest type, and is adequate if the tank is likely to be emptied on the average almost as soon as it is full. To avoid waste, however, you fit a ball-cock which admits water in inverse proportion to the existing water level. Now there is no waste at all, and the rate of filling can be as fast as the supply pressure and capacity permit. But you have a more elaborate reflex mechanism which might go wrong and if you are wise you will leave the overflow pipe too, just in case, to ensure failure-to-safety.

Now note how, from outside the tank, you could distinguish the first system from the second. In the first place there would be steady 'spontaneous' activity in the input and there would be two alternative outputs, the siphon or the overflow, related in such a way that when the first was operated the second was inhibited and the first would only operate if the second was already working. In the second system on the other hand the input would only appear *after* the siphon was operated and then for a fixed time, during which the siphon would be inhibited. To take the analogy a step further, if you decide that the whole system should be automatic in the sense of not requiring an initiating stimulus, you could either arrange for an inverted U-tube siphon (which would empty the tank quickly and completely whenever it was full, the frequency of discharge being a linear function of the input rate), or add to the reflex system a clock which would initiate the sequence of siphoning and filling at regular intervals. This last would ensure relative independence of filling rate and supply pressure. It could also be linked with a receptor to provide information about when the discharge would be most effective, thus forming a second-order reflex, with further possibilities of devices for estimating contingency between apparently independent events, conditional probability, and so forth. In these more sophisticated arrangements, inspection would reveal 'spontaneous rhythmic activity' which might be significantly related in its phase relation to the pattern of incoming signals, but would show little connexion with the characters of the energy supply. Above all, the more perfect and intricate the dynamic balance, the more characteristic and varied would be the internal spontaneous activity. (Obviously this word 'spontaneous' is an awkward one. This is no place to discuss it in detail. Many other terms have been used: 'autochthonous', 'autogenous', 'autogenic' and so forth.)

We are still debating whether in the brain small populations of cells or individual cells do really exhibit gratuitous, autogenous activity. In any case, whether an isolated cell, or a slab of cortex or a whole brain or organism is considered, wherever rhythmic or repetitive activity is observed, there must be a 'feedback' of some sort. This is true even of a pendulum; so it is not surprising that we find such effects in profusion in animals or that they are often inversely related to outward function or operational activity, for as in the case of our water tank in the household they are usually essentially administrative rather than operational.

This bring us back to the basic question: can we hope to distinguish in ourselves, in children, between on the one hand the administrative homeostatic mechanisms which, from the point of view of mentality and behaviour are concerned with parameters (A) and on the other the operational, speculative processes, the manipulation of essential variables, which gives us such deep satisfaction—happiness as opposed to comfort?

Now I must reply more explicitly to Piaget's questions to me.

The first question dealt with the possible forms of psychobiological development, of which I suggested six. Piaget proposed another to describe the construction of logical relationships, which he feels is an important stage at 7-8 years, and he describes this as *Learning by successive equilibrations*. For me this presents few problems since I consider such learning as a *special case* of 'stochastic' learning just as I consider logical reasoning as a special case of statistical reflexion. I agree of course that propositions such as A=B, B=C, therefore A=C are unlikely to be worked out by children under 7-8, but I think of this class of propositions as a member of the (larger) class: 'A usually implies B, B usually implies C, so there is a reasonable chance that A will imply C.' Remember that in such a chain of *probabilities* the uncertainty is multiplied at each stage, so that the chance of an organism making the *logical* inference is quite small unless the probability is near unity on every occasion and at each stage. In the example Piaget gave of his friend counting pebbles (Vol. II, p. 59), he counted them several times, changing the order and making sure that the cardinal sum was invariant with order. Piaget's point was that the organism here was actually manipulating the environment, and I agree that this is of basic importance. But I maintain that in the development of an assembly of statistical associations a stage will *sometimes* be reached at which a completely invariant component will emerge and this may become a basis for logical reasoning. This is really quite familiar, and is sometimes described as the search for redundancy; for example, in the question of cardinal number and ordinal number, the pebbles or the fingers are found to be 'redundant'. The relations sometimes described as Natural Laws are in fact examples of enormous redundancy. In general, the degree of redundancy, the completeness of invariance of Natural Laws, cannot be determined without experimental verification, that is, physiological action by the organism. There is only a very poor chance of the signals received passively by an organism providing enough information for it to draw a general conclusion. Hence the need for 'speculation', the active and assiduous exploration of promising relations; in scientific work the experimental testing of plausible hypotheses. This is included in my class of Learning by Association since a large proportion of the relevant information received by the brain is from proprioceptors responding to muscular and glandular action, rather than from exteroceptors.

It seems to me that the 'learning par équilibrations successives' of Piaget would be better translated as 'matching' (a word which cannot be translated into French; it is used often in technical French in phrases such as 'Pour assurer un minimum de distorsion dynamique il faut que les selfs soient *matchés* . . .': the inductances must be matched). This is a most important concept, but is not outside the mechano-physiological classification I put forward. Learning by matching obviously implies the existence within the organism of some sort of model to match with experience and I suggest that a child is *unlikely* to acquire enough information to build up in his brain a stock of 'logical' models before the age of 7 or so.

This is just the sort of question I had hoped to be able to answer by experiment. We have evidence—in reply to Piaget's second question to me—that elaboration of sensory signals is rare in children below the age of 7 or so. Is this because elaboration depends upon progressive matching of internal models with external experience and this cannot be done until there has been time for a stock of internal models to be built up, or is it because the neural apparatus is not there at all before this age? This should be a straightforward problem and seems to me a basic one, but it cannot be answered, I fear, without experiments of a fairly intricate nature.

This leads on to my answer to Piaget's third question; why is there so thin a correspondence between EEG and cognitive development? I think this is true only if one is limited to subjective consideration of the passive EEG features. If one makes quantitative studies of the EEG *and other physiological variables* during activity, particularly during a learning experiment, very exciting relationships emerge which do indeed seem to encourage the search for a firm passage between physio- and psychological domains. Such experiments are, alas, still very involved and expensive, but I don't feel anything simpler is worth doing. Some of you may well feel that our claims are exaggerated and that we make too much technical fuss —you may be right, but the old method of taking a passive EEG and glancing through the record is rather as though Tanner were to glance at one of his child subjects and say vaguely, 'Yes, that's a well developed child.' May I give another analogy—suppose we were trying to decide how to teach children gymnastics and the question arose, at what age should we expect a particular child to be able to raise itself up to a horizontal bar? Would it be enough to measure the girth of the upper arm at rest? Would we not have to consider practice, incentive, competition, physical proportionality? Our psychophysiological experiments are rather like that; we are trying to find out how and when people become capable of performing certain mental gymnastics. At the present stage it looks as though there are definite turning points in development, when certain mechanisms reach a threshold of operational efficiency and begin to have external effects. I must stress again the serious difficulties this raises—classical methods of observation and analysis do not allow readily for non-linear or threshold effects. The popular psychological notion of 'insight' is one of these. In my model (Vol. II, Fig. 11, pp. 32-33) there is a component labelled 'insight' which indicates when the 'experience' of the model is adequate to justify external action. Mechanically it is a threshold device which does nothing until the stress on it reaches a certain value when it 'fires' and transmits a single 'bit' (binary digit) of information to a storage register. This is an abrupt event which apparently—seen from outside—has no precedent; that is to say, nothing seems to be happening for a long time, then suddenly the whole situation is changed. Actually, within the box plenty is happening but it is not reflected in action. There is nothing mysterious in this of course, but it is important to realize that the link between a great deal of selective activity at the input and a quite elaborate novel action at the output is just a single 'bit' of information which tells the storage system that a certain degree of improbability has been surpassed. This relation is very hard to put into words, and beyond my capacity to condense into algebra, which is why I made the model; when met with in a living organism it is terribly confusing and impressive.

That is why the existence of step functions or thresholds in physical development *apart* from behavioural effects such as 'insight' must be investigated very carefully; if a system contains the two together the problem may be very nearly intractable. None of us is really trained to handle this sort of problem—it is hard to preserve one's dignity and poise going upstairs on skis. I say again—mind the step!

J. M. TANNER

Comments on Professor Piaget's Paper

Two of the main questions raised by Piaget concern me closely: the existence of stages of development, and the mechanism of transformation from one stage to another. The first of these questions I think largely spurious; that is I consider it chiefly a matter of the different use of words by different members of the group. Here I am in total agreement with the remarks made by Lorenz on this subject at the third meeting (Vol. III, p. 162). An example below will, I hope, make my standpoint clear. It will show, amongst other things, that I assume Piaget's conditions for existence of a stage numbers 1, 2, 3 and possibly 4 (pp. 13-14) as existing all the time throughout growth and governing continually the physical growth of the organism from moment to moment. I would not myself consider these conditions sufficient warrant for the use of the word 'stage'.

The second question, that of the mechanism of transformation, I consider the most fundamental question in our whole field and probably the most important. I am only sorry that I can contribute practically nothing to its elucidation, whereas as a physiologist I might be expected to contribute perhaps the most. The fact is that physiological ignorance on this matter is profound, and professional physiological interest and experiment almost non-existent.

Dealing now with the specific questions addressed to me:

1 (and 3). The *immediate* cause of the chief phase of acceleration, that at adolescence, is well known. The spurt in bodily growth is caused by the release of hormones from the gonads, adrenals and pituitary. The cause of the increase in gonad and adrenal secretions is the release of other pituitary hormones, and the release of these pituitary hormones is caused by certain events, the nature of which is obscure, in the C.N.S.

The most we can say about this at present is that at some stage of development some areas in the C.N.S. reach a state of maturity X, and as soon as X is reached, messages pass to the pituitary to release hormones previously stored there, and adolescence ensues. But what causes state X to appear? This question is in my view the fundamental one in all the study of physical growth.

61

We can sum up all we know about X by saying:

(i) X does not depend much on the size of the organism; it depends more on the percentage of ultimate adult size achieved, i.e. X appears more nearly at say 80 per cent final size than at a size of so many grams.

(ii) If the organism is starved and growth retarded, X is retarded. If the organism is given food after a length of time spent at constant weight, then X appears at about the same percentage of adult weight reached, quite irrespective of how many days have passed. The appearance of X is related to *internal maturational time*, not to chronological time.

(iii) The moment when X is reached can be best predicted from observing the previous course of growth. It will then be seen that X occurs chronologically early in organisms all of whose progress-to-maturity has been swift or 'advanced'. That is, children with a bone age of 11 at chronological age 9 reach X earlier than children with a bone age of 9 at chronological age 9.

This leads one to suppose that the stage X proceeds from state W, which in turn proceeds from state V, etc. One can think of growth and development as a continuous series of states $\to U \to V \to W \to X \to$: the organism may be temporarily arrested in any of the states, but the *order* in which they occur is always the same. One cannot proceed, for example, from U to W except through V, unless some pathological disturbance supervenes.

This formulation lends itself to a symbolization of what I believe to be the relation between those who use the concept of stages (Piaget for cognition) and those who prefer the concept of 'continuous' development (Piaget for perception, myself for physical growth). If we symbolize *observable* change by length of arrow and state by length of dotted line associated with the capital letter, we have:

Stages: $\to$.... U ......$\to$...... V ......$\to$...... W......$\to$
Continuous: ———$\to$. U .————$\to$V .————$\to$. W .————$\to$

In part, I feel sure, the idea of 'stages' arises from an inability to measure small increments of function; but in part the idea may truthfully reflect a situation where in one part of the organism no change is occurring (while continuous growth meanwhile goes on in another part).

As to the mechanism of these $U \to V \to W \to$, and the question of equilibria: we know very little about this and I can only repeat what I said at our first meeting—that the process of maturation seems to me like a series of clocks, the signal for the starting of one being the running-down of another. I would now complicate this a little by adding that there are many clocks all going at once, and clock B starts when A reaches four o'clock, clock C when A reaches six o'clock, and so on.

62

Undoubtedly there are feed-back mechanisms wholly within the C.N.S. governing the U → V → W mechanism. Whether there are feed-backs of the sort C.N.S. → endocrines → C.N.S. or C.N.S. → endocrines → peripheral tissues → C.N.S. we do not know. (Equally we have no really clear idea of how far environmental stimulation, e.g. by social conditioning or simple physical exercise, can enter the feed-back circuit.) We do know of various substances (both oestrogens and androgens) which will speed up maturation of particular bits of the organism—for example the ossification of the bones at the wrist, or the appearance of pubic hair—but we do not know of any substances or any treatment (except starvation) which will speed up or slow down the rate of development of the organism as a whole, that is, while maintaining its normally balanced structure.

2. Our knowledge of anatomical and histological changes in the human brain after the age of six months is virtually nil. Probably by the age of nine months, and almost certainly by one year, all the cells and all the fibres of the C.N.S. are present, and all the fibres ultimately to receive myelin have begun to become myelinated. After this time, however, the diameters of the myelin sheaths increase, and probably also the size of some nerve cells increases. About detailed histological changes at the periods $1\frac{1}{2}$-2; 7-8; 11-12, we have no information whatever. I leave the question of EEG evidence for functional changes to Grey Walter to answer: apart from the EEG I do not think there are any useful physiological data on C.N.S. function during this time.

RENÉ ZAZZO

Comments on Professor Piaget's Paper

Professor Piaget's essay on the general problems of the psycho-biological development of the child has given me once more the opportunity to take up the thread of our discussions.

1. *The concept of interaction between factors affecting development*

Partitioning into compartments is dangerous, but it is necessary to distinguish between factors. This second proposition must be stated as clearly as the first if we are to avoid falling from atomistic error into a confused globalism.

Moreover the interaction Piaget mentions presupposes the existence of factors. Of course, it must be pointed out that these factors do not act as independent variables. It is, for example, an organism which 'chooses' and organizes its environment in accordance with its heredity, and in turn this environment acts on the expression of the heredity, and perhaps eventually on its transformation. I agree here with Piaget, and the only fault I would find in his formulation would be undue caution. He says 'The interactions (of factors) are at least as important as their respective actions.' It seems to me that there are *no* isolated actions. The action of a factor is accomplished and can be analysed only through interactions even if, in extreme cases, this action of a factor strongly dominates the others.

Wallon and I tend to trace everything back to the maturation of the nervous system and to the social factor. Two very important matters must be made quite clear however:

(*a*) I do not consider these factors of maturation and environment to be additive. They determine each other in a progressive integration. Moreover the conception of the social factor runs the risk of creating misunderstanding if by it one means only the general framework within which the individual's activity is carried out. The conception of syncretic sociability defined by Wallon at the stage of pure emotivity implies a very archaic level of the 'social' and at the same time stresses the original interdependence of the organism and the social. I personally have used the method of twin investigation more

64

in order to study the dialectics of inter-individual relations than to solve the classical problem of the relative importance of Heredity and Environment (which seems to me a very ambiguous problem in any case). This corresponds with what Piaget (p. 20)—using a debatable term—calls molecular phenomena of social life. The term is debatable in my opinion because the idea of the molecule may lead us to think that social life in the 'molar' sense (general form of society) is only the combination of individual interactions.

(b) Mind ('psychism') cannot be reduced to factors. The human being is not reduced to the conditions of his existence. A new reality arises from the processes of integration of the different factors. Through his actions and his conscience (whatever the definition given to conscience) the individual becomes in turn the *agent* of his development and his behaviour. Although I am reluctant to admit that equilibrium is a factor, I nevertheless consider that, in the dynamics of development, effects become in turn causes. Here we reach the problem of conscience, of interiorization, and of autonomy, which scientific psychology cannot solve by denial.

2. *Concept of equilibrium*

The phenomena of equilibrium and regulation are incontrovertible. But I am not quite sure:
(a) of understanding exactly the explanatory significance Piaget gives to the conception of equilibrium considered as a factor;
(b) of agreeing with him as to the wide extent which he attributes to the phenomenon of equilibrium in all natural fields—physical, psychological and sociological.

First of all I find it rather difficult to admit under the same category of factors heredity, environment, and equilibrium. It seems to me that equilibrium is always a relationship, a *law* of organization between elements or between various causal series. If one classes equilibrium as a fourth factor alongside material causes and conditions one runs the risk either of *substantializing*, of hypostasizing the laws of equilibrium, or else of *dematerializing* the material factors of development, making them disappear in a pure game of intemporal relations, a mental algebra.

Moreover, I was very much struck by the fact that the concrete examples Piaget gives of the *independence* of the equilibrium 'factor' are in relation to the solution of a problem at a given stage of development and not to an actual *genesis*: as if what was essential was the equilibrium, a sort of final cause, transcending the conditions of development. Here he stresses *that which does not change* (the eternal and general laws of logic) and does not consider, as such, *that which changes*.

In any case it seems to me necessary to distinguish between the process of equilibrium *during genesis* (an equilibrium established between well-defined material conditions) and the process of equilibrium as the *search for a solution*.

3. *The concept of a common language*

The scientific mind requires, of course, that the same things should be said in the same terms and that the same term should be applied exclusively to the same thing. Specializations are accompanied by conceptual organizations and jargons which are often undecipherable from one specialization to another.

However, one may sometimes be led to believe that the idea of a common language and the isomorphism of the different levels of reality are interdependent, for example if one speaks of the 'translation from one viewpoint into another'. In the case of the EEG, intellectual operations and social relations, their common laws of strategy, economy and equilibrium might authorize a common language and, of course, the more clearly the identity of the laws emerges from the diversity of the phenomena, the easier would it be to establish a common language. Moreover, scientists have a strong tendency to attempt this reduction of reality, this 'identification', as Emil Meyerson has shown so well in his famous thesis.

But we cannot postulate what still remains to be demonstrated and consequently we must not base a common language on what is only a heuristic attitude or a working hypothesis. In short, if 'common language' signifies use of common terms to designate the same things, then I am in agreement with Piaget; if 'common language' is the expression of a postulate of isomorphism, then I am not.

Certainly our various languages must become inter-coherent in their attempt at expressing the coherence of the various levels of reality. We must look for analogies, parallelisms and common laws and also, within the same field and from one field to another, relations between cause and effect where the effect cannot be reduced to its cause.

Practically speaking, the search for a common language is not just limited to the search for common terms in special scientific fields, but includes the statement of clear definitions, that is to say definitions communicable without ambiguity outside the narrow circle of a speciality.

4. *The concept of stages of development*

I do not think I have understood very well Piaget's criteria of the concept of stage. However, I have here two preliminary remarks to make:

(*a*) I am not certain that his definition applies to everything that might be considered as a stage. He has defined the concept of stage on lines suggested by the study of intelligence. If one demands criteria—particularly the characteristic of structural equilibrium—which are perhaps peculiar to cognitive functions, one runs the risk of neglecting in other fields the existence of stages which would be expressed only by a constant order of succession and by integration. There is a risk of ending up for example with the syllogism which would sterilize all scientific initiative: the stage is an equilibrium structure, therefore there are no stages in the development of personality.

In the present state of our knowledge it seems to me more profitable to agree upon a much less restrictive definition, having as criteria only *constant order* and *integration*.

(*b*) I am not certain that I have correctly understood Piaget's attitude concerning the evolution of non-cognitive functions. Sometimes it seems to me that he is sceptical about the existence of stages other than intellectual stages: in particular, he mentions on several occasions that the cognitive factors correspond to the structure of behaviour whereas the affective factors correspond only to their energy component.

5. *Mechanisms of passage from one stage to another*

We must certainly come to an agreement as to what we mean by the word stage. But that is not enough. We must be fully aware of, and state clearly if necessary, the concepts which take account of the mechanisms and the dialectic of change: concepts of threshold, passage from a quantitative growth to a qualitative transformation, etc.

I should like therefore to come back to some commonplace affirmations which have been neglected during our discussions on the existence of stages:

1. The continuity of a growth (level of calcification, length of limb, increase in angle measuring muscular extensibility, degrees of myelinization) does not exclude *a priori* a transformation or a *discontinuity* on a functional level.

2. At a higher level of complexity the continuity of growth of physiological components or conditions can cause the appearance of stages at the psychological level. Thus we must look for the coherence of development rather in causal liaisons than in the correspondence of stages, whether or not the development occurs in successive levels.

3. The psycho-physiological evolution of the individual leads him into increasingly complex and extensive *environments* which can act as external organizers and thus cause stages.

4. It is true that the statement of dominant characters is frequently arbitrary. However, we must distinguish between a *subjectivity* which brings with it no proof, and an entirely legitimate *relativity* of points of view. The stages can vary according to the codes one uses for deciphering, but obviously each code must be clearly defined.

5. The hostility of many authors towards a denial of the conception of stages frequently arises from the desire to preserve whatever might be qualitative in the transformation of the individual, whether in psychology or physiology. It is necessary to stress strongly that a *qualitative transformation* (of the personality, for example) *can well be conceived without discontinuity*: a gradual transformation, as in light spectra. In this respect the concept of crisis remains to be clearly stated.

LUDWIG VON BERTALANFFY

Comments on Professor Piaget's Paper

As I am a newcomer to the Group, the present memorandum is intended to give some idea as to the contribution I may be able to make to the discussion at the Fourth Meeting. I am basing my remarks on Professor Piaget's paper.

I. *The quest for a common language*

Professor Piaget has admirably emphasized that, in order to arrive at some co-ordination and synthesis of various fields, a principal problem is that of a common language which, so to speak, is translatable from one field to the other.

1. I believe I can make a suggestion in this respect. In the last few years, a development has taken place which seems to correspond well to Professor Piaget's quest. It is the development of General System Theory (G.S.T.).

G.S.T. is intended to elaborate such principles as apply to 'systems' in general, irrespective of their particular kind, the nature of their component elements, and the relations or 'forces' between them. It thus provides a superstructure of theory generalized in comparison with the conventional fields of science. It is capable of giving exact definitions to many notions, such as, for example, wholeness, interaction, progressive differentiation, mechanization, centralization, dynamic and homeostatic (feedback) regulations, teleological behaviour, etc., which recur in all biological, behavioural, and social fields, have had some vitalistic or mystical flavour, and were not accounted for in the so-called 'mechanistic' approach. In such a way, G.S.T. accounts for the isomorphy of theoretical constructs and of the corresponding traits of reality in the diverse fields of science.

G.S.T. has been rather extensively applied in various fields during recent years, and it may be mentioned that a *Society for the Advancement of General Systems Theory*, which is a group within the *American Association for the Advancement of Science*, attempts further development and application of this field. The principal goals of G.S.T. are: (*a*) in trying to integrate individual branches of science in their general principles; and (*b*) in offering a theoretical structure and models to those fields of science—especially the behavioural sciences—which still lack them.

Ashby's formulations (1952) referred to in previous meetings are closely related to those mentioned above. Even though he does not use the term General System Theory, he starts with the same mathematical model as I do. As Ashby and I have drawn different derivations from the same model, our work is complementary.

2. I am not going to review in this memorandum what has been done in this line as it may be found in the literature (Bertalanffy 1949, 1950a). Rather, I would like to give some clarification as to the bearing as well as the limitations of G.S.T. and interdisciplinary constructs in general. What will be said applies equally to other attempts at a 'common language', such as information theory, game theory, decision theory, cybernetics, and so forth.

Being an experimentalist with strong leanings towards physics myself, I am vividly aware of a danger apparent in much of current literature in the behavioural fields. Nothing is accomplished by loosely applying to unexplained or unco-ordinated facts some fashionable term—be it 'system', 'homeostasis', 'feedback', 'information', 'minimax solution', or whatever the case may be. Attaching some new verbal label must not be mistaken for a new insight or understanding.

What G.S.T. (and related constructs) can do is what Hayek (1955) has aptly discussed as 'explanation of the principle'. In physics (and to a certain extent other fields such as biophysics, genetics, etc.), there is a hypothetico-deductive system of laws, the appropriate parameters of which can be inserted; so we have explanation and prediction of individual empirical phenomena, such as the positions of the planets at any time in the past or future, the behaviour of atoms, or the result of some cross in *Drosophila*. Many biological and most behavioural phenomena (except such rather trivial aspects as e.g. mortality statistics) are too complicated and obscure in their structure to allow for such explanation and prediction. The best we can do—at least at present—is some 'explanation in principle'. What this means can best be illustrated by a few examples.

There is a highly elaborate mathematical theory of population, both from the ecological (Volterra, D'Ancona, Gause and others) and genetical (Fisher, Sewall Wright, etc.) viewpoints. All biologists agree that this theory provides an important basis for understanding the struggle for existence, biological equilibria, etc., and evolutionary processes, respectively. It is difficult, however, to prove quantitatively, say, Volterra's laws of population growth even in laboratory experiments, and it is nearly impossible to do so in the field as the complexity of natural ecological and genetical systems prohibits giving concrete values to the relevant parameters (coefficients of reproduction, extinction, and competition; selective advantage, coefficients for drift and the like).

Economics and econometrics provide theoretical models which are more or less generally accepted. As a rule, however, professors of economics are not millionaires, showing that though they can give 'explanations in principle' for the economic process, they are not in a position to predict the fluctuations of the market with respect to a definite date or an individual stock.

Game theory (referred to as a possible model by Piaget, at p. 7) is a novel and original mathematical field. However, I understand from competent authorities that hardly any examples except trivial ones can be figured out specifically in the way a physicist or engineer would calculate a phenomenon or a machine, even though the theory may provide explanations 'in principle' for psychological and social phenomena.

Similar considerations apply to G.S.T. It is in a position to offer 'explanation in principle'; but it cannot be blamed for not giving quantitative solutions for phenomena like embryonic regulation, psychobiological development, etc., where the complexity of the process and the lack of definition of the relevant parameters are prohibitive.

So much about G.S.T. and theoretical models in general. What more can it offer for the problems of psychobiological development?

II. *The question of an equilibrium factor*

1. Professor Piaget suggests that, besides the factors customarily envisaged in development, another principle should be considered which he calls the 'equilibrium factor'.

In principle, I am in full agreement with Professor Piaget, but I believe that this viewpoint can be considerably improved if, instead of the notion of 'equilibrium', somewhat different conceptions are taken as the starting point.

Looking first at the organism from the physiological viewpoint, it is a basic characteristic that it is not a system in equilibrium. On the contrary, for a system to be living presupposes that it avoids the state of equilibrium. If equilibrium—chemical, osmotic, thermodynamic, etc.—is reached, this means death.

This avoidance of equilibrium is possible because the organism is an open system, maintaining itself in continuous exchange, building up and breaking down its components. An open system and an organism may reach a time-independent state where it appears to remain macroscopically unchanged; but this is not 'equilibrium' but a 'steady state'.

Although this seems to be trivial and the living organism has been called a 'dynamic equilibrium' for a long time, only in recent years has the theory of open system and steady states—kinetic and thermodynamic—been developed. The laws governing open systems and steady states are characteristically different from those governing the conventional closed systems and equilibria. Again I have to forsake a more detailed explanation and refer to current literature (for a general orientation: cf. Bertalanffy, 1950b, 1953a, 1954; Bray & White, 1954; Jung, 1956). I am taking up only a few aspects which may be important in relation to problems of behaviour.

It is a basic tenet in biology and psychobiology that the organism tends to maintain itself 'in equilibrium', that is, to react to stimuli in such a way as to return to a state of rest. This is also at the basis of the notion of homeostasis, although this introduces some new ideas as to the mechanisms concerned (feedback, circular processes). Intimately connected with this is the 'automaton model' of the organism, that is, the conception that the organism is essentially a reactive system, set into motion only by external influences (stimulus-response scheme).

These models are unrealistic. That the organism is not a resting but a primarily active system is shown by phenomena as diverse as metabolism, spontaneous movements of lower animals, of foetuses before the establishment of reflexes or after deafferentation (Lorenz, *First Meeting*, Vol. I, p. 108 ff.), the EEG of the unstimulated brain, '*in vacuo*' behaviour, and innumerable others. Liddell gave a nice illustration of the bias imposed by model conceptions (or rather metaphysico-political superstitions) when he told us (Vol. II, p. 142) how for the Pavlov school spontaneous behaviour in the dog was unorthodox, 'against the rules', and politically suspect.

In contrast, according to the open-system model, the organism is an intrinsically active system. Furthermore, the theory of open systems accounts for just those properties of the living organism which were considered 'vitalistic', that is, violating the laws of physics such as the equifinality of development (Driesch's 'first proof of vitalism'), and the apparent contradiction between the trend towards increasing disorder in the inorganic world following 'the second principle of thermodynamics, and the trend toward increasing order in biological development and evolution (another 'proof of vitalism' according to DuNoüy and others). These vital characteristics are in contrast with the conventional physics of closed systems, but are perfectly legitimate within and, indeed, necessary consequences of, a generalized physics of open systems. Also the problem of biological time, referred to by Grey Walter (Vol. II, p. 34, 66) comes under the theory of Irreversible Thermodynamics and biophysics of open systems.

Both Lorenz and myself (Bertalanffy, 1937, p. 10 ff., 133 ff.; 1952, p. 17 ff., 114 ff.) have for a long time stressed that the organism should be considered as an essentially active system—Lorenz in his theory of instinct and behaviour, connected with von Holst's criticism of classical reflexology; I in the context of general biological theory, eventually leading to the modern expansion of kinetics and thermodynamics, as briefly indicated above.

2. Coming to psychobiological matters, we find the development closely parallel. An important basis of Freudian theory is the 'principle of stability' he adopted from Fechner. The supreme tendency of the organism, biological and mental, supposedly is to get rid of stimuli, and come to rest in a state of 'equilibrium'. It is in the same vein when the concept of homeostasis is applied to any sort of behavioural or mental activity—from mountain climbing to science or composing sonatas (cf. Stagner (1951) and the criticism of the concept of homeostasis by Toch & Hastorf (1955) and Bertalanffy (1951a)).

The above theoretical notions do not seem to account for those aspects which are variously called play-activities, exploring, creativity and the like, going along with 'function pleasure' (Karl Bühler, cf. Mead's remarks, Vol. II, p. 139), which is so characteristic of human behaviour in general, and mental development of the child in particular. As Lorenz has always emphasized (e.g. 1943), these activities have their forerunners in animal behaviour. Just as the physical organism avoids a state of equilibrium, so does the mental organism, an essential aspect of which seems to be not relieving of tensions but rather building up new tensions.

Neo-Freudian theory tries to account for this state of affairs. Thus Alexander (1948) states that 'the basic function of the mental apparatus consists in sustaining the homeostatic equilibrium' but adds that besides the principles of 'stability' and 'inertia' (the latter identical with 'progressive mechanization' as mentioned above) another principle of 'surplus energy' is required. The Montreal experiments, reported at this Conference by Dr. Bindra (Vol. II, p. 75 ff.), dramatically show that the human organism just cannot stand a state of non-stimulation, of complete rest and of 'equilibrium'. The hallucinations occurring in absolute seclusion are a vivid demonstration of the 'autonomous activity' of the psychophysical organism.

So, physiologically, the organism is an instrinsically active system, tending to a steady state and allowing even for 'anamorphosis', i.e. spontaneous transition toward higher order. Psychologically, this implies what may be loosely called 'creativity'; and in terms of general theory, these are consequences of the organism being not a closed system attaining equilibrium but an open system.

3. Naturally, it remains to be seen in how far the open-system model can be applied to behavioural or psychobiological science. Attempts in this direction have been made by Krech (1950) and Pringle (1951) and in the transactional viewpoint, often quoted nowadays, by Bentley (1950). A 'biologistic' reductionism would be no better than 'physicalism'. Trivially, open systems as treated in physics and biophysics are something quite different from what the psychologist is speaking of. I propose, however, that as a tentative model or analogue, 'open system' with 'autonomous activity' and 'anamorphosis' is a better construct to start with than 'closed system' (which actually is at the basis of Gestalt psychology, behaviourism, cybernetics, and Freudian theory) (cf. Bertalanffy, 1951b, p. 33 ff.), 'primary reactivity' (the stimulus-response scheme), and mental organization conceived as an apparatus to maintain 'equilibrium'.

III. *Stages or continuous development*

In view of the foregoing, the controversy whether development is 'continuous' or taking place in 'stages' seems to acquire a few new aspects.

1. One relevant notion has already been introduced, namely that of step functions as discussed by Ashby, meaning that the process is not discontinuous but shows more or less rapid transitions toward higher levels or plateaux (cf. the discussion in Bertalanffy, 1956).

2. Obviously there are no all-embracing steps as Gesell (1956) seems to presuppose when speaking of the 'personality of the 10-11-year-old', etc., as distinct entities. So far as somatic development is concerned, a glance at the figure reproduced by Tanner (Vol. I, Fig. 1, p. 37) shows that all organs do not follow the same pattern of development.

There are, however, periods where not all but quite a number of characteristics change. Trivially, puberty is one of them. In this sense it seems legitimate to speak of 'phases' or 'cycles' of somatic and mental growth.

3. As a somewhat less trivial notion, I would like to introduce that of equifinal steps. As has been indicated, equifinality is a characteristic of open systems if and when they tend toward a steady state. Equifinal phases are such as to be reached from different starting points and in different ways, and maintained over a time till a change in conditions—external or internal—causes a new development in the system and brings it on the way toward another equifinal phase. This is related to Piaget's conception of successive equilibria stages or levels, but brings in a few new viewpoints. I am illustrating this by way of a few examples deliberately taken from very different fields.

(*a*) The early development of an ovum is very different in the various animal classes or orders, being what is technically known as holoblastic, meroblastic, discoidal, or superficial segmentation. This depends upon factors such as the content and distribution of yolk; it varies in different species and is even changeable experimentally. However, an essentially similar two-layered stage, the gastrula, is reached anyway. Similarly, early development in amphioxus, fish, amphibian, reptile, bird, and mammal is very different. Nevertheless, the vertebrate neurula with its characteristic arrangement of primordial organs is strikingly similar in all classes.

(*b*) Everybody is agreed that species have not arisen by separate acts of creation, as Linnaeus had it, but by natural evolution, presupposing transition from one species to another. However, what we find in nature is separate species, with hardly any intermediates. The nearest explanation is that species are relatively stable systems in genic balance, which therefore show up abundantly in the present fauna and flora and in the palaeontological record, while intermediates are unbalanced, short-lived stages of transition, which for this very reason, usually are 'missing links' (for a more detailed discussion, cf. Bertalanffy, 1952, p. 95 ff.). It is in the same vein that Huxley (Vol. III, p. 200)) emphasizes that most species become stabilized at a certain level of organization.

(*c*) In the history of architecture, we distinguish the Romanesque and Gothic and Baroque styles. There are transitions between Romanesque and Gothic ('Uebergangstil' of the German art historians), and between Gothic and Baroque. However, specimens of these transition styles are rare. Suppose Europe were to be exposed in a new war to even more efficient bombing than took place in the Second World War. Then, for statistical reasons, the few specimens of transition style would be extinguished while a number of Romanesque and Gothic churches would still remain. So the art historian of the future would see a jump from Romanesque to Gothic— exactly the same picture as the palaeontologist sees in the animal and plant world. Romanesque, Gothic, and Baroque would appear to be stages of relative 'balance' which therefore are maintained for quite a while, till new influences (perhaps Arabic in the first instance, Renaissance in the second) upset this 'balance' and lead to a new development and relatively stable state.

Again, early automobiles were a lot of fancy carriages of every imaginable shape, type of propulsion, etc. But when the development became stabilized, that is, a near optimal solution of the technical problem was reached, nothing much happened any more. So present cars of whatever brand are pretty much alike, and the car makers are at pains every year to advertise a 'new' model, that is, one which is a little different in trimming from last year's crop. The parallel to evolution of new species is obvious. I notice that Piaget has already hinted at 'cultural equifinality' in his questions to Margaret Mead (p. 25).

(*d*) Something similar seems to apply to the psychobiological development of the child. If I am correctly informed, the age of 10 to 12 represents a stage of internal balance. Then the beginning action of the sex hormones, etc., leads, somatically, to a second acceleration of growth ('adolescent spurt' of Tanner); correlated, electrophysiologically, with the change from theta to alpha rhythm (Grey Walter, Vol. I, Fig. 15, p. 145); psychologically, to a second 'negative' or sulking phase; scholastically, the transition to secondary school (cf. Zazzo, Vol. I, p. 166 ff.). Eventually a new balance is reached in the adult. More detailed are Piaget's (and Freud's) phases of early mental development.

So development seems to take place in a series of equifinal levels, and this seems to take out much of the sharpness of contrast between 'stages' and 'continuous development'. Unnecessary to repeat that these stages are not all-inclusive, and that maturation does not take place simultaneously in all processes, physiological or mental.

JEAN PIAGET

Reply to Comments Concerning the Part Played by Equilibration Processes in the Psychobiological Development of the Child

This is perhaps not the place to thank my colleagues and to express my appreciation of the very varied replies which they drew up for our last meeting following my attempt at a synthesis. The discussions which took place at that meeting,[1] in addition to indicating clearly my gratitude, showed above all how much attention I have paid to their comments. However, in view of the fact that these discussions have ended in a measure of agreement much greater than seemed possible at the outset, particularly by clearing up certain semantic misunderstandings, I was asked to draw up, after the meeting, a brief reply to the documents prepared beforehand.[2]

The aim of this reply is simply to show that if it is granted (contrary to the impression my report may have given) that the organism is an open and essentially active system then development cannot be explained without having recourse to equilibration processes. In fact, although mental, like physical, life (and even more so) is a perpetual process of construction (and sometimes even of invention), it is by no means incoherent because of this, and what is required is to understand how the mechanism bringing about this continual construction may constitute at the same time a regulating mechanism ensuring coherence.

In the field of the cognitive functions in particular, the problem is to understand how new learning, discovery and creation may not only be reconciled with but take place at the same time as control and verification in such a way that the new remains in harmony with the acquired. This is once more a problem of equilibration. However, although everyone stresses the activity and renewal aspect of development, the equilibration aspect is only too often forgotten. Above all,

---

[1] Reported in Part II.
[2] It is, of course, understood that I alone am responsible for this reply which must remain without an answer.

it is often not sufficiently realized that these two aspects are inseparable and that the very same agencies which effect the new constructions are also those which simultaneously ensure their regulation.

An example of this is afforded by logical operations, under their double aspect of agencies of indefinite construction and coherent reversibility. Although this example is almost unique, as we shall stress, from the viewpoint of degree of perfection in equilibrated adaptation, it constitutes no more than the final term of a long series of regulations of all kinds, which come into play with the most elementary learning and perception, and whose semi-equilibrated mechanisms of retroaction and anticipation provide the basis for the logical reversibility which characterizes logical operations. Furthermore, this example illustrates well what is doubtless true in general, namely, that analysis of regulation, in other words of equilibration, throws some light on the mechanism of construction itself (in the case of operations, in fact, every new construction, and consequently every invention, is reversible from the outset and therefore can be equilibrated).

1. The result of stabilization and, in particular, compensation processes, can be designated by the term equilibrium[1] or by that suggested by Bertalanffy, 'stable state in an open system'. Whatever the vocabulary employed, however, it must be stressed at the outset that such processes always exist in a living being, which amounts to saying that, for it, equilibrium does not represent an occasional or extrinsic characteristic but an intrinsic one, subsuming a certain number of specific functions. Thus, for a pebble, the fact of being in stable, unstable, or metastable equilibrium in no way affects its other properties: thus, its equilibrium is an occasional or added characteristic and the proof thereof is that in order to define a state of stable equilibrium the physicist calls in a system of 'virtual work' which exists only in his mind and not in the pebble itself. On the other hand, a higher vertebrate which could not stand on its paws would be pathological; here a homeostatic disorder constitutes a disease. From the mental viewpoint, an adult whose thinking remains unstable as regards definitions, inferences or decisions is considered to be abnormal. In each of these latter cases, equilibrium under one form or another constitutes an intrinsic and not an extrinsic characteristic of the fields considered. (Naturally this does not signify that we have here a specific property of life, but only that wherever there is life there is also equilibration.)

2. In the second place, it must be stressed that the equilibration

---

[1] A translation of the original French word 'équilibre'. It should be noted that in French this word has a broader sense than the words 'equilibrium' or 'balance' in English. See pp. 92, 94.

process which thus constitutes an intrinsic characteristic corresponds, in living beings, to specific needs, tendencies, or functions and not merely to an automatic balance independent of the activities of the subject. Thus, in the case of the higher cognitive functions, there exists a tendency to equilibrium which manifests the need for coherence. In the case of the elementary cognitive functions (perception) the same holds true, although the forms of equilibrium attained are more fleeting and less stable. In other words, the force of the tendency is not entirely determined by its results, and this is why it is better to speak of *equilibration* as a process corresponding to a tendency rather than of equilibrium only.

3. To these needs, tendencies or functions correspond special mechanisms or agencies of equilibration whose activity is complementary to that of all behaviours aiming at the exploration or modification of the environment during the exchanges between it and the organism. Thus, all sensorimotor activity is accompanied by regulation of posture and tonus, etc. In the case of the cognitive functions, one may conceive of the elementary logical operations as constructing new forms or new assemblies within the environment (classifications, seriations, correspondences, etc,); but these activities are necessarily accompanied (necessarily, because this is a condition of their success) by a stabilization of their forms and elements (conservation, etc.). From this viewpoint, it may be said that the inverse and reciprocal operations taking place in this stabilization constitute the equilibrium agencies, it being understood, however, that these mechanisms or agencies are indissolubly linked with those affecting the new constructions.

4. In the sense in which we understand the term, then, equilibrium is therefore essentially bound up with the activities of the organism, not only because equilibration presupposes activities, but also because the stable states or equilibrium forms reached at the end of equilibration processes always represent the play of compensation between activities proper. Stable equilibrium may be defined locally by assuming that if a small perturbation $\triangle E_p$ is introduced in a state E by the observer or by nature, the subject reacts by a spontaneous movement of the same order, $\triangle E_s$, which returns the system to the state E, or to a state close to this. It is then said that the reaction $\triangle E_s$ constitutes an activity.[1]

5. If we prefer the term equilibrium (mobile or dynamic) to that of stable state, it is because the concept of equilibrium implies that of compensation and because the activities of the subject (see 4) are always compensatory at the same time as constructive. This

[1] For more detailed definitions, see the publication on logic and equilibrium which is being prepared by the *Centre international d'Epistémologie génétique.* Geneva.

79

concept is of general importance, since it doubtless concerns the fundamental mechanisms of assimilation or learning. If these mechanisms are assumed to be on a simple process of association, the problem then remains of understanding why certain associations are unstable (for example, conditioning considered as merely association remains temporary or unstable) whereas others are stable. The problem can be solved only to the extent that a stabilization factor is introduced, in the form of the satisfaction of a need (which is thus a compensation in the sense that filling a gap is a compensation). In other words, in the event of a stable association between x and y, y is not only associated (externally) with x, but assimilated to x in the sense that y is merged into the x schema and fills a momentary gap (need) relating to this schema.

These considerations confirm what has been said (under 3) regarding the complementary and indissociable nature of equilibration and of assimilation; the concept of assimilation explains more than does that of association precisely in so far as it includes a stabilization factor.

6. The compensatory activities just discussed (5), which therefore constitute the specific agencies of equilibration (cf. 3), play a considerable part at all levels of behaviour, in the form of retroactive processes necessary for the anticipations involved in construction. In this respect, it may be considered that the agencies of equilibration correspond in general to all regulatory systems in their dual retroactive and anticipatory aspect. However, these concepts recur continually in all theories explaining behaviour, from the 'feedback' common in the Anglo-Saxon countries to the reafferences and models of action of Soviet psychology. Even in a theory of learning as associationist as Hull's, retroactions play an essential part.

7. However, even if all this is commonplace, it is not often understood that the higher cognitive operations constitute, with their characteristics of combined retroaction and anticipation, structures similar to those of the regulations (and the silence of my colleagues in the study group on this point shows that I continue to be not very comprehensible in this connexion). However, there are two differences, namely, that they attain complete equilibrium and that, thanks to the complete reversibility which characterizes this equilibrium, the operational structures take an algebraic form simpler than the mathematical expression of 'feed-back'.[1]

8. Thus, reversibility for an operation leading from state A to state B consists in the presence of an inverse operation leading back from state B to state A. Reversibility (in the form of inversion or reci-

[1] These operational structures take simple forms such as groups, groupings, lattices, etc., while a 'feed-back' must be expressed as a complicated integral.

procity) is thus a special case of retroaction: that in which the retro-action brings about a complete return to state A and not only to a state A', close to A. It may therefore be said that, in the case of operations, operation BA is the same as operation AB, but reversed (an identity which is indicated by the consideration that when a subject understands an operation he also understands, by this very fact, the possibility of its inverse), whereas, in the case of a regulation, no matter of what kind, the two actions which lead from A to B and from B to A or A' respectively, are different. Apart from this distinctive characteristic, however, operational reversibility is nothing more than retroaction. It may therefore be said that operations represent a direct prolongation of regulations and it may even be considered that, from the viewpoint of equilibrium, the three great structures which dominate mental life and arise in hierarchic order during development are the basic rhythms, the regulations and the operations. These logical structures consequently do not represent an isolated sector of mental life (or a characteristic formed from outside by language, etc.) but the final stage of an edifice all of whose parts are interdependent.

9. However, the value of an equilibration theory is precisely in explaining this completion of the activo-cognitive structures (if they can be so termed). Indeed, it is this progressive equilibrium of the compensation ($\triangle E_s$ in relation to $\triangle E_p$) which underlies operational reversibility, and not the reverse. If it were necessary to explain equilibrium by reversibility, it would be impossible to under-stand from whence the latter could arise, whereas one can understand (in outline) how coarse compensations become finer and how, with the aid of symbolic function and representation, these compensations may finally bring about, *in thought*, exact reversibility. To employ a comparison, which is more than a mere image, it might be said that when a physicist describes the equilibrium of a body, he calls into play systems of 'virtual work' which exist in his mind and not in the said body, while in bringing about the equilibrium of his interiorized actions (which are his operations), a living and thinking subject establishes an interplay of compensations between the different components of virtual work, which then play an effective role in his actual thought.[1] This system of virtual work con-stitutes, in fact, a system of all possible operations for a given structure and it is precisely these possible operations which represent logic.

10. From such a viewpoint, logical structures are the only completely equilibrated structures in the organism (apart from a few similar

[1] We might thus define virtual work without calling on concepts of force, etc., but considering merely $\triangle E_s$'s which are imaginable (in the true sense of the word) without being actually carried out.

81

structures which approach without attaining the same precision, i.e. perceptive constants and certain sensorimotor schemata relative to space and objects). As such, the operational structures constitute a very special case, whose properties cannot be generalized for the whole of mental life, even under its cognitive aspect. But as this special case also represents, at the same time, the final point of a very general process of equilibration and as this process concerns the regulations as a whole (and, beyond them, more basic rhythms), the study of logical structures is very important in order to determine the real significance of equilibrium mechanisms.

11. It should be noted further that, although equilibration thus constitutes a developmental factor to be added to the three classic factors of heredity, environment (external or internal), and social education, it is a factor which cannot be dissociated from them. To be more precise, equilibrium is a form (and equilibration a structuration), but this form has a content and this content can only be hereditary or acquired by physical or social learning. However, as none of these three factors acts alone, it would be useless to try to isolate the equilibration factor; it intervenes in every hereditary or acquired process, and intervenes in their interactions. It is in this sense that it is the most general of the four, but this in no way signifies that it is superimposed on the other three by an additive process.

12. In particular, the equilibrium factor is dominant in exchanges between the organism and the environment. These exchanges correspond to what is generally termed 'adaptation' (and Lorenz suggested that I replace the term 'equilibrium' by 'adaptive interaction'). However, all adaptation, both mental and physical, includes two poles: one corresponding to the assimilation of energy or matter from the environment by the structure of the organism (or mental assimilation of data perceived in the environment to the schemata of action followed by the subject); the other corresponding to the accommodation[1] of structures of schemata of the organism or subject to environmental situations or data. Adaptation is then nothing more than an equilibrium between this assimilation and organic or mental accommodation. This is why the most elementary exchanges between subject and object are already determined by the equilibrium factor.

Conclusion

This last remark (12) enables us to conclude by putting the equilibrium factor in its true perspective, which is a biological and not a

---

[1] We use this term in the sense of 'accommodates' or phenotypes, i.e. variations undergone by the organism in relation to the environment.

logical one, although the special equilibrium of logical structures is one of the finest achievements of living morphogenesis.

We shall therefore conclude by saying that life, like thought (or thought, like life) is essentially active because it constructs forms. From this viewpoint, thought forms are a prolongation of living morphogenesis through the intermediary of nervous co-ordination, sensorimotor schemata of action, etc., without forgetting social structures, since the operation of reason is always dependent on co-operation. However these forms or structures, whether biological or mental, must constantly comply with the double requirement of assimilation of objects or external data to them and, in return, of accomodation to these objects or data. Without assimilation, the organism or subject would be like soft wax, as in the reproach levelled against empiricism, ceaselessly modified by chance encounters or changes in the environment. Without accommodation, the organism or the subject would be withdrawn within itself and beyond the reach of any external action. This equilibrium between assimilation and accommodation can only be limited and relatively unstable on the organic level, since the effects of one are attained at the expense of the other: equilibrium is only a compromise at the level of organic morphogenesis or variation of the species. With nervous organization and mental life, on the contrary, a twofold power of retroaction and anticipation, of reconstitution of the past and the foreseeing of the future, considerably enlarges the field of this equilibrium and replaces fleeting compromises by actual syntheses. Schemata of action already constitute such syntheses, with their power of general assimilation and multiple accommodation. Nevertheless equilibrium is only attained, from the operational and cognitive viewpoint, with logico-mathematical structures capable of assimilating the whole universe to thought, without being ever broken or even shaken by the innumerable accommodations called for by experience. We have studied the background of this cognitive equilibration in the modest sector represented by child development: but, even within this limited field, it is remarkably instructive and becomes much more so once properly situated in its general perspective.

PART II
DISCUSSION

INTRODUCTORY DISCUSSION

DR. CANDAU (Director-General, World Health Organization):
Ladies and Gentlemen; I am very happy to welcome you here at Geneva today and to open the fourth meeting of the Study Group on the Psychobiological Development of the Child, which is to be the last of the present series. As I understand it, the Group intends, during the coming week, to try to synthesize the points of view of the disciplines which it represents and to reach some general agreement as to the interaction of factors involved in the child's development, the way characteristic stages follow one another, and the actual mechanisms involved when one stage succeeds another. It has been agreed that searching for a common language to facilitate understanding between representatives of different specialities is of fundamental importance.

Considerable preparatory work has been undertaken for this meeting. Professor Piaget, who was requested to make the initial presentation, has circulated to the Study Group members a stimulating paper on the general problems of the psychobiological development of the child. This has evoked much comment from the members, and a series of preparatory papers give their points of view and replies to specific questions addressed to them by Professor Piaget (see Part I). I am happy that the World Health Organization has been able to contribute to the preparation of this meeting, in particular by aiding in the making of a film by Professor Piaget and Mlle Inhelder on some aspects of the child's intellectual development. I look forward to the further discussion with very great interest.

FREMONT-SMITH (Chairman, Study Group):
We have much reason to be grateful to Dr. Candau, and first I want to express our thanks to him, and to Dr. Peterson and his staff. We are particularly grateful for the fact that we have been clearly designated as a Study Group which is distinct from an Expert Committee, and given the job not of passing resolutions but of interacting, learning, growing, doing something which we are studying in this Study Group on the Psychobiological Development of the Child—developing ourselves.

Professor von Bertalanffy, as our only new member on this occasion, would you be kind enough very informally to introduce yourself by telling us in three or four minutes those highpoints in your career which you think we would like to hear about? (See Vols. I, II and III for similar introductions by other members.)

87

BERTALANFFY:

When I read the proceedings of the previous meeting I noticed that in introducing themselves the members of the Group emphasized nurture and somewhat underplayed nature, even though in many of you—for example Julian Huxley and Konrad Lorenz—the hereditary traits would be quite obvious. So, for a change, let me reverse this procedure. As my name reveals, I am a Hungarian of a sort, meaning that my stock is Hungarian even though I do not speak a word of this language. The first Bertalanffy of some shadowy literary merit appears to have been a Jesuit, Bertalanffy Pál, who in the early 1700s wrote a pious book of sermons. He, having been a Catholic priest, obviously cannot be in my direct ancestral line. To what extent traits of the Jesuitic mind are discoverable in my way of thinking is for you to decide. Anyway, this book seems to be one of the first printed in the Hungarian language and quite a bibliophilic item. Only two copies have come to my attention—one was once in my possession and was burnt with my other belongings during the war, and the other one is in the British Museum.

One of my grandfathers also was quite a character. He was a trained lawyer, but eloped with a wandering theatre troupe—with a road-show I think you would say—and ended up as the director of the Stadt Theatres in Graz and Vienna. I read in a book that the Graz theatre was never at a lower artistic level than under my revered grandfather's direction, but also was never better off financially. Unfortunately I did not inherit his businesslike mind.

As far as I myself am concerned, my work has been in the field of theoretical and quantitative biology, experimental medicine, and cellular and comparative physiology. In the present connexion, however, my philosophical background will perhaps be more interesting. It is a rather chequered one. In my youth I was strongly attracted by German mysticism. Indeed, it is one of my small triumphs that back in 1928 I published a selection of the works of Nicholas of Cusa—that extraordinary figure of the Quattrocento who, being a Roman Cardinal, was at the same time the last of the line of great German mystics and the first of the line of modern science and enlightenment which later led to Copernicus, Galileo and Newton, as well as to Giordano Bruno and Leibniz. This was some years before Nicholas of Cusa was brought to the more general attention by the Heidelberg Academy's great edition of his works. On the other hand I was a student and pupil of Moriz Schlick, the founder of the Vienna circle of logical positivism. I was also on very good terms with the blind philosopher Hans Vaihinger, the author of the *Philosophy of As If*. Such influences at least lead a person to be broadminded, and what today I would call a 'perspectivistic' viewpoint is, in modern terms, the dictum of Nicholas of Cusa 'ex omnibus partibus relucet totum', meaning that any part or any viewpoint in some limited way reflects the universe.

If I am asked what I would consider as my moderate achievements, I would perhaps point to the following. First, I have been advocating that viewpoint in biology known as the organismic conception. The concept that the organism must be considered and investigated as a whole is a triviality nowadays, but it used not to be so, and was indeed under heavy fire when I tried to advance it during the 1920s. This viewpoint was partly the background of a good part of my laboratory work, which was concerned with metabolism, growth, and related problems in their quantitative aspects. Furthermore the concept of the organism as an open system and a steady state led me into physical chemistry, kinetics and thermodynamics, and here I was confronted with a rather amazing fact. Obviously the organism is a system showing continuous exchange, import and export of matter and is thus an open system—but there was no theory in conventional physics to account for such systems and their laws. Eventually I was led to the concept of the general system theory as a sort of generalized superstructure of science, applicable particularly to fields outside physics.

After many years at the University of Vienna, the course of my life has led me, with the exodus of Austrian scientists after the war, first to Canada where I directed a department of research in medical biology at the University of Ottawa, and then to the west coast of America. After a year at the Centre for Advanced Study in the Behavioral Sciences in Stanford, I recently came to Los Angeles. My laboratory is particularly engaged in cancer work, and at present we are studying the application of fluorescence microscopy to cancer diagnosis. However in recent years my interests have increasingly concentrated on behavioural science and the basic theoretical questions of psychiatry.

Now it remains to me to thank you for your kind invitation, and I certainly do not need to tell you how much I am looking forward to this conference, hoping to contribute whatever little I can to the fundamental problems this Group is investigating.

FREMONT-SMITH:
Thank you very much, Dr. von Bertalanffy.

PIAGET:
This essay of mine (Part I) which was sent to you was a kind of experiment. When I tried to carry out the task which you gave me the honour of undertaking, that is, of attempting a synthesis as a starting point for our discussions, I found myself in a very awkward situation. A synthesis is either a common doctrine—which is

obviously impossible in a group such as ours with such multiple and diverse points of view—or it is a common hierarchy of the problems, a common search for general ideas or general models. Now to write a paper simply on the problems and ideas that can be used would not be very exciting. I therefore chose to make a sort of compromise; I tried to draw up a paper which would stress particularly the problems of a common language, of the factors affecting development, and of developmental stages and the mechanisms of transition from one stage to another. Apart from this, I included in my paper some personal opinions which I have not developed fully, but which I put in, to be quite frank, as a challenge to provoke contradiction and discussion. I added a few questions for the same purpose.

The experiment I wanted to make concerned the two following questions: (1) would there be real reactions, by which I mean reactions not merely for the sake of courtesy, but constituting a real discussion of the problems posed, and (2) would these reactions be relatively convergent or, on the contrary, would they disperse in all directions? If the responses were real and sufficient convergence were achieved, we could consider the experiment successful and consequently speak of the possibility of making a synthesis; otherwise it would have meant failure, and we should have had to look for something else.

I hope it does not surprise you if I conclude that there was a much greater convergence in your replies than one might have expected. It is a convergence which is partly implicit and our job here is, of course, to get it to stand out more clearly. It is a convergence also achieved frequently at my expense, that is, in contradiction to what I said. That is of no importance, that was just the point of the experiment. Moreover, I think that as regards this last point it is more a question of appearance than reality, and the lack of agreement which may be found between your responses and my paper is not very fundamental. I think I can agree very sincerely with almost all the objections which have been made to my paper, except for one point which is of major importance to me, and that is the role of logic in cognitive functions.

On reading your replies I got a very encouraging impression of freshness, of much more that was new than each of you would probably imagine from your own reply. Authors frequently make themselves best understood in connexion with a discussion of general problems, and I have to admit that on reading your papers I understood a number of points concerning your thoughts which I had previously missed. I am forced to confess that up to then I had misunderstood certain points in the thinking of Margaret Mead, for example, and of Bowlby, of Lorenz, and of several others, and that their replies seemed to me not only highly instructive and illuminating, but also very constructive as regards the synthesis which we are seeking to establish during this last meeting of the group.

I should like to give a few examples of these new points contained in your papers and about which it seems to me almost unanimous agreement is possible.

As the first example I will take the problem of stages as dealt with by Bowlby in his reply. I had already understood from previous discussions between Bowlby and myself that we fundamentally agreed on the problem of relations between an individual's past experience and his present organization. I had understood that Bowlby does not consider, as did Freud in certain passages, that we are fixed in the past and that there is necessarily regression into the unconscious during the utilization of this past, but rather that the past is continually reorganized according to present needs and present structures. But though I had already understood this point, I did not know how to reconcile the Freudian stages with the stages of cognitive development in the child. Now, Bowlby's reply contains an idea which seems to me very clear and fertile. He says that an affective reaction in the child—for example, the relations between the child and his mother—is the product of a group of reactions which are at first isolated or unco-ordinated between themselves, such as suckling or smiling or imitating, but later becomes more and more closely co-ordinated until they finally constitute a whole. Thus Bowlby suggests—and this is the idea which seems to me fundamental —that the stages which are important in the field which interests him are not stages of the same type as the Freudian ones which stress chiefly the dominant aspect at a certain period and which refer essentially to the content of behaviour patterns and not to their form. They are instead stages which depend chiefly, if I have understood Bowlby properly, on the progressions in this development from isolated elements into a co-ordinated whole. In these processes of affective co-ordination, then, we can find stages which might correspond to, or would at least compare more closely with, the stages of cognitive development.

I will take another example, that furnished by Lorenz's reply. I am forced to confess after reading it that up to now I had not understood Lorenz at all well. I had realized this and attempted to do something about it—in particular I suggested that one of my students at the Sorbonne should write a thesis on the ideas of Lorenz and Tinbergen; the thesis was excellent, but did not entirely clarify my thinking. But Lorenz's paper in reply to mine contains a series of statements which seem to me of great importance, and are hard to find in his other writings. For example, I had always thought that his idea of spontaneous activity of an organism was tinged with apriorism or almost with vitalism; but in his paper Lorenz makes an absolutely clear statement against apriorism and preformism in favour of a constant interaction between the spontaneous activities of the organism and environmental influences, so that I am entirely in agreement with this whole section of his reply. In my mind, 'spontaneous' had seemed to contradict this constant interaction; if this is not so, the synthesis of our views becomes easier. Instinctive activities have to be considered as a particular case of morphogenetic activities in general, and I think that cognitive activities are also comprised in morphogenetic activities. It follows that all the work of Lorenz's school on this morphogenesis from the point of view of 'spontaneous' activity could be of direct interest to my research on the development of cognitive structures.

Now I am coming to the main point of my presentation which was discussed by everybody: the idea of equilibrium as a factor in development. On this point there is a very remarkable convergence in your written replies. All the replies made reservations and alterations along the same lines.

(1) Bertalanffy's paper proposes substituting for the word 'equilibrium' the idea of a stable state in an open system.

(2) Lorenz would agree with what I wrote if I replaced 'equilibrium' by 'adaptive interaction'. I think that the idea of adaptation presupposes precisely an equilibrium; in adaptation there is always an assimilation of external factors, whether energetic or chemical, etc., from the environment by the organism and, on the other hand, an accommodation of the organism to the situation in which it finds itself; the adaptation then is already an equilibrium between assimilation and accommodation, and that is why I prefer personally the term 'equilibrium'. But the idea of adaptive interaction is absolutely fundamental.

(3) Margaret Mead says she agrees with the language of equilibrium but she wonders whether the model of gains and losses is the best model. I shall come back to this, if you permit, when we speak of cognitive equilibrium; for the moment I would simply mention that when speaking of gains and losses I am of course speaking of gains and losses of information and I remark that the word used by Margaret Mead to ask whether this model is the best is the word 'rewarding'. Well, it is precisely in the sense of 'rewarding' that I am speaking of gains and losses; that is to say that there are ideas which are rich in information, and there are ideas which lead to losses.

(4) Grey Walter makes two remarks in his paper which seem to me fundamental to our discussion. The first remark is that the best dynamic equilibrium always corresponds to the maximum activity. The second remark is that equilibrium and in particular equilibration is a particular case of a stochastic process and that the idea of equilibrium must be interpreted in a probabilistic sense.

(5) Finally, everyone made the remark that the organism never is in equilibrium.

Here then are the different points on which I received replies. I think personally I am about a hundred per cent in agreement with these different remarks. I think that the divergence depends mainly on terminology, on vocabulary. There is only one point where I do not agree with the replies given on this idea of equilibrium and I will begin with this point so as to clarify what I wanted to say.

Here is the question. Naturally I am ready to admit that the organism is never in equilibrium; equilibration processes always occur but we never find complete equilibrium is attained. There is, however, a special field where one can speak of equilibrium (which is why I am preoccupied by this idea) and it is precisely the field of logical structures. Take logical or mathematical structures such as the system of whole numbers. When a child of seven or eight years has managed to construct a series of whole numbers, when he has understood the series 1, 2, 3, 4, etc., then this structure will remain in equilibrium (if you prefer another word I do not mind) until death unless the individual goes mad. Now this does not mean that there is any state of rest; the individual will all the time make use of these ideas in action on objects or in exchange with other individuals. This system will also be integrated into other systems; that is to say that after having learnt whole numbers the individual will discover fractions, irrational numbers, complex numbers, transfinite numbers and so on. But whatever the new systems into which the system of whole numbers is integrated, this number system will not be changed any further. It remains in an equilibrium which is characterized by mobility and activity and which is founded on operations constituting actions of adding a unit or taking one away.

This equilibrium is characterized above all by the idea of reversibility, a reversibility which I will define as being the possibility of making an operation correspond to one and only one reverse operation which cancels it out. Now, the point that I did not manage to make understood, it seems to me, is that this reversibility of mental operations, which characterizes the equilibrium of a cognitive structure, constitutes the limiting case or final outcome of a process which is of much wider occurrence than logical structures. This process is found in all fields which deal with retroactive mechanisms, feedback mechanisms, anticipatory mechanisms, etc. I will take an example of behaviour showing these retroactions or anticipations which ensure a certain equilibrium: it is the classical example which has been quoted everywhere as being a suitable demonstration of feedback in the ordinary behaviour of individuals, the example of a driver on an icy road who tends to slide to the left. He makes a correction to the right, tends to slide back again to the right, corrects to the left and so on. At first he makes his corrections with big movements causing wide oscillations but after a time he manages to make corrections in advance, that is to say, by progressive anticipation before there has been any deviation. There you have an equilibrium which derives from probabilistic considerations: every movement made by an individual, each of his successive actions, comprises a probability determined by the resultant of the preceding behaviour according to a series of sequential controls easily describable from the probabilistic point of view. With the trial-and-error retroactions and anticipations of ordinary behaviour you never have complete compensation; thus though you certainly find equilibration processes you never get to perfect equilibrium. With intellectual co-ordinations, on the other hand, you have a system of operations which finally does reach equilibrium. These operations, since they are actions to start with (the operation of addition is the action of putting together; the operation of subtraction is the action of taking a part, etc.) remain actions like the others, actions which first gave rise to tentative trials and obey the same laws as the actions of the driver on the icy road. However, they show this notable peculiarity that, in the course of sufficiently general actions, such precisely as logical operations, the compensation obtained becomes finally a complete compensation.

But this is only a particular case in the wider problem of equilibration processes in general. As far as this general problem is concerned I think, in common with all the authors of the replies, that equilibrium in the sense in which I use the term is not a state of rest but essentially an active state and that the best equilibrium will always correspond, as Grey Walter said, to a maximum of activity. I think, secondly, that equilibrium is never achieved except in the case of certain special structures like the logico-mathematical ones. Finally, I think, as Grey Walter suggests—that all these equilibrium mechanisms have to be interpreted in a probabilistic, stochastic fashion.

I wanted to present these few preliminary remarks in order to show that there is a much greater convergence than one might have imagined between my paper and the replies.

In consequence, we can justly consider the making of a synthesis at this last session, a synthesis which will not be one of doctrine of course, but which will consist of an arrangement in order of possible questions and explanatory models, so as to delimit the field of interdisciplinary research which will be most usefully followed in our subsequent work.

BERTALANAFFY:

'Equilibrium' is a term that presents considerable linguistic difficulties. The terms are well defined in English, but the French expression, *état stationnaire*, is equivocal, and in German I had to introduce a new term, *Fliessgleichgewicht*, which is now generally accepted. It might be of some use if I give a precise definition of the terms relating to 'equilibrium'. These definitions are in terms of physics, but are applicable to biological phenomena.

(1) A *stationary state* (état stationnaire; stationärer Zustand) means a state of a system where the rate of macroscopic changes becomes zero; that is the system does not show macroscopic changes in time. This is irrespective of the kind of system.

(2) An *equilibrium* (équilibre; Gleichgewicht) is a time-independent state of a system where all macroscopic magnitudes remain constant and all macroscopic processes stop. A state of equilibrium must be attained in a closed system according to the second law of thermodynamics and is defined by a maximum of entropy.

(3) A *steady state* (no accepted term in French; Fliessgleichgewicht) is also defined as a time-independent state where the system remains unchanged macroscopically, although macroscopic processes of import and export of matter are going on—in contrast to the equilibrium state of a closed system. There is no simple thermodynamic definition for a steady state and it is not defined by maximum entropy; it can be defined in kinetic terms.

These are the meanings so far as physical chemistry is concerned. I should mention that, for example, the equilibrium which is spoken of in stochastic models or in game theory is again something different.

PIAGET:

If I understood Bertalanffy properly, he has defined 'steady state' exactly in the sense in which I speak of equilibrium in my parlance. In our Centre International d'Epistémologie Génétique here in Geneva, we have been searching for a year, with the assistance of a physicist, Mandelbrot, for an idea which might be applied to psychological behaviour which would not imply physical apriorism; something analogous to the idea of forces, or minimum potential energy, which themselves have no meaning in psychology. I would propose then the following definition (Apostel, Mandelbrot & Piaget, 1957).

The most general definition on which we can agree starts from the state E which is relatively stable, that is, does not change macroscopically. Then there are introduced, either by nature or by the observer, perturbations in the experiment which modify the set-up. Thus you have a perturbation $\triangle E_p$. Then a 'spontaneous' movement of the organism or of the subject, which I would call $\triangle E_s$, may respond to this perturbation. Now if $\triangle E_s$ is equivalent to $\triangle E_p$, that is to say, brings it back to the initial state, I will speak of

95

equilibrium. I am avoiding the 'equilibrium of forces' which would have no meaning in psychology and I am avoiding using the term 'minimum potential energy'. My general definition corresponds to Bertalanffy's 'steady state' rather than to the word 'equilibrium', but in French I prefer the term 'équilibre'—because it introduces the idea of compensation. This idea of compensation is of central importance because it is by studying the compensations that one can establish degrees of equilibrium. Thus it is ascertained that imperfect compensations can exist, for example in the trial-and-error and in the retroactions and anticipations which I was speaking about a little while ago. But you can have a strict compensation between $\triangle E_s$ and $\triangle E_p$, that is to say that here the equilibrium will take the form of a group, that is the transformation 1 will be corrected by the transformation 1^{-1}. Thus you have reversibility, or strict compensation as a limiting state towards which the compensations brought into proximity will tend.

You see that this vocabulary is exceedingly simple and makes no physical presuppositions. However, there remains the whole immense problem of the relations between equilibrium and chance. Is this equilibrium, this equilibration, the result of a series of probabilities developing in an analogous way to developing entropy or, on the contrary, is it a question of antichance or of an organizatory process resisting disorder?

BERTALANFFY:

I have two remarks to make to Professor Piaget's definition. One is that the definition Professor Piaget gave now is a bit more general than the considerations in his paper, where he refers to stochastic processes, game theory and so forth. And secondly that all these concepts are models we apply, and we can take what model we please for our particular purpose. For certain purposes, for example, if you consider physiological processes and the like, the model of the open system will prove very useful and important. For other considerations, you will use a model from information theory or game theory. It depends on the problem; your only obligation is when you have chosen a model, to stick to it and apply it consistently.

FREMONT-SMITH:

Would you agree that you may also need to use several models simultaneously sometimes in relation to the same problem, to give flexibility of approach?

BERTALANFFY:

I absolutely agree and could even give illustrations of this from physics. In thermodynamics, for example, you can describe things in

96

classical terms, using concepts like total and free energy, entropy, and so forth, and you can also describe the same processes by statistical mechanics which speaks in terms of probabilities and uses quite a different language. Furthermore, you can translate one into the other. Something similar is true for wave mechanics and quantum statistics according to Schrödinger and Heisenberg respectively. Here also are two descriptions using different mathematical structures, but one model and set of laws can, so to speak, be translated into the other.

SECOND DISCUSSION

Equilibration and the
Development of Logical Structures

PIAGET:
Today I hope to reply to the different questions put to me and to speak about the factors affecting development and about equilibrium. I will begin with factors affecting development. I said that we must add to the three classical factors of heredity, physical environment and social influence a fourth factor, equilibration, that is the equilibration of the three factors between themselves and equilibration within each one.

The three classical factors are indissociable and non-additive. For example, the influence of the environment is not simply added to that of heredity, because the organism chooses one or other environmental influence according to its hereditary structure, so that there is from the beginning an interconnexion between hereditary influences and influences from the physical environment. Now if the co-ordination of these influences is not simply the product of a chance mixing then necessarily the problem of equilibration arises. This is why I think a fourth factor is necessary, a factor which plays a part in the actual connexion of the three other factors. Zazzo, in his reply to my paper, says that this factor is no more than a system of relationships, whereas the other three factors seem 'real' to him. Personally I do not think that there is a difference in kind between the equilibrium factor and the others, because as soon as one analyses closely a hereditary mechanism, or an exchange between organism and environment, or more particularly a social mechanism, one finds they are only increasingly complex systems of relationships. One could perhaps say that the equilibrium factor is unlike the others in that it does not derive from simple causality; but it is necessarily inherent in a statistical form of causality. To speak of heredity, of environment or of society as causes in the sense of classic causality is certainly no more than a first approximation, and as soon as one goes beyond this one comes to probabilistic systems and statistical casuality.

Now I want to repeat that the problem of logical structures is a special one because this is the only field where one attains complete equilibrium. I think that in the affective field one would also find the equivalent of what logic is in the cognitive field; it would be structurations of social concepts in the form of scales of moral values; however this does not concern me and I will limit myself to what I have experience of, that is to the facts of logical structures. I will take first of all as an example the ideas of conservation. We observe that these ideas of conservation cannot be explained by the three classical factors alone. For the child to reach the idea of conservation (normally at about 7 or 8 years), of course maturation must have occurred: a prerequisite is that the nervous system should have reached a certain level of functioning which derives from a hereditary element. But this hereditary element is not sufficient, that is to say these ideas of conservation are not innate; one observes their gradual construction under the influence of experience. Also they vary very much from one child to another, and particularly from one social environment to another.

Secondly, this is not a mechanism which can be explained simply by physical experience or by the experience of objects. Of course experience plays a part; children manipulate objects and learn by observing the results. But this factor of experience is not by itself sufficient for the following reasons. The first is that we have never seen a child spontaneously verifying any conservation by systematic experiment. Either the child does not believe in conservation or else suddenly he believes in it and when he believes in it there is a totally different approach, and an expression of full understanding, of full comprehension of a new intellectual instrument; he says that it is obvious that there is conservation. We have never seen a child not believe before, then make an experiment, and then believe afterwards. Sometimes we encourage him to make experiments, for example on the conservation of volume with the water level, or the conservation of weight, giving him a balance, but the child does not try of his own accord. In the field of physical conservation, it is most remarkable that the first of the ideas of conservation to appear is not that of weight or volume but of substance. What is substance without weight and volume? It is nothing at all, it cannot be shown by experiment, it is a kind of empty form which begins by being the first idea of conservation; it is not a product of experience. Finally there is feeling of necessity; conservation appears as obvious as soon as it is understood. The feeling of necessity does not come from experience; it is the accompaniment of the understanding of the logical relationship.

Thirdly, of course, there are the social factors in this establishment of conservation, but these factors are not by themselves enough either.

One can give all kinds of proofs of that: for example, the most primitive form of conservation, the permanent object on the sensori-motor level, appears before language. Then comes the formal level when the child reaches structures of groups with four transforma-tions (inverse, reciprocal, correlative and identical); these structures go beyond language, they cannot be expressed by language and yet they influence thought in a very clear manner. Also there is a tem-poral sequence in which these notions appear and this cannot be explained by language or social factors. In manipulations of the ball of clay, for instance, the idea of conservation of substance is seen on the average at about 7-8 years; weight at about 9-10 years; and volume at about 11-12 years. But the child arrives at these three stages exactly by the same reasoning using the same words. If this were the effect of a verbal structure why should he not apply it immediately to everything? And then finally, the fundamental experiment, there are the deaf-mutes. Oléron (1951) has shown that operatory structures develop quite normally in deaf-mutes. Of course in deaf-mutes there is some symbolic function, such as language by gesture, etc., but there is not the normal social transmission by language. Consequently I think that in this field none of the three factors is sufficient alone; one must have recourse to the factor of equilibration.

During development we observe that there are stages where the child's ideas of conservation, etc., are not stable, but alter. Later the child arrives at a stability of these ideas which normally would last throughout the whole of his life. Now the problem is how to explain this progressive stabilization. First of all I will try to translate equilibrium in terms of activities and strategies. There is one pre-liminary circumstance we must note in order to understand the strategies which are to be mentioned. It is that in all arrangements where the problem of conservation appears we have to deal with two kinds of qualities or variables which from the observer's point of view vary inversely one to the other. Objectively therefore we are from the beginning faced with a group structure. Take for example the ball of clay which you change into a sausage: it gets longer: that is the first variable, but on the other hand it gets thinner: this is the second variable, which gets modified inversely as the first. Take the same ball and cut it up into pieces; these pieces can be few in number—the first variable—and they can be large or small—the second variable—and if the number is large, the pieces are small; if the number is small, the pieces are large, and we have again two inverse variations. Take the correspondence between elements which you space out: you have the length of the series which increases, but you have the density which decreases. Take the two horizontal bars which are then made to overlap: one projects beyond the other at one side but it recedes compared with the other on the other side; thus we again have two complementary variables.

I shall call the first variable characteristic *A* and the second characteristic *B*; *A* is not necessarily positive and *B* is not necessarily negative; they simply vary inversely one with the other. Having said this we observe through studying the reactions of these arrangements certain common mechanisms which I shall call strategies. We can distinguish four strategies: (Apostel *et al*, 1957). (1) *First strategy*: the child deals with only one of the two characteristics. This is what I shall call a focusing of the attention on one, *A*, of the two characteristics. The child ignores the other, *B*. The child says, for example, that the clay ball has got longer and that consequently there is more clay; he does not trouble about its thinness. Or else on the contrary he says that it has got thinner, therefore there is less clay; but he does not trouble about the length. (2) At a given moment appears the *second strategy*: the child deals with characteristic *B* which he suddenly discovers; but he then forgets characteristic *A* and he will go on reasoning according to characteristic *B*, ignoring what went before. (3) *Third strategy*: oscillation between *A* and *B*, with the beginning of a link between the two, but first one and then the other is uppermost. At times there is a direct oscillation from one to the other and at times the child reconciles them for small changes but is not able to do so for big changes. We have here an intermediate strategy, wherein one can distinguish substrategies or particular tactics. (4) Finally you have the *fourth strategy* which consists in understanding that the two characteristics are inversely related to each other as if they were balancing each other. At this moment the idea of conservation appears.

We note therefore a progression; *A*, *B*, oscillation between *A* and *B*, and finally linking up of the two. Let us now try to translate these strategies in terms of a theory of games. Let us attempt to speak of gains and losses of information. We note in fact that there are strategies which are more or less costly and correspondingly produce a greater or smaller yield. The primitive strategy of focusing on one single characteristic is the simplest and least costly. It costs no effort of information—there is simply a focusing of attention on one point with neglect of all the rest and the reasoning starts just from these data. At the same time it is the strategy which gives the least yield; no security, no possibility of prediction; at each modification of the arrangement, the child hesitates again; there is no stable generalization, there is no instrument which permits deduction. At the other extreme we note that strategy 4 is the most costly—it presupposes progressive synthesis; the very fact that there are intermediate stages shows how much has to be elaborated in order to achieve the idea of inverse relationships. But though the most costly, at the same time

101

it is the one which represents the greatest yield from the point of view of security, and from the point of view of the possibility of prediction, because the child discovers a general law which is going to be applied to all transformations in a particular field.

Since we are faced with a sequential process in which each element is determined by the preceding one, I propose to explain the choice of these successive strategies using a probabilistic language. I am using probability in the statistical sense of the probability of a certain event occurring out of a universe of possible events. The problem then is to know what are the possible events and to make an exhaustive list of them. In this case I will propose a simple solution. We shall call possible cases those cases which can be realized and we shall choose as a criterion of what can be realized that which actually is realized at the end of the process. In other words, the possible cases will be all those which are attained at the last stage. We can then construct an exceedingly simple group of events starting from this criterion. We have the events *A or B*, the events *A and B*, and furthermore we have the transformations leading to these states. The child can deal either simply with these configurations—he looks at the changed ball, he does not trouble about the transformation itself—or else he can deal also with the transformation. What has happened between the initial state and the final state? The ball has been drawn out and this transformation then controls both *A* and *B*.

Having admitted this group, we have first to explain why strategy 1 appears first. The hypothesis is that the choice of a single characteristic out of the two is the most probable solution. Why? Because the facts show us that the child can reason on one out of two characteristics without troubling about the other. From the point of view of the subject the two characteristics appear to be independent, although from the point of view of the observer they constitute a group structure. However we are reasoning from the point of view of the subject and not at all from the point of view of the observer. Therefore, if the probability that *A* will be focused upon is 0·5 and that *B* will be focused upon is 0·5, for them both to be focused upon at the same time would be 0·25, that is to say the product of the two. It is obvious then that strategy 1 is the simplest and the most probable at the beginning in the absence of all information on the structure of the objective relationships which come into play.

Secondly, the child is going to generalize—he starts for example from the length in the case of the ball which you are continually drawing out. He continues to reason about length, using his first strategy in all situations as long as it works. However, at a given moment it no longer works. The problem arises then of the transition from strategy 1 to strategy 2, a problem which does not comprise any modification in the body of events, but which must account for a modification in the probabilities attached to these strategies. I shall call probability A, p_1 and probability B, p_2. At first p_1 is greater than p_2, but at a given moment we have a reversal which characterizes strategy 2. This reversal may be due to external or internal causes, One of the external causes is the effect of perceptive contrast. One cannot reason indefinitely on the length. When the clay ball is changed into a sausage which lengthens into a string, the child ceases to say that there is more clay than at the beginning. At a given moment the other characteristic, the thinness, forces itself upon his attention. Secondly, there are internal factors which must derive from questions of subjective security or insecurity. In particular there is a lack of satisfaction about always using the same solution when it is not accompanied by certainty. Therefore both for reasons of subjective lack of satisfaction and objective contrast, character B finally takes precedence. And when B takes precedence, the same reasoning begins over again, but in the reverse sense.

However, this cannot go on indefinitely because even at the beginning there was a certain focusing upon A. That is to say that at a given moment the child who is reasoning this time on the thinness and forgetting the length is going to remember the length. An oscillation is then produced, which is the most probable strategy when the subject has gone from A to B and then recalls A. We observe then the whole classical process: oscillation first with retroaction, but later becoming anticipatory. From the moment the child oscillates between the two characteristics A and B, he begins to foresee that one of the characteristics is not modified without the other. In other words, the probability that A *and* B will take precedence over A alone or B alone occurs as soon as a retroactive process is produced. It becomes increasingly strong when the oscillations are at the same time retroactive and anticipatory. When the subject reaches this stage, the consideration of transformations is introduced. Up to this point the child has reasoned only on *configurations*—which is much simpler: the configuration is the state of the moment which can be concentrated upon without the other state being dealt with. Thinking about a *transformation* is on the contrary thinking about several states at once, about the point of departure and the point of arrival, with intervals between the two which are also states. The same reasoning that I indicated just now to show that A *and* B are less probable than A *or* B explains why the child begins with configurations. But as soon as these processes of retroactive and anticipatory oscillations occur, the consideration of transformations becomes probable. It becomes so because the subject possesses the two extremes of the transformation and all that is left is to introduce the transformation itself.

In short, the pattern of my explanation would be the following:

you are dealing with a series of sequential controls, such that each strategy is made probable by the preceding one. Strategy 4 is not the most probable at the beginning: it is the least probable then, but each strategy becomes the most probable following the results of the preceding one.

A few more words about operatory structures themselves—only a few words because the process is the same. Within the framework of an operatory structure like seriation (the placing in order of varying-sized sticks, for example), characteristic A would be the relationship 'greater than' (or 'smaller than') and characteristic B would be the inverse relationship. The child reasons first of all on only one of these relationships. To reach the correct seriation he must co-ordinate the two relationships. The operatory method in seriation is acquired at the precise moment when the child reasons at the same time about A and about B, that is to say when he looks for an element which will be at the same time larger than all the preceding ones and smaller than all those which remain to be classified. Thus strategy 4 here corresponds exactly to the definition above: that is to knowing how to manipulate simultaneously both characteristics one conversely to the other.

It is the same thing for classification. You can classify by adding the new classes through successive additions, that is uniting; or else you can classify by dichotomy, by dividing one class into two and so on. Uniting and dividing are the two characteristics A and B, and this is not merely theoretical, as is shown by the experiments on inclusion. For example, bunches of grapes, some white and others black, are put on the child's table and he is asked: 'Are there more grapes or more black grapes?' One observes then that up to about 7-8 years the child has great difficulty in including the part in the whole. Now it is easy to show that this including of the part in the whole presupposes just that connexion of two methods of uniting and dividing, and that it is a question of being able to pass from the whole to the part and from the part to the whole at the same time. As long as he can only make this passage in one direction and not in the other simultaneously he will make classifications which empirically are satisfactory, but he will not have the logical idea of inclusion.

I should like to add a final remark in connexion with Zazzo's reply to my paper. The substance of Zazzo's reply is: your process of equilibration seems likely in the particular case of the solution of specific cognitive problems, but does it apply in a more general way to development, acquisition and learning? Naturally I think it does. I will put the question in the following way: is an acquisition due to a system of associations or of assimilations? If it is a matter of associations it is simply that a piece of behaviour is repeated n times and it becomes stable by repetition: there is no problem of equilibration. But a difficulty arises: why do these simple repetitions give rise to liaisons which are stable in some cases but not in others? Everyone knows that this is the big problem of the conditioned reflex: Pavlov's dog will not salivate indefinitely if he only hears the bell and if he never again gets the food which should confirm that the bell has a significance. Conditionings which last are those which correspond to a need and those which are confirmed. In other words the association itself is not an explanatory principle; the association does not become stable in accordance with the number of repetitions but only in so far as it implies a need at the point of departure and a satisfaction at the point of arrival. When there is no satisfaction there is no stabilization. What is fundamental here is not the association itself, but the assimilation into the pattern. But as soon as assimilatory patterns appear we are faced with a problem of equilibrium. In fact all adaptation comprises two poles: assimilation to the structures and the previous activities of an organism, and accommodation to the present situation—and this brings up a problem of equilibrium. I think then that processes of equilibration occur from the beginning of development and that the pattern I have tried to propose to you is included in the theory of learning, being the particular case of learning without external reinforcements, without the 'reinforcement' of Hull, etc. Only the subjective reinforcement which is the pleasure of action or of understanding plays a part.

LORENZ:

I very strongly doubt that there is no reinforcement in this case; the simple matching of theory to facts gives very great satisfaction. You remember Harlow, the primate psychologist in Wisconsin, showed that in monkeys the solution of puzzles without the slightest reward was self-reinforcing. The solution was its own reward.

PIAGET:

Precisely. I said that there was no *external* reinforcement. There is an *internal* reinforcement through the pleasure of feeling satisfaction in having found a solution. But there is no external reinforcement, no means of objective control, no punishment nor recompense.

ZAZZO:

Professor Piaget, there remains for me a somewhat strange feeling: when you speak of equilibrium you make me think of Bergson when he speaks of duration—excuse me, but after all Bergson had a great mind, didn't he?—because Bergson considers duration as being independent and apart from the things which last (or durate) and I sometimes have the impression that you consider equilibrium independently from what is in equilibrium. For you it is a factor which is added to and combines with the others but seems not to be resultant of all the material causes which can act. In other words you frequently give the impression of explaining the logic of evolution by the evolution of logic!

PIAGET:

As regards this particular case of logical structures, I should like to get rid of a misunderstanding which seems to me to persist in this discussion. I have not the slightest desire to generalize from the case of logic to all the rest of mental life. Logic is the only field where equilibrium is fully achieved; in the other fields we are faced with partial equilibria which do not reach the measure of operation but only that of regulations and feedbacks. If I had had the time I should have spoken of perception, and shown you that one finds exactly the same processes: strategy 1 is a focusing, strategy 2 another focusing, strategy 3 is the passage between the two, the defocusing, etc., but I should particularly have shown you that in all the perceptive mechanism we studied we found the first three strategies but never the fourth; the fourth appears to be peculiar to logic.

Logic is a particular case but, on the other hand, as far as the first three of its strategies are concerned it is a case which is a part of a much wider category; of a category of all the phenomena where processes of retroaction and anticipation occur, which is almost all vital phenomena. That is why I think that the pattern of equilibrium is a very general pattern but is achieved in its complete form with strategy 4 only in the field of logic amongst cognitive functions. When Zazzo says that my theory of development is actually a history of logic he goes beyond my thinking: but logic is a specially instructive case because everything is found there, whereas in all the other fields one finds only regulations, near-reversibility, semi-equilibrium, etc.

LORENZ:

I want to say that a sigh of relief was audible at this part of the table when you said that complete equilibration was only achieved in cognitive functions. Much as I am in agreement with this thesis, I think that nevertheless I would add a type of function which is not usually thought of as a cognitive function, but which at least is analogous, and that is the phenomenon of perceptual constancy. You say that complete equilibration never occurs in perception—but I believe it does. Let me give an example—if I move my eyes to and fro this room doesn't seem to move, it remains stationary in my perception—we don't see the walls wobble. And you know that the explanation of this non-production of subjective illusion is due to a very complicated regulating mechanism only lately discovered.

The principle of 'reafference' plays a most important part in the physiology of perception, and I might explain in a few words what it is. If I turn my eye sideways passively, by shoving a finger into the eye-socket, I do get the illusion of the environment moving in the opposite direction. If, on the other hand, we fix the anaesthetized eye, by pressing a little ring to the eyeball, so that it cannot move, and then try to look to our right, the whole room about us seems to pivot in the direction of our intended eye movement. This is the important point: that we have not actually moved the eye, we have only sent out the voluntary motor impulses which would have moved it under normal circumstances. It is the sending-out of the motor impulse which creates, all by itself, the illusion of a movement of the environment in the direction of the intended eye movement. This illusory movement is the exact reverse of what happens to the retinal image when the eyeball is allowed to move freely. The illusory movement caused by the impulse itself, and the real retinal movement caused by the turning of the eye, counteract and extinguish each other completely. If we move our eye to the right, of course our retina shifts in the opposite direction. We should see our environment moving correspondingly, if it were not for this process of compensation, in which the movement of the retinal image is extinguished by an 'illusory movement'. In order to make all this more intelligible, I might describe the same process in an anthropomorphic parable, putting a reasoning human mind in the place of the mechanisms of perception—which Helmholtz did quite seriously, when he interpreted this kind of process on the basis of 'unconscious reasoning'. The moment the voluntary command to turn the eye to the right is sent to the muscle, a correlatory message is dispatched to the visual cortex, telling it what movement is to be expected, in consequence of the impulse, from the retinal image. Thus the central receptor is warned not to interpret as a movement of the environment what really is caused by a movement of the organism. The consequence of the message to the central receptor was termed 'Reafferenz-Erwartung' (Reafference Expectancy) by Holst, a term which he later dropped because of its anthropomorphic quality. This message paralleling the motor impulse is now termed 'Efferenzkopie'.

The principle of preventing an illusion by actively creating another one counteracting it is even more widely found among the processes of perception than is the principle of reafference. Let me give you an example of this. If we stand before a long and high wall and look at its straight and horizontal upper edge, we see it as a straight line. But, in consequence of perspective, what really is projected on our retina is a wide arch with its convex side upwards. If, in complete darkness and without any other points of reference, we look at an equally long and straight horizontal luminescent line presented above the level of our eyes, we do perceive it as a wide arch with its convexity upwards. It is this 'illusion' which enables us to perceive straight horizontal lines as straight when they are above, or, for that matter, below eye level, in spite of the fact that in this position their retinal image is distorted by perspective.

All these mechanisms of constancy are very much akin to cognitive functions in that they 'abstract', out of the information contained in the sensory data, properties which are constantly inherent in the perceived object. One of the chief functions of perception in general and constancy effects in particular is true objectivation, just as is the case with cognitive functions.

I think that constancy effects are attained by a process of equilibration which, in some of the instances I cited, is just as complete as in cognition. And I think that this exception from the rule stated by Professor Piaget is one that actually proves the rule, because constancy perception is functionally so closely akin to cognition in its objectivating function that it might also be subsumed under the conception of cognitive processes.

PIAGET:

I am delighted with what Lorenz has just said. Firstly, when I was using the term cognitive functions I was not thinking only of intelligence but also of perception. Secondly, in perception it is of course the constancy phenomena which are closest to the phenomena of conservation. It is the same thing on another scale; for years we have been working on the relation between the perceptive constancies and operatory conservations, and I entirely agree with everything Lorenz has just said. Consequently I think this shows the general nature of the problem of equilibrium, it being understood that logic remains the only cognitive field where complete equilibrium is attained.

In fact, as regards perceptive constancies, can one actually speak of a strict total equilibrium? If it is true, I would say that there is a logic of perception. But in all the cases we have studied experimentally up to now we have found a mechanism which is analogous with that of conservation, but for a constancy which is not absolutely strict. I will give you as an example the constancy of sizes in depth (Piaget & Lambercier, 1951). The rule in the adult, among hundreds of subjects that we have measured now, is not absolute constancy but a super-constancy, that is to say that a stick of 10 cm shown four metres away from the subject is seen by the adult as being rather larger than 10 cm. The average is about 9·5 cm for it to be seen equal to 10. In other words, we have a regulatory mechanism which goes beyond the exact balance, an anticipatory mechanism which is a precaution taken against error. If you wish, it is almost logic, but this little excess shows that it is still regulation and not quite operation.

GREY WALTER:

I want to emphasize what Konrad Lorenz said. Recently there have been some disturbing discoveries made about perception in intact animals which, in effect, show that there are mechanisms within the brain which act like traffic cops for incoming information and actually damp down and modify the action of the receptors themselves. It has been shown that the information which is allowed to reach the brain from the outside world is a function of its novelty and significance. The level of the receptor itself, the actual eye or ear, is cut down, as though the central nervous system were to say: 'I'm not interested in what you're sending me.'

The recent work by Hernandez-Peon and Jouvet (1956) on the ear seems particularly clear. The point is that the information reaching the central nervous system is even more corrupt than we thought before, not merely because of differentiation or fatigue or adaptation but also because of this very positive traffic control system.

MONNIER:

I do not think that the physiological experiments of Granit on sensory organs really support the conception of compensatory illusions expressed by Lorenz. They prove only that the receptivity, the 'Bereitschaft', of the sensory receptors is regulated by efferent fibres. By virtue of this mechanism the threshold of the muscle spindle may be lowered and the muscle receptors may become more or less ready to detect external or internal stimuli. This occurs for example in the knee-jerk reflex, which may be reinforced by a voluntary movement of the hands.

LORENZ:

Similar mechanisms of analogous function but obviously working at a higher level of integration exist also in the central nervous system. My point is that all of them work on the principle of creating a compensatory illusion in order to exclude unwanted information. When you stand for some time looking at a lake on which the waves are all travelling quickly to your left and then raise your eyes to the opposite bank, you see, to your surprise, that the bank seems to be gliding towards your right. And if you have been driving a car for a very long time, and then stop, the landscape seems to float smoothly backwards. This is always my illustration for the fact that we cannot, on principle, distinguish between the illusion created by central compensatory mechanisms and the real sensory information: again and again, when suddenly forced to stop before a railway crossing after a long drive, I felt my car sliding smoothly backwards and said to myself: 'Aha, that is the well-known illusion'—and did not do anything about it, until the man behind me started blowing his horn in utmost alarm because I really was rolling back on him. Your laughter shows that the phenomenon is known to most of you! The point it proves is that even if you are interested in making the difference between sensory information and compensatory illusion, you simply cannot do it.

I think that failures of constancy mechanisms in really achieving constancy, or in overdoing it, are quite frequent. There is one example we found in making animal films which concerns a failure of time constancy. If, in a film, you show a cat licking her kittens, first taken from a distance, and, immediately after that in a close-up, the close-up must be slowed down quite considerably, else you get the unavoidable impression of a speeding-up of movements with the enlargement of the picture. If the face of a kitten covers most of the screen and the mother's tongue travels, with each stroke, from lower left to upper right, our constancy effect breaks down and we see that tongue travelling at enormous speed. We cannot correlate speed to size correctly and in order to counteract this phenomenon one had to take all close-ups of quick movements in a slow-motion of a measure nearly equal to that of the enlargement.

The more complicated constancy phenomena seem to be much less precise in most animals than in Man. That's a very sweeping generalization, and in swift-moving animals, of course, size-constancy must be very well developed. On the whole, though, complicated Gestalt-constancy is much less good in animals than it is in Man.

GREY WALTER:

There is still some doubt in my mind as to whether these stages of intellectual development are inevitable stages or simply the results of experience. It is very important to know whether development by these stages occurs because the machine simply matures that way, or whether it is due to the gradual acquisition of sufficient information from the environment finally to permit, for example, abstractions of action. Professor Piaget, do you think these changes of thought in children are the result of the accumulation of redundant information from a large amount of experience or do yourself in your heart think that these are stages which will develop inevitably even without accumulation of information?

PIAGET:

The problem is to know whether a progressive nervous organization occurs or whether an accumulation of external information is sufficient. I do *not* think that one can explain intellectual operations simply by the accumulation of information, because there is not just information there, there is the way the information is structured and co-ordinated.

GREY WALTER:

I am not suggesting that the truth may lie entirely on one side or the other, but one would like to know the proportional importance of learning and maturation. To what extent are there inevitable, self-sustaining processes in the nervous system which make the child ready to walk, ready to talk, ready to perform these various cognitive or affective operations, irrespective of his experience? Or to what extent is it all modifiable or modified by experience?

FREMONT-SMITH:

Coghill, you remember, said *experience is growth* as far as the nervous system is concerned. One might say there are two inter-dependent aspects of development of the nervous system. One is the growth in terms of size and complexity at the more macroscopic level, and the other is the structuring and complexity resulting from experience. Perhaps you really couldn't get a fully developed brain without information being received by it.

GREY WALTER:

I think Coghill's data are a little bit facile, really. For example, there is information now from the comparison of premature babies and mature children born at full term (Douglas, 1956). The prematures are a month old at the time most children are born, but there is no difference from full-term children, in the time at which they walk, calculated as post-conceptual ages, despite their having had a month more of extra-uterine experience. It looks rather as though walking is a more or less inevitable development, a matura-tional growth process.

LORENZ:

I myself am quite convinced that in the interaction of maturation and learning in the progression from stage one to stage four, there is very little carry-over of learning from one experience to the next and that it is, say, 3 per cent learning carried over from previous experience and 97 per cent maturation process in the central nervous system. My impression is that if you should make a large series of experiments with children who are daily faced with these problems and children who are faced with them for the first time at a given age, you would find as little difference as my pupil Grohmann found with pigeons prevented from making flying experiences and those that were not (Vol. I, p. 52).

I have certain misgivings about speaking of 'factors of development' even though they are said to be 'interacting'. I think you cannot say there are hereditary and environmental 'factors' as if they could be isolated. With a slight exaggeration you might say that everything is inherited and everything is environmental. It is a truism for genetics that what actually is inherited are not characters but what Woltereck has called *Reaktionsnormen*, i.e., potentialities to develop certain characters, given certain environmental conditions. Perhaps the best illustration is what the geneticists call penetrance. There are some characters like the blood groups which show up under any circumstances if the organism develops at all; there are also characters which even though they are genetic and inherited manifest themselves only under rather special circumstances or in an irregular way. Similarly, there is no 'equilibrium factor' in physical systems; there is only a constellation of forces which may (or may not) lead to equilibrium.

The 'equilibrium factor' in Piaget's sense is, as I see it, nothing else but the establishment of the categories of cognition. It is the unique and profound contribution of Piaget to have shown us how these develop. While, according to Kant, the forms of intuition and categories of experience were supposed to be *a priori* and universal, we realize, to a large extent owing to Piaget, that cognition and experience of the world do not follow hard and fast rules. Rather the categories of experience depend on the one hand on the psychophysical organization of the living being concerned, and on the other hand on linguistic and cultural factors.

For example, the category of substance, which is unavoidable and obvious to our way of thinking, seems to be connected with our linguistic habits, the constructing of sentences with substantive and adjective in the Indogermanic languages, which led to the Aristotelian distinction between substance and attributes (see Bertalanffy, 1955a). In languages like Hopi or Chinese, there are quite different categories to bring order into our experience (Whorff, 1952). Thus it appears that the categories which have been considered to be absolute and *a priori*, in fact are different in different cultures and are slowly formed during the mental development of the child. I would think Piaget's equilibrium factor would have a different course of development in different cultural and linguistic conditions.

LORENZ:

I agree on the principle that *some* ways of thinking are dependent on verbalization. Existentialist philosophy, for instance, could never have developed in a culture which was not in command of the verb 'to be', it is a deification of the German 'copula', the auxiliary verb 'to be'. But I emphatically disagree with the belief that verbalization has to do at all with the category of substance; the development of the notion of substance is connected with the development of perceptual constancies.

BERTALANFFY:

But you remember Charlotte Bühler (1930) has shown that perceptual constancies themselves develop during the maturation of the child, the error in estimating size, for example, being considerably larger in the two-year-old child than in the three- or four-year-old.

As far as verbalization is concerned, I think one of the difficulties preventing us from arriving at satisfactory theories in matters involving psychology is our dependence on our linguistic bondage. Our language describes psychological happenings in physical metaphors. For this I quote two different and excellent authorities. One authority is Konrad Lorenz himself who, in 1943, emphasized that our way of dealing with psychological experience is based upon physical similes. 'Comprehend' means 'grasping something'; a 'connexion' is a physical link between things; even 'time' is represented in terms of visualized space when we speak of a certain 'span' of time, and so forth. My other authority, from quite a different field, is Benjamin Lee Whorff. From the view point of anthropology and linguistics, he said essentially the same thing, namely, that we are using spatial or corporeal metaphors in order to express psychological experience. What applies to our way of expression in the vernacular, also applies to the models we use in science. When you speak of 'equilibrium', 'homeostasis', 'open system', and so forth, it is always a physical metaphor which is used. Freud, in his 'dammed-up libido', and Lorenz's concept that instinctual energy is built up and discharged if a certain level is surpassed (even without stimulus as in *in vacuo* behaviour), both use the same hydrostatic model. Again, it is physical models that psychoanalysis uses in concepts such as incorporation, intrusion, elimination, and the like. Unfortunately, within the structure of our language and thinking, we can hardly do otherwise, and can only try to make the best of it.

This, it seems to me, is one of the reasons why psychological theory is so difficult. It might be easier, for example, in the Hopi language where there are fundamentally different categories to bring order into experience. There are no tenses. They make no distinction between present, past, and future. Rather the distinction is between what one may call the manifest, that is, all that is accessible to sensory experience, and the un-manifest, which comprises both the future and what we would call mental. So the future and the mental processes go under the same category. Such language would lead to the

113

formation of categories which are impossible, or very difficult, to approach from our standpoint.

MEAD:

You must remember that this doesn't mean at all that people who use such different categories can't build a house, that they don't know the difference between yesterday, today and tomorrow. The most striking example is the Trobriands where there is no recognition of causality of any sort in the language. A seed never turns into a plant that turns into a larger plant. You have a seed, then you have a plant and then you have a larger plant as if they were all coming preformed from somewhere. The Trobriands refuse to recognize physical paternity, they refuse to recognize that the food goes into the body and is added to it. The body is simply a tube and you take the food in and you excrete all of it and nothing from the food goes to you. But this doesn't interfere with their having an adequate marriage system, disapproving of illegitimacy, making roads that go some place and building houses that stand up. All of these observations of the external world, which we have disciplined into a system, they leave in an implicit non-verbalized state and all the things that we put into a dream state and only permit to poets they put into a system.

On the other hand the Manus child would be dead if it made the mistakes in real life that some Swiss children make in the experimental situation of Piaget's tests. They don't think that when they change the shape of something they change its weight. If they did they couldn't handle their canoes, and load things from one to another. They have to know *in activity* all these things that they are only able to conceptualize much more slowly. Progression in Piaget's tests seems to me a process of maturation meeting with a process of teaching and conceptualization which is culture-bound. Let me give a complementary illustration. There are people who mature in dreaming, as we mature in our ability to understand logic and use mathematics. There has been a study made of three different primitive people with three different levels of dreaming. The children's dreams were alike in all three of the societies, and showed no formal differences. But in one society you get a second stage where you can use your dream as a directive for yourself on how to get well and things of this sort; and in the third society (the Penang of Malaya) there is a higher level of 'maturity' in which you can turn your dreams into useful social instruments. Here there are schools of dreaming, young people sit around and their dreams are criticized, and they gradually mature to the stage where they can use their dreams in a different way. Now, if we had precise and sensitive techniques to study this capacity I think we would find a series of steps of maturation with age in it too. But the society that can teach people how to dream constructively would reflect these maturational stages differently from ours. I might add that we can't do this, and one of the reasons we can't do it is probably because we are so busy teaching children to carry out the type of logical thinking which Professor Piaget is examining.

The Definition of Stages of Development

PIAGET:

We are now going to discuss the problem of stages of development. I will not repeat what is in my paper (in Part I); I shall merely reply to the objections which were made: not for the purpose of defending myself but in order to raise problems of general interest.

I will begin with Margaret Mead's reply, in which she maintains —and I entirely agree with her—that the stages cannot be characterized by average chronological ages, since these average ages, of course, vary considerably from one social environment to another even in the same society, and still more from one social culture to another. On the other hand, she agrees with the criterion of the order of succession, and in particular the criterion of successive equilibrations, and shows that a series of researches could be undertaken in this field to give precision to the stages and their implications. Therefore I should like to put before her a programme of possible research with the collaboration of several different members of the Group if possible, but in any case between Margaret Mead and ourselves.

The research is to determine how far certain stages are found in all cultures, and other stages not found. I will simply give four examples in the field of cognitive functions; the examples show at the same time that even in the cognitive field the value of stages can differ greatly according to the structures involved.

1. The first comparative experiment on stages has to do with the reversible operations of which Bärbel Inhelder and I have often spoken, but operations benefiting from the help of perceptive configurations in a field where perception is not in conflict with operation. A good and a very simple example which according to our forecasts should be found in the most different cultures is seriation. A child is given a certain number of little sticks in disorder to put in order from the smallest to the biggest. They must be sticks which are not too different, because if they are too different it is simply a matter of perceptive reading without reasoning. You need, for example, sticks differing by about half a centimetre in 10 to 20 centimetres

116

to force the individual to compare them two by two. Here in Geneva we find three stages (Piaget & Szeminska, 1941). There is a first stage where the child puts together a small and a big stick in pairs, which he does not manage to co-ordinate; or else he makes little series of two or three, but he does not manage to co-ordinate the series. We find a second stage where the child proceeds by trial and error; he begins by making series which are fairly but not quite regular, then he corrects them and finally he manages to make the exact series. We find a third stage—and this for us is the criterion for acquiring the operation—when the child takes all the relationships into account from the beginning. He looks for the smallest stick and compares it with all the others. When he has found it he looks for the smallest of those that remain, and then he puts it next to the first, then the smallest of all those that remain, and so on. In other words, he understands the relations according to which any element is at the same time both larger than those already put down and smaller than those which remain.

Now do we find these three stages in different cultures? This is a very simple experiment. This year Bärbel Inhelder and some collaborators carried out a very interesting variation of it by asking the child not to handle the sticks straight away, but to anticipate by mental imagery, by language, and especially by drawing, how he is going to make his series of sticks (he is given sticks of different colours with different coloured pencils to see how he can solve it by drawing). We then got the result, that at stage 2, that of empiric trial and error, certain children are capable of anticipation: when it is a matter of making a plan before handling the sticks they make an absolutely correct drawing. They say to you: 'I am going to put them like that', (and when the drawing is in black it is fine; when it is in colours it is the same problem as with the manipulation itself, it is more difficult). Nevertheless, the child does not afterwards manage to make the series in an operatory fashion because the anticipatory pattern is not an operation, it is a progression in a single direction. In the operatory system he must take into account the two relationships of going up and going down which are not found in the anticipatory pattern, which is only a configuration based on perception.

2. For the second experiment I will take an operation again, but without the assistance of perceptive configuration and on the contrary in conflict with it. Here we can think simply of pouring beads from one vessel to another (Piaget & Szeminska, 1941). We have two jars of the same dimensions and the child himself has put a bead into one of the jars every time he has put one into the other, until he has ten on each side. He thus knows there is the same number in each jar. He then pours the beads from one of the similar jars into a jar of a different shape and is asked whether there are as many, if there

117

are more, or less, etc. We find three stages: the little ones deny conservation, they will tell you that there are more because it is higher, or that there are less because it is thinner; in a second stage there is conservation for smaller transformations but not for large ones; and during a third stage conservation is affirmed as being evident and necessary.

3. Thirdly, we can take an example of pure operation, but with the assistance of language. The question is: is 5 equal to $3+2$, using the same technique of correspondence between two series, but with the possibility of counting (Apostel *et al.*, 1957). Language can here assist the investigation of the elements and favour conservation.

The experiment is carried out as follows: the child is given 5 red and 5 blue counters, each red one paired with a blue one. He knows that there is an equality, that there are as many blue counters as red counters. Then the red counters are displaced, but without the length of the row or the arrangement of the parts being altered. Generally the child agrees that there is still equality. Then this collection is changed into two sub-collections of 3 and 2 and the child is asked whether there is still the same number of counters (I am speaking here of small collections of 5, but of course the experiment can be done with 15, 20 or 30 counters). We find then the following stages. The youngest subjects that can be questioned (about 4 years old) say 'it isn't the same thing any more. Now there are more because you have two packets, while over there there is only one packet.' Then you find children will begin to count in order to verify, but an intermediate stage is observed which is very strange, where the child counts but is not convinced by spoken numbering. I remember a child, for example, who said '1, 2, 3, 4, 5 and 1, 2, 3, 4, 5. Well, I find 5 on each side but there are more here' $(3+2)$. This reaction disappears later. The child uses counting in order to verify an equality and he admits that there is an equality of quantities of sums when there is an equality of numbers, but only up to a certain number. Another child, for example, admitted that $10=8+2$, $12=8+4$, that $15=10+5$, and for 16 it was still all right, but for 17 he began to count and said 'Well, I can see there are 17 here and 17 there, but now it is not the same any more.' In other words he goes back here to behaviour left over from the previous stage. Finally, at the last stage, the child no longer needs to count. He says 'Of course, it will always be the same thing, it is the same collection, you have just divided it in 2 or 3 parts,' etc. 'It is not worth while counting, I know, I am quite sure.' So the final analytic process is the result of a development where we find all the transitions. By questioning a few more children, I discovered even finer transitions.

4. Fourthly, I will take a problem of representation without operation; of simple representations with language but without any

logical problem. For example, the questions of animism (Piaget, 1929) which I think Margaret Mead has already dealt with among children in New Guinea.

According to our forecasts, which are of course purely hypothetical, I think that the first experiment, that of seriation or operatory configuration with the assistance of perceptive configuration, must be most general and must be found in almost every culture. Experiment 2 is perhaps a little less general; experiment 3 is certainly less general because spoken counting comes in, and counting is a collective and cultural technique. Then in the fourth experiment (animism, etc.) there are no operations and I think therefore that there is no reason why there should be uniformity of reactions from one cultural environment to another. In this last field I do not think that one would find general (that is cross-cultural) stages.

This is, of course, only a very short sketch. It would be necessary to study much more closely a table of operatory tests. I have given this simply as a basis for ideas and to furnish concrete examples.

MEAD:

When I said that I didn't think discussing the average performance of a child at some designated stage was very much use, Professor Piaget interpreted that as a statement about a difference *between* cultures. I only meant it partly as that; I meant it even more importantly as a difference between individuals *within* a single culture. It seems to me that an average for any stage obscures most of the things that are interesting and important. Each culture differentially selects from among the available types or styles or ways of learning which are potential in any reasonably large sample of the human race. For example, there are some societies that won't let a child walk before it talks and others that won't let the opposite happen. So a certain group of children will be held back until another group is ready to catch up with them, and a great deal of social pressure will be expended to obtain uniformity at a point where a uniformity would not otherwise exist. Thus a child may not be permitted to crawl till it has a certain number of teeth.

Another gross social intervention amongst the varieties of maturation which I think makes an enormous difference in the end is saying in a given society that a child can't get to school until it is six. If children are taught to read at four, which is quite possible, and used to be done, then those children will approach language and every other problem differently from those that don't strike any type of symbolization either in mathematics or in reading until, say, eight or until they are adults.

Thus I see the significance of cultural intervention in biological development as only explicable if one includes individual differences

119

in patterning. These differences include evenness and unevenness of physical maturation which we're beginning to know a good deal about, and include the fact that some children seem to be able to come into a particular period much earlier than others. When Professor Piaget described the experiments that he was suggesting that he and I do together, he said 'I remember a child who . . .' and then he mentioned the particular one who could do the sixteen and not the seventeen items. That child disappears in a general statement of stages—whereas actually I think every one of the differences amongst these children is significant. If we think only cross-sectionally, and leave out these individual differences, then in effect we leave out the cultural differences also.

Piaget presented these four experiments saying that he expected when you got to the verbal level that the tests would not be done in different cultures in the same way, whereas at the perceptual or the manipulative level he expected great similarity. But that leaves out of account what cultures actually have done. Some cultures have emphasized one of these levels and other cultures another. There are cultures in which people can do a great deal of manipulation of language, but will not be able to count beyond 20; there are others where people can count to 400,000 but are bored with language and do almost nothing with it. My comment on the question of averages was designed to include these two kinds of differences. Individual personal differences—whether they're seen as types or as patterns—have almost disappeared in the papers that we wrote in Part I although they've been present in our discussion over and over again.

The second point that I wanted to make was to welcome this suggestion for cross-cultural co-operation on a group of children. I think this will be a cumulative process during this meeting in which each one of us will have ideas of co-operation that ought to build up by the end of this session to some plan by which the different approaches can be grounded in identified living children, and not remain floating around in the air as attributes of something called 'the child'.

PIAGET:

I will now pass on to Zazzo's objection which is connected with the definition of stages. Here I should first like to remind you that in my paper the definition of stages is simply a reproduction of what Bärbel Inhelder said in our first meeting (Vol. 1, p. 84), when she attempted to find criteria for the stages. She indicated five criteria: (1) the order of succession; (2) integration of the acquisitions at one stage into the following stage; (3) a whole structure characterizing the total aspects of a stage; (4) the fact that one stage prepares the following; and (5) that the new stage constitutes the culmination of what is prepared in the preceding stage, in other words an equilibrium step. Now Zazzo replies that these definitions are too limiting, and that naturally if one defines the stages in too limiting a way it will be easy to say afterwards that there are no general stages. He proposes, therefore, a much more elastic definition of stages.

I will simply reply that these are degrees of the possible structuration of stages, and, that, of course, one can be content with one or two degrees within the five. One can very well conceive of a series which can be called stages which would conform only to the first criterion, that is to say, to the constant order of succession. One can very well imagine another series of stages where there would be at the same time order of succession and integration. One can very well conceive of a third series of stages where there would be the first three requisites and not the two last, etc. I do not think that these criteria constitute a kind of *a priori* framework. The criteria I have presented are what can be found in a field where stages are clearest; there is no question of generalizing these requirements for all stages in all fields.

ZAZZO:

That reply seems to me very satisfactory because it admits differing definitions for different levels, and I think that links up with what Tanner said in his paper.

PIAGET:

I now come to the big problem: the problem of the very existence of stages; do there exist steps in development or is complete continuity observed? Now, Tanner, upholding the position which he has adopted during all the meetings of our Group, shows that in somatic development one finds only continuity. He therefore naturally tends to generalize this idea and in opposing the idea of relative discontinuity in other fields he makes an objection which seems to me extremely serious: it is that when we are faced macroscopically with a certain discontinuity we never know whether there do not exist small transformations which would be continuous but which we do not manage to measure on our scale of approximation. In other words, continuity would depend fundamentally on a question of scale; for a certain scale of measurement we obtain discontinuity when with a finer scale we should get continuity. Of course this argument is quite valid, because the very manner of defining continuity and discontinuity implies that these ideas remain fundamentally relative to the scale of measurement or observation. This, then, is the alternative which confronts us: either a basic continuity or else development by steps, which would allow us to speak of stages at least to our scale of approximation.

2E

I think Bertalanffy's paper brings to this point documentation of great value. Bertalanffy takes his examples from fields as different as architecture, the history of automobile technique and the evolution of species in order to demonstrate that this is a general problem. In the evolution of species it is remarkable that one has great difficulty in finding intermediate types between two species. Stable species are found, as if there were no evolution; one observes only very few transitional forms which would enable evolution to be demonstrated. Thus the solution proposed by Bertalanffy, using the ideas of equifinality and equifinal steps, is that the intermediate types are unstable, whereas the species themselves are steady open states. In the case of species there would, then, be equilibrium steps for certain morphogenetic organizations, whereas the cases of transition would be unstable.

This conception of Bertalanffy's seems to me to correspond exactly with what Inhelder and I have found in the field of cognitive stages. On the one hand we find stages which characterize a certain proportion of individuals at any given age. On the other hand, we always find sub- or intermediary stages, but as soon as we try to pin these intermediary stages down we enter a sort of cloud-dust of sub-intermediaries because of their instability. Other organizational steps are relatively more stable and it is these that one can consequently consider as 'stages'.

The usual reproach made about stages like those I have been reminding you of is that in making them continuity is neglected. This is exactly Tanner's argument; and generally, every time we constructed a series of stages in one field or the other of the cognitive functions, Inhelder and I came up against the same objections of exaggerating a discontinuity and neglecting a continuity which we might have found if we had made a finer analysis.

This year, however, in the work of our Centre for Developmental Epistemology in Geneva I met with the reverse objection from one of our collaborators; that is to say, he systematically saw discontinuity everywhere where I tried to show him transitions and continuity from one stage to another. The problem was one which interested our Centre and which goes perhaps rather beyond the interest of psychologists: it was the problem of what is called in logical empiricism the analytic and the synthetic. The question was to establish whether there exists between analytic and synthetic statements a complete opposition (Carnap) or a continuity of transition (Quine). It was for this reason that we carried out the psychological experiment (amongst others) on counting and verifying $3+2=5$, that I described above. The idea was to take a statement considered by all the logicians to be strictly analytic, but which I wanted to show actually began in the child by being experimental and consequently synthetic.

However, despite this, my collaborator maintained that if the changes were slight they were nevertheless always made by sudden reorganization and discontinuous steps. He was a logical empiricist who insisted on the distinction between the analytic and synthetic, and I did not manage to convince him that there was continuity. In another field I should perhaps easily have convinced him. In other words, these notions of continuity and discontinuity depend not only on the scale of measurement but also on the general system of interpretation.

I will conclude, then, by saying that stages of development appear to me to be a reality, but differ from one field to another; they are more or less defined, more or less precise and accentuated according to the fields. As regards general stages common to all fields of development, I am in some doubt. I can neither affirm nor deny their existence. One can only decide by successive approaches, which would consist in establishing a series of correlations, correspondences and parallelisms—work which is almost entirely still to be done. Lastly, the idea of stages seems to me necessarily linked with the idea of equilibrium, or steady states.

GREY WALTER:

The definition of 'stage' is essential to our whole philosophy about children. We can't escape the general axiom that in dealing with an organism there are bound to be thresholds; there are bound to be stages below thresholds at which nothing happens, stages above thresholds when something does happen. But the difficulty arises when one has many thresholds, that is many processes each with a different threshold, in which a series of step-functions may overlap. Piaget seemed to me to be saying that in studying the *whole behaviour* of a child, there may well be so many thresholds that the various jumps superimpose and produce a smooth curve. It seems to me that one of our tasks is to see if we can dissect out the various step-functions and thus isolate particular psycho-physiological functions in the child for further investigation. The origin of some of our misunderstandings may be that some of us are looking at individual functions—for example, the existence of a particular type of brain activity in the EEG, or the existence of some drive in sexual behaviour —whereas others are looking at whole behaviour in which there is a blurring of these otherwise critical stages of development.

TANNER:

I was going to say very much the same thing. Piaget acknowledged the force of the argument that something which appears as a stage

123

may do so because it has been measured on a coarse scale and that if the scale is made finer one may discover there is continuity. In my turn I agree that if you go still further down in refinement, down to the cellular level, you again come to step-functions. Thus there are some behavioural levels where stages appear, other levels, for example of physical measurements, where continuity appears, and then the cellular level where ultimately there is again discontinuity. It is chiefly for this reason that, as I said in my comment on Piaget's paper, I don't feel the question of stages is a very real one. I think that stages are useful only in certain operational situations and that it would probably be a mistake to discuss as a question of philosophic importance whether stages do or do not exist in the disembodied or decontexed sense.

PIAGET:

I should like to make a quotation. It is from Henri Poincaré and he said 'Scientific research consists in making what is discontinuous continuous and in making what is continuous discontinuous'!

INHELDER:

Certainly in the field of cognitive functions stages have no absolute significance. What actually does a stage signify if not a change of a qualitative order, a sort of metamorphosis? We can speak of stages only when we observe a real change in behaviour in a defined situation. Such a transformation can be marked by a change in the way of thinking. It may happen, for example, that a child for a shorter or longer time tries to find a solution to a problem by the method of trial and error. He gets close to the correct solution through a series of successive adjustments, without, however, achieving success. Then almost abruptly he changes his tactics and reasons in a perfectly logical way with a feeling that it has become self-evident. It is then that we are faced with a new form of thought qualitatively different from the previous form. This new method or tactic will itself serve as a basis for new trials and errors in connexion with more complex problems. This metamorphosis of thought is particularly clearly seen in respect of ideas of conservation.

BERTALANFFY:

Here a question occurs to me. We have the stages as analysed by Professor Piaget. On the other hand, we can compare the curve of brain growth (Vol. I, Fig. 1, p. 37) with the 'age curve of intelligence' (see Fig. 1) based on the Berkeley Growth Study. It seems that these curves of brain growth and mental growth show a remarkable similarity. Would you say that the smooth Berkeley curve is caused by a smoothing-out of Professor Piaget's stages?

FIG. 1

A PROPOSED AGE CURVE OF INTELLIGENCE, BIRTH TO 50 YEARS

Based on data from the Berkeley Growth Study, the Terman Gifted Study, and Owen's Iowa Study (after Bayley, 1955).

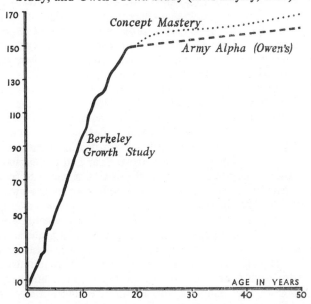

INHELDER:

Yes, I suppose it is a cumulative effect.

The effect of pseudo-regularity in curves of development can result from the way the tests are grouped. It has been noted that different ideas of conservation, of an arithmetical, geometrical, physical, etc., order are not formed at exactly the same moment. The processes involved are parallel, but not synchronous because one finds more difficulty in structuring one aspect of reality than others. These overlaps are one of the reasons why for many years I refused to believe in general stages of cognition. It was only later on after I had noticed the surprising concordance of structural order in the mechanisms of thought that I was able to show steps within cognitive functions. These steps are characterized by structures.

These structures in the concrete thought of the child or in the formal thought of the adolescent always represent the *optimum* of his operatory capacity. Naturally, during each day the child goes through oscillations of thought, and both the adolescent and the adult are far from reasoning formally all the time. The attainment

125

of a cognitive stage merely means that an individual under optimal conditions becomes capable of behaving in a certain way which was impossible for him before.

PIAGET:

This is the same point that Bowlby raised when in his reply to my essay he said 'I wonder if Piaget accepts the idea that, at all ages, behaviour is regulated by cognitive processes of different degrees of development—that in some of our actions we operate with a fully-fledged intelligence and in others none at all, and that in respect of any one activity we may shift from one level to another?'

Well, I fully accept this idea. Our cognitive functions are certainly not uniform for every period of the day. Although I am mainly engaged in intellectual operations, I am for example at an operatory level for only a small part of the day when I devote myself to my professional work. The rest of the time I am dealing with empirical trial and error. At the time when I drove a car and my engine went wrong it was even empirical trial and error on a very low level, as you can imagine. Every moment I am indulging in pre-operatory intuition. At other times I go even lower and almost give way to magical behaviour. If I am stopped by a red light when I am in a hurry it is difficult for me not to link this up with other preoccupations of the moment. In short, the intellectual level varies considerably, exactly like the affective level, according to the different times of the day, but for each behaviour pattern I think we shall find a certain correspondence. For example, for a primitive emotion a very low intellectual level, and for a lofty aesthetic or moral sentiment a high intellectual level. We shall always have this correspondence between the two aspects.

BERTALANFFY:

I think we all agree that we do not invariably find stages, but in certain phenomena we find more or less continuous curves, and in others, distinctive steps. The growth curve of body-weight in a fish, for example, is quite smooth and without inflection. In the rat, however, a lower mammal, the curve is in general similar, but a more detailed analysis reveals that it is actually composed of two 'growth cycles', the transition from the first to the second cycle being relatively sharp and corresponding to the beginning of puberty. Finally, in man there is a very apparent growth-cycle added to the basic curve at puberty—the increase in growth-rate that Tanner calls the adolescent spurt (see Vol. I, p. 36). I want to emphasize that such steps are real. In physiological phenomena in the rat, for example, you find continuity with respect to certain characteristics and with respect to others you have breaks. For example, make an allometric plot

FIG. 2
RELATIVE GROWTH IN THE ALBINO RAT
(A) SIMPLE ALLOMETRY. (B) CHANGES IN ALLOMETRY

The discontinuities in relative growth appear at a body weight of circa 100 g., i.e. the time of puberty. A similar break is found in the growth-in-time curve of the rat. The figures give only regression lines: complete data and statistical analysis in Bertalanffy and Pirozynski (1952, 1953): Racine (1953).

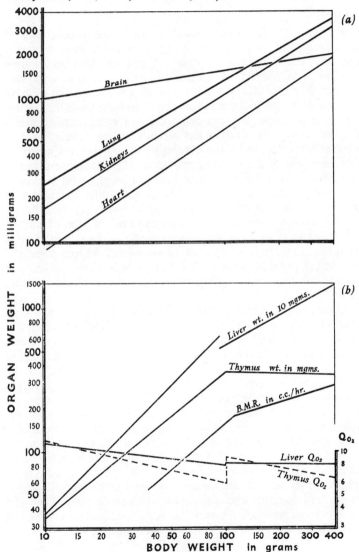

(Fig. 2), taking total weight as the abscissa and some physiological variable as the ordinate. For the allometric growth of the heart, for example, we get an allometric regression line without a break, and the same applies to the relative growth of the brain. However, in the relative growth of the liver, we find a break; similarly, in basal metabolic rate and other phenomena. But when and if breaks occur, they all take place approximately at the same period, namely, at a body-weight of about 100 g, that is, just preceding puberty.

LORENZ:

I want to say a few things about stages in the development of behaviour in birds. I could not disagree less with what Professor Piaget has said about general stages. A general stage occurs only where the development of different functions coincides, is synchronized. The probability of such coincidence is small and we have true synchronization in the behaviour patterns of animals only where an obvious selection pressure has evolved a synchronizing mechanism. We have done two studies recently on the development of behaviour in birds: one is Ilse Prechtl's still unpublished paper on the development of the gaping response, or the begging response in little birds, and the other is Helga Fischer's longitudinal studies in geese. Now, there are two events in a bird's life, hatching and fledging, at which it is very necessary to synchronize function. When a bird comes out of the egg it must start to breathe, it must start to eat, it must start to move in a very specific manner, and it must start at once to learn several things, to learn what not to eat, mainly. Thus you can say that the newly-hatched goose is a very well-defined general stage. The same applies to fledging, when the bird suddenly begins to fly.

These are the only general stages which I could find in a bird's life because in studying, as we have done now, the development of certain activities in geese, we find that, although there is a very strict succession of stages for every single one of the activities studied, nothing in the morphology or the behaviour of the bird varies as much as the relative speed of development of different activities. The unsynchronization, the variations of these speeds of development may give rise to certain syndromes which always occur if certain desynchronizations have taken place. To give you a very clear example of this: in lightly-domesticated geese—they must have some domestic blood to achieve this—the mother-child relationship, in other words the following-mother relationship, which is a clearly-defined type of behaviour, may survive abnormally long, and sexual activities may, in these semi-domestic animals, appear abnormally early. Then you get a syndrome which is the most beautiful Oedipus behaviour you can imagine: the bird insists violently on copulating with its mother

128

and with nobody else. If he has a father who is non-domesticated, whose sexual activity therefore arises later in the spring, the father doesn't object to this. We have a Canada domestic hybrid who is called Oedipus for this very reason, and I can guarantee to get the complex of Oedipus behaviour experimentally at will. I only have to take a wild Canada gander, and a domestic goose, and pair them, and have them raise their children and this behaviour appears regularly.

Now, Helga Fischer has shown how more subtle non-synchronization and occasional skipping of a stage results in a very interesting disturbance of pair-formation. For instance, the ganders are more active in certain pre-copulative sexual activities called distance courtship, which is the only behaviour pattern at this stage to show sexual dimorphism. It is this distance courtship which sorts out heterosexual pairs, and if it is skipped, which may happen for environmental reasons, then homosexual pair-formation occurs for the reason that the only other sexually dimorphic behaviour patterns appear much later in relation to real copulation. Thus again, de-synchronization and/or skipping of a stage results in highly specific disintegration of behaviour.

Thus I wanted to say how necessary it is to study the stages of *each* behaviour pattern, of each type of behaviour, thoroughly, and then look for co-ordinating mechanisms. We do find very definite co-ordinating mechanisms which may effect re-integration of this disrupted behaviour at a later stage.

You may be surprised at the difference of age at which the stages may occur. We have case-histories of distance courtship, the normal beginning of pair-formation, occurring at one year old in one bird, and at over five years old in perfectly normal others. A species with such a tremendous life-span as a greylag goose can afford to spend quite a few years on pair-formation; no very important selection pressure is brought to bear on the quick formation of pairs because a pair once formed survives for a very long time.

Ilse Prechtl has described some very interesting cases of overlap of function giving rise to non-adaptive behaviour. There is a mechanism which orientates the gaping of the young bird upward as long as it is blind, and a later-arising mechanism which visually directs the bird's gaping towards the parent; and there is a time when both are active with the result that the bird gapes in the resultant of the two orientation responses. In cave-nesting birds the first gaping response is released by auditory functions, and this releasing mechanism is switched off from one hour to the next at the time this bird begins to gape visually. This switching off of the auditory releasing mechanism is reversible because if you stick a little black paper on the bird's eyes it begins to gape on acoustic stimulation again. So this shows definitely that there must be a survival value for the bird, not only in each of the two things, but also in a definite mechanism for making a jump where originally there was an overlap.

I mention this to show that synchronization, in other words a general stage, is a secondary effect due to a particular mechanism necessary to effect it. In the development of animals, there is a definite survival value in *not* synchronizing the development of different functions and/or structures because if you change too much at once there is danger of disintegration. The instability of transitional stages couldn't be emphasized more dramatically than by the animals dying. Anybody who has bred cichlids knows that the brood perish either immediately after hatching, or at the point of metamorphosis from the non-swimming, beak-fed stage, to the swimming stage. Those are the two metamorphoses in a cichlid's life. In a bird, anybody who has bred ducks and geese knows that there are also two points of danger—one is after hatching and the other is at fledging. These are the two points which, like the disintegration of human behaviour in puberty, are stages where necessarily many things must be changed at once. Otto Koenig in Vienna did a very beautiful study with the child-psychologist, Sylvia Klimpfinger, on the ontogenetic development of behaviour in hounds; and they showed that the mortality of young hounds was greatest at the phase of accelerated transition.

I was going to say exactly the same thing Grey Walter said about thresholds, that of course overt behaviour very often begins quite suddenly from one hour to the next when the threshold is reached. It varies from case to case, however: some instinctive activities begin slowly and get more and more intense from day to day, whereas with others the sudden crossing of a threshold makes an apparently huge jump; either may happen.

PIAGET:

I must now go on to give a definition of affectivity as Lorenz, Bowlby and others have requested. French-speaking psychologists speak frequently of affectivity in contrast to cognitive functions, but a word with such significance does not really exist in the English language. Consequently, we must come to some agreement here about the implications of this distinction: is it only relative to a certain cultural language or does it correspond to something real in psychological fact?

I would mention first three authors whose psychological work is very different, but who have each dealt with this distinction. I am thinking of Kurt Lewin, Pierre Janet and Claparède. Kurt Lewin, as you know, introduced the idea of 'Gestalt' into the study of social and affective psychology and for him the problem was one of characterizing affectivity from the theoretical approach. Lewin proposed extending the original notion of 'field' in Köhler's language to what he called the 'total field', which would include the ego of the subject with his reactions to objects and not only what is perceived or conceived in the external world by the subject. In the total field Lewin introduced a distinction between the *dynamics* of the field and the *structure* of the field. These are two characteristics which are indissociable because there is never structure without dynamism or dynamism without structure, but they are never reducible one to the other. In Lewin's language affectivity is the dynamics of the field and the cognitive functions are the structuration of the field. This seems to me a relatively clear criterion.

Pierre Janet distinguished in behaviour two sorts of action which are also very different but are always found at the same time: what he called primary action and what he called secondary action. Primary action is the relation between the subject and the objects; for example, the action of going in the direction of any place in space, or of manipulating objects. Secondary action, on the contrary, is the energetic—or, as Janet calls it, the economic—regulation of the primary action. These regulations consist of regulations of activation: activation in the positive sense like effort, pressure, etc., or activation in the negative sense, like fatigue or depression, which slow down action. On the other hand, there are regulations of termination and not only of activation, some of them positive (that would be joy or the feeling of success) and the others negative (which would be sadness or the feeling of failure). In all elementary behaviour Janet thus always finds the primary action which corresponds to what Lewin calls the structure of the field and then the secondary action which corresponds to Lewin's dynamics of the field.

Claparède tells us that in all behaviour there is an aim pursued and means used to attain it. On the one hand we have the value of the aim; on the other hand we have the method for attaining this aim. The value of the aim is affectivity, the technique is intelligence (in other words the cognitive functions of perception, sensorimotor co-ordination, intelligence, etc.).

Thus in three different authors I find the same dichotomy of two indissociable and complementary aspects of action, but two aspects which are irreducible. Agreeing with this—I would say that affectivity is the regulation of values, everything which gives a value to the aim, everything which releases interest, effort, etc., and then I would say that cognitive functions are the total of structural regulations.

I will take two examples: one very elementary example from the point of view of the level of development—that of instinctive conduct. In French we have no word to designate the sum of instinctive behaviour, we just say 'instinct'. In German there are two words which correspond precisely to the dichotomy I was speaking of just now. In German one says 'Trieb' for the valuation of the aim and the pressure which directs towards the aim, and 'Instinkt' for the technique, that is to say for the cognitive functions. This is exactly the dichotomy I was thinking of for affectivity and the cognitive functions. At the other end of the scale I will take a higher behaviour pattern such as mathematical reasoning. Mathematical reasoning is highly cognitive of course; it is a combination of symbols, operations, etc. This is the structure of the field. Mathematical reasoning also necessitates, however, interest and effort; there can be fatigue, there can be reinforcements (will-power, etc.) and then there are sentiments such as the aesthetic (every mathematician will say, 'An elegant demonstration', or, 'A clumsy demonstration'). All this corresponds to an energetic regulation of the action, it is affectivity.

I think, then, there are two dimensions to every behaviour pattern, whatever it may be, and that it is legitimate to use a general word to designate the two terms of this dichotomy.

LORENZ:

I would like to call attention here to the very old paper of Wallace Craig who died last year—*Appetites and Aversion as Constituents of Instincts*, in which he gave exactly these two conceptions and in an identical way. It is a very interesting symptom of the effects of my participation in this group that I now miss badly at this table an American psychologist, a good behaviourist, a good learning man, because I would like to put to him just one question: whether a learning theorist would be content with my definition of affectivity which I think is more or less identical with Piaget's.

I would say what we call affectivity is the subjective side of all processes which effect positive or negative conditioning—which is the objectivistic behaviouristic way of saying goals and aims. I have been re-reading McDougall lately and I have always been struck by the ease with which he can be translated into pure objectivistic terms, if only he wouldn't insist on being a vitalist! Now I am sure that very many of my American friends on hearing Piaget's exposition of affectivity would accuse him of being a vitalist, just as he accused me! Still, a short time ago I was a vitalist. I want to translate what Piaget has said in such a way that the wisest Watsonian couldn't object to it. Now in even the purest kind of cognitive behaviour you still have to have an aim, you have to have an emotional signal flag as the goal for which you are striving, and I think that you could get the behaviourists to agree by saying that this is reinforcement. Everything that is a gain is a reward and every reward is by definition

132

something which is a reinforcement. The reward is in our subjective experience but this still constitutes reinforcement. Everything that we experience as punishment constitutes the opposite. And that's all in Craig.

This affective aim, the rewarding flag at the end is, of course, characteristic of all behaviour and McDougall is quite right that this aim is still there even if the animal doesn't move. It is there in what Monica Holzäpfel so aptly termed the appetitive behaviour directed at quiescence. This does not mean the animal is going to sleep, but signifies its appetence for the state of rest from disturbing stimuli which causes all the responses by which an animal is driven into its optimal habitat. Running down a scale of humidity or up a scale of temperatures, are responses which Monica Holzäpfel has termed 'Appetenz nach höheren Zuständen'. And this is what in Wallace Craig's terminology would be called aversion. In Wallace Craig's terminology everything ending in the performance of an instinctive act is an appetite. And everything that acts in quiescence is aversion. The psychology is doubtful because, while it is true that in most cases where you strive at a consummatory act like eating or copulation, it is for pleasure, the converse is not true. When you run away from cold or you run up a temperature scale there is pain on one hand but there is still pleasure on the other; it's punishment *and* reward. So in the case of appetite it is true that the thing works on the reward principle but it is not true that the Appetenz nach höheren Zuständen works exclusively on the punishment principle, as Wallace Craig thought.

MONNIER:

I should like to bring to the definition of stages of development in the child, some facts concerning EEG changes with age.

A qualitative analysis of the EEG development in three boys of the same family (6 to 11, 12 to 15, and 13 to 15½ years) in a longitudinal series shows that the development of cerebral activity occurs continuously and progressively, according to a structural plan which is expressed partially in the record of each subject at each age, but completely only in early adulthood. Thus the 15-year-old adolescent shows a definitely organized pattern, towards which the still imperfect structures of previous periods were tending.

The characteristics of complete development illustrated by the electrographic pattern of the 15-year-old boy are: progressive differentiation, systematization and localization of the cerebral electrical activities. These features are particularly true as concerns the alpha rhythm, whose polyrhythmic components diminish in favour of a few dominant components; thus the alpha rhythm becomes more monorhythmic and more monomorphic. These dominant components increase in frequency, abundance, and regularity in the posterior part of the brain, with a clear tendency to a more precise location in the occipital region and with predominance on one side. Moreover, the alpha rhythm becomes better organized into harmonious spindles. Parallel to the organization of the alpha rhythm in the posterior region, the activity of the temporal region

FIG. 3

DEVELOPMENT OF ELECTRICAL ACTIVITY OF THE BRAIN
IN ONE CHILD (VINCENT) FROM 6 TO 11 YEARS AND
ANOTHER (FRANÇOIS) FROM 12 TO 15 YEARS

The cross-hatched zones indicate the times of apparent discontinuity or stages. On the right are frequency and voltage of alpha rhythm.

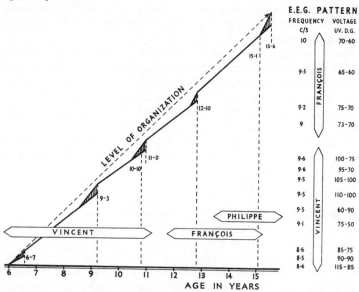

becomes also less polyrhythmic and polymorphic; the small components of the delta band diminish in abundance and voltage, and the theta-rhythm frequency band becomes narrower. Finally, the theta components also decrease in voltage; their traces interfere with traces of rapid beta components. This theta rhythm more or less entirely disappears in resting conditions towards adolescence, between 12 and 15 years. We may find it later, of course, under emotional conditions.

Many data suggest however the existence of stages within the continuous development. Fig. 3 shows on one axis the pattern of

134

organization, and on the other axis the age in years. The pattern has been analysed qualitatively and to some extent quantitatively in frequency and voltage. The average frequency increases from 8·4 to 9·5 cycles/sec. in one boy. In the two older boys, the frequency also increases, from 9 to 10 cycles/sec.

Within the continuous development of the brain rhythms, one can distinguish certain epochs at which the organization of the electro-graphic pattern becomes better defined, structured, and consolidated. These epochs, which produce the impression of a certain discontinuity in development, perhaps more apparent than real, can be called stages. Thus, the youngest child reaches a first stage of development at 6·7 and 7 years. Then a second one at 9·3. This first step is very typical. The predominance of the alpha rhythm on the right side becomes irreversible. Once this last stage has been reached, further examinations carried out during the tenth year do not show abrupt alterations any more; however, at 10·10 new improvements allow one to foresee a next step towards 11 years. Consequently, we may postulate the existence of three stages of development in this child, at 6·7 to 7, 9·3 and about 11 years. As concerns the stages of development during the prepubertal and pubertal period, we have got some data from the shorter series of examinations carried out in this boy's brothers. At 12·10 one boy's EEG develops some more homogeneous and less polyrhythmic pattern. Finally, in both older boys, the pattern of adolescent cerebral activity is achieved towards the fiftheenth year. If we compare the rate of development of the cerebral activity in two subjects during a similar period (12-15 years), we are able to distinguish individual differences. The EEG shows certainly a higher degree of organization in one boy at 15 years than in his brother.

My conclusion will be very brief. If we compare the characteristics of the stages defined by Piaget and Inhelder on the basis of their psychological investigations with the characteristics of our EEG stages, we recognise some correspondences. We detect a constant order of succession in the transformation of the EEG with the age. We have noted at one stage in the EEG signs of preparation for the following stage. Furthermore, we observed signs of growing equilibrium in the form of more and more monomorphic, localized, systematized and structured rhythmic activity with definite irreversibility. Once a pattern has been acquired, it will not regress to the previous stage, unless disease occurs.

FOURTH DISCUSSION

Psychosexual Stages in Child Development

ERIKSON:

This meeting I am going to present a restatement of the 'Freudian' phases of early infantile psychosexuality. At the last meeting (Vol. III) I discussed *psychosocial* development in general and the development of the sense of identity in particular; and my desire to do so then sprang from my feeling that if one really wanted to speak of *human* ethology it was necessary to take into account the whole span of the first twenty years. It seemed necessary for somebody to point out that we cannot forever continue to compare the *small* human child with the *young* animal and think that the two will have parallels which will explain the principles of human ethology. Human ethology, rather, must encompass the whole, ever-widening circle of the pre-adult human's mutuality and fittedness: in relation to the maternal person, the parental persons, the play- and school-mates, the training and the teaching adults, and the institutions which represent the ideology of the whole group. That all of this taken together is as important to a person when he is in his late teens as his mother was to him when he was at the earlier age is what I tried last time to illustrate with the history of a breakdown at the threshold of young adulthood.

But now I am grateful for the opportunity in the eleventh hour of this group's work to come back to the early Freudian stages. When the members of this Group speak of the 'Freudian stages' they mean, of course, the psychosexual stages of orality, anality and genitality; and it is entirely true that what Freud had first in mind was a reconstruction of early sexuality, that is psychosexuality, on the basis of psychopathological material. It is up to each of us to decide how much of Freud's original reconstruction in the psychosexual area he wants to accept—how much of it he thinks he recognizes in his patients' neurotic regressions, dreams, character deformations, or in the direct observation of children. But it has seemed to me now for 20 years that these stages have an importance for child development and psychosocial development in general which is mostly overlooked —by my psychoanalytic colleagues as well as by those in other fields.

136

'Oral', 'anal' and 'genital' are terms which refer to body zones: meaning zones around the mouth and the upper nutritional tract, the eliminative organs, and the genital organs. And it was Freud's theory that a certain amount of libido or sexual energy is attached to these zones during successive stages of development; that the child has experience of a highly libidinal, emotional, affective kind centring in and around these zones; that societies are more or less prohibitive in regard to the employment of these zones in infantile habits, and that the human being suffers from society's interference with the naïve, sensual, sexual experiences attached to the zones. What Margaret Mead said about the cognitive stages as developed by Piaget and Inhelder holds true for the psychosexual stages as well: they are part of 'a process of maturation meeting a process of education'—education not only in the sense of prohibition or guidance, but also in the sense of the transmission of the particular culture's version of reality. In order to see this, however, one must add to the concept of the psychosexual *zones*, that of 'organ *modes*' —modes meaning ways of 'going at' something—modes of aggression, if you wish, in the original Latin sense of *adgredere*. The appearance of a new stage is, most generally, the appearance of a new dominant mode of going at things, by way of a newly-matured executive part of the organism. In this sense then I would postulate that during those stages described by Freud as 'psychosexual' a number of organ modes become the highly affective modes of going at things, and that at the same time, these modes become the concern of child training.

'Incorporation' would be the dominant organ mode for the zone around the mouth, the oral zone. It represents a general attitude of 'accepting' experience of a kind that is *offered* rather than the kinds that one must know how to take or to reach out for. One may say, however, that such incorporation at the beginning of life is also the dominant mode for a number of other zones, such as the eyes, the ears, the senses in general, and the whole tactile surface. Therefore I would speak not of an oral stage but of an oral-sensory-tactile stage. Nevertheless, the mouth, as the organ of nutritional and libidinal intercourse with the nipple and other sources of food, remains the centre of this organization of incorporative organs.

To the dominant first mode there is soon added a dominant second mode. The second incorporative mode would be incorporation by way of *taking*—more active incorporation through a more co-ordinated reaching out and seeking out: biting, grasping, focusing, etc.

As these get established libidinal attention as well as growth-energy shifts to another zone-organization: retention (*retenere*) and elimination (*ex* and *limen*) are the modes dramatized in the sphincters

137

and the muscle system, this occurring during the second year. There is a certain innate 'ambivalence' in the organ systems which have to alternate and synchronize both retention and elimination, which is what the sphincters have to learn. It is obvious in the motion of alternate opening and closing that the organism becomes ready at this time alternately to hold in and to let go, to grasp and to throw away, to hold on and to repudiate in a number of organs and in a variety of social interactions.

Later, development as well as libidinisation shifts to locomotor and infantile-genital organs: intrusion, in the Latin sense of *intrudere* —'thrust into'—is the organ mode connected with psychosexual sensations in the phallic-urethral zone, in the third and fourth year. Inclusion becomes the dominant mode for the female genital organs. Both come from a common matrix which boys and girls share, even as they share a common maturation in locomotor development and locomotor passion, as brought about by individual idiosyncrasy or cultural provocation.

Each mode, then, is originally 'attached' to a focal zone (Freud's erotogenic zones): (1) mouth and throat; (2) rectum and urethra; (3) genitals; and a peripheral contact system: (1) sensory and tactile; (2) muscular; and (3) locomotor.

I really don't feel able to discuss in brevity the question as to whether these mode-maturations are the function of 'instinct' or not. There is something quantitative about them, an amount of urge which must find its action, which Freud has called *Trieb*. To Freud this was primarily an energy concept—a fact which is often forgotten for semantic reasons: in English the German *Trieb* becomes 'instinct' whereas *Trieb* should really be 'drive'. I make this matter easier for myself by speaking of *instinctual energy* and *instinctive patterns*, i.e., of instinctual forces which endow instinctive patterns of contact-seeking with energy. It is one of the main aspects of human life that in man's long childhood instinctive patterns are more variable and instinctual energies more displaceable than they are in the animal. I think we would save much misunderstanding if we would always assume that Freud is speaking of a quantity of instinctual energy temporarily or permanently 'attached' to a particular organ system and its particular patterns of behaviour. These instinctual energies are obviously related to Professor Piaget's 'affective' energies. On the other hand, there are also instinctive patterns (such as the organ-modes) which are related to the maturation of the cognitive systems; so the problem remains how to study the overlapping of the energy aspects and the pattern aspects of that long period of maturing, playing, and learning called childhood.

Let me now discuss the probability that in the existence of organ-modes and in their relations to each other we have a set of pheno-

138

mena akin to what Konrad Lorenz referred to as 'relatively autonomous processes'—processes which stubbornly seek an equilibrium within themselves; but which also, just because they are so stubborn, create critical periods for the human being in that they refuse to be harmonized with the various reaction velocities of other systems. This in fact is what I think Freud first saw in his psychopathological investigations. Let us first look at a figure (Fig. 4) which tries to indicate the inner relation of the organ modes to each other.

FIG. 4

INNER RELATION OF ORGAN MODES

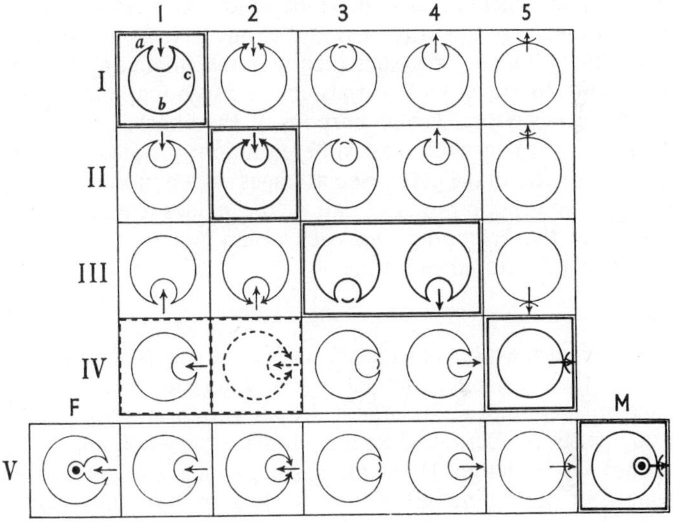

This diagram is a systematization growing out of the observations of children's symptoms and children's play, and out of the comparison of child training patterns in various cultures. I.1 is a sign for the incorporative mode. II.2 is the sign for the second incorporative mode of clamping down, grasping, biting on, taking. III.3 is the retentive mode, meaning closing for the sake of holding in or keeping out. III.4 represents the eliminative mode, IV.5 the intrusive mode, and IV.1 and 2 the inclusive mode.

MEAD:
You ought to add that this chart is really set up for males only.

ERIKSON:
Yes. The letter *a* represents the oral zone, *b* the anal/urethral zone, *c* the genital zone. As you see, *all the modes, and not only the dominant*

139

one, 'exist' at the same time (horizontally) in all zones, and can, in fact, become relatively dominant—for pathological, idiosyncratic or cultural reasons. This is one rule this chart demonstrates. However, if any of these secondary modes is over- or under-emphasized, then there is an interference with the supposedly dominant mode *and* with the next mode which can either be called into life too early or too intensively. Inappropriate clamping down (I.2) for example, can happen if the baby is either inclined or forced to close up. And there can be also an intrusive pattern (I.5) of—as it were—screwing himself on the breast. But the dominant mode at the first stage, the mode that must be mature enough to meet the particular system of child training which in turn must be ready to meet the mode, is incorporation, I.1. Thus, any early and strong deviation, modification or variation will show up systematically in the whole organization of modes—and to trace such variations in psychopathology and in anthropology was the second purpose of the chart.

Progression by growth and differentiation proceeds along the diagonal (as it did in the psychosocial stages shown in Vol. III, p. 168). This is the epigenetic principle: all of the modes are present in all organs from the beginning, but each organ has a dominant mode which has its developmental time.

LORENZ:

What strikes me quite particularly is that the stages of first grasping only and then grasping and letting go alternately, are very well marked in locomotion. In practically all vertebrates who walk on feet you get first a period when the animal is very well able to grasp but is not able to let go. He just hangs on, which is of survival value of course for not falling out of the nest. I think that these two stages of grasping—first grasping and then retention and elimination alternately—are highly characteristic of the ontogeny of locomotion in all vertebrates that are not born in stage 3.

KRAPF:

I would mention the very early appearance of the grasping reflex in the human neonate, a grasping in which the infant also cannot let go. It already appears in the foetus, and is undoubtedly one of his first manifestations of motor behaviour.

ERIKSON:

I would be intensely interested in a systematic comparison between these matters of human development and phylogenetic material; and I hope that sometime we can look at all of this in an ethological way. But I must emphasize that I am not now talking about maturing *capacities*. I am talking about something which Professor Piaget

140

calls affective, and others call emotional—that particular investment in subjective experience which Freud calls libidinal; that ambitious, stubborn, and excited interest, in going at things in certain ways, of completing an act, coupled with the high degree of frustration from not being permitted to complete it or not being able to complete it.

I must emphasize this, because in most of the discussions of this group this central problem has remained peripheral.

LORENZ:

I entirely agree with this and I hadn't misunderstood you, but all you said now about affectivity applies exactly to the affectivity of motor patterns. I was thinking about the development of monkeys which Katerina Heinault has particularly studied. All this theory about frustration applies exactly to everything a little baboon does, not with his mouth or his genitalia, but quite exactly to what he does with his hands and feet. *Quite* exactly! I emphasize that this is not an objection, it's an illustration.

ERIKSON:

A very important illustration. What I want to get to next is a reformulation of these stages as a series of *encounters* such as only human life institutionalizes. Each stage permits an intensive encounter with particular educative measures. Cultures have, of course, every interest in fully meeting the child's maturational readiness in these respects, and they have done so, one after the other, with highly emotional and magical measures of training. This the chart cannot illustrate. It only indicates a maturational sequence of 'readinesses', and like all maturational diagrams (only more importantly) it fails to take into account such elements as intensity and duration, which are widely influenced by the environment.

MEAD:

Don't you think too that the chart was highly influenced by being made up in America at a time, in the early 1930s, when nobody could think about anything but zones, when books on children would have sometimes a hundred pages on toilet training and two on talking, and the culture was treating the child as a set of zones on the trunk of the body. Writers on child care ignored arms and legs, ignored speech, ignored cognitive development. When I first saw the chart I found I could put half my cultures in these terms because they also were obsessed by zones and trunks, but I could do nothing at all at first with a culture where the emphasis was on the whole body and a great deal of importance was given to the locomotor and tactile systems. You now include these in your statement.

Well, the chart depicts only the organ modes centred in the eroto-genic zones which (for good biological reasons) *are* on the trunk. In my book (Erikson, 1950) muscles and limbs are already acknowl-edged in so far as they are concerned in this particular problem of organ modes. But I'm glad Margaret Mead referred to the problem of transitory one-sidedness in psychoanalytic concept formation; it occurred to me that I should say something about this. Psycho-analysis develops in a highly dialectical way. Somebody said to Freud once: 'Five years ago you said exactly the opposite', and Freud said 'That was right then'. In a dialectical way Freud always wrote as much against as for something, and many of his statements become clear only in the context of the then necessary antithesis. Take, for example, the question as to whether a memory reported today is more representative of the situation in which it emerges, or of the past situation of which it claims to be a remnant. In the debate between Dr. Bowlby and Professor Piaget at the last meeting (Vol. III, pp. 156,160) Bowlby quoted Freud as saying that 'memories are indestructible'. Actually, Freud said that 'early structures' (and that is more than isolated memories) are 'never quite destroyed'. Now that was written in a general climate in which it was assumed that the child was not affectively aware of many of the most important things that were happening to him, did not care to be aware, and did not, later on, remember. Freud concluded from later disturbances that such 'silent' events had, in fact, been deeply experienced and very deeply registered. To my mind this does not mean that memories as such are indestructible; Freud after all was the one who described what happens to early experiences, how they are disguised, trans-ferred, displaced, repressed—he described the laws of their destruction while maintaining that some of their energy and essential imagery persisted. At any rate, the point I want to make is: when you quote Freud, you must say what he wrote *against* at the time.

Every step in psychoanalytic theory has the most far-reaching implications, for the philosophy of life, for the treatment of children, for one's attitude toward one's own neurosis, and so on. It is always significant on that frontier of living where we touch the irrational, the 'inhuman', the ugly, the frightening. So in response to every change in emphasis (it is happening now to my concept of identity) a hasty kind of pseudo-integration takes place, a pseudo-synthesis of everything that is known up to then, a totalization, you may say, of partial knowledge. In psychology, this reaches into the ethical and philosophical much more quickly and deeply than do similar pseudo-integrations in other scientific fields. In order to give security to their children and to their patients, people have to offer premature closures of knowledge which, though the best one can have at a given time, may still be conceptually spurious. It is for this reason that in psychoanalysis as a 'movement' we have had any number of Utopias which have had to be undone or left by the wayside before the next step could be made.

FREMONT-SMITH:
This is not true only of psychoanalysis. I think almost every scientific development has its eras of Utopia, and its needs of undoing. In fact, one of the things that this Group has come together for is for a bit of mutual undoing!

LORENZ:
The most beautiful example of this relative truth is behaviourism and purposive psychology. If you don't know whom McDougall is arguing against, you will think that this great genius is a perfect fool; and exactly the same is true of behaviourism. Behaviourism and purposive psychology give a wonderful example of Hegel's doctrine that the thesis is only true with its antithesis.

ERIKSON:
Coming back to Fig. 4—in the first three stages we assumed a mode development independent of sexual differences. This is unlikely, but a chart can do only so much; and, as a chart, it does presuppose that the later stages are present in the earlier ones. In IV.5, then, the intrusive mode dominates the others in the boy's life. Yet, since there is a high degree of bisexuality, the 'feminine' mode of inclusion, a kind of 'enveloping' attitude (IV 1.2), is secondarily emphasized in the boy. In the girl this mode is dominant, while the intrusive mode becomes secondary. Incidentally, this arrangement makes oral incorporation (I.1) a precursor of genital inclusion (IV 1.2). This gives the girl's whole chart a different slant of great significance.
The further development of these modes, in so far as they remain sex-bound, is indicated with the little sign of a circle with a dot inside (V). It represents the fact and, if you wish, the instinctive knowledge of the fact, that deep inside the body procreative modes are waiting. Their physiological focus is obviously in the boy the *Anlage* of the semen and in the girl that of the ovum. This something inside the body gives all these modes a particular meaning, lending libidinal energy to the whole complex of wanting to be a father, of playing with bows and arrows or guns and automobiles, or whatever the equivalent technological symbol is to express both intrusion and locomotion. In the modes of inclusion, there is also an increasing orientation towards a future role of incorporating for the sake of developing something inside. This again was at one time a rather important thing to say because psychoanalysts tended to consider

143

pregenitality a mere preparation for exercising potency, and for learning to join in the genital climax, omitting the further development of the libido to what I call generativity. This then is represented by the addition of an inner centre to all the psychosexual modes.

Now before I come to the main point, I would like to indicate briefly where this chart overlaps with the chart on psychosocial development which I presented at the third meeting (Vol. III, p. 168). You will remember that the problem of Basic Trust vs. Basic Mistrust was the first psychosocial problem, occurring in the first year of life. This would correspond in the present chart to the problems of incorporation. Basic trust is the lasting capacity to overcome basic mistrust in spite of everything that life may bring. The child acquires the basis for such faith, as Bowlby so dramatically shows again and again, in the at first 'incorporative' meeting with the giving maternal figure in the first year. The second psychosocial problem, autonomy vs. doubt and shame, develops with and out of the interplay of retaining and releasing, which culminates in a certain pushing away of the mother while yet holding on to her. It needs basic trust to develop autonomy, while shame and doubt at that age would make the child want to go back and check up on mother (and her reality and morality). This coincides with the second stage, that of retention and elimination. All this is dramatically illustrated in psychopathology, and popularly in what the Germans call *Trotzperiode*. Finally the psychosocial alternative of initiative and guilt is related to the stage of intrusive-inclusive differentiation: for it is out of this third stage that children have to retain the capacity to develop the uninhibited ability to exercise male and female initiative according to the ideals of their culture.

The point I want to make now is that Freud, by finding in his psychopathological work the greatest relevance of the connexions which I briefly illustrated in the diagram, really pointed to more than he cared to elaborate at the time when he was exclusively interested in the importance of this system for the development of healthy or morbid psychosexuality. The early encounters of these maturing organ modes with the specific educative processes, which are meant to meet them half way, establishes, I think, a basic grammar of what I call *social modalities*. For example, in order to get something in the incorporative way you have to have somebody give something— and the general setting for the act of giving and receiving will, in large or small details, vary from couple to couple and from culture to culture. In the interplay of getting and giving, then, a certain basic style materializes for the experience of getting and being given on the part of the child and, on the part of the maternal person, for giving to somebody who needs to be given to. The satiation of the recipient, his signs of thankful gratification, and the satisfaction of the giver,

144

and her feeling of having done a good job in the eyes of her society, complete a cycle comparable to those described in animal ethology. But human cultures vary in their ways of giving things to the baby and of withholding things from it and of justifying their particular way of doing so. In any given culture, therefore, a child experiences the modes in a special form. Here, an important thing has to be added; good and evil permeate human life to such an extent that each of these modes can take on a highly negative and a highly positive connotation: human health as well as virtue depend on their balance. To get by being given can, on the one hand, become an excessively demanding attitude in life, and it can also become the modality of receiving with good grace. Any number of variations are possible between those two.

As we think of such combinations it is good to become aware of the language in which we express them. There is a relationship, I think, in any language, between certain very basic terms and the basic social modalities. One cannot help noticing to what extent the whole culture, in its technology and in its personal relations, expresses itself already in those early encounters. To take (that is, the second mode) can mean to acquire, to secure, to learn to grasp; but also to snatch, to rob, to take away from someone. Then 'to hold on' can become to hold in, to hold away from, not to give up; on the other hand it can have the positive connotation of holding, of maintaining. Especially is the expression 'to have and to hold' a very nice one in English. It means you hold on, but for the purpose of taking care of what is held. Maintaining can be stubborn and negative, or positive, as in maintaining interest and sustaining an activity. Then 'eliminative' would be in English 'to let go', which can mean to let, to let be, or to let pass. On the other hand it can mean 'to eject', to let loose destructively. Finally, the intrusive and inclusive modes are best expressed in the term 'to make' as a form of 'to conquer' a person. One speaks of 'making a girl' which means to take her, to intrude upon her; one also can 'make a job', meaning you did it, you managed it. Intrusion and inclusion are forms of 'making people'. You can make them by intruding into them, or by snaring and attracting them. Genitality in its generative aspect is later contained in the nice English word 'to beget' which means to intrude or include in order to create a child. This of course is the more mature, more mutual form of making something and making something with somebody. This comes late in the human, who has to learn first to make things in the sense of finishing them, of doing them with somebody in some division of labour—which is where the school age begins. The social modalities, I would mention in conclusion, develop out of an interplay between the ability cognitively to complete certain operations in regard to the physical world, affectively to

145

interact with a growing radius of relevant people and things, and ultimate to integrate and maintain both.

If there were time to present a case-history I think I could show more convincingly how organization of organ modes tends towards an equilibrium of its own. This could be seen in comparing a child's social behaviour with his play behaviour, his phantasies and his habits. Such an equilibrium could also be shown in a systematic comparison of all the permissive, provocative, and punitive trends dealing with the zones and modes in a homogeneous child training system. Freud, of course, saw mainly the punitive in child training systems—which he viewed as mostly arbitrary or hypocritical or at any rate senseless—an idea which easily suggests itself if you consider only the victims of a system. However, if you look at the various cultural systems you find in each at least an 'instinctive' rationale, which is the best we have until we can develop a universal, rational child training system. I have tried to show this in comparing two American Indian tribes (Erikson, 1950).

When Bärbel Inhelder is testing a child, that child is supposed, for example, to match cards depicting two containers of water. But he may for a moment become more interested in seeing the water run out of the upper container into the lower container than in concentrating on the cognitive problem. In other words anyone motivated to concentrate on the cognitive has to suppress the mere enjoyment of making the thing function and the playful wish to match things aesthetically. Professor Piaget told us yesterday something about the equilibrium of the cognitive function. But as this is being established there must be some more general tendency in the child which permits him to concentrate on that which will lead to a cognitive equilibrium and to exclude other aspects of the mind which are seeking *their* kind of equilibrium: the psychosexual, the psychosocial, etc. This equilibrator behind all equilibrated functions is, I think, what we call the ego in psychoanalysis. This important aspect of psychoanalytic theory has been ignored in the precirculated essays in Part I.

There has been in these essays and in the discussion an exclusive emphasis, it seems to me, on the instinctual and energetic side in psychoanalysis. What has been completely ignored is the long development of structural concepts combined in what is called 'ego psychology'. Freud, back in 1920, in *The Ego and the Id* called the ego 'a cohesive organization of mental processes', i.e., an agency for a central equilibrium (the equilibrium of the child and not of its part-functions). In psychoanalytic ego psychology there is a whole literature on 'inner structure', on the development of a cohesive organization of mental processes which tends to create or to restore the whole child's equilibrium when he finds himself in a situation where one function is to be concentrated on and others to be put aside.

In regard to the term ego, of course, one again has to overcome very great semantic difficulties. As far as the variety of its implications in different languages is concerned, the term 'substance' has nothing on the term 'ego'! When we say in America 'that woman has an *ego*!' we mean vanity, egotism. The German 'Ich', especially in its heavy existential implications, means something very different, and so does the 'moi' of *'L'état c'est moi'*. Nor is the psychoanalytic ego the 'self' as it appears, for example, in a Jewish story. An old Jew comes to his physician and says, 'Doctor, my feet hurt me, my stomach aches and my head is heavy. And you know, doctor, I myself don't feel so good either.' That is the self but it isn't the ego.

Brain physiologists before Freud called ego an area in the brain which is coherent and maintains its coherence, its equilibrium. Such equilibrium theories seem to be related to early economic theories. At any rate, from the beginning Freud paid attention to the problem of inner structure, to the balancing machine, as it were, for which his energies are the fuel: only that the human organism is a growing machine in which new structure forms through growth and through experience. Many aspects of what has been referred to here as 'organizing thresholds' and 'step functions', or as the reorganization of the total mental condition at times of 'multiple breaks', were anticipated by Freud a good forty years ago, while only his instinctual theories became popular, even among scientists. One must grant, however, that Freud's papers are always concerned with a more mystical central function rather than with observable part-functions, and they have a highly speculative character. Nevertheless a conceptual convergence clearly exists between Piaget's and Freud's ideas of mental structure.

Let me, in conclusion, repeat the obvious. When we speak of the human child, the distance from hatching to fledging, from birth to maturity, is tremendously longer, tremendously more complicated, than in other animals, and also tremendously dependent on variations in the environment. Therefore, it is necessary to study all the stages of instinctive, cognitive, symbolic and social equilibration that are necessary to build up to the time when human fledging can occur successfully—that is, at the end of adolescence. I understand very well and I certainly agree with John Bowlby that from an ethological point of view it is important to investigate early biological mechanisms such as those which permit a child to stand separation from the mother. I personally feel, however, that from the beginning to the end of childhood, society plays a decisive role. At the end, as I tried to illustrate at our third meeting, society must verify with ideology, and with opportunities, what the child has learned from the long dependence on his parents. At the beginning, some kind of organized faith must provide the mother with a periodic restoration of that basic trust through which she can become trustworthy—so that trust may be created in the baby.

INHELDER:

It seems to me very important to remember, as Eric emphasized, that one should study not merely the development of the ego but also how the social environment of the individual stresses certain norms of behaviour. We must, of course, seek not only internal laws of equilibrium concerning the individual as such but also laws of equilibrium regulating interactions between the individual and his social environment. Thus, in our society, social norms which played a part in education became more flexible during the last decades, partly owing to the influence of psycho-analytic ideas. Nevertheless I see a certain danger in the superficial extension of these ideas, since they also impose new norms of behaviour which become more or less obligatory, at least for certain individuals. My own opinion is that the individual contributes very largely to his own equilibration and is not merely in some way the inevitable victim of either an internal development occuring *sui generis* or of social pressure. Complete autonomy is only achieved when an individual feels free from the need for approval of those surrounding him.

Turning to our general problem, we are attempting to establish certain correspondences between different series of facts. Personally I do not think it is possible to establish these correspondences between facts as such, but between *mechanisms of development*. It is the mechanisms of transformation which are our common denominators. Thus I should like to know more about just how these 'modes' you have described are transformed, how one becomes part of another or how one is replaced by another, in what way there is conflict between them. I think this is the crucial point for enabling us to find a common system for our future discussions.

LORENZ:

When I made the statement that the principle of grasping and ungrasping was applicable not only to overt oral movements but to locomotor and other movements of the striated musculature in general, I was only doing a thing which I always do with Freudian assertions: I first try to generalize them to the utmost extent—and then I try to reverse this process and 'ungeneralize' them. With Freud you always know that he is seeing something of extreme importance and you never know whether he has over-generalized or under-generalized, and quite usually he over-generalizes as I think is the case with the Oedipus complex, which develops in the way I have already pointed out. Now in the case of sexual differences in behaviour, such as 'intrusiveness' and 'inclusiveness' and so forth, I find myself in the rare position of wanting to generalize something that Freud said farther than he did. What irks me about the diagram which Erikson has just shown us demonstrating these differences, is that it can be applied, with very little or no change, to animals which do not have, never have had, and never will have either a penis or a vagina. So the zone-theory certainly does not hold for these animals, but the principle of the diagram goes.

I want to point out to Eric modes of pair-formation, the mechanism by which partners of different sex are enabled to find each other. This was a real riddle with some cichlid species in which there is not the slightest sexual dimorphism either in bodily characters or in instinctive movements and in which, nevertheless, heterosexual pairs are formed with the same regularity as in organisms with a sexual dimorphism like that of a golden pheasant. When I set my pupil Beatrice Oehlert to tackle this problem I certainly did my best to handicap her with a prejudice: I was convinced that sex-recognition must somehow be effected by some kind of releaser characteristic of one of the sexes. Miss Oehlert's very thorough analysis of conflict behaviour brought to light an altogether different mechanism which, in my opinion, has a great deal to do with what Freud explained on the basis of the zone theory. If animals which, during the non-sexual period, are unsocial and territorial, are brought into contact with each other by the awakening of sexual drive, the unwonted proximity of a conspecific invariably activates, besides sexual responses, also those of escape and aggression. This 'conflict' is not, by any means, anything pathological, it is normal and necessary that all three drives are simultaneously activated. Indeed, the two fish would not approach each other, if ad-gression, in the literal sense of 'going there' did not bring them together.

Now you must realize that in these fish we really know to a considerable extent what movements are activated by which drive. We really know that this little erection of the dorsal fin or that spreading of the gill membrane means aggression, and that this slight sideways tilt of the body and folding of the median fins means activation of escape drive or that this little sideways twitch of the head denotes sexual excitation. Our knowledge is borne out by correct prediction of what the fish will do in the next second. In short, you may believe me that we really know what drive is at the moment contending with what other drive within one of these cichlids.

The important thing which Beatrice Oehlert found on this basis was the following: In both sexes, aggression, sexual drive and escape are being activated all the time, as long as both fish keep responding to each other. In both sexes, each of these three drives exerts a certain

149

inhibiting influence on the two others. But these inhibiting effects are not the same in the two sexes. In the male, aggression does not inhibit sexual behaviour, or inhibits it only very slightly. In other words, aggressive behaviour and sexual behaviour are perfectly mixable in the male; they can be superimposed on each other. But, in the male, escape behaviour effects an almost complete inhibition of sexual behaviour. In other words, if he is even very slightly afraid of the female, he is completely unable to respond sexually to her. In the female, it is the other way round. Beatrice Oehlert found that mixed forms of aggressive and sexual behaviour—which are so frequent in the male—do not occur in females. In the female, aggressive behaviour completely inhibits sexuality, even if sexual motivation is very strong. Quite on the contrary, females that are full of spawn, and stand badly in need of a male, are only all the more furious in their attack against any male which does not, in his turn, intimidate them. On the other hand, escape behaviour and sexual behaviour are compatible in the female.

Now this comparatively simple dimorphism in the inhibitory interactions between escape, aggression, and sexuality is—surprisingly—quite sufficient to explain the formation of heterosexual pairs in animals lacking any other form of sexual dimorphism. I am quite convinced that the same principle holds true for all those birds in which both sexes are potentially able to act either as male or female, dependent only on the social rank-relation to the partner.

Thus the parallel between the role played by male 'aggressiveness' in my example, and male 'intrusiveness' in Freud's theory is, I think, obvious. In other words I do not believe that males are intrusive because they have a penis, I believe that in vertebrates it is the males, and not the females, that have developed a penis, because ages before the first penis was ever evolved, males were more aggressive and the little mechanism of pair-formation, which Beatrice Oehlert discovered, was in full operation.

MEAD:

I think this illustration brings out beautifully the point that it isn't the penis and the vagina that create modes of behaviour; the penis and the vagina in human children and human adults are used as a form of communication. Communication among creatures differently equipped genitally would go on differently.

The things that the child has to learn as he matures are used as modes of communication, and one culture emphasises one thing and another another. One school of psychologists says that the trouble with anthropologists is that in one culture they will discuss orality and weaning as a clue and in the next culture they will discus anal training. This is because we follow what is done in the culture itself

with its emphatic patterning of interrelationship to the child at a particular stage. In a culture which emphasizes the anal retentive mode, we may find insistence on the child getting a certain kind of oral training as part of anal training and discipline of movement. The emphasis on rhythm and on sitting in a certain way, moving in a certain way, defaecating at a certain time, eating a certain kind of food in a certain sort of way, may give a hypertrophy of maintenance function and an extraordinary impairment of initiative or operational functions as Grey Walter calls them. Manus culture twenty-five years ago heavily emphasized these control rhythmic functions at the expense of individual initiative and individual integration (Mead, 1956). You got this even reflected in the view of the self or the ego. Twenty-five years ago a Manus didn't have a whole personality. He had eight or nine names and each name was attached to the amount of property that had been given at his birth and people called him by one of these names in terms of their particular relationships to him. His emotions were located in different parts of his body, so that he thought with his neck, got angry with his belly, felt grief in his eyes and fright in his buttocks. And the society itself had no boundaries. It was a system of compensating pressures on the individual. An individual did things because other people did other things to him. There was no real centralized political idea of leadership. Now today, when they have come into the modern world, taken over the idea of being a little nation with boundaries, with membership in larger groups, with structure, with a fence around each village, with organized leadership, the individual now has something called a mind-soul, which is a single principle inside the individual directing people's relationships to each other and to a rather odd version of a Christian God. As this is developed the regulative inhibiting aspects of the toilet training and muscular training that existed twenty-five years ago have decreased and the emphasis on initiative has increased.

The extreme child-training in our own societies of thirty years ago was a perfect way of making a good accountant in a bank who took the same train every morning and who wanted to take the same train every morning and never made a mistake either. But it was a very poor way of making an individual who had more initiative and autonomy.

TANNER:

I have a specific question to ask Erik. In child development, is the location, so to speak, of the organ modes primarily in the brain or is it primarily peripheral? When you say the organs create the modes do you mean it in the literal peripheral-organ sense? There is a crucial question on this which should be able to be answered and that is what do you know about the psychosexual development of pseudo-hermaphrodites? Their brains, as far as we know, are probably normally male- and female-developed, but their peripheral genital organization varies from case to case and is always more or less muddled up.

FREMONT-SMITH:

I can give a very short answer to this last question. I think the best data have been collected by Drs. Hampson, Money and Hampson (1956) under Dr. John Whitehorn at Johns Hopkins University. These investigators showed in quite a large group of pseudo-hermaphrodites of different forms of mal- or incomplete development of the genital organs that the mode followed by the child was determined not by the internal organ (whether it was testes or ovary) nor by the external organ (whether it appeared to be more male or female) nor by the presence of XX or XY chromosomes as determined in the skin, but by the social pressure, by the expectation of the family and the social group as to whether this little human object was a boy or girl. The family and social attitude was the most important one to be considered in planning a successful gender for the child.

LORENZ:

May I answer that question from another point of view? You know that the motor patterns of copulation are quite ambisexual in most mammals and that the females are able to execute the pelvic thrust exactly in such a way that it would effect introduction of the penis if they had one. If you watch the cows coming down from the Alps now they are slightly excited, and you can often see them performing male sexual movements, which shows that at least in them the behaviour pattern is built into the central nervous system.

TANNER:

Yes, I know. This is why I addressed my question to Erik, because what I am really trying to do is to pin down to what extent these descriptions in psychoanalytic language of the erotogenic zones and the stages of development are symbolic only and to what extent they are quite concrete.

ERIKSON:

I would say they are both; they *must* be both in the human. The abortive phallic thrust-movements which occur in the cow are, indeed, mode fragments, lacking only the proper executive organ; but they are not comparable to the mode-fragments in the human which become integrated only by becoming symbolic at the same time as they become real: i.e. they become social, aesthetic and moral

152

modalities at the same time as they become an expression of the organism. At any rate, the modes and modalities have a highly symbolic quality from the beginning. The highly affective tone in the parents' warnings and approvals give the child the feeling that an event is a significant reality, has a high symbolic value; and I would think it is both the affectivity in the child's specific drivenness at a particular stage *and* the affectivity of the guiding adults which give it that value. This is probably the very reason why full sexual consummation is delayed so long in the human—so that society has the opportunity to bring together drive-energy, instinct-fragment, and symbol-communication in such a way that important values are once and for all transmitted.[1]

ZAZZO:

I think we should stress the point that at no age in his life does the child have an equilibrium of his own, an autonomous equilibrium such as an animal would have; but that the child's equilibrium always necessitates adult intervention and this intervention is variable from one civilization to another and gives to each age its own particular aspects. I think we tend too much to study childhood as a psychogenesis through mechanisms within the child without considering that at each stage, each moment, the adult intervenes and that without the adult there is no human child.

ERIKSON:

I entirely agree. Certainly it is one of the human problems that an inner regulation is accomplished only by a gradual internalization of an outer regulation first presented by the maternal person, then by the parental persons, by the basic family and so on. I also think the superego is nothing else but the beginning of adulthood in the child. It is the taking over of the moral self-regulation. You can often *see* when the child's superego is developing by the way he treats younger children; he treats younger children as if he were already an adult. That often looks like a caricature; and we know the tremendous burden which spurts of precocious adulthood can be on the child's equilibrium. Whatever the ego is, its dominant area of equilibration at the threshold of adulthood can only be psychosocial. This is why we have to protect children for so long, why we have to educate them for so long, and why we owe them a whole functioning society—and not just a good mother.

Yet, many adult egos and superegos, joined in a society, must come to a relative cultural equilibrium with one another, in order to

[1] It is important to note that, in this discussion, I am employing the more general use of the concept symbol, and do not refer to the specific case of 'Freudian' symbols.

2F

create that prolonged state of protection which we call childhood. But such a cultural equilibration, necessary as it is for the survival of each individual, is at some times and in some ways antagonistic to the individal's equilibrium. We would like to simplify this matter in claiming, for example, that a 'sane society' makes sane people, but it probably is not that simple. You probably can't have a society without its own forms of 'insane' tensions, just as you can't have individuals without conflicts. It is in the nature of social equilibrium that there must be people who 'pay' for the society's equilibrium—just as individuals 'pay' for their personal equilibrium with some sacrifices of wishes, capacities, opportunities.

General System Theory
and the Behavioural Sciences

BERTALANFFY:
You will have seen that my memorandum (Part I) offers for consideration in this Group a certain theoretical structure called General System Theory; and I want now to discuss the application of this structure to problems in the behavioural sciences.

Before doing so, I would like to make an introductory remark about the use as well as the limitations of models in science. A model never *is* the thing concerned; it only represents certain *aspects* in a more or less adequate way. To be aware of this is of primary importance. There is a very general tendency for symbols and models to be taken for the things of which they represent certain aspects only. The outcome of this tendency is what we may call the fallacy of the nothing-but. If we fall into the fallacy of the nothing-but, we have propositions such as—all phenomena in the world are nothing but the mechanical play of atoms; the reaction of an animal is nothing but an aggregate of reflexes; the brain is nothing but an electric calculator; the psyche is nothing but id, ego, and superego; and so forth *ad infinitum*. All such propositions are quite valid in so far as they are taken as a description of certain aspects of reality, but they are preposterous and easily refuted if the model is taken for a metaphysical entity. All scientific theories are constructs, models or, if you will, mythologies. Consequently, they must be remodelled and improved with increasing knowledge and must never be taken for granted and never taken as absolute or as an expression of ultimate reality.

One of these models is what is called General System Theory. Perhaps the simplest way to introduce you to this is to tell you how I myself came to the idea. If we survey the development of modern science, we realize that very similar general viewpoints and concepts have appeared in independent fields, often without the research worker in one field knowing of the work done in the other. For example, problems of organization, of wholeness, and of dynamic interaction are the most urgent ones in modern physics, chemistry, physical chemistry and technology. In biology, in contrast to the analytical way of thinking and experimenting, that is, isolating components such as chemical compounds, cells, reflexes, or whatever the case may be, problems of an organismic sort appear everywhere, and the question again is about wholeness, organization, and dynamic interaction. We have a parallel development in psychology, starting with Gestalt psychology and manifest in many other modern trends. And if we look at the social sciences, again it is problems of wholeness, interaction, organization, etc., which appear to be most important and pressing.

There is a second and even more interesting aspect. We find not only a parallelism in the general development of science, but quite often isomorphic laws in fields which have little or nothing to do with each other. For example, in the theory of populations of animal or plant species, certain systems of equations have been developed by Lotka, Volterra and others for the so-called ecological equilibrium, the struggle for existence and so forth. Later on, it turned out that the same sort of differential equations may be used in problems of chemical kinetics. The entities compared are totally different, but it appears that the general conceptual model, an ecology, so to speak, on the one hand of animal species, and on the other hand of molecules, is essentially the same. The origin of such correspondences is obviously the fact that isomorphic models can be and actually are applied in quite different fields.

So I came to postulate a new discipline which would deal with these matters, and which is called General System Theory. This theory deals with models and laws applicable not to one particular system, but to systems in general.

The argument leading to such generalized theory runs something like this. If we look at physics, we find that it investigates systems of various levels of generality: from very special systems as they are used by the engineer who builds a bridge or an automobile, up to laws such as those of thermodynamics, which apply to systems of a very general nature, whether they are caloric, mechanical, chemical or whatever else. However, there seems to be no limit or border-line. Why not ask for principles and laws holding for systems in general, not only for physical systems but also for systems in the biological, behavioural and social fields? And actually it turned out that it was possible to elaborate such a theory of generalized systems.

I think the first time I talked about this idea was at the University of Chicago in 1938. Then came the war, and I also was afraid of what Gauss, the mathematician, called the *Geschrei der Boeotier*. I feared that my reputation as an experimentalist would be damaged if my preoccupation with such highly theoretical matters were

156

uncovered! So nothing was published until after the war. Then, however, I soon found that this idea was not a personal idiosyncrasy or fancy, but rather was one expression of a trend which was present in various quarters. I found that quite a number of scientists in different fields had thought on essentially similar lines. Some even used the same mathematical model I had used, drawing from it, however, rather different deductions. This was, for example, the case with Ross Ashby. In addition, there were other new developments, such as information theory, cybernetics, game theory, decision theory, and operational research which used mathematical models which were different, but had a similar general interdisciplinary aim. So General System Theory is an expression of a rather general trend, prevailing in various fields of modern science.

GREY WALTER:

You speak of 'General System Theory' as a theory of theories. I'd like to ask: do you use the word 'model' as being essentially synonymous with 'theory'?

BERTALANFFY:

Yes. I don't clearly see the difference between 'theory' and 'conceptual model'—the latter being the more fashionable term. What is essential is the hypothetico-deductive character of a construct so that consequences can be derived from it.

GREY WALTER:

But don't you think it is worth distinguishing between hypotheses in three forms: a verbal form, using language; a mathematical form, which of course is a language but a very special form of language with rules of its own; and a working model form, which is neither linguistic nor mathematical and which has limitations and advantages of its own? For example Ashby, whom you mentioned, differs from you in that he made a machine before he wrote his book, and he therefore discovered in making and working and observing his own machine where he was wrong. For me, and for many other people who are thinking on convergent lines, the value of a working model is that it is a 'crystallized hypothesis'. It is absolutely clear, it is quite brittle, and when it breaks, it breaks with a loud bang. There's no question of it being bent, almost imperceptibly, to fit new facts. We know words can change their meaning almost imperceptibly. Mathematics bends less easily and there are many brilliant mathematical biologists who have promoted generalizing theories, but nobody I know understands them. They use eccentric, idiosyncratic algebras—even Ashby, who has tried very hard to systematize his thinking in his recent book *Introduction to Cybernetics* (1956), is

157

hard to understand for those of us who have not had formal and prolonged mathematical training. I should have thought that the word 'model' should usually be kept for those hypothetical propositions which are in the literal sense mechanical. They are not equivocal as words are, and they are intelligible as mathematical expressions usually are not. If we use 'model' interchangeably with 'theory' then I think we're liable to condemn theory because it has the limitations of models, and condemn models for having the limitations of theory.

BERTALANFFY:

I think our difference is largely semantic. We can distinguish material models and conceptual models. Material models are your tortoises, or Ashby's homeostat, or Lillie's iron wire. Conceptual models are theoretical constructs. I most heartily agree with what I suppose was in your mind, namely that conceptual models may be so general that you can do little with them. I would not draw an absolute border-line between verbal and mathematical models however; mathematics is only a highly formalized form of language and thinking.

GREY WALTER:

Well, yes. But I think there is a very important distinction between ordinary vernacular and mathematical language. The rules of mathematics are invariable, whereas the virtue of what we are saying now is that it is essentially poetic, it can be misunderstood, it means different things to different people. Mathematics is unambiguous— there is no noise in it. It is an absolutely noise-free channel, which is a special case of communication.

BERTALANFFY:

This discussion is related to the question Konrad Lorenz raised in his memorandum (Part I); whether with such general conceptions, there is danger of throwing away the specific and essential character of the phenomenon concerned. The answer is emphatically 'yes'. This danger is a very real one, but it is present everywhere. We do this all the time, only we must be careful to be aware of doing it. For example, take the system of mechanics, which is certainly a legitimate science. It tells you that Newton's apple and the planets and the tides follow the same law—the law of gravitation. Now this is all right as far as it goes; but it does not mean that apples and planets and the ocean are all the same. Or to put it a little differently, there are innumerable other aspects of apples and planets which you just don't handle with this particular kind of model. It was the pitfall of the so-called mechanistic view of the world that it took mechanics as the all-embracing model of all phenomena in the world.

LORENZ:

I am always very strongly conscious that all our experience, all we know of the world, is also a model. As the pictures are modelled in the grain of our retina, so everything is modelled in the grain of our central nervous system. That is of course a truism, but I want to call attention to it because this fact makes it so difficult for us to remember that our consciously made models are models of a model.

GREY WALTER:

A model of a model is a model.

LORENZ:

A model of a model *is* a model, of course. But that's why the two aspects must be kept apart in our thinking, because there is only a difference of degree between them.

BERTALANFFY:

Our world picture is a model conditioned on the one hand by biological factors, meaning our organization as a primate with certain characteristics of sensory apparatus, a certain organization of the nervous system, etc., and, on the other hand, by cultural and linguistic factors. What aspects we pick out depends on biological as well as cultural factors. In scientific thinking, however, there is the reverse tendency, which I have called progressive deanthropomorphization (Bertalanffy, 1953b). By this I mean that the elements which are specific to our biological organization and to our cultural and linguistic bias are progressively thrown out of the scientific world picture. What eventually remains is a conceptual system—in the best case a mathematical system—which does represent certain aspects of reality, whatever this means, even though certainly quite different modes of description and quite different aspects would be possible. In this becoming free from our biological and cultural biases lies, I believe, the dignity of science.

Coming back to General System Theory, we can also look at the problem in a somewhat different manner. Most of you will know a remarkable paper by Warren Weaver, the founder of information theory, on Science and Complexity. Weaver (1951) gives a brilliant exposé of one basic problem which is involved here, the line of argument being something like this: Classical physics or, to speak in a more general way, the mechanistic approach, has led to an elucidation of processes where one-way causal chains can be isolated. The classical approach was also very successful with respect to what

Weaver calls laws of unorganized complexity, that is, where the behaviour of a whole can be considered as the statistical result of practically innumerable elementary events. These are laws of disorder which, in the last resort, stem from the second principle of thermo-dynamics. But then, we have also posed to us the problem of *organized* complexity, that is, of laws of interaction within a finite number of elements. It is here that the classical approach lets us down. You can rephrase this by saying that the great problem is what are the laws of organization. These are very difficult to state; remember, for example, that even the three-body problem in mechanics is insoluble, or solvable only by way of approximation; or think of the difficulties appearing in simultaneous differential equations when the condition of linearity is abandoned. This problem of organized complexity appears particularly in fields like the biological, behavioural and social sciences. I think it is reasonable to say that all these modern approaches, general system theory, cybernetics, game theory, etc., are different attempts to tackle this problem.

Thus the main functions of general system theory and of the related approaches just mentioned would be essentially two: (i) to develop a superstructure of science applicable in different fields and providing a basis for the unity of science; and (ii) to provide conceptual models, principles and laws in those sciences which at present lack them—that is particularly the biological, behavioural and social sciences.

General System Theory does not claim any monopoly, and the only claim it makes is that for certain aspects or for certain kinds of problems it seems to be useful, while with respect to other aspects and problems, approaches like that of information theory, cyber-netics, or game theory, etc., might be better. Even so, there are certain indications that further unification of these approaches may even-tually be possible. For example, if you take cybernetics and the feedback model, it will probably turn out as a special case of a more general model of dynamic interaction (Bertalanffy, 1951a). Again, information is defined as negative entropy in information theory, but negative entropy also plays an important role in the thermodynamics of open systems. Perhaps there will be found a way to translate one approach into the other, comparable to the translation between quantum statistics and wave-mechanics which are different mathe-matical descriptions but give the same results. However, in the present stage it will be best to follow up one model and see how far we can get.

Quite a number of applications of General System Theory have been made (Society for the Advancement of General Systems Theory, 1956). However, for this presentation, I would like to enumerate only a few consequences of possible interest to this group.

General system theory permits the exact definition of many notions which are alien to physics but are indispensable in the behavioural, biological and social sciences (Bertalanffy, 1950a; Ashby, 1952; Miller, 1955). This applies to concepts such as hierarchichal order, differentiation, centralization, control, the whole and its parts, and teleology in its various forms. General system theory is able to give exact definitions of such concepts in mathematical terms which, so to speak, strip them of the metaphysical or vitalistic character which was often associated with them. In the social sciences for example Narroll and I tried to give a quantitative measure of social organization in terms of the numbers of craft specialties in a society versus population, using the principle of allometry (Narroll & Bertalanffy, 1956).

I am sure I have much agreement here when I say that the notion of teleology, while taboo in the mechanistic world view, is now taken seriously; we are quite well able to give concrete models for different aspects of teleological behaviour. Some material models of this sort were presented by Grey Walter; other models are equifinality, trial and error by step functions following Ashby, etc. I think it is important to point out that notions of this kind are not taken to be vitalistic or metaphysical any more, but are considered amenable to scientific thinking and research.

It seems to me that General System Theory offers a better model of behaviour than previous theory did. It appears that in what may be called the classical theory of behaviour, three aspects have been fundamental.

(a) The first is linear or one-way causality as expressed in the classical reflex-arc and stimulus-response scheme, and also in the feedback scheme of homeostasis (Fig. 5). Even though the latter assumes a circular process, one-way causality remains unchanged.

FIG. 5

FEEDBACK SCHEME

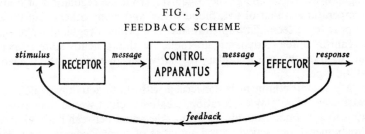

(b) The second characteristic is the consideration of all behaviour from an economic or utilitarian viewpoint, that is, as serving the maintenance of an equilibrium or biological survival. This is essentially the concept of homeostasis.

(c) The third is the viewpoint of the primary reactivity of the psychobiological organism, as expressed in the stimulus-response scheme. The organism is considered essentially as a penny-in-the-slot machine, set into action by external stimuli.

I have already mentioned some criticisms of this classical scheme in my precirculated paper, and Konrad Lorenz has advanced similar ideas. Thus, it can be said that the classical model is inadequate because: (i) behaviour as a whole precedes linear-causal or reflex reactions, as can be abundantly shown ontogenetically as well as phylogenetically: ontogenetically, if you think of the observations on early foetuses by Coghill and others; phylogenetically if you consider the behaviour of some lower animal like a jellyfish where there is behaviour as a whole but no definite one-way reflexes (Bertalanffy, 1952). (ii) Consideration of all behaviour as homeostatic, in the nature of 'coping with reality', a 'defence mechanism' and the like overlooks those activities which fall under the category of play, creativity, and so on. (iii) Primary activity ontogenetically and phylogenetically precedes stimulus-response and reactive behaviour.

The homeostasis model which is fashionable nowadays still adheres to the classical viewpoints mentioned, one-way causality, economic consideration of behaviour, and primary reactivity of the organism. In contrast, general system theory provides the background for a new concept of the organism and of behaviour, emphasizing action-as-a-whole as primary, allowing for non-utilitarian activities, and taking into account that intrinsic activity generally precedes reactive behaviour.

In criticism of the notion of homeostasis I would like specifically to emphasize two points. The closest German translation of this term is *Regelmechanismen* which is an appropriate word, as it expresses that 'mechanisms' are under consideration. Now mechanisms of the Cannon or homeostasis type of course are present in many regulative phenomena of the organism, from the regulation of body temperature to that of pH, blood sugar, and many others. But these appear to be secondary apparatuses. The primary regulability of the organism is due to dynamic interaction within a steady state. Superimposed on this are secondary regulative mechanisms of the homeostatic type.

My second comment is concerned with those activities which are variously called play exploration, creativity, etc. I would take exception to a distinction made by Franz Alexander between maintenance (or homeostatic) activities and activities of surplus energy, the latter including propagation, play and creative activities, etc. It seems to me difficult to distinguish between them. For example, you have a rat or mouse, and it is running around in its cage. This would be surplus activity, as the animal doesn't need to do it, and could just sit down and eat chow from the container. On the other hand, in the natural environment the rat must run around to explore and to find

162

the necessary amount of food, so it is really a maintenance activity. Or a young colt is hopping around in the corral for no particular reason, seeming to be a playful animal. But such play activities do have a survival value, hence are 'homeostatic' mechanisms. It seems difficult to draw a borderline between immanent maintenance activity and surplus activity.

LORENZ:

I could not disagree less with what you have just said about the impossibility of finding surplus activities. You would find that in these species in which surplus activity seems to abound, the whole system of action of the species was built up on the presence of surplus activity. All these animals with a huge differentiation of exploratory behaviour *live* by the exploratory behaviour. What I call the specialists in non-specialization like rats, like *Corridae* in birds, like man, are the most tremendous successes biologically that you can imagine; and if you ask why, the ecological answer is very simple.

Let me take the raven as an example: the raven can live in the desert, leading the life of a vulture, and it can live on bird-islands leading the life of a skua, and so on and so forth because in its youth it treats everything as if it were biologically important. If you see a raven dealing with an unknown object, you will find that its overt behaviour consists successively of (a) escape reaction, (b) attack reactions, (c) feeding responses, and (d) the very special response of hiding. It first treats the object as a potential enemy by being very careful, then attacks it from a certain angle—from behind, if it has a head, which is an IRM for front end and rear end—and ends up by performing all the hiding activities, by taking this thing, tearing it to pieces and hiding it in clefts. Now you might think that the bird wants to eat that thing, but this is not the case. This activity is so preponderant that in a state of exploratory behaviour, you cannot lure away the raven by the best baits, by the most delicate morsels even if it's hungry. Anthropomorphically and functionally speaking, this raven does not want to eat this thing, but it wants to know whether it is eatable *in theory*. This is research, you see, and the rat as well as the raven, and man also, lives by virtue of exploratory behaviour. That is their main adaptation. The animal lacking in many specific adaptations has one particular adaptation and that is exploratory behaviour—and it's certainly not a surplus activity. Your rat running about or your lion running up and down a cage only seem to do surplus things if you keep thinking on the basis of reflex theory. . . .

BERTALANFFY:

That's what I call the 'error of the cage'.

LORENZ:

That's the error of the cage, exactly! And the moment you know about automatic activities, it is perfectly clear that this poor animal must somehow get rid of the endogenous impulses it is producing all the time. So I couldn't disagree with you less.

FREMONT-SMITH:

Could one say that the homeostatic mechanism is superimposed on the primary activity of the organism, but superimposed in order to free the organism to exhibit its primary activity in a wide variety of environments—to return to Claude Bernard again?

BERTALANFFY:

Certainly. It is a general principle that specialization permits higher efficiency and entails loss of regulability. You have a primitive society —everybody is his own own tailor, farmer, engineer, doctor and what have you, and everybody can do everything, but on a pretty low level. Then you come to a highly specialized society. Here doctors are supposed to be better and tailors definitely are and farmers also. On the other hand, the specialists become irreplaceable and if a major catastrophe occurs, for example, the engineers of the water-works of London or New York go out of business, this means absolute disaster. Something similar applies to the specialization of the biological organism. Specialized homeostatic mechanisms do set the organism free of changes in the outer world, allowing it to devote its activities in a broader range of environment, and at a higher level.

GREY WALTER:

I make a distinction between the administrative and the operational aspects of organic life, which is similar to Alexander's, but the distinction is, in my mind, a *vectorial* distinction, not a scalar one. The essence of the administrative or homeostatic functions, their diagnostic character, is that the feedback is a negative feedback. It is an error-operated system of the most primitive type, a reflex; it is very easy to imitate and as I mentioned in my memorandum is to be found in most well-regulated households in the water-closet— which came even before the thermostat.

Now on the other hand the operational aspects of life are those which have a *positive* feedback and are therefore essentially unstable. This is a vectorial distinction; it is the sign and not just the scale that is distinctive. By experiment it is sometimes possible to move the vector around from negative to positive or vice versa and thus to show that in certain cases, but not in others, a homeostatic or administrative function or mechanism which mediates stability can be converted into an operational or unstabilizing one.

164

The reason I think this distinction is important is that it enables one to design experiments in terms of the vector or sign of the information flow, without recourse to such rather vague notions as autonomy or energy. I think you should be able to design experiments to find out whether an animal running around freely is behaving homeostatically or operationally. For example, if the application of a stress induces torpor or indifference or sleep, that would suggest that the effect involves increasing negative feedback; if there is increased irritability and instability the vector is becoming positive. This is where I should expect signs of personality to appear, particularly in higher mammals. To return for a moment to our terms of reference, human children may respond to stress by withdrawal and apparent indifference or by aggression and agitation; it may be worth considering whether in the first case there is aggravation of a homeostatic process and in the second evocation of an operational one. Furthermore there may be critical phases in development when one or the other mechanism is more likely to appear under stress.

BERTALANFFY:

What Cannon meant by homeostasis is indicated by examples like the regulation of body temperature which represents a feedback circuit like that shown in Fig. 4. I would criticize the use of the word 'homeostasis' for designating adaptation in general, as is often done, because regulation on the basis of dynamic interaction seems to be the primary phenomenon, and mechanized and structure-bound feedback regulations appear to be superimposed as a secondary layer. As a classical example, take regulations in early embryonic development. A normal sea-urchin ovum yields a normal larva. You divide the ovum in two halves, and each half becomes a complete larva. You bring two eggs to fusion—again you get a normal larva. This was Driesch's so-called first proof of vitalism. However, we can explain this, at least in general terms, within the theory of open systems as an example of equifinality. But certainly you cannot imagine feedback mechanisms being involved because there is a dynamic interaction of practically an infinite number of parts. I am critical of using the term 'homeostasis' as synonymous with adaptation because this inflates the notion so that it may lose its original meaning.

ERIKSON:

I want to say one word about the pleasure I feel in hearing all this because it gives, as it were, the theoretical underpinning for something which clinically has impressed me in the last few years. This theory of the surplus in play, of course, goes back to the idea that those animals play most that do not have to take care of their

165

own food supply and of their own security because either their mothers take care of it or humans do. The origin of all these theories lies in the economic doctrines of the last century, the influence of which on Freud has been vastly underestimated. You find theories in the classical economics of the last century which already speak of humans in the aggregate as pleasure-and-pain machines, in terms of gains and losses. I personally would say that nothing has done more harm in psychoanalysis and in its application than the Weltanschauung, one might almost say the ethics, which grew out of this 'economic' trend of thinking. Thus, the ego has been treated in psychoanalysis as a kind of merchandising agency which bargains for pleasure and self-expression. By this, I do not mean that Freud's psycho-economics is not fruitful; but it is the anthropomorphic equation of man with one of his functions, which has made him 'nothing but' a storehouse of inner bargains.

Speaking practically, we at Riggs have taken quite a number of chances with patients during the last few years, and found out that patients were able to do things which, according to our theories, they were unable to do. We found that we were inclined to keep them ill by imposing on them interpretations concerning an inner economic determinism, telling them *why* they couldn't do what they couldn't do, without realizing that they were in a state of latent activity—where something active is going on which is merely waiting for a chance to meet the world of opportunities. The combination of interpretation and encouragement of specific activity brings about an entirely different inner economic state. We have recently had experiences where the patients have made our life difficult by suddenly wanting to do things which patients are not supposed to be able to do and we had to change the structure of our institution and the relationship of the institution to the community. Only an integration of our ego-theories with such theories of functioning as Piaget advances can get us closer to the nature of this problem.

BERTALANFFY:

What Erik has just said gives me an excellent start for my concluding remarks. Psychobiologically it is customary to consider all behaviour, and particularly the behaviour of the child, as 'coping with reality', as 'defence mechanisms' and the like. Now, yesterday, instead of going to Montreux as I was advised to do, I spent the time preparing the present talk. But certainly our charming Chairman did not force me to do so and so far as I am able to see I have put it together, not as a homeostatic device for maintaining my disturbed mental equilibrium or as a defence reaction against this group, or as an outflow of my Oedipus complex, but mostly for the fun of it.

ERIKSON:

The last two things are not mutually exclusive!

BERTALANFFY:

No, I agree. But what I want to emphasize is that the psycho-biological organism is characterized by primary activity. Reflex mechanisms crystallize, so to speak, out of this primary activity in the way of progressive mechanization.

LORENZ:

Someone once said that the amoeba is less of a machine than a horse is!

BERTALANFFY:

That is exactly what I wanted to say.

One, though by no means the only, aspect of general system theory is its consideration of *open systems*. This is an important aspect in so far as it has led to original developments in physics, physical chemistry and biophysics. Conventional physics by definition deals only with closed systems, that is, systems which do not exchange matter with the environment. So physical chemistry, in kinetics, tells about the reactions, their rates and the chemical equilibria eventually established in a closed reaction vessel where a number of reactants are brought together. In a similar way, conventional thermodynamics expressly declares that its laws apply to closed systems: according to the first principle, in a closed system energy is constant; according to the second, in a closed system entropy must increase. This implies that eventually the process comes to a stop at a state of maximum entropy. As you know, the second principle can be formulated in different ways. One of these is to say that entropy is a measure of probability, hence a closed system tends towards a state of most probable distribution. This, however, is a state of complete disorder. If you have, for example, red and blue beads, then it's very improbable that all red beads should be on one side and all blue beads on the other side of a container; the most probable state is that all the beads are mixed up. Something similar applies to molecules having different velocities: it is improbable to have all fast molecules (or a high temperature) on one side, and all slow molecules (or a low temperature) on the other; the most probable state is to have them evenly distributed over the space, resulting in a state of thermic equilibrium.

However, we find systems in nature which by their very definition are not closed. The most important, though by no means the only, example is the living organism. The living organism is an open system where there is import and export, continuous building up and breaking down of material. So we are confronted with a rather embarrassing situation, namely that the laws of conventional physics, by definition, do not apply to the living organism, or, speaking more precisely, apply only to limited aspects and processes of it. For example, the transport of oxygen from the lungs to the tissues is based upon the establishment of chemical equilibria between reduced haemoglobin, oxyhaemoglobin and oxygen. We can apply the conventional principles of kinetics in this particular case because this is a fast reaction which comes to an equilibrium in a short time. However, we cannot apply the familiar formulations of kinetics and thermodynamics to the organism as a whole because these are slow processes which don't go to equilibrium but rather are maintained in a steady state.

So, in order to arrive at a true biophysics, a physics of the living organism, we have to generalize the principles of physics to include open systems. Such a theory leads to a large number of consequences which in our limited time obviously I cannot discuss. I want to clarify only one point: namely, that the theory of open systems is not a clever *aperçu* or a mere programme of things to be done, but is a well-developed theory, by no means consummate but progressing rather rapidly at the present time. The generalization of physical chemistry, of kinetics and thermodynamics, has been made and applied to very different problems. I may mention that the so-called irreversible thermodynamics, of which the thermodynamics of open systems is a part, is a major development in modern physics and has led to novel developments and solutions in thermo-electricity, thermo-osmosis, electro-osmosis, thermo-diffusion, the so-called 'fountain effect' of helium II, and many other problems which do not belong to the present discussion.

The applications of the theory of open systems in biology and biophysics include, for example, the kinetics of open systems in isotope experiments. The theory of the transmission of excitation in the nerve, as developed by Hill and Rashevsky, is a special case of the theory of open systems. So is the theory of sensory and, in particular, visual perception, as developed by Hecht, and the theory of growth, as developed by myself. The phenomena of overshoot and false starts which are not found in conventional chemical systems going towards equilibrium, but are seen in many physiological phenomena, can also be interpreted in terms of the theory of open systems. Such theory also allows calculation of the energy requirements for maintenance of the steady state of the organism.

The theory also leads to consequences of a general character. One is the so-called principle of *equifinality*. Briefly, this means the following. In a closed system the final state is unequivocally determined by the initial conditions. For example, when you have a chemical equilibrium then the final concentrations eventually established by the reactants will depend on the initial concentrations, namely, what you have put in in the beginning. In contrast to this, equifinality is a characteristic of open systems; if and when an open system approaches a steady state this will be the same, irrespective of the initial conditions and the course taken by the process in approaching the steady state. This can be easily shown mathematically; if the kinetic equations of an open system are solved for the steady state, the parameters of the initial conditions drop out and the steady state is defined only by the system-constants, the parameters of reaction and transport.

It may be noted that this equifinal behaviour was considered to be the foremost 'proof of vitalism'. As already mentioned, a normal and complete larva develops, for example, from a normal ovum of the sea urchin, from each half of an experimentally divided ovum, or from the fusion of two ova. This proves, according to Driesch, that biological regulation cannot be explained in terms of physics, but only by the action of a vitalistic 'entelechy' directing the processes in anticipation of the goal. It is interesting to note that Driesch's argument is quite correct so far as conventional physics goes; for in the physics of closed sytems, equifinal behaviour is not found. However, the so-called proof of vitalism evaporates when you take into account the physics of open systems.

There is a second problem which constitutes another allegedly vitalistic feature of the living world: the question of entropy and the living organism. The problem can be formulated in the following way. There appears to be a sharp contrast between inanimate and animate nature, or, as it was sometimes stated, a violent contradiction between Kelvin's degradation and Darwin's evolution, between the law of dissipation in physics and the law of evolution in biology. According to the second principle of thermodynamics, the general trend of physical events is towards states of maximum disorder and levelling down of differences with the so-called heat death of the universe as the final outlook when all energy is dissipated into heat of low temperature and the world process comes to a stop. In contrast, the living organism is a system of extreme improbability and highest degree of order which nevertheless is kept fairly constant in so far as we are considering the adult stage. Furthermore, we find, in embryonic development and in phylogenetic evolution, a transition toward higher order, heterogeneity and organization. The ovum, in ontogenesis, advances from a seemingly undifferentiated state to the extremely complicated structure of the developed organism. In evolution we find a transition from the lower to higher and highest organisms.

In fact, this problem is an easy one, for the apparent contradiction

169

between entropy and evolution disappears within the generalized thermodynamics of open systems. Perhaps I should make this point a little more technical.

There is a modern development called Irreversible Thermodynamics in contrast to classical or conventional thermodynamics. The equation of classical thermodynamics are applicable only to closed systems. It can be said that the classical doctrine should rather be called 'thermostatics'—as is frequently done at present. Conventional thermodynamics or thermostatics proves to be insufficient in so far as states of nonequilibrium, processes of transport in and out of the system, and irreversible processes come into play.

The modern generalization of kinetics and thermodynamics is a remarkable development which was partly stimulated by biological considerations. It remains a pleasing thought to me that I was one of the first to pose the problem and to propose the concept of the 'open system' from the biological viewpoint in 1934. Only much later, I learned that a Belgian, Defay, had spoken of the thermodynamics of open systems in 1929. I developed some basic principles of the kinetics of open systems in 1940, and a similar approach was made almost simultaneously by the Canadian biophysicist, Burton (1939). Irreversible thermodynamics was started in Germany by J. Meixner, and its development is particularly due to the Belgian school of thermodynamics, Onsager, Prigogine, de Donder, de Groot, and others.

Irreversible thermodynamics is characterized by the fact that it introduces a number of principles which are novel compared with classical thermodynamics. Essentially they are the following: (1) the generalization of the entropy function which I am going to discuss in more detail in a moment; (2) the so-called phenomenological laws; (3) the Onsager reciprocity relations; and (4) the principle of microscopic reversibility. From these principles, irreversible thermodynamics as a generalization of classical thermodynamics can be derived, as reviewed in the books by de Groot (1951) and Denbigh (1951). This is not the last possible generalization and further work is in progress of which I would like to mention that of Reik (1953) which seems to be the most general formulation of thermodynamics hitherto achieved.

On the basis of the theory of open systems the apparent contradiction between entropy and evolution disappears. In all irreversible processes entropy must increase. Therefore the change of entropy in a closed system is always positive and order is continually destroyed. In open systems, however, we not only have production of entropy due to irreversible processes but we also have import of entropy which may well be negative as in the case of the living organism which imports complex molecules high in free energy.

170

The basic principle in the classical thermodynamics of closed systems is that entropy must increase:

$$dS > 0$$

which is the simplest expression for the second principle. However, a generalized entropy function was introduced by Prigogine which also covers open systems and reads:

$$dS = d_eS + d_iS$$

This equation states that the change of entropy in an open system is composed of two parts, namely the change of entropy by transport d_eS, and the entropy production within the system, d_iS, due to irreversible processes such as chemical reactions, diffusion, heat conduction, etc. Now according to the second principle, d_iS must always be positive. However, d_eS, meaning entropy transport, may be positive, zero, or negative. It is negative if material rich in free energy is introduced into the system. Consequently, the total change of entropy, dS, can, according to the amount and the sign of d_eS, be either positive or negative, and there is no contradiction between the second law and the thermodynamics of open systems. Open systems, and in particular the living organism, can avoid the increase in entropy and maintain a thermodynamically improbable state; or they may even advance toward states of decreased entropy or increased organization.

LORENZ:
I take it this means that life increases entropy to the Universe.

BERTALANFFY:
Yes. What you choose as an open system or as a closed system depends on what you want to investigate.

LORENZ:
Considering the Universe as a closed system, because there isn't anything else, life lives at the cost of the entropy increase of the Universe.

BERTALANFFY:
Yes, this is true.

PIAGET:
As we are here for a synthesis and to make a certain number of interdisciplinary transitions I should like to transfer to a problem which interests me very deeply and which is one of the aspects of my essay. If you translate the ideas of thermodynamic entropy into

171

ideas of entropy relative to information, the problem life-and-entropy which you have just dealt with appears again in the following form: are logical structures going to correspond to an entropy maximum or, on the contrary, to an anti-entropy process, a sort of antichance or Maxwell's demon before all the corrections which have been introduced into this idea since Szilard; or on the other hand must another solution be investigated, a tertium? Well, at the moment I have the impression, without having had time to think it over, that your solution for the biological field corresponds to this tertium which we are seeking in the logical field. In the cognitive field also there is exchange because there is an open system without this being opposed to increase in entropy. It would thus be a question of seeing how one could transpose the terms of your solution into terms of information and logic. We could admit that logical operations are the organ of exchange, whereas the total content of these exchanges would necessarily obey the laws of chance.

GREY WALTER:

I was going to say exactly the same thing as Piaget. In many approaches to this problem there has been a temptation to compare the integral equations describing entropy and those describing information, which look very much the same, and to consider information as negative entropy: I wonder if one might say that logical reasoning is a closed system in which information can never increase, in fact is bound to diminish.

But what I called in my commentary on Piaget's paper 'statistical reflexion', is in a sense an open system in which information may actually increase. If this is so then there may be a corresponding loss of information elsewhere, just as entropy is increasing in the Universe as a whole, if we assume a simple naïve view of the Universe. If we may actually reduce the rate of increase of entropy in statistical reflexion (of which I suggested logical reasoning in a special case just as closed systems are a special case of open systems) then one may actually get a paradoxical gain of information, which has always puzzled people and gives one an excuse for some sort of vitalistic notion of creative mentality.

PIAGET:

I am not at all sure that logical reasoning is a closed system. I should like to have Bertalanffy's opinion.

BERTALANFFY:

It certainly appears that in some way the thermodynamics of open systems and information theory have to be brought together, even though at present we don't know exactly how this is to be done (cf.

172

Quastler, 1954). In this regard, I would like to mention one point which is often overlooked. Information theory is essentially concerned with possible decisions, that is, probabilities. In its present form, it is not concerned with what is sometimes called semantic information. To put the problem in the simplest way: a royal flush in poker is called a highly 'improbable' event, and in fact it requires a considerable number of 'bits'. But by itself, a royal flush is not more improbable than any odd combination of cards, a ten of spades, plus the five of hearts plus the queen of diamonds, etc. The royal flush is 'improbable' only if we lump together the probabilities of all other combinations against one singular case. But why the flush is a singular case is not defined in terms of decisions or bits of information. This problem of 'semantic information' naturally appears also in other applications of information theory and information theory in its present form is not capable of defining why a certain state is singular as compared to others.

PIAGET:
I agree with practically everything Bertalanffy has said, except on one point which is very general, and which no doubt depends more on wide conceptions and interpretations than on data which can be verified by experiment.

Bertalanffy tells us that two systems exist in an organism. There is a primary system which is a total of dynamic interactions within a stable state and then there are secondary mechanisms, that is to say homeostases, which occur later as regulations in the primary mechanism. It is this duality which worries me. I do not see any decisive reason for introducing duality instead of admitting a steady state open system with regulations straight away.

In fact this primary mechanism has two characteristics: it is steady and it is open. Well then, if it is open, in order for it to be steady there must already be regulations. If not, and precisely because it is open, it is exposed to all the alterations due to external perturbations and will stop being steady. It follows that there are regulatory mechanisms from the beginning, mechanisms which have not been added but which are inherent. In other words, this system of dynamic interactions already contains what in my language I call equilibrium and what Bertalanffy in his language calls stability. In short, I myself would see unity from the start where Bertalanffy sees duality.

This brings me to a second question: the position of logic. Grey Walter tells us in his paper in Part I that logic is a sort of closed system which teaches us nothing, which is a collection of redundancies, and that the important reality is constituted by the statistical system of information within which logic becomes crystallized.

I have a remark to make here which brings us back to unity. I

173

think we must carefully distinguish in our discussion between the logic of the logician and that of the individual, and the only thing which is of interest for the aims of our group is the logic of the individual. The logic of the logician, of course, *is* a closed system because it is an axiomatization made after the event and made so that it constitutes precisely a closed system. This logic does not teach us anything, I agree: it is only an instrument of control and not of information or increasing information. But if we turn to the logic of the individual—the logic which develops in the child and which results in a state of equilibrium in the adolescent and the adult and of which the logician makes an axiomatic system after the event—the logic of the individual is above all an operatory system. Now an operatory system constitutes a group of activities which are in equilibrium in the sense in which I have used the term, that is to say in a sense which is both very special because it is the only state where one really achieves equilibrium and at the same time very general, because the system of operations in equilibrium is in fact only a special case of a vast whole, that of regulations and homeostases, etc. Just as a short time ago I was upholding the fact that there was unity where Bertalanffy introduces duality, I think equally that in the problem of relations between logic and information there is complete unity between logic and the acquisition of information. Logic is not the result of the putting together of information, it is a structuration and organization, which is what permits exchange between the individual and the external world. It is the total sum of the regulations which permit this bringing in of new information, this bringing of external entropy into Bertalanffy's equation.

BERTALANFFY:

It was certainly not my intention to establish a dualism between dynamic regulations on the one hand and fixed machine-like regulations, feedback and the like, on the other. If I created such an impression it is only due to the necessary brevity of my remarks. You may have noticed that I have spoken of a 'progressive mechanization' which implies that there is no dualism of regulations but a gradual transition. I had best quote from a paper where I discussed this question in detail:

'. . . There is no sharp border-line between "dynamical systems" and "machines" . . . . The construction of a "machine" essentially means that, within a system of forces, conditions of constraint are introduced, so that the degree of freedom in certain causal chains is restricted, usually so that only one course is possible, and causality runs one way. But even in man-made machines, we have all transitions from fixed to loose coupling, allowing for only one, or for several degrees of freedom. But this is precisely what we mean and what

174

we find in nature. The primary and basic regulations seem such as in systems with a minimum of constraint and therefore a high degree of freedom. Ontogenetically and phylogenetically, conditions of constraint evolve, making, on the one hand, the system more efficient, but limiting, on the other, dynamic interaction, degree of freedom, and regulation after disturbance. . . .

'In this sense, feedback represents an important, but special type of system behaviour. "Dynamics" is the broader theory since we can come, from general system principles, always to regulations by machines, introducing conditions of constraint, but not *vice versa*.' (Bertalanffy, 1951a, p. 360.)

Lastly I want to emphasize that, speaking of 'systems', we must distinguish two different kinds: one is the 'material' or 'natural' system, the other the 'conceptual system' such as mathematics and logic. The term 'system' is thoroughly misleading if this is not borne in mind. Naturally what I have said about closed and open systems refers to material or natural systems. A conceptual system like geometry or logic—that's quite another story.

FREMONT-SMITH:

And alas, at least for the present, we have no next instalment for it to be continued in. But my idea of a study group of this sort is one that generates a discussion which ends open-ended, and I think that this is a very good end to open on, or open to end on.

REFERENCES

ALEXANDER, F. (1948) *Fundamentals of psychoanalysis*, New York (the theoretical principles reprinted in *Dialectica*).

APOSTEL, L., MANDELBROT, B. and PIAGET, J. (1957) *Logique et équilibre*. In: *Études d'épistémologie génétique*, 2. Paris.

APOSTEL, L., MAYS, W., MORF, A. and PIAGET, J. (1957) *Les Liaisons analytiques et synthétiques dans les comportements du sujet*. In: *Études d'épistémologie génétique*, 4, ch. 4. Paris.

ASHBY, W. R. (1952) *Design for a brain*, London.

ASHBY, W. R. (1956) *Introduction to cybernetics*, London.

Association de psychologie scientifique de langue française (1956) *Le Problème des stades en psychologie de l'enfant*. Symposium. Paris.

BAYLEY, N. (1955) *Amer. Psychologist*, **10**, 805.

BENTLEY, A. F. (1950) *Science*, **112**, 775.

BERTALANFFY, L. VON (1937) *Das Gefüge des Lebens*, Leipzig.

BERTALANFFY, L. VON (1949) *Biol. gen. (Wien)*, **19**, 114.

BERTALANFFY, L. VON (1950a) *Brit. J. Philos. Sci.* **1**, 139.

BERTALANFFY, L. VON (1950b) *Science*, **111**, 23 (partly obsolete).

BERTALANFFY, L. VON (1951a) *Hum. Biol.* **23**, 346.

BERTALANFFY, L. VON (1951b) *J. Personality*, **20**, 24.

BERTALANFFY, L. VON (1952) *Problems of life*, New York and London.

BERTALANFFY, L. VON (1953a) *Biophysik des Fliessgleichgewichts*. Translated by W. Westphal, Vieweg, Braunschweig.

BERTALANFFY, L. VON (1953b) *Sci. Monthly (Wash.)*, **77**, 233.

BERTALANFFY, L. VON (1954) *Scientia (Milano)* 48th year.

BERTALANFFY, L. VON (1955) *Main currents in modern thought*, **11**, 75.

BERTALANFFY, L. VON (1955a) *Philos. Sci.* **22**, 243.

BERTALANFFY, L. VON (1956) *Sci. Monthly*, **82**, 33.

BERTALANFFY, L. VON, HEMPEL, C. G., BASS, R. E. and JONAS, H. (1951) *Hum. Biol.* **23**, 302.

BERTALANFFY, L. VON and PIROZYNSKI, W. J. (1952) *Evolution*, **6**, 3287.

BERTALANFFY, L. VON and PIROZYNSKI, W. J. (1953) *Biol. Bull.* **105**, 240.

BERTALANFFY, L. VON and RAPOPORT, A. (1956) *Yearbk. Soc. Advancement of General Systems Theory* 1, Ann Arbor.

BRAY, H. G. and WHITE, K. (1954) *New Biology*, **16**, 70.

BÜHLER, C. (1930) *Kindheit und Jugend*, Leipzig, 2nd ed.

BURTON, A. C. (1939) *J. Cell. Comp. Physiol.* **14**, 327.

DENBIGH, K. G. (1951) *The thermodynamics of the steady state*, London and New York.

DOUGLAS, J. W. (1956) *Med. Offr.*, **95**, 33.

ERIKSON, E. (1950) *Childhood and society*, New York.

FREUD, S. (1949a) *An outline of psycho-analysis*, London, p. 14.

FREUD, S. (1949b) *Three essays on the theory of sexuality*, London, p. 75.

FREUD, S. (1950) Construction in analysis. In: *Collected papers*, V, London.

GESELL, A. (1956) *Youth: the years from ten to sixteen*, New York.

GROOT, S. R. DE (1951) *Thermodynamics of irreversible processes*, New York.

HAMPSON, J. G., MONEY, J. and HAMPSON, J. L. (1956) *J. clin. Endocr. Metab.* **16**, 547.

HAYEK, F. A. (1955) *Brit. J. Philos. Sci.* **6**, 209.

HERNANDEZ-PEON, R., SCHERRER, H. and JOUVET, M. (1956) *Science*, **123**, 331.

INHELDER, B. and PIAGET, J. (1955) *De la Logique de l'enfant à la logique de l'adolescent*, Paris.

JUNG, F. (1956) *Naturwissenschaften* **43**, 73.

KLEIN, M. (1952) In: Klein, M., Heimann, P., Isaacs, S. and Rivière, J. *Developments in psycho-analysis*, London.

KRECH, D. (1950) *Psychol. Rev.* **57**, 345.

LEWIN et al. (1943) In: Barker, R. G., Kounin, J. S. and Wright, H.F. ed. *Child behaviour and development*, New York.

LORENZ, K. (1943) *Z. Tierpsychol.* **5**, 235.

LORENZ, K. Z. (1950) In: *Symp. Soc. exp. Biol.* Cambridge, No. IV.

MEAD, M. (1956) *New lives for old. Cultural transformation in Manus 1928-1953*, New York and London.

MILLER, J. G. (1955) *Amer. J. Psychol.* **68**, 513.

MONNIER, M. (1951) *Dialectica* **11**, 167.

NARROLL, R. and BERTALANFFY, L. VON (1956) In: *General systems. Yearbook of the Society for the Advancement of General Systems Theory*, **1**, 76.

OLÉRON, P. (1952) *Ann. psychol.* **52**, 47.

OLÉRON, P. (1951) *Ann. psychol.* **51**, 89.

PARSONS, T. and BALES, R. F. (1955) *Family, socialization and interaction process*, Glencoe, Ill.

PIAGET, J. (1929) *The child's conception of the world*, London.

PIAGET, J. (1950) *La Construction du réel chez l'enfant*, Neuchâtel, ch. 1.

PIAGET, J. and LAMBERCIER, M. (1951) *Arch. Psychol. (Genève)* **33**, 81.

PIAGET, J. and SZEMINSKA, A. (1941) *La Gènese du nombre chez l'enfant*, Neuchâtel and Paris.

PRINGLE, J. W. S. (1951) *Behaviour*, **3**, 174.

QUASTLER, H. (ed.) (1953) *Information theory in biology*, Urbana, Ill.

RACINE, G. E. (1953) *A statistical analysis of the metabolism of rats and mice*. Thesis, University of Ottawa, Canada.

RAPAPORT, D. (In press) In: Koch, S., ed. *Systematic resources of psychology*, New York.

REIK, H. G. (1953) *Ann. Phys.* **11**, 270, 407, 420; **13**, 73.

RICKMAN, J. (1951) *Brit. J. med. Psychol.* **24**, 1.

Society for the Advancement of General Systems Theory (1956) *General Systems. Yearbook of the Society for the Advancement of General Systems Theory*, **1**, Ann Arbor, Mich.

STAGNER, R. (1951) *Psychol. Rev.* **58**, 5.

TANNER, J. M. and INHELDER, B., (eds.) (1956) *Discussions on child development. The first meeting of the World Health Organization Study*

Group on the Psychobiological Development of the Child, Geneva, 1953, London and New York, p. 75.

TOCH, H. H. and HASTORF, A. H. (1955) *Homeostasis in psychology: a review and critique.* Mimeograph, Center for Advanced Study in the Behavioural Sciences, Stanford (Calif.)

WALTER, G. (1953) *The living brain,* London.

WEAVER, W. (1951) *Amer. Sci.* **36,** 4.

WEISS, P. (1955) In: Willier, B. H., Weiss, P. and Hamburger, V. eds. *Analysis of development,* Philadelphia.

WEISS, P. (1950) In: *Symp. Soc. exp. Biol.* Cambridge, **4,** 92.

WHORFF, B. L. (1952) *Collected papers on metalinguistics,* Washington.

INDEX

acceleration: at adolescence, cause of, 61; phases of, 26
accommodation, 82–3, 92, 105
achievement, 14
action: economy of, 18; primary and secondary, 131
activation, regulations of, 131
activity, 79–80; latent, 166; maintenance, 162; surplus, 162–3
adaptation, 82
Adler, Alfred, 54
adolescence, 61
affective: reactions, 91; stages, elementary, 6–7
affectivity, 31, 40 ff., 130–1; definition of, 130–1; development of, 12; stages of, 17–8
affects, and cognitions, 24–5, 42 ff.
age: for appearance of stage, 13, 49; bone and chronological, 62; critical, for cognitive stages, 26; variation between children at given, 53
aggression, modes of, 137, 149
Aktualgenese, 9, 10, 25
Alexander, F., 73, 162
alpha rhythm/waves, 22–3, 76, 133–5
ambivalence, 138; and love object, 46
Ambrose, Anthony, 35
analytic and synthetic, 122–3
anamorphosis, 73–4
androgens, 63
animism, 119
Apostel, L.. et al., 95, 101, 118
Appetenz nach höheren Zuständen, 133
apriorism, 91–2; dynamic, 4, 28; preformist, 29; static and dynamic, 24
architecture, 75
Ashby, W. R., 9, 26, 54, 55, 56, 70, 74, 157, 161
assimilation, 80, 82–3, 92, 105; of new influences, 18, 19

association, 105
Association de Psychologie scientifique de langue française, 14
attributes, inherited and acquired, 4
automaton model, 72
automobiles, 75–6
autonomy, 144, 148
averages, 116, 119–20
aversion, 133

Bayes strategy, 8
beads and jar, 117–18
behaviour: affective and cognitive, 24–5; escape and sexual, 150; exploratory, 163; learned, and humanity, 50; spontaneous, 72; structuration of, 44; three aspects, 161–2
behaviour patterns: and affectivity, 40–1; and cognitive development, 42–3; and simple mechanisms, 55
behaviourism, 143
Bentley, A. F., 74
Bergson, Henri, 105
Berkeley Growth Study, 124–5
Bernard, Claude, 164
Bertalanffy, L. von, 29, 30, 48, 54, 56, 70, 72, 73, 74, 75, 78, 92, 112, 122, 159, 160, 161, 175; biography, 88–9
Bindra, 73
birds, behaviour development in, 128–30
birth, 36
bisexuality, 143
Bowlby, John, 5, 8, 13, 18, 19, 24–5, 32, 33, 55, 56, 91, 126, 142
brain changes, 63
Bray, H. G., and White, K., 72
Bühler, Charlotte, 113
Bühler, K., 73
Burton, 170

180

184

teleology, 161
temperature, variation of, 56
tendons, transplantation of, 43
tests, operatory, 117 ff.
thermodynamics, 167; irreversible, 168, 170
thresholds, 123, 130, 147
time: Bergsonian and Newtonian, 54; biological, 72; internal maturational, 62
Tinbergen, N., 91
Toch, H. H., and Hastorf, A. H., 73
transitions/transformations: between stages, 13–4, 15 ff., 24, 45–7, 67–8; mechanism of, 26, 61–3; without discontinuity, 68
Trieb, 138
Trobriands, 114
trust, basic, 144, 148

understanding, mutual, 32
units, natural, 31–2
unity of personality, 15
Utopias, 143

values, positive and negative, 18
variables, complimentary, 100 ff.
velocities, developmental, 34
verbalization, 112–13
vitalism, 24, 28, 72 132 165, 169
Volterra, 70, 156

Wallon, H., 4, 11, 37, 42, 64
Walter, Grey, 4, 6–7, 22, 25–6, 30, 72, 76, 92, 94, 161
water-closet, 57, 164
Weaver, Warren, 159
weight, 62
Weiss, Paul, 42, 43, 44
Whorff, B. L., 112, 113
Wiener, N., 54
Woltereck, 112
work, virtual, 78, 81
Wright, Sewall, 70

Zelditch, Morris, jnr., 8
zones, 141; anal, oral, and genital, 137; focal, 141